W9-AFL-252

CRYPTOGAMIC BOTANY

Volume I

ALGAE AND FUNGI

McGRAW-HILL PUBLICATIONS IN THE BOTANICAL SCIENCES

Edmund W. Sinnott, *Consulting Editor*

ARNOLD An Introduction to Palebotany
CURTIS AND CLARK An Introduction to Plant Physiology
EAMES Morphology of the Angiosperms
EAMES Morphology of Vascular Plants: Lower Groups
EAMES AND MACDANIELS An Introduction to Plant Anatomy
HAUPT An Introduction to Botany
HAUPT Laboratory Manual of Elementary Botany
HAUPT Plant Morphology
HILL Economic Botany
HILL, OVERHOLTS, POPP, AND GROVE Botany
JOHANSEN Plant Microtechnique
KRAMER Plant and Soil Water Relationships
KRAMER AND KOZLOWSKI Physiology of Trees
LILLY AND BARNETT Physiology of the Fungi
MAHESHWARI An Introduction to the Embryology of the Angiosperms
MILLER Plant Physiology
POOL Flowers and Flowering Plants
SHARP Fundamentals of Cytology
SINNOTT Plant Morphogenesis
SINNOTT, DUNN, AND DOBZHANSKY Principles of Genetics
SINNOTT AND WILSON Botany: Principles and Problems
SMITH Cryptogamic Botany
 Vol. I. Algae and Fungi
 Vol. II. Bryophytes and Pteridophytes
SMITH The Fresh-water Algae of the United States
SWINGLE Textbook of Systematic Botany
WEAVER AND CLEMENTS Plant Ecology

There are also the related series of McGraw-Hill Publications in the Zoological Sciences, of which E. J. Boell is Consulting Editor, and in the Agricultural Sciences, of which R. A. Brink is Consulting Editor.

CRYPTOGAMIC BOTANY

VOLUME I

Algae and Fungi

GILBERT M. SMITH

Stanford University

SECOND EDITION

McGRAW-HILL BOOK COMPANY, INC.

New York Toronto London

1955

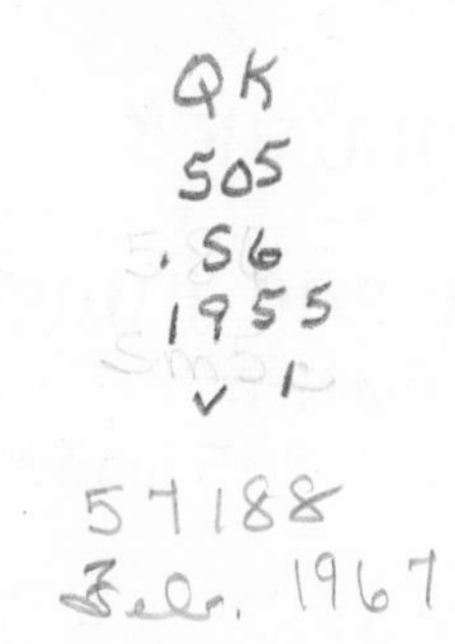

CRYPTOGAMIC BOTANY, Vol. 1

Library of Congress Catalog Card Number 54-8808

IX

58839

PREFACE

The general plan of the first edition has been followed in preparing this revised edition. The general discussions of the major taxa have been entirely rewritten and numerous changes have been made in descriptions of the various genera selected as "types." In certain cases, especially in the red and the brown algae, genera with a wider geographical distribution have been substituted for those described in the first edition.

As in the case of the first edition, this book is designed for students who have had an introductory course in botany and who wish to make a more intensive study of plants below the level of seed plants. It is written from the standpoint that a thorough knowledge of a representative series in each of the major groups is better than scraps of information about a large number of members of each group. This has been done with full knowledge of the danger of presenting the subject through a series of "types," and with a full realization that students are apt to substitute the type for the group and to consider all Fucales identical with *Fucus*, all Mucorales identical with *Rhizopus*, and all Marchantiales identical with *Marchantia*. However, it is hoped that introductory discussions to divisions, classes, and other taxa will help call attention to those characters of the selected representatives which are characteristic of the taxon as a whole and those which are special to the representative itself. In certain cases, as with the diatoms and the blue-green algae, it has been thought more advantageous to present the group as a whole instead of discussing selected representatives.

An attempt has been made to make the space devoted to each group proportional to its diversity and to check the natural tendency to overemphasize groups in which an author is especially interested. I realize that some botanists will disagree with the allocation of space, especially in the relative proportions devoted to the algae and to the fungi. There has also been the problem of selecting representatives for each of the groups. Wherever possible the genera selected are found in the United States and are of widespread distribution. In some cases this has meant the selection of a highly specialized rather than a generalized type, but it is felt that the availability of living material for study in the laboratory offsets this disadvantage.

Any general discussion of a group involves inclusion of subjects that are a matter of controversy. An attempt has been made to present both sides of controversial subjects, but I have not hesitated to express an opinion upon the relative merits of the arguments. Any attempt to group plants in a natural system of classification necessitates a consideration of phylogeny, a subject upon which no two botanists are in entire accord. Phyletic diagrams are included in this book because it is thought that a graphic presentation is the best method by which the student may visualize the suggested interrelationships between the various taxa. However, they are presented with a full realization that every botanist will disagree in minor or in major points.

The bibliographies at the ends of the chapters are to be looked upon as indicating the sources where a student may find fuller discussions of the subjects, rather than as a documentation justifying the various statements. References to the entire literature on the various subjects would have involved an expansion of bibliographies to an extent inappropriate to a book of this size. Wherever possible, the references selected are to journals with a wide circulation in this country.

A large proportion of the figures have been especially drawn for this book. Figures designated as *semidiagrammatic* are those in which it has been impossible to draw all details of a preparation cell for cell. Figures designated as *diagrammatic* are more or less conventionalized drawings based upon one or more preparations. Theoretical drawings not based upon any particular preparation or preparations are designated as *diagrams*. Illustrations taken from other authors are designated as *from* when copied in facsimile, and as *after* when redrawn for this book. A large majority of the original drawings have been made by the author. Most of the habit sketches of red and of brown algae were drawn by Mrs. Carl F. Janish and Mrs. Fred Addicott; the habit sketches of fungi were drawn by Mrs. Janish.

The completeness of the series of original figures is due to the courtesy of other botanists in furnishing material and preparations. Professor E. M. Gilbert and the late Professor J. I. W. McMurphy furnished preparations of many fungi. Dr. D. A. Johansen granted me free access to his extensive collection of preparations. Many of the figures are based upon preparations made especially for me by Dr. Johansen, whose skill in sectioning and staining refractory material has made possible illustrative material that would otherwise have been unavailable. Certain of the new illustrations in this edition were drawn from special preparations made by W. K. Bowen, microtechnician of the Department of Biology of Stanford University. Professor G. J. Hollenberg has supplied preparations of *Polysiphonia;* Dr. H. C. Gilbert preparations of *Ceratiomyxa;* and Professor J. G. Dickson preparations of *Puccinia* and *Ustilago.*

Professor G. F. Papenfuss and H. L. Blomquist have furnished preserved material of *Dictyota;* Professor W. R. Taylor and Dr. Jean Feldmann have furnished preserved material of *Dudresnaya;* and Dr. Laura Garnjobst has furnished cultures of *Neurospora.*

Thanks are due Professor Alexander H. Smith, the Kelco Company, and the Johns-Manville Company for supplying photographs.

I am under deep obligation to my colleague Professor Robert M. Page for supplying cultures of various fungi, for answering various questions about fungi, and especially for his critical reading of the chapters on the fungi.

GILBERT M. SMITH

CONTENTS

PREFACE v

CHAPTER 1. The classification of spore-producing plants 1

2. Chlorophyta 12

3. Euglenophyta 139

4. Pyrrophyta 148

5. Chrysophyta 165

6. Phaeophyta 217

7. Cyanophyta 275

8. Rhodophyta 291

9. Myxomycophyta 346

10. Eumycophyta—Introduction 364

11. Phycomycetae 371

12. Ascomycetae 422

13. Basidiomycetae 469

14. Deuteromycetae 514

15. Lichenes (Lichens) 516

INDEX 527

CHAPTER 1

THE CLASSIFICATION OF SPORE-PRODUCING PLANTS

The classification of plants has undergone many changes since Aristotle (384–322 B.C.) and his pupil Theophrastus (372–287 B.C.) first grouped them into *trees*, *shrubs*, and *herbs*. Beginning with the herbalists of the sixteenth century, there came a gradual realization that the most obvious characters are not necessarily the most important. Their gradual recognition that the structure of the flower is of more fundamental importance in classification than are vegetative characters paved the way for the "sexual system" of Linnaeus in which he grouped plants according to the number of stamens and carpels, their union, and their presence or absence in the flower. This system, although wholly artificial, had the great advantage that an unknown plant, when discovered, could be easily interpolated among those already known. Linnaeus divided the plant kingdom into 25 classes, one of which, the *Cryptogamia*, included all plants with "concealed" reproductive organs. He[1] characterized the class as follows: "*CRYPTOGAMIA continet Vegetabilia, quorum Fructificationes oculis nostris se subtrahunt, & structura ab aliis diversa gaudent.*" He divided the Cryptogamia into the following four orders: *Filices* which included all known pteridophytes; *Musci* which included all known mosses and leafy liverworts; *Algae* which included algae, lichens, and thallose liverworts; and the *Fungi*.

Natural systems of classification, that is, those in which plants were grouped according to what were thought to be their natural affinities, were established long before Darwin proposed the evolutionary theory. The first natural system, that of De Jussieu,[2] divided plants into three major groups, *Acotyledones*, *Monocotyledones*, and *Dicotyledones*. His Acotyledones are the approximate equivalent of Linnaeus' Cryptogamia, and the various orders he recognized among the Acotyledones are equally heterogeneous. Many other natural systems for the classification of plants were proposed during the first half of the nineteenth century, but all of them[3] are very inadequate as far as spore-producing (cryptogamic) plants

[1] Linnaeus, 1754. [2] De Jussieu, 1789.

[3] See Lindley (1847) for a summary of the various systems.

are concerned. The decade following Darwin's announcement of the theory of evolution in 1859 is marked by the appearance of true natural systems in which the fundamental basis for the classification of plants is phylogeny and in which they are arranged in an ascending series from the most primitive to the most complex.

The system[1] which places the cryptogamic portion of the plant kingdom in three divisions (*Thallophyta, Bryophyta, Pteridophyta*) was introduced about 1880. It soon became widely adopted and is still followed in a more or less modified form in many present-day textbooks. A decade or two after the turn of the century botanists began raising the question of whether or not the Thallophyta and the Pteridophyta are natural divisions. To date, botanists are universally agreed that the Bryophyta are a natural division.

Validity of the Thallophyta. The Thallophyta, with its two subdivisions the *Algae* and the *Fungi*, may be distinguished from other plants on the basis of structure of their gamete- and spore-producing organs. Sex organs of Thallophyta are one-celled, or when multicellular (as in certain brown algae) they do not have the gamete-containing cells surrounded by a layer of sterile cells. Bryophytes and pteridophytes have multicellular sex organs in which there is an outer layer of sterile cells. Sporangia of Thallophyta are always one-celled; those of more advanced plants are many-celled. Another distinction between Thallophyta and other plants is the fact that zygotes of Thallophyta never develop into multicellular embryos while still within the female sex organ.

Granting the common distinctive morphological features distinguishing algae and fungi from other plants there then arises the question: is this due to an evolution of the fungi from the algae, or have these common features been evolved independently in the two? If the fungi have been evolved from the algae there is some justification for maintaining the division Thallophyta. But, as will be shown in chapters dealing with the various classes of fungi, the evidence favors the view that none of the fungi has been evolved from algae. From this it follows that the Thallophyta are not a valid division, and that the subdivisions Algae and Fungi should each be placed in one or more divisions.

Organisms to Be Placed among the Algae. Before discussing whether the algae should be placed in one or more than one division it is necessary

[1] This is frequently stated to have first appeared in the third edition of Eichler's "Syllabus" (1883). Credit for establishment of these divisions should go elsewhere since they are not recognized in the second edition of Eichler's "Syllabus" (1880) and they are to be found in the synopsis of the plant kingdom published by Schimper in 1879. The division name *Thallophyta* was first introduced by Endlicher (1836), who called it a kingdom. The names *Bryophyta* and *Pteridophyta* were first (?) introduced by Haeckel (1866) but he was not the first to give these groups the rank of a division.

to take up the question of what organisms belong in this assemblage. Until the beginning of the twentieth century it was customary to recognize the following four classes of algae: *Chlorophyceae*, *Phaeophyceae*, *Rhodophyceae*, and *Myxophyceae* (*Cyanophyceae*). Diatoms were universally included among the algae and placed either in the Phaeophyceae or in a class distinct from other classes. During this time botanists rarely questioned the practice of protozoologists who placed all motile unicellular and colonial flagellated organisms with chlorophyll in the class Mastigophora of the phylum Protozoa. An exception must be made in the case of the volvocine series culminating in *Volvox*. Here, beginning a century ago,[1] botanists began calling certain members of this series algae but made no attempt to assign them a definite place among the algae. This was first done by Rabenhorst (1863), who placed the *Chlamydomonas-Volvox* series in the group of grass-green algae to which he gave the name Chlorophyllaceae.

When, at the beginning of this century, the *Xanthophyceae* (*Heterokontae*) were segregated[2] from the grass-green algae (*Chlorophyceae*) certain pigmented flagellates were included in the class.

Later, the chrysomonads and the dinoflagellates each were shown[3] to be related to organisms of an unquestionable algal nature. The euglenoids and the cryptomonads are also related to organisms of an algal type, but types not so highly advanced as in the algal types related to the chrysomonad and to the dinoflagellate series. Thus, with the possible exception of the chloromonads, all the various groups (orders) which protozoologists place in the subclass Phytomastigina of the class Mastigophora are phylogenetically related to organisms of a truly algal nature.

Classification of the Algae. It has become increasingly clear during recent decades that physiological characteristics of vegetative cells and the morphology of motile reproductive cells are the fundamental bases upon which algae should be classified. One important characteristic of vegetative cells is the nature of the pigments in their plastids, and throughout each of the classes of algae the plastids contain certain distinctive pigments not found in other classes of algae (Table 1). Correlated with this is the fact that the type of food reserve accumulated by the cell runs consistently throughout each class of algae and the type differs from class to class. Throughout each class there is a striking constancy in position of flagella of motile cells. In some classes all flagella are alike in structure. In other classes one flagellum is of the "whiplash" type and the other of the "tinsel" type (Fig. 91, page 168).

The Chlorophyceae and the Phaeophyceae may be cited to illustrate these differences. The Chlorophyceae have a predominance of chlorophylls in their plastids, contain certain unique xanthophylls, and almost always

[1] Braun, 1851; Cohn, 1853. [2] Luther, 1899. [3] Pascher, 1914, 1925, 1927.

TABLE 1. PRINCIPAL PIGMENTS OF THE DIFFERENT CLASSES OF ALGAE (BASED ON STRAIN, 1951)

	Myxophyceae	Rhodophyceae	Xanthophyceae	Chrysophyceae	Bacillariophyceae	Phaeophyceae	Dinophyceae	Chlorophyceae	Euglenophyceae
Chlorophylls:									
Chlorophyll *a*....	+++	+++	+++	+++	+++	+++	+++	+++	+++
Chlorophyll *b*....	0	0	0	0	0	0	0	++	+
Chlorophyll *c*....	0	0	0	...	+	+	+	0	0
Chlorophyll *d*....	0	+	0	...	0	0	0	0	0
Chlorophyll *e*.....	0	0	+	...	0	0	0	0	0
Carotenes:									
α-Carotene.......	...	+	...	...	0	0	0	+	
β-Carotene.......	+++	+++	+++	+++	+++	+++	+++	+++	+++
ε-Carotene.......	...	...	...	...	+	0	...	0	
Flavicin.........	+	...	...	...	0	0	...	0	
Xanthophylls:									
Lutein...........	?	++	0	+	0	0	0	+++	?
Zeaxanthin.......	?	...	0	...	0	0	0	+	
Violaxanthin.....	...	...	...	...	0	+	0	+	
Flavoxanthin.....	...	...	...	...	0	+	...	?	
Neoxanthin......	...	...	0	...	0	+	0	+	
Fucoxanthin.....	...	?	0	+	++	++	0	0	0
Neofucoxanthin A	...	...	0	...	+	+	0	0	0
Neofucoxanthin B	...	...	0	...	+	+	0	0	0
Diatoxanthin.....	...	...	0	...	+	?	0	0	0
Diadinoxanthin ..	...	...	0	...	+	?	+	0	0
Dinoxanthin.....	...	...	0	...	0	?	+	0	0
Neodinoxanthin..	...	...	0	...	0	0	+	0	0
Peridinin........	...	...	0	...	0	0	++	0	0
Myxoxanthin....	++	...	0	...	0	0	0	0	0
Myxoxanthophyll.	++	...	0	...	0	0	0	0	0
Unnamed........	?	?	++	?		+			+
Phycobilins:									
r-Phycoerythrin..	0	+++	0	?	0	0	0	0	0
r-Phycocyanin....	0	+	0	?	0	0	0	0	0
c-Phycoerythrin..	+	0	0	?	0	0	0	0	0
c-Phycocyanin....	+++	0	0	?	0	0	0	0	0

+++ indicates the principal pigment in each of the four groups of pigments.

++ indicates a pigment comprising less than half of the total pigments of the group.

\+ indicates a pigment comprising a small fraction of the total pigments of the group.

? indicates small quantities of a pigment whose source or identification is uncertain.

0 indicates known absence of a pigment.

... indicates lack of knowledge concerning the presence of certain pigments in some classes of algae.

store photosynthetic reserves as starch. Motile vegetative and reproductive cells have terminally inserted flagella that are all of the "whiplash" type and equal in length. The Phaeophyceae have a predominance of carotenoids in their plastids, contain certain unique xanthophylls, and store photosynthetic reserves as laminarin. Motile reproductive cells have laterally inserted flagella, one of the "whiplash" type, the other of the "tinsel" type.

According to the foregoing bases the algae are generally[1] divided into the following classes: *Chlorophyceae* (with or without segregation of the charas as a separate class, the *Charophyceae*), *Euglenophyceae, Xanthophyceae, Chrysophyceae, Bacillariophyceae, Phaeophyceae, Dinophyceae, Myxophyceae, Rhodophyceae, Cryptophyceae.*

Pascher[2] was the first to point out that certain of the classes mentioned above are sufficiently distinct to be recognized as divisions of the plant kingdom, whereas other classes have so many features in common that they are evidently related to one another. Thus, the number of divisions necessary for a complete classification of the algae is less than the number of classes. The first recognition of an affinity between certain classes was that which showed[3] a relationship between the Xanthophyceae, Chrysophyceae, and Bacillariophyceae. Features in common to these three classes include cell walls composed of two overlapping halves, silicified cell walls, motile cells with similarities in flagellation, a distinctive type of resting cell (cyst), and similarities in the nature of food reserves. Despite differences in chlorophylls and xanthophylls (see Table 1), there seems to be good ground for placing the three in a single division, the *Chrysophyta.* The golden brown chromatophores of Phaeophyceae have much the same color as chromatophores of many Chrysophyta but there are differences in the pigments causing the brown color (Table 1). Since there are striking differences in the food reserves and in insertion of the flagella of reproductive cells, the Phaeophyceae should be placed in a separate division, the *Phaeophyta*. The Myxophyceae and the Rhodophyceae are the only algae in which there are phycobilin pigments, but the phycobilins are not identical in the two.[4] The differences in nuclear organization, localization or nonlocalization of pigments in chromatophores, and presence or absence of sexual reproduction are so striking that there does not seem to be a phylogenetic connection between the two classes. Thus the Rhodophyceae are to be placed in one division, the *Rhodophyta;* and the Myxophyceae in another, the *Cyanophyta*. The chlorophycean series, including the charas, is also so distinctive that it should be placed in a separate division, the *Chlorophyta*. Similarities in pigmentation of Euglenophyceae and Chlorophyceae tempt one to place the Euglenophyceae in the

[1] Fritsch, 1935, 1944, 1945; Pascher, 1914, 1921, 1931; Smith, 1933, 1950.
[2] Pascher, 1914, 1921, 1931. [3] Pascher, 1914. [4] Strain, 1951.

Chlorophyta, but for the present it seems better to place them in a separate division, the *Euglenophyta*. The Dinophyceae have sufficient distinctiveness to be placed in another division, the *Pyrrophyta*. Opinion is divided as to whether the Cryptophyceae should be included in the Pyrrophyta,* or should not be included.[1] For the present it seems better to consider the Cryptophyceae a class of uncertain systematic position and not to place it in any of the divisions mentioned above. The question of the proper disposition of the chloromonads is even more difficult, and in their case, also, it seems best to group them among algae of uncertain systematic position.

Classification of the Fungi. The true fungi are universally divided into the following four classes: *Phycomycetae*, *Ascomycetae*, *Basidiomycetae*, and *Deuteromycetae* (Fungi Imperfecti). At one time some botanists placed the slime molds (*Myxomycetae* or *Mycetozoa*) in the animal kingdom, but today practically all botanists consider them related to the fungi. The Myxomycetae differ so markedly from other fungi that they should be placed in a separate division, the *Myxomycophyta*.

Whether the true fungi should be placed in a single division or in more than one division depends upon their mode of origin. One group of botanists holds that the Phycomycetes arose from algae that were either Chlorophyceae or Xanthophyceae; and that algae referable to the Rhodophyceae gave rise to the Ascomycetes which, in turn, gave rise to the Basidiomycetes. If this is correct the true fungi should be placed in two divisions; one containing the Phycomycetes; the other containing the Ascomycetes, Basidiomycetes, and Deuteromycetes. According to another group of botanists, the Phycomycetes arose from protozoa and in turn gave rise to the Ascomycetes and Basidiomycetes. Since, as will be shown in Chaps. 12 and 13, this seems the more probable, these three classes, together with the Deuteromycetes, may be grouped in a single division, the *Eumycophyta*.

Validity of the Pteridophyta. For a long time ferns, lycopods, and horsetails were thought to be sufficiently related to be placed in a single division, the *Pteridophyta*. Question as to the validity of the Pteridophyta arose when Jeffrey[2] showed that there are two fundamentally different types of vascular plants. He called these types "stocks." Ferns, gymnosperms, and angiosperms, a "stock" which he called the *Pteridopsida*, have macrophyllous leaves and leaf gaps when the vascular cylinder is siphonostelic (see Vol. 2, Chap. 6). Lycopods and horsetails, a "stock" which he called the *Lycopsida*, have microphyllous leaves and no leaf gaps when the vascular cylinder is siphonostelic. Jeffrey does not indicate

* Pascher, 1914, 1927. [An asterisk will be used hereafter to indicate a *discussion* source.]

[1] Graham, 1951. [2] Jeffrey, 1902.

whether these two "stocks" should be considered divisions or subdivisions of the plant kingdom. Scott[1] was the first to give them formal rank as divisions and to segregate the horsetails as a separate division, the *Sphenopsida*. Later, Scott[2] gave the Psilophytales the rank of a division but retained the ordinal name as a division name.

Ferns, lycopods, and horsetails are three series diverging from psilophytes; and seed plants are a series or group of series derived from ferns. The problem is that of what rank should be accorded diverging members of the collective series. Some botanists[3] place the collective series in a single division, the *Tracheophyta*, and divide it into four subdivisions: *Psilopsida, Lycopsida, Sphenopsida*, and *Pteropsida*. This reduction of the four to the rank of subdivisions minimizes their marked divergence one from another. In the opinion of the writer the differences between the psilopsidan, lycopsidan, and sphenopsidan series are of the magnitude of a division. There still remains the question of the degree of divergence among members of the pteropsidan series. Although ancestral to seed plants, the ferns seem to be sufficiently distinct from them to be placed in a separate division. Distinctive differences include gametic union by means of free-swimming antherozoids, gametophytes that are free-living from the beginning or eventually become so, uninterrupted growth of sporophyte from zygote to maturity, and absence of seed habit.

Finally, if psilophytes, lycopods, horsetails, and ferns are each to be given the rank of a division what names should be applied to these divisions? The International Code of Botanical Nomenclature as amended in 1950 recommends that all names of divisions end in the suffix -phyta and that subdivisions of vascular plants end in the suffix -opsida. Therefore although Lycopsida and Sphenopsida have been used as division names[1] they are inappropriate. The earliest system[4] in which the various classes of the Pteridophyta were each given the rank of a division used the name *Lepidophyta* for the lycopodian series and *Calamophyta* for the equisetaceous series. The division name Pteridophyta was restricted to include only the ferns. Because of the widespread use of the name Pteridophyta when all vascular cryptogams are grouped in a single division, the name *Pterophyta* is proposed for the division composed solely of ferns. The psilophytes should be grouped in a separate division, the *Psilophyta*.

Interrelationships. The various algal divisions mentioned on preceding pages seem to be phyletic series entirely independent from one another. The answer to the question as to whether they arose independently or from some common ancestral stock is obscure and purely a matter of speculation. However, numerous physiological and morphological features

[1] Scott, 1909. [2] Scott, 1923. [3] Eames, 1935; Tippo, 1942.
[4] Bessey, 1907.

in common suggest that they may have had a common origin in some primitively organized ancestral stock. The common physiological features include ability to elaborate food photosynthetically, ability to form enzymes, common features in permeability, and similarities in responses to external stimuli. Most of them also have such common cellular morphological features as a differentiation of the protoplasm into cytoplasm and nucleus, a localization of photosynthetic pigments in plastids, and a qualitative division of the nuclear material.

It is impossible to decide which of the algal divisions was the first to be evolved. The Cyanophyta are simpler in cell structure and in organization of their colonies, but this does not necessarily mean that they were the first to appear. In the Chrysophyta, Pyrrophyta, Euglenophyta, and Cyanophyta there has been but little advancement in evolution of the plant body, and in all of them the reproductive organs are simple. The Phaeophyta and Rhodophyta have attained a high algal level insofar as certain of each have a relatively large plant body of complex external form and with some internal differentiation of tissues. However, in neither the red nor the brown algae does there seem to have been an evolution of a true land plant.

If, as appears to be the case, the divisions of a fungal nature have evolved from protozoa they have no phylogenetic connection with other divisions of the plant kingdom. The two fungal divisions (Myxomycophyta and Eumycophyta) may have had a common origin but it is more probable that they were evolved independently.

Nowhere in the Chlorophyta are there algae as complex as are found in Rhodophyta and Phaeophyta. In spite of this, the presence of identical pigments in Chlorophyta and in true land plants, and the fact that the end product of photosynthesis in both is starch, suggests very strongly that all green plants at a higher evolutionary level than an algal organization have arisen from the Chlorophyta. The most primitive of these higher green plants are the Bryophyta. The Psilophyta are widely considered to be the most primitive of pteridophytes; but there is disagreement as to whether they were evolved directly from the Chlorophyta, evolved from the ancestral line leading to the Bryophyta, or evolved from one of the lines (classes) within the Bryophyta. As will be shown in Vol. 2, Chap. 6, the evidence seems to favor their origin from an anthocerotan type of bryophyte. Evolution from the Psilophyta proceeded in three distinct pteridophytic lines. Two of these lines, the Calamophyta and the Lepidophyta, did not evolve beyond the pteridophytic level. Seed plants were evolved from the third line, the Pterophyta, but it is beyond the province of this book to discuss the origin and classification of seed plants.

The relationships of plants are usually shown by a diagram having the form of a much-branched tree. A more accurate diagrammatic representation of evolutionary relationships among plants would be that of a tree adjoined by eight shrubs (Fig. 1). The tree would represent the Chlorophyta and the land plants derived from them. The shrubs would represent the other algae and the fungi. Four of the algal shrubs would be very low. The other two, representing the Phaeophyta and the Rhodophyta, would be somewhat taller.

Divisions and Classes of Cryptogams. The divisions and classes into which cryptogamic plants are here divided may be tabulated as follows,

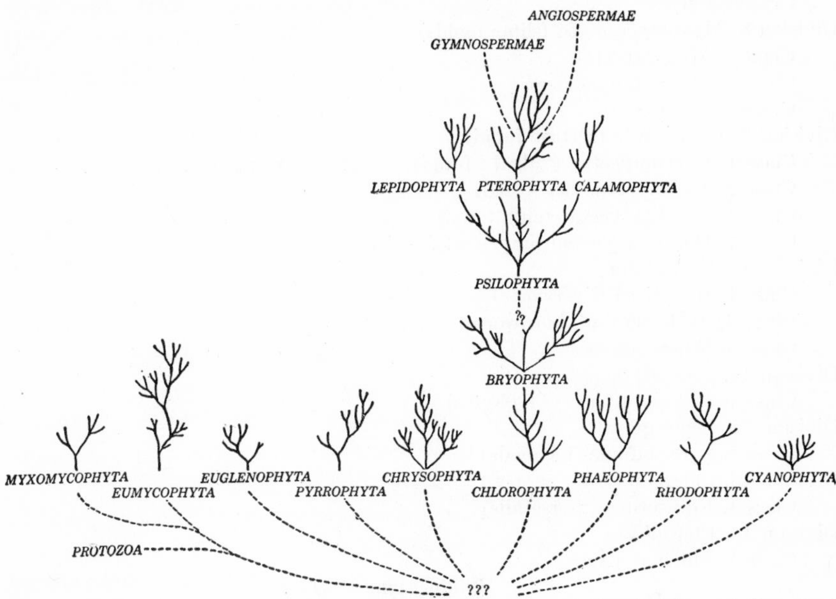

Fig. 1. Diagram showing the suggested interrelationships of the divisions of the plant kingdom.

but it should be noted that the sequence in which the algal divisions are arranged does not necessarily imply that the first on the list are the more primitive.

Division 1. Chlorophyta
- Class 1. Chlorophyceae (grass-green algae)
- Class 2. Charophyceae (stoneworts)

Division 2. Euglenophyta
- Class 1. Euglenophyceae (euglenoids)

Division 3. Pyrrophyta
- Class 1. Desmophyceae (dinophysids)
- Class 2. Dinophyceae (dinoflagelloids)

Division 4. Chrysophyta
- Class 1. Chrysophyceae (golden brown algae)
- Class 2. Xanthophyceae (yellow-green algae)
- Class 3. Bacillariophyceae (diatoms)

Division 5. Phaeophyta (brown algae)
 Class 1. Isogenerateae
 Class 2. Heterogenerateae
 Class 3. Cyclosporeae
Division 6. Cyanophyta (blue-green algae)
 Class 1. Myxophyceae
Division 7. Rhodophyta (red algae)
 Class 1. Rhodophyceae
Algae of Uncertain Systematic Position
 Chloromonadales
 Cryptophyceae
Division 8. Myxomycophyta (slime molds)
 Class 1. Myxomycetae
 Class 2. Plasmodiophorinae
 Class 3. Acrasieae
Division 9. Eumycophyta (true fungi)
 Class 1. Phycomycetae ("algal" fungi)
 Class 2. Ascomycetae (sac fungi)
 Class 3. Basidiomycetae (club fungi)
 Class 4. Deuteromycetae (imperfect fungi)
Division 10. Bryophyta
 Class 1. Hepaticae (liverworts)
 Class 2. Anthocerotae (hornworts)
 Class 3. Musci (mosses)
Division 11. Psilophyta
 Class 1. Psilophytinae (psilophytes)
Division 12. Lepidophyta
 Class 1. Lycopodinae (lycopods)
Division 13. Calamophyta
 Class 1. Equisetinae (horsetails)
Division 14. Pterophyta
 Class 1. Filicinae (ferns)

Bibliography

Bessey, C. E. **1907.** *Univ. Nebr. Studies* **7,** No. 4: 1–99. [Classification of plants.]

Braun, A. **1851.** Betrachtungen über die Erscheinung der Verjüngung in der Natur. Leipzig. 363 pp. 3 pl.

Cohn, F. **1853.** *Nova Acta Acad. Leop. Carol.* **24:** 103–256. 6 pl. [Development of algae and fungi.]

Eames, A. J. **1936.** Morphology of vascular plants. Lower groups (Psilophytales to Filicales). New York. 433 pp. 215 figs.

Eichler, A. W. **1880.** Syllabus der Vorlesungen über specielle und medicinisch-pharmaceutische Botanik. 2d ed. Berlin. 47 pp.

1883. *Ibid.* 3d ed. Berlin. 68 pp.

Endlicher, S. **1836.** Genera plantarum secundum ordines naturales disposita. Vindbonae.

Fritsch, F. E. **1935.** The structure and reproduction of the algae. Vol. 1. Cambridge. 791 pp. 245 figs.

1944. *Bot. Rev.* **10:** 233–277. [Classification of algae.]

1945. The structure and reproduction of the algae. Vol. 2. Cambridge. 939 pp. 336 figs.

Graham, H. W. **1951.** Pyrrhophyta. In G. M. Smith (editor), Manual of phycology. Waltham, Mass. Pp. 105–118. 3 figs.

Haeckel, E. **1866.** Generelle Morphologie der Organismen. Bd. 2. CLX + 462 pp. 8 pl.

Jeffrey, E. C. **1902.** *Phil. Trans. Roy. Soc. London B.* **195:** 119–146. 6 pl. [Stelar theory.]

De Jussieu, A. L. **1789.** Genera plantarum secundum ordines naturales disposita. Paris. 498 pp.

Lindley, J. **1847.** The vegetable kingdom. 2d ed. London. 911 pp.

Linnaeus, C. **1754.** Genera plantarum. Holmiae. 500 pp.

Luther, A. **1899.** *Bih. Kgl. Svensk. Vetensk.-Ak. Handl.* **24,** Afd. 3, No. 13; 1–22. 1 pl. [Xanthophyceae.]

Pascher, A. **1914.** *Ber. Deutsch. Bot. Ges.* **32:** 136–160. [Classification of algae.]

1921. *Ibid.* **39:** 236–248. 6 figs. [Classification of algae.]

1925. *Arch. Protistenk.* **52:** 489–546. 1 pl. 10 figs. [Classification of algae.]

1927. *Ibid.* **58:** 1–54. 38 figs. [Classification of algae.]

1931. *Beih. Bot. Centralbl.* **48:** 317–332. [Classification of algae.]

Rabenhorst, L. **1863.** Kryptogamen-Flora von Sachsen, der Ober-Lausitz, Thüringen und Nordböhmen mit Berücksichtigung der benachbarten Länder. Abt. 1. Leipzig. 655 pp.

Schimper, W. P. **1879.** Palaeophytologie. In K. A. Zittle, Handbuch der Palaeontologie **2,** Lief. 1: 1–152. 117 figs.

Scott, D. H. **1909.** Studies in fossil botany. 2d ed. Vol. 2. London. 321 pp. 95 figs.

1923. *Ibid.* 3d ed. Vol. 2. London. 446 pp. 136 figs.

Smith, G. M. **1933.** The fresh-water algae of the United States. New York. 716 pp. 449 figs.

1950. *Ibid.* 2d ed. New York. 719 pp. 559 figs.

Strain, H. H. **1951.** The pigments of algae. In G. M. Smith (editor), Manual of phycology. Waltham, Mass. Pp. 243–262.

Tippo, O. **1942.** *Chronica Botanica* **7:** 203–206. [Classification of plant kingdom.]

CHAPTER 2

CHLOROPHYTA

The Chlorophyta (grass-green algae) have their photosynthetic pigments localized in chromatophores which are grass green because of the predominance of chlorophylls *a* and *b* over the carotenes and xanthophylls. There are several xanthophylls not found in other algae, and of these lutein is the most abundant (see Table 1, page 4). Photosynthetic reserves are usually stored as starch and its formation is intimately associated with an organ of the chromatophore, the pyrenoid. Motile stages have all flagella of the whiplash type and equal in length. With a few exceptions the zoospores and motile gametes have two or four flagella. Although sexual reproduction is not a feature distinguishing Chlorophyta from other algae, it is a phenomenon of wide occurrence within the division, and in the various orders it ranges all the way from isogamy to oögamy.

Occurrence and Distribution. Approximately 10 per cent of the species are marine and 90 per cent are fresh-water. Certain orders, as the Ulvales and Siphonales, are predominantly marine; other orders, as the Ulotrichales, are predominantly fresh-water; and still others, as the Oedogoniales and Zygnematales, are exclusively fresh-water.

Most of the marine species live in shallow water along ocean shores, often being attached to rocks at levels that are exposed at low tide. In tropical waters certain attached species grow as much as 100 meters below the surface of the ocean. A majority of fresh-water species are submerged aquatics, but the number of species that do not grow submerged is surprisingly large. These include the species growing on soil, on rocks and cliffs, on damp wood or the bark of trees, and on snow or ice. There are also a few species that are internal parasites of land plants or epizootic upon land animals.

Many of the marine species have a definite geographical distribution, which is primarily dependent upon the temperature of the water. The same does not hold for fresh-water species; and, except for certain desmids and certain other species, all of them are cosmopolitan and may be expected anywhere.

Cell Structure. A few of the more primitive Chlorophyta have naked protoplasts, but in the great majority of cases the protoplast lies within a definite wall which is a secretion product of the protoplast. Even when, as in certain unicellular Volvocales, there is no cell wall the exterior portion of the protoplasm is rigid and has a definite shape. The characteristic shape of cells in genera with a cell wall is, therefore, probably due to the protoplast itself rather than to the enclosing wall. All cells which are surrounded by a wall have one composed of at least two concentric layers. The innermost layer is composed wholly or in large part of cellulose[1] except in the Siphonales where the innermost layer usually contains callose instead of cellulose.[2] External to the cellulose is a layer of pectose, and it is very probable that this is produced directly by the protoplasm and filters through the micellae of the cellulose layer. In many species the outermost portion of the pectose is converted into a water-soluble pectin that dissolves in the surrounding medium. It is very probable, also, that the formation of pectose is a continuous process throughout vegetative life of the cell. There are many algae, including the Zygnemataceae, where the amount of pectose secreted just about balances the amount dissolved away. The result is a sort of equilibrium in which the thickness of the pectose layer remains practically constant.[3] If the formation of pectose ceases, as it does during conjugation in Zygnemataceae, there comes a time when the pectic layer becomes dissolved away and there is nothing external to the cellulose layer. Proof of this is seen in the lack of epiphytes on actively growing cells of *Zygnema* and *Spirogyra* (because the surface upon which epiphytes would grow is continually dissolving away) and the frequent presence of epiphytes upon old and conjugating filaments of these genera. Not all algae establish this balance in the gelatinous portion of the wall and certain of them, as *Gloeocystis*, have the gelatinous portion continually increasing in thickness. There are also genera in which the outermost portion of the pectose becomes impregnated with an insoluble substance that prevents dissolving away of the underlying pectose. *Cladophora* and *Oedogonium* are examples of Chlorophyta with an insoluble outermost wall layer. The chemical nature of the insoluble substance is in dispute, some holding that it is chitin,[4] others denying this.[5] Walls of green algae may also be impregnated with lime. This is especially the case with certain Siphonales of tropical seas, and in them lime may accumulate in such quantity that the alga is greenish white.

The photosynthetic and associated pigments (see Table 1, page 4) are borne in definite plastids—the **chloroplasts.** These are grass green because of a predominance of the chlorophylls over other pigments. How-

[1] Tiffany, 1924; Wurdack, 1923. [2] Mirande, 1913. [3] Tiffany, 1924.
[4] Wurdack, 1923. [5] von Wettstein, 1921.

ever, the amount of pigments present is extremely variable from species to species and ranges all the way from a quantity sufficient to color the plastid a brilliant grass green to an amount so small that there is only a tinge of color. Certain Volvocales, as *Polytoma*, completely lack photosynthetic pigments. Vegetative cells of certain genera and zygotes of many genera have the green color masked by a red pigment called **hematochrome.** In vegetative cells of *Trentepohlia* the so-called "hematochrome" is beta-carotene, and in vegetative cells of *Haematococcus* the "hematochrome" is a ketonic carotenoid—euglenorhodone.[1] The color of cells of certain Zygnemataceae may also be modified by anthocyan pigments dissolved in the cell sap.

Chloroplasts of green algae always have a shape characteristic for the particular genus or species. Old cells of *Scenedesmus*, *Hydrodictyon*, and several other algae seem to have the pigments diffused throughout the cytoplasm, but young cells of all of them have definite chloroplasts. The shape of the chloroplast is extremely varied from genus to genus. The massive cup-shaped chloroplast characteristic of so many species of *Chlamydomonas* is also found in many other Volvocales and Tetrasporales. The widespread occurrence of cup-shaped chloroplasts among these primitive Chlorophyta gives good reason for supposing that this is the primitive type. However, even in *Chlamydomonas* there are species where the chloroplast is stellate or is **H**-shaped in optical section. More advanced green algae, as the Ulotrichales, usually have cells with a chloroplast that is parietal in position, laminate, and entire or perforate. Siphonales usually have numerous small discoid chloroplasts in the peripheral portion of the cytoplasm. The most elaborate of all chloroplasts are those found in the Desmidiaceae, and the range in shape from species to species, and genus to genus, is almost infinite.[2]

Most chloroplasts contain a special organ, the **pyrenoid.** Structurally it consists of a central proteinaceous core, which in turn is ensheathed by minute plates of starch. Strictly speaking, the term should be applied only to the proteinaceous core, but in common usage it is often applied to both the core and the surrounding starch plates. The first study of pyrenoids with the aid of modern cytological techniques was on *Hydrodictyon*.[3] This study holds that the core of a pyrenoid becomes differentiated into two parts, one destined to become impregnated with starch, the other to remain unchanged (Fig. 2). The part undergoing change gradually gives more and more of a starch reaction, eventually moves away from the unchanged part, and becomes one of the starch plates surrounding the central core. A somewhat similar relationship between starch and the central core has been reported[4] for certain other green algae. Accord-

[1] Strain, 1951. [2] Nellie Carter, 1919*A*, 1919*B*, 1920, 1920*A*.
[3] Timberlake, 1901. [4] Bold, 1931; Lutman, 1910; McAllister, 1913.

ing to another interpretation[1] starch grains are at first minute granules external to the proteinaceous body; later on the granules increase in size by deposition of starch on all sides.

Pure cultures of green algae furnish considerable evidence on the role of the pyrenoid in starch formation. When cells are grown in total darkness but in the presence of glucose or some other carbon source, there is an accumulation of starch around the protein core. This seems to show that the first steps in photosynthesis are carried on by the chlorophyll-containing portion of the chloroplast and that the last step or steps in formation of starch are performed by the protein core of the pyrenoid.

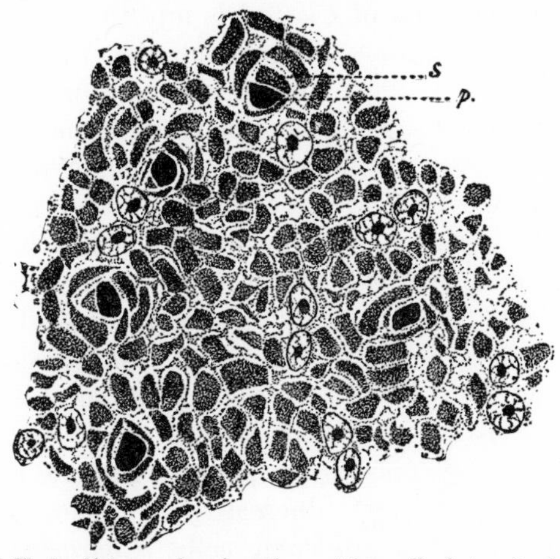

Fig. 2. Pyrenoids of *Hydrodictyon*, showing the cutting off of starch plates. (*From Timberlake*, 1901.)

Cells of small size with one chloroplast and those with many small chloroplasts usually have but one pyrenoid in a chloroplast. Cells with large chloroplasts have many pyrenoids, either irregularly distributed as in *Oedogonium*, or in a linear series as in *Spirogyra*. Mature cells whose chloroplasts contain numerous pyrenoids may have but a single pyrenoid when young and the number increases as the chloroplast grows in size (*Hydrodictyon*), or there may be several pyrenoids even in the youngest chloroplast (*Oedogonium, Spirogyra*). Species whose chloroplasts contain one pyrenoid when the cell is mature may have the pyrenoids formed *de novo* in the daughter cells,[2] or pyrenoids of daughter cells may be formed by division of the pyrenoid in the parent cell.[3] Pyrenoids need not be present to have starch formed in cells of green algae. This is the case in certain heteroplastic Siphonales whose chloroplasts are without pyrenoids and in which all starch accumulates in leucoplasts.[4]

[1] Czurda, 1928. [2] Geitler, 1926; McAllister, 1913; Smith, 1916, 1916*A*, 1918.

[3] Acton, 1916; Bold, 1913; Geitler, 1926; Potthoff, 1927; Vlk, 1939.

[4] Czurda, 1928; Ernst, 1902, 1904; Feldmann, 1946.

Chlorophyta also store reserve foods as oil. The oil droplets so frequently found in old vegetative cells and in zygotes are undoubtedly conversion products from starch. A formation of oil, instead of starch, is a regular phenomenon in vegetative cells of *Schizochlamys* and *Mesotaenium*.

All green algae have a definitely organized nucleus with a distinct nuclear membrane, one or more nucleoli, and a chromatic network. The amount of chromatic material in a nucleus is often so scanty that the space between nucleolus and membrane is almost colorless; but nuclei of certain genera, as *Oedogonium*, *Cladophora*, and *Spirogyra*, have considerable chromatic material. Nuclear division, except occasional amitotic divisions in internodal cells of *Chara*,[1] is mitotic and similar to that in higher plants. Vegetative cells of all Volvocales are uninucleate, and the same is true for many genera of a more advanced type. A multinucleate (**coenocytic**) condition is known both for Chlorophyta which have no vegetative cell division and for those whose cells divide vegetatively. In genera without vegetative cell division, as in *Pediastrum*, the number of nuclei may remain small until just before formation of zoospores or gametes and then suddenly increase in number. Other genera with such cells (*Characium*, *Hydrodictyon*) have a gradual increase in number of nuclei throughout the entire vegetative life of a cell. Coenocytic cells of the type found in *Cladophora* have a gradual increase in number of nuclei as the cell increases in size, and not a sudden increase in number just prior to cell division.

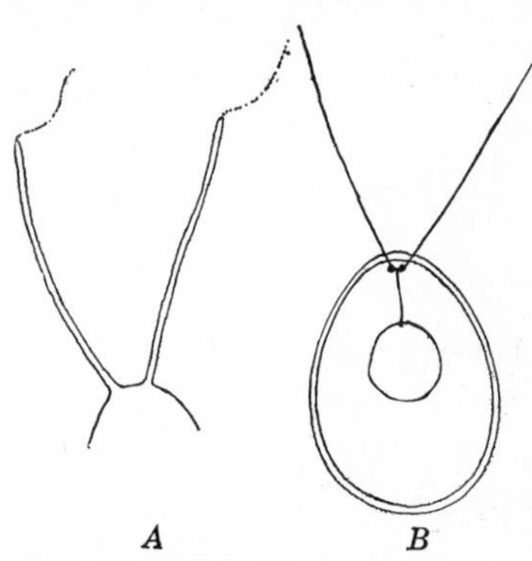

FIG. 3. *A*, flagella of *Chlamydomonas dorsoventralis* Pascher stained to show the endpiece. *B*, cell of *Chlamydomonas nasuta* Korshikov, with all protoplasmic structures but flagella and neuromotor apparatus omitted from the drawing. (*A*, *after Vlk*, 1938; *B*, *based upon Kater*, 1929.)

Vegetative cells of most Volvocales and reproductive cells of most other green algae are bi- or quadriflagellate and with the flagella inserted at the anterior end. Motile reproductive cells of Oedogoniales and of *Derbesia* have a transverse whorl of many flagella. Flagella of a sufficient number of Volvocales, and of swarmers of other Chlorophyta, have been investigated[2] to warrant the assumption that there is but one type of flagellum throughout the division. This is of the whiplash type and one in which an axial filament (**axoneme**) is surrounded by a cytoplasmic sheath for a greater part of its length. The cytoplasmic sheath usually ends abruptly, the naked portion of the axoneme extending beyond it being known as the endpiece (Fig. 3*A*). Flagella of Volvocales are inti-

[1] Sundaralingam, 1948. [2] Owen, 1949; Petersen, 1929; Vlk, 1938.

mately associated with a **neuromotor apparatus.** A neuromotor apparatus (Fig. 3*B*) consists of a granule (**blepharoplast**) at the base of the flagellum, and the blepharoplasts connected by a transverse fiber (the **paradesmose**) which is connected with a descending fiber, the **rhizoplast.** The rhizoplast runs down to and connects with a centrosome that may lie within[1] or just outside[2] the nucleus.

The **eyespot** (**stigma**) of motile cells usually lies toward the anterior end of a cell but it may be median or posterior in position. It is a photoreceptive organ that seems to be concerned with directing the movement of flagella in phototactic responses. Evidence for this is seen in certain colorless unicellular genera of Volvocales where the species with eyespots respond phototactically and those lacking them do not.[3] On the other hand, a mutant of *Chlamydomonas reinhardi* Dang. without an eyespot does show a phototactic response but not so pronounced as in strains with an eyespot.[4] In *Chlamydomonas* (Fig. 4*A*) the eyespot is described[5] as consisting of a biconvex hyaline photosensitive portion which overlies a curved pigmented plate. *Gonium*, *Eudorina*, and *Volvox* are described[6] as having a biconvex lens exterior to cup-shaped photosensitive and pigmented portions (Fig. 4*B*). Phototactic responses in these eyespots are thought to be due to selective reflection from the shaded concave surface of the pigmented portion.

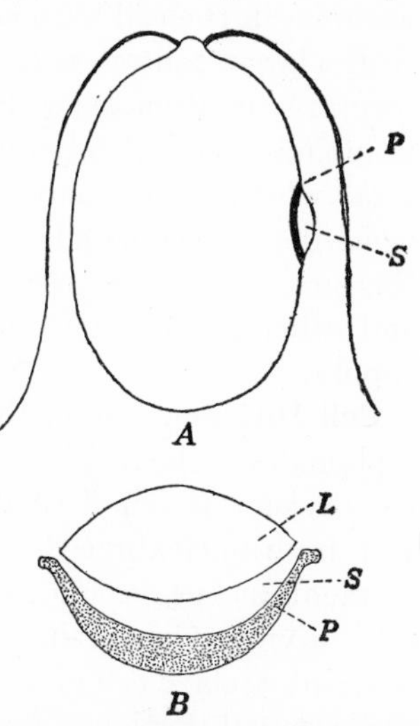

FIG. 4. *A*, diagram of an eyespot of *Chlamydomonas* showing the pigment cup (*P*) and the photosensitive substance (*S*). *B*, diagram of a vertical section of the eyespot of *Volvox* through the lens (*L*), photosensitive substance (*S*), and the pigment cup (*P*). (*Modified from Mast*, 1928.)

Vegetative cells of most Volvocales and of certain Tetrasporales have **contractile vacuoles.** In most biflagellate genera, there are two contractile vacuoles and they lie near the base of the flagella. Some biflagellate genera have more than two vacuoles, and these, as in *Haematococcus*, may lie beneath any part of the protoplast's surface. When two vacuoles are present these usually contract alternately. The contraction is sudden and the distention is slow. Because of this the contractile vacuoles are sometimes called **pulsating vacuoles.** It is thought that contractile vacuoles are excretory organs and that the liquid discharged from them is expelled from the cell. Contractile vacuoles of Chlorophyta are not inter-

[1] Entz, 1918; Kater, 1929. [2] Elliot, 1934; Kater, 1925.
[3] E. G. Pringsheim, 1937. [4] Hartshorne, 1953.
[5] Mast, 1928. [6] Mast, 1916, 1928.

connected to form the complex systems that are found in certain Chrysophyceae and protozoa.

The vacuoles present in cells of genera more advanced than Tetrasporales are of the familiar type found in most plant cells. Immature cells developing from zoospores, as those of *Hydrodictyon*, have innumerable minute vacuoles scattered throughout the cytoplasm. Many of them gradually increase in size, and now and then two or more of the enlarging vacuoles coalesce. Gradually, therefore, the number of conspicuous vacuoles in the cell becomes smaller, and eventually they unite to form a single large **central vacuole.** Sometimes, as in *Sphaeroplea*, there are several large vacuoles within a mature cell; or, as in *Spirogyra*, the central vacuole is incompletely divided by strands of cytoplasm. Species of green algae which do not have a conspicuous central vacuole are chiefly those which have become adapted to a subaerial existence. It is thought[1] that this lack of large vacuoles is the chief reason why *Protococcus*, *Trentepohlia*, and other aerial algae can live where there is a greatly reduced water supply.

Cell Division. One of the characteristics of the Chlorococcales and the Siphonales is the inability of their cells to divide vegetatively. Vegetative cell division is found in all other orders and occurs in both uninucleate and multinucleate cells. Division is intercalary in most unbranched filamentous species and, except for the basal cell, any cell in a filament may divide. Genera in which the thallus is a branching filament may have intercalary cell divisions, but more often cell division is restricted to the terminal portion of branches though not necessarily to the apical cell of a branch.

Cytokinesis of uninucleate cells is always preceded by a mitotic division of the nucleus; multinucleate cells may or may not have a division of the nuclei immediately preceding cell division. Cell division is usually by a transverse furrowing that takes place midway between the poles of the plasma membrane and only in rare cases[2] is cell division by means of a cell plate (phragmoplast). In division by furrowing the furrow deepens until it has cut entirely through the protoplast and so produced two daughter protoplasts. Although division by means of a furrow is almost universal, there is great variability in the time at which a transverse wall is formed between the two daughter protoplasts. Most cells dividing by means of a furrow secrete wall material within the deepening furrow. In fact, cross-wall formation follows so closely upon the furrowing that cell division is often thought to be caused by an inward growth of a transverse septum. Completion of cytokinesis before the beginning of wall formation is found in *Microspora* and in Oedogoniales. *Microspora* has an intercalation of an **H**-shaped piece of wall material between the daughter protoplasts;

[1] de Puymaly, 1924. [2] Mainx, 1927; McAllister, 1913, 1931.

Oedogoniales have the secretion of a transverse wall after elongation of the unique lateral ring of wall material (see page 70). Cell division in constricted desmids, to which the great majority of species belong, begins with a nuclear division and an elongation of the isthmus between the two semicells (see page 86). After a transverse division in the region of the isthmus each of the two daughter cells consists of one semicell and half of the isthmus portion of the parent cell. The old semicell remains unchanged, but the isthmus portion enlarges until it is identical in size and ornamentation with the old semicell (Fig. 40, page 86).

In cells with a single chloroplast, cytokinesis divides the chloroplast into two daughter chloroplasts. The division may be in the transverse axis of the cell (*Spirogyra* and *Ulothrix*) or in the longitudinal axis of a cell (*Chlamydomonas*). Uninucleate cells with a chloroplast axial to both poles of the nucleus have a transverse division of each chloroplast and a migration of a daughter nucleus to a point midway between each pair of daughter chloroplasts. There then follows a bipartition of the cytoplasm that results in two daughter protoplasts each with a nucleus and two chloroplasts axial to it. Siphonales and other green algae with numerous chloroplasts have no division of the chloroplasts at the time of cell division.

Many of the Chlorophyta show a very marked diurnal periodicity in the time at which nuclear and cell division takes place. In the great majority of cases these divisions take place during the night. Nuclear division usually begins within an hour or two after sundown and is often completed by the early morning hours. The occurrence of division at night rather than during the daytime may possibly be correlated with the greater accumulation of reserve foods following the photosynthetic activity of the daytime.

Vegetative Multiplication. In colonial genera, cell division increases the number of cells of a colony but does not bring about a formation of new plants. Accidental breaking of a colony, especially in the case of filamentous genera, may result from such external causes as animals feeding upon the alga, or it may result from the action of water currents. The formation of zoospores, aplanospores, or zoogametes in certain parts of a filament is often followed by a breaking of the filament at points where there are empty cells. In some cases, as in Oedogoniales, the cell wall breaks transversely when zoospores are liberated and so severs the filament into two or more portions.

Some filamentous species, as those of *Stichococcus* and small-celled species of *Spirogyra*, have a strong tendency to separate into individual cells or short series of a few cells each. Such fragments may then grow into long filaments. Fragmentation is especially frequent in species of *Spirogyra* that have an annular infolding of the transverse walls (replicate end walls); the fragmentation resulting from the eversion of the replicate walls induced through changes in turgidity of the cells. It has been held[1] that many of the transverse walls of filamentous algae have a middle lamella of pectic material. If this is true of filaments which tend to fragment, changes in composition of the middle lamellae might be one of the causes of fragmentation.

Asexual Reproduction. The commonest method of asexual reproduction is by a formation of **zoospores.** From the phylogenetic standpoint, zoospores may be looked upon as a temporary reversion to the primitive ancestral flagellated condition. Zoospore formation, like cell division, frequently takes place at night, and the spores are liberated at daybreak. Sudden changes in the environment often induce profuse sporulation, and it is no unusual experience to find such algae as *Stigeoclonium* and *Draparnaldia* sporulating so profusely the day after collection that but few traces of the original filaments remain. Change from light to dark, a transfer from an aerial to an aquatic environment, and a change from running to quiet water also stimulate a formation of zoospores. However, change of external environmental conditions does not bring about zoospore formation with the regularity that has been claimed,[2] and one cannot always be certain of obtaining zoospores at a desired time by modifying the environment.

Zoospores are usually formed in vegetative cells morphologically similar to others in the colony, and only in a few cases, as in the Trentepohliaceae, are they formed in special cells (**sporangia**). All vegetative cells in a colony may be able to produce zoospores, or spore formation may be restricted to certain cells. The restriction of zoospore formation to certain cells is especially prominent in genera with branching filaments, where it usually takes place only in young vigorously growing portions of the filament. Colonies with all cells potentially capable of producing zoospores rarely have all of them doing so simultaneously and spore formation at any given day is usually restricted to isolated cells or short series of cells.

Zoospores may be formed singly or in numbers within a cell. When a uninucleate cell produces more than one zoospore the number of zoospores is two or a multiple thereof and usually 4, 8, or 16. This is due either to repeated bipartition of the protoplast, or to successive simultaneous nuclear divisions followed by a cleavage into uninucleate protoplasts. Coenocytic cells also have a cleavage into uninucleate protoplasts that become zoospores, but their number is not necessarily a multiple of two. Cleavage of coenocytic (multinucleate) cells may be **simultaneous;** or it may be **progressive** and into masses with smaller and smaller numbers of nuclei (Fig. 46*F–G*, page 93). Irrespective of whether formed by

[1] Tiffany, 1924. [2] Klebs, 1896.

simultaneous or progressive cleavage, the ultimate uninucleate protoplasts are then metamorphosed into zoospores with a specific number of flagella.

Liberation of zoospores is generally through a pore in the surrounding wall of the old parent cell, but it may also be effected by a breaking or gelatinization of the wall. In *Cladophora* (Fig. 27*A*, page 67), pore formation is obviously due to a local gelatinization of the cell wall, and it is probable that the same is true for many other green algae. Zoospores of most genera may swim freely in any direction after liberation, but in many cases the direction in which they swim is influenced by external factors, especially light. The duration of swarming is dependent both upon the particular species and upon environmental conditions. Normally the zoospores of most species swarm for an hour or two, but the swarming period may be as short as three or four minutes (*Pediastrum*) or as long as two or three days (*Ulothrix*). Zoospores are without a wall throughout the entire swarming period. When swarming ceases, the great majority of genera have the zoospore coming to rest upon some solid object in the water. Shortly after the cessation of swarming the zoospore retracts or loses its flagella, secretes a wall, and thus becomes a vegetative cell. If, as is usually the case, this cell is resting upon some solid object the pectic material in the wall cements it to the substratum. Colonial species soon have the one-celled stage thus formed developing into a many-celled colony.

Not infrequently there is a formation of nonflagellated **aplanospores** instead of zoospores. Zoospores lack walls; aplanospores have a definite wall distinct from the wall of the parent cell. Aplanospores are usually formed singly within a cell but there may also be a formation of more than one. Aplanospores are to be interpreted as abortive zoospores in which the motile phase has been omitted. They are regularly formed in certain genera, including *Microspora* (Fig. 16*C*, page 48), and only occasionally in other genera such as *Ulothrix*. Aplanospores may be liberated from an old parent-cell wall before they germinate, or they may begin developing into a new filament before they are liberated. Aplanospores with greatly thickened walls are usually called **hypnospores.** If an aplanospore has the same distinctive shape as the parent cell it is an **autospore**, and these are the only known method of reproduction in certain families of the Chlorococcales. The number of autospores produced by a cell is two or a multiple thereof. Autospores may separate from one another after liberation or all autospores produced by a cell may remain permanently united in an **autocolony** whose cells are always arranged in a specific manner characteristic for the genus (Fig. 52*A–B*, page 100).

Vegetative cells may also develop into spore-like stages with much thicker walls and more abundant food reserves. These **akinetes** may always be distinguished from aplanospores by the fact that the additional wall layers around the protoplast are fused with the wall of the parent cell. A formation of akinetes is of regular occurrence in certain genera, including *Pithophora* (Fig. 5), and occasional in others. An akinete is not a modified zoospore or a stage in formation of zoospores. Instead, it is a direct modification of a vegetative cell and one resulting in a structure better adapted to tide the alga over unfavorable conditions. Akinetes of certain genera may develop directly into new plants (*Pithophora*), or, as is usually the case, have the protoplast dividing into a number of zoospores which escape from the enclosing wall.

Sexual Reproduction. The Chlorophyta are algae in which gametic union is of widespread occurrence. In the simplest and most primitive case there is a fusion of a flagellated gamete (**zoogamete**) with another zoogamete of identical size and structure. Among algae with this **isogamous** gametic union it is impossible to make morphological distinctions between male and female gametes (Fig. 8*B*, page 33). Isogamy leads to a condition of **anisogamy** where both gametes are flagellated, but where one of a fusing pair is regularly larger than the other. The differences in size between the two may be relatively small (Fig. 24*E–F*, page 62), or it may be pronounced (Fig. 60*E–F*, page 114). In anisogamous species the smaller of a fusing pair is considered the male and the larger the female. Anisogamy leads, in turn, to a condition of **oögamy** where there is a union of a small flagellated male gamete (**antherozoid**) with a large nonflagellated female gamete (**egg**). Isogamy, anisogamy, and oögamy represent a progressive series in differentiation of gametes, a differentiation that has arisen independently in at least five different phyletic lines among the green algae. The occurrence of oögamy in three different genera of unicellular Volvocales (*Chlamydomonas*, *Chlorogonium*, *Polytoma*) shows that an evolution from isogamy to oögamy is not necessarily correlated with an increase in complexity of colonial organization.

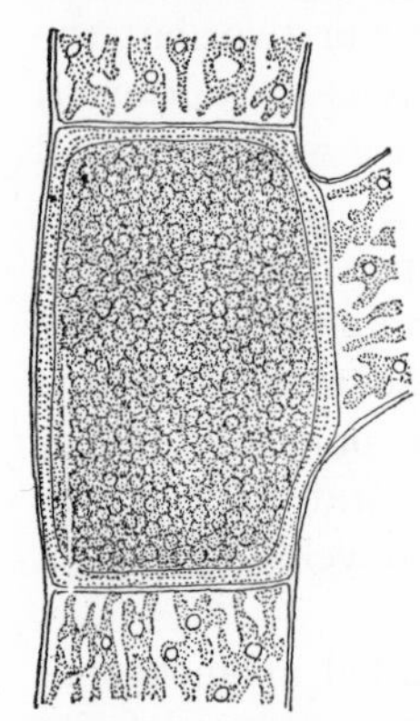

FIG. 5. Akinete of *Pithophora oedogonia* (Mont.) Wittr. (× 300.)

Study of green algae in unialgal and pure culture has shown that certain species are **homothallic** (**monoecious**) and can have a union of gametes derived from a single parent cell. Other species are **heterothallic** (**dioecious**) and have the gametes fusing in pairs only when the two come from cells of different parentage.

Among a few one-celled Volvocales two vegetative cells may function directly as gametes and fuse in pairs. This occurs among both homo- and heterothallic species of *Chlamydomonas*. Most green algae produce flagellated or amoeboid reproductive cells whose special purpose is to function as gametes. In many cases, as in *Ulothrix* and *Ulva*, reproductive swarmers are biflagellate when gametes and quadriflagellate when zoospores. In isogamous and anisogamous species there is rarely a formation of gametes within a special cell of distinctive shape (**gametangium**) whose sole function is the production of gametes. Practically all oögamous green algae have gametangia of distinctive shape and ones in which the male gametangium (**antheridium**) is morphologically different from the female gametangium (**oögonium**). Isogamous and anisogamous Chlorophyta discharge their gametes from the parent cell, the formation and ripening of the zygote occurring external to the alga. With a few exceptions, oögamous genera do not liberate their eggs from the oögonium. Gametic union takes place within the oögonium, and the resultant zygote is liberated only when the oögonial wall decays.

Aplanogamy, a union of amoeboid gametes (**aplanogametes**) without flagella, is a feature immediately distinguishing the Zygnematales from other Chlorophyta. Most Desmidiaceae have the aplanogametes escaping from and uniting in pairs external to the parent-cell wall. Zygnemataceae have no liberation of aplanogametes and have an establishment of a tubular connection (**conjugation tube**) between two cells containing aplanogametes. Some of these, as certain species of *Zygnema*, are truly isogamous and have the two aplanogametes meeting and fusing in the conjugation tube; others, as *Spirogyra*, are morphologically isogamous but not physiologically isogamous because one aplanogamete is actively amoeboid and the other passive.

A gamete that has not united with a gamete of opposite sex may develop **parthenogenetically** into a new plant. This has been demonstrated by culture in certain species.[1] Clear proof of parthenogenesis in certain species of a genus does not mean that all species of the genus are parthenogenetic. For example, *Ulva lactuca* L. is parthenogenetic,[2] whereas *U. lobata* (Kütz.) S. and G. is not.[3]

The Zygote and Its Germination. Zygotes of Chlorophyta are of two types, thin-walled zygotes which germinate within a day or two after gametic union, and thick-walled zygotes which remain dormant for some time before germinating.

Isogamous and anisogamous species forming thick-walled resting zygotes usually do not have a disappearance of flagella when gametes unite and the zygote may be motile for several hours before it comes to rest, loses its flagella, and begins to form a wall. All zygotes of oögamous species are immobile from the beginning, and all begin to form a wall within a fairly short time. When first formed the wall of a resting zygote is a thin homogeneous structure, but as ripening proceeds it becomes much thicker and often differentiated into three layers, the outer two of which contain

[1] Føyn, 1934, 1934*A*. [2] Føyn, 1934*A*. [3] Smith, 1950.

cellulose. At first the protoplast of a resting zygote is of a bright green color and contains such food reserves as were present in the gametes. Photosynthesis by the ripening zygote results in an accumulation of still more reserve food. In young zygotes the food reserve consists almost wholly of starch; later on, there is often a conversion of the starch into oil. Ripening of a zygote is generally accompanied by a development of "hematochrome" in sufficient abundance to color the protoplast a bright red or an orange-red.

Sooner or later, the two nuclei contributed by the two gametes fuse with each other. The fate of the chloroplast or chloroplasts contributed by each gamete is very difficult to follow in the case of resting zygotes. For *Zygnema*[1] and for certain desmids[2] it seems fairly certain that chloroplasts derived from the female gamete persist and those contributed by the male gamete degenerate.

Fusion of gamete nuclei (**syngamy**) is followed by meiosis in the case of thick-walled resting zygotes. For green algae this was first demonstrated in *Coleochaete*.[3] Since then a meiotic division of the fusion nucleus in thick-walled zygotes has been found among certain members of the Volvocales, Ulotrichales, Oedogoniales, Chlorococcales, and Zygnematales. Meiosis usually occurs just before the zygote germinates. However, the time interval between gametic union and ability to germinate varies greatly from genus to genus. For example, zygotes of *Chlamydomonas* may be capable of germination in 10 days, those of *Ulothrix* in 5 to 9 months,[4] and those of *Oedogonium* in 12 to 14 months.[5] Except in Zygnematales, meiotic division of the fusion nucleus into four nuclei is usually followed by a cleavage of the protoplast into four uninucleate protoplasts, each of which becomes a zoospore; but there are cases where the number of nuclei becomes 8, 16, 32, or 64 before cleavage and with a resultant formation of 8, 16, 32, or 64 zoospores. Degeneration of one, two, or three nuclei immediately after meiosis results in a production of three, two, or a single zoospore by a germinating zygote. The zygote wall cracks open after the zoospores are formed but they usually do not become motile until after they have been extruded from the zygote wall. In germination of zygotes of Zygnematales there may be a formation of one, two, or four protoplasts after meiosis but these protoplasts are not metamorphosed into zoospores. They develop directly into new plants.

Zygotes of the thin-walled type which germinate within a day or two after gametic union have a mitotic division of the zygote nucleus and a direct development of the zygote into a new thallus.

Life Cycles. The simplest possible type of life cycle is that found in *Chlamydomonas*. Here, division of a vegetative cell results in the forma-

[1] Kurssanow, 1911. [2] Potthoff, 1927. [3] Allen, 1905.
[4] Gross, 1931. [5] Mainx, 1931.

tion of 2, 4, 8, or 16 motile daughter cells which may function as gametes. Zygotes resulting from gametic union have a meiotic division of the fusion nucleus and produce zoospores which function directly as one-celled vegetative plants. The life cycle of this primitive green alga consists of an alternation of a one-celled haploid phase with a one-celled diploid phase. Such an alternation is not obligatory in the sense that the haploid phase must always give rise to the diploid phase, and there may be a succession of haploid phases before production of the diploid phase. The alternation is obligatory in the sense that the diploid phase cannot give rise to further diploid phases but must always form the haploid phase.

Most green algae with alternating unicellular haploid and diploid phases have the vegetative functions, especially photosynthesis, centered in the haploid phase. *Chlorochytrium* may be cited as a green unicellular alga where the opposite condition obtains, and where the vegetative functions center in the unicellular diploid phase. This alga must be considered as having obligatory unicellular haploid and diploid phases, if the very temporary coenocytic condition during gametogenesis is not taken into consideration.

Beginning with the primitive condition of an alternation of unicellular haploid and diploid phases, there may be an evolution of a multicellular condition on either the haploid or the diploid side of the life cycle. The great majority of Chlorophyta have this on the haploid side. This has resulted (as in *Spirogyra*, *Oedogonium*, or *Coleochaete*) in a life cycle in which a multicellular haploid generation alternates with a unicellular diploid phase. Many such green algae have a reduplication of the haploid generation by means of zoospores or other asexual reproductive bodies. *Codium*[1] represents a case where there has been an interpolation of equational (mitotic) divisions of the diploid nucleus between syngamy and meiosis. Here we have what is essentially a multicellular diploid generation alternating with a unicellular haploid phase.

Particular interest attaches to those green algae in which a multicellular haploid generation alternates with a multicellular diploid generation. Most of these algae are **isomorphic**[2] and with the two generations morphologically identical; but in some genera, including *Stigeoclonium*,[3] the alternation is **heteromorphic** and the two generations morphologically dissimilar. The cycle of alternation may be strictly obligate, with the two generations following each other in regular succession; or there may be a parthenogenetic reduplication of the haploid generation.

An alternation of multicellular haploid and diploid generations has arisen independently in three families not closely related to one another (Cladophoraceae, Ulvaceae, Chaetophoraceae). As to the origin of this type of life cycle it is not improbable that this came from close relatives

[1] Williams, 1925. [2] Fritsch, 1935. [3] Juller, 1937.

whose life cycle consists of an alternation of a multicellular generation and a one-celled diploid phase. Support for this view is seen in the fact that each of the three families just mentioned has genera with an alternation of a multicellular haploid generation with a unicellular diploid phase. An alga with such a life cycle may have mutated in such a manner that the zygote nucleus divided mitotically instead of meiotically. The contribution by each haploid gamete of an identical set of genes for size and shape of thallus would result in the zygote's growing into a diploid thallus identical with the haploid multicellular thallus. The capacity for meiosis, originally present in the zygote nucleus, is transmitted throughout each cell generation in development of the diploid generation. Whether or not a cell of the diploid generation exhibits the capacity for undergoing meiosis is dependent upon the particular genus. All the cells of the diploid generation may have the nuclei dividing meiotically and the cells producing zoospores as in *Ulva* and *Entromorpha;* or, as in *Cladophora*, meiosis and zoospore formation may be restricted to young actively growing cells such as those at the tips of branches.

Evolution among the Chlorophyta. It is universally agreed that the unicellular Volvocales are of the primitive type from which all more advanced Chlorophyta have been evolved. It is also generally agreed that the colonial Volvocales represent an evolutionary dead end.

There is also practically unanimous agreement that both the palmelloid (Tetrasporales) and coccoid (Chlorococcales) green algae have been evolved directly from motile unicellular green algae. Opinion differs concerning relationships of these two groups to more complex green algae. According to one view[1] the ulotrichaceous algae have been derived from tetrasporaceous algae. According to another view[2] the ulotrichaceous algae have been derived directly from motile unicellular forms.

Most phycologists think that the siphonaceous green algae have been derived from coenocytic chlorococcoid forms and that *Protosiphon* represents an intermediate between the two. Many[3] think that all the multicellular coenocytic algae have, in turn, been derived from the siphonaceous green algae. Others[4] think that the Sphaeropleaceae and the Cladophoraceae are related to the ulotrichaceous series and the remaining multicellular coenocytic genera are derived from the siphonaceous genera. Still others[5] think that the siphonocladaceous, dasycladaceous, siphonaceous, and cladophoraceous series have been evolved independently from coenocytic chlorococcine algae. As between the foregoing diverse views it seems most probable that the multicellular coenocytic

[1] Blackman, 1900; Smith, 1938, 1950; West, 1916. [2] Fritsch, 1935.

[3] Blackman and Tansley, 1902; Feldmann, 1938; Pascher, 1931; Printz, 1927; West, 1916.

[4] Fritsch, 1935, 1947; Iyengar, 1951. [5] Egerod, 1952; Papenfuss, 1951.

green algae are not derived from the siphonaceous green algae. One feature favoring this interpretation is the discovery of two unique xanthophylls in siphonaceous green algae[1] and their absence in multicellular coenocytic genera.[2] As to the relationship of multicellular coenocytic algae to other Chlorophyta, the best interpretation seems to be that *Sphaeroplea* and the cladophoraceous series have been derived from ulotrichaceous forms and the remainder from chlorococcoid forms (Fig. 6).

Both the Oedogoniales and the Zygnematales are not closely related to other green algae. One theory[3] holds that the Oedogoniales are a phyletic

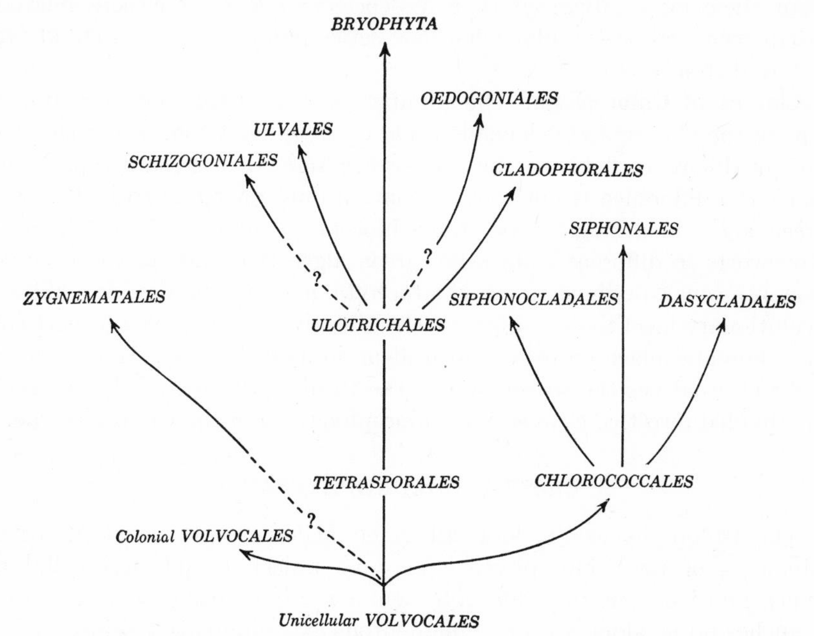

FIG. 6. Diagram showing the suggested interrelationships among the Chlorophyceae.

line derived from a unicellular motile green alga with the same distinctive flagellation as in zoospores and antherozoids of Oedogoniales. On the other hand, it seems more probable that the distinctive type of swarmer in Oedogoniales is a modification of the bi- and quadriflagellate swarmers found in other Chlorophyta. Evidence for this is seen in "*Derbesia*," a form unrelated to Oedogoniales but with the same type of swarmer. According to this interpretation the Oedogoniales may be a remote offshoot from the ulotrichaceous series.

The Zygnematales are immediately set off from other green algae by their aplanogamy. The occasional occurrence of amoeboid instead of

[1] Strain, 1951. [2] Personal communication from H. H. Strain.
[3] Blackman and Tansley, 1902; Bohlin, 1901; West, 1916.

flagellated gametes in *Chlamydomonas*[1] and the presence of various types of chloroplast in this genus suggest the possibility of a direct derivation of Zygnematales from motile one-celled ancestors. On the other hand, certain members of the ulotrichaceous series also have the ability to form amoeboid instead of flagellated reproductive cells.[2] There is, therefore, an equal possibility that the Zygnematales are an offshoot that arose at an early or a relatively late stage in evolution of the ulotrichaceous series.

The Charales (stoneworts) are more remote from other green algae than are members of any other order. Obviously they must have arisen from algae more advanced than Volvocales. The most closely related group seems to be the ulotrichaceous series but the Charales stand far removed from them.

Classes of Chlorophyta. The number of classes that one recognizes among the Chlorophyta depends upon one's opinion concerning the degree of difference between the stoneworts and other green algae. Some think the difference is not greater than ordinal rank and so include all green algae in a single class, the Chlorophyceae. Others consider the stoneworts so different from other green algae that they merit recognition as a separate division, the Charophyta, and one standing at a higher evolutionary level than an algal level. Still others place the stoneworts in one class and place all other green algae in another class. Among these three alternatives the writer prefers the third in which the Chlorophyta are divided into two classes, the Chlorophyceae and the Charophyceae.

CLASS 1. CHLOROPHYCEAE

The Chlorophyceae include all green algae except the stoneworts. Members of the Chlorophyceae may be unicellular or multicellular. When multicellular, the Chlorophyceae never have transverse whorls of branches borne along a central filamentous axis differentiated into nodes and internodes. Chlorophyceae also differ from Charophyceae in lacking ensheathing structures around the sex organs.

There are approximately 425 genera and 6,500 species of Chlorophyceae.

Classification. Phycologists are in general agreement concerning the genera to be assigned to many of the families (as the Volvocaceae, Hydrodictyaceae, Ulvaceae, Cladophoraceae, Oedogoniaceae, Zygnemataceae, and Desmidiaceae) but there is great diversity of opinion concerning the limits of taxa larger than the family. Some phycologists[3] recognize the *Volvocales* and *Tetrasporales* as separate orders, whereas others[4] reduce the Tetrasporales to a suborder of the Volvocales. Those who place the

[1] Pascher, 1918. [2] Pascher, 1915.
[3] Pascher, 1931; Prescott, 1951; Smith, 1933.
[4] Fritsch, 1935; Iyengar, 1951; Oltmanns, 1922; Papenfuss, 1951.

tetrasporaceous green algae in the Volvocales think that there is but little difference between them and the palmella stages formed by many unicellular Volvocales. However, the fact that the immobile phase is transitory in unicellular Volvocales and the motile phase is transitory in tetrasporaceous algae seems to justify the placing of the two in separate orders.

Both the branched and unbranched filamentous genera with a ulotrichoid type of cell are generally placed[1] in a single order, the *Ulotrichales*, but there are those[2] who segregate the branching genera in a separate order, the Chaetophorales, because of their heterotrichous habit.

Opinion is about equally divided as to whether the Ulvaceae should be placed in a separate order, the *Ulvales*,[3] or placed among the Ulotrichales.[4] The same holds for the Prasiolaceae, where some place them in a separate order, the *Schizogoniales*, and others include them in the Ulotrichales. In both these families the parenchymatous thallus differs so markedly from one of the filamentous type that the two families should not be included among the Ulotrichales.

The orders *Oedogoniales*, *Zygnematales* (Conjugales), *Chlorococcales*, and *Siphonales* are recognized by all phycologists. There is general agreement concerning the content of the first three, but not in the case of the Siphonales. Many phycologists include only the unseptate coenocytic siphonaceous genera in the Siphonales, but there are those who think[5] that many of the septate coenocytic genera are so closely related to the siphonaceous genera that they should be included in the Siphonales.

Formerly, those who restricted the Siphonales to the unseptate genera placed all multicellular coenocytic genera in a single order, the *Siphonocladales*. It is now generally agreed that the Sphaeropleaceae belong among the Ulotrichales. There are also those[6] who place the Cladophoraceae in a separate order, the *Cladophorales*, but this treatment of them has been vigorously opposed.[7] Cell division in Cladophoraceae is so different from the segregative cell division in Siphonocladaceae that the separation of the Cladophorales from the Siphonocladales seems justified. The Dasycladaceae are frequently placed among the Siphonocladales but differences in structure of their chloroplasts and the verticillate organization of the thallus justify the proposal[8] that this family be placed in a separate order, the *Dasycladales*.

[1] Oltmanns, 1922; Papenfuss, 1951; Pascher, 1931; Printz, 1927; Setchell and Gardner, 1920; Smith, 1933; West, 1916.

[2] Fritsch, 1935; Iyengar, 1951.

[3] Papenfuss, 1951; Prescott, 1951; Setchell and Gardner, 1920; Smith, 1933; West, 1916.

[4] Fritsch, 1935; Iyengar, 1951; Oltmanns, 1922; Pascher, 1931.

[5] Fritsch, 1935, 1947; Iyengar, 1951.

[6] Fritsch, 1935; Papenfuss, 1951; Prescott, 1951; Smith, 1938.

[7] Børgesen, 1939; Feldmann, 1938. [8] Feldmann, 1938.

When all the foregoing diverse views are taken into consideration the most natural classification of the Chlorophyceae seems to be that which divides them into the following orders: Volvocales, Tetrasporales, Ulotrichales, Ulvales, Schizogoniales, Cladophorales, Oedogoniales, Zygnematales, Chlorococcales, Siphonales, Siphonocladales, Dasycladales.

ORDER 1. VOLVOCALES

The Volvocales are the only order in which the vegetative cells are flagellated and actively motile. Some genera are unicellular; other genera are multicellular, with the number of cells in a colony a multiple of two and with the cells arranged in a definite manner. Asexual reproduction in unicellular genera is by division into a definite number of cells, and in colonial genera is by all or by certain cells of a colony dividing and redividing to form a daughter colony. Sexual reproduction may be isogamous, anisogamous, or oögamous.

There are more than 60 genera and 500 species of Volvocales. Almost all of them are fresh-water in habit and frequently they develop luxuriantly in waters rich in soluble nitrogenous compounds.

Most genera have more or less ovoid cells, but some have cells that are compressed or with an irregular outline. Some genera have naked protoplasts, but most of them have a definite cell wall with a cellulose layer next to the protoplast. Frequently there is a layer of pectic material external to the cellulose, and in colonial genera the pectic layers around the individual cells may be completely fused with one another to form a homogeneous colonial matrix. The general organization of the protoplast throughout the order is more or less like that of *Chlamydomonas*. However, there are a few genera, including *Polytoma*, which lack photosynthetic pigments and where the nutrition is saprophytic.

The Volvocales are generally divided into five or six families. Of the families discussed below, one is representative of those whose cells are solitary; the other is representative of those whose cells are united in colonies.

FAMILY 1. CHLAMYDOMONADACEAE

The Chlamydomonadaceae include all the unicellular Volvocales with a definite cell wall except those with a wall composed of two overlapping halves or those with a protoplast containing numerous contractile vacuoles and cytoplasmic strands to the cell wall. The cells may be bi- or quadriflagellate. Asexual reproduction is by division of the protoplast into two, four, or eight daughter protoplasts which form cell walls while still within the parent-cell wall. Daughter cells are liberated by a rupture or by a gelatinization of the parent-cell wall. If there is a gelatinization of the wall, the daughter cells may not escape before they produce a new cell generation or new cell generations. Such **palmella stages** are known for a number of genera, and in each of them the cells may become motile at any time.

Gametic union may be isogamous, anisogamous, or oögamous; and study in pure and unialgal culture has shown that some species are homothallic and others heterothallic. Zygotes form a thick wall and undergo a period of rest before the protoplast divides to form four or more flagellated cells. Cytological and genetic study of certain genera has shown that division of the zygote nucleus is meiotic,[1] and the same is probably true for all genera.

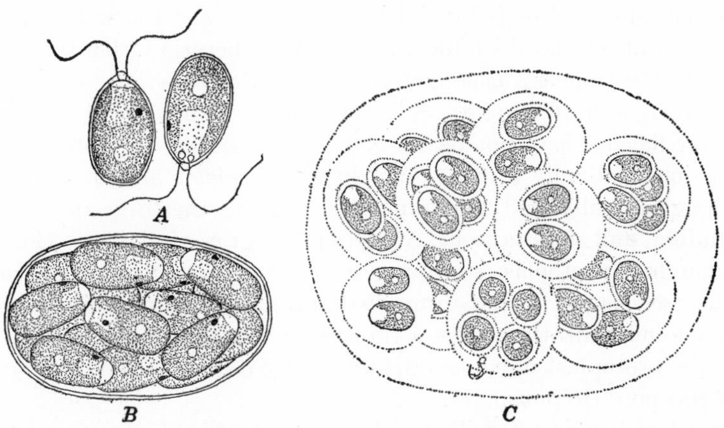

Fig. 7. *A–B*, *Chlamydomonas snowiae* Printz. *A*, motile vegetative cells. *B*, daughter cells before liberation from mother-cell wall. *C*, palmella stage of an undetermined species of *Chlamydomonas*. (× 1,000.)

Chlamydomonas, with some 325 species, is a widely distributed fresh-water organism in standing water and on damp soil. It often grows in abundance in waters rich in ammonium compounds, as pools in barnyards.

The cells (Fig. 7*A*) are biflagellate; and ellipsoidal, pyriform, subcylindrical, or spherical. The two flagella are anterior in insertion, lie fairly close together, and the contour of the cell may or may not be distinctly papillate in the region bearing the flagella. There is always a definite cellulose wall, and motile cells of some species have a gelatinous pectic sheath external to the cellulose layer. Most species have a single cup-shaped chloroplast. Chloroplasts of this type may be massive and occupy most of the protoplast, or the sides of the cup may be relatively thin. Other species have laminate or stellate chloroplasts, or have chloroplasts that are **H**-shaped in optical section.[2] Chloroplasts of most species

[1] Moewus, 1935, 1936, 1938, 1944; Schulze, 1927; Strehlow, 1929.
[2] Pascher, 1927.

contain a single pyrenoid; but those of certain species contain two pyrenoids, several pyrenoids, or no pyrenoids at all. Typically there are two contractile vacuoles near the base of the flagella and in a plane at right angles to them, but the number and position of vacuoles are not constant for the genus. The shape and position of the eyespot are fairly constant for any given species, but taking the genus as a whole the eyespot may lie anywhere between insertion of the flagella and the base of a cell. All species are uninucleate. Species with a cup-shaped chloroplast have the nucleus lying in the colorless cytoplasm filling the cup; other species may have the nucleus axial and midway between the two poles of a cell, or axially excentric.

Asexual reproduction is by division of the protoplast into 2, 4, 8, or 16 daughter protoplasts which form walls before liberation from the parent-cell wall. Most species usually form 4 daughter cells but some species usually form 8 or 16 daughter cells. Dividing cells are usually immobile, but their flagella may not be retracted or discarded. A protoplast first divides longitudinally into two daughter protoplasts and these then divide longitudinally and simultaneously. Any further divisions are also longitudinal and simultaneous. After the last series of divisions (Fig. 7*B*) each daughter protoplast secretes a wall and develops a neuromotor apparatus (see page 17) that forms two flagella. Daughter cells are liberated by a gelatinization or by a rupture of the parent-cell wall. In rare cases[1] the protoplast of a vegetative cell may round up and develop into an aplanospore (hypnospore).

Instead of forming flagella and becoming motile, daughter cells may remain within the matrix formed by gelatinization of the parent-cell wall. Division and redivision of these daughter cells may produce an amorphous colony with hundreds or thousands of cells, all embedded within a common gelatinous matrix. Such palmella stages (Fig. 7*C*), so called because phycologists formerly thought them to be species of *Palmella,* are regularly formed when *Chlamydomonas* is growing on damp soil or is cultured on agar in the laboratory. Within a few minutes after a palmella stage is flooded with water the cells develop flagella, become motile, and escape from the gelatinous matrix.

Some species are homothallic; others are heterothallic; and gametic union may be isogamous, anisogamous, or oögamous. In most isogamous species there is no formation of special gametic cells but any cell may function as a gamete when conditions are favorable. Such cells are usually so densely filled with starch that the structure of the chloroplast is obscured. Most species with vegetative cells functioning as gametes have the protoplasts escaping from the enclosing wall immediately prior to gametic union (Fig. 8*A–B*); but certain species, including *C. eugametos*

[1] Wille, 1903.

Moewus,[1] do not have an escape of the protoplasts. Gametic union begins by two cells becoming apposed to and fusing with each other at the anterior end (Fig. 8*C–D*). Species with a shedding of cell walls have this followed by a lateral fusion to form a quadriflagellate zygote (Fig. 8*E*). Species without a shedding of cell walls have the two cells remaining apposed in tandem until gametic union is completed. In either case the quadriflagellate zygote remains motile for several hours, and in certain species[2] it may remain motile for as many as 15 days. In the anisogamous heterothallic *C. braunii* Gorosch. a cell of a male clone divides to form 8 or 16 male gametes and one of a female clone forms 2 or 4 female

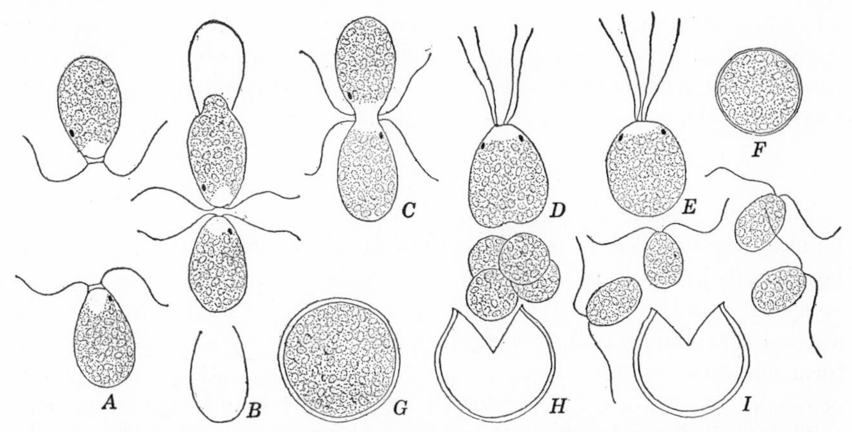

FIG. 8. *Chlamydomonas snowiae* Printz. *A–B*, mutual approach of cells and escape of protoplasts from walls immediately prior to gametic union. *C–D*, early and late stages in gametic union. *E*, quadriflagellate zygote. *F–G*, young and mature resting zygotes. *H–I*, germination of zygote. (× 1,300.)

gametes.[3] These gametes do not shed their walls at the time of gametic union. In the two oögamous species, *C. coccifera* Gorosch.[4] and *C. oögamum* Moewus,[3] a male cell divides to form 8, 16, or 32 small biflagellate antherozoids, one of which unites with a large female cell that becomes a globose egg without flagella.

Disappearance of flagella from quadriflagellate zygotes of isogamous and anisogamous species is followed by formation of a wall around the zygote. The wall may be smooth or spiny. In a few species there is no increase in size of the resting zygote and all food reserves within it are contributed by the gametes. In most species the resting zygote enlarges to two to five times its original diameter and additional food reserves are formed photosynthetically (Fig. 8*F–G*). During later stages in ripening of these zygotes much of the reserve starch is converted into oil. In

[1] Moewus, 1944. [2] Strehlow, 1929.
[3] Moewus, 1938. [4] Goroschankin, 1905.

ripening of zygotes of most species the protoplast eventually becomes reddish because of formation of a "hematochrome" that masks the chlorophyll; but there are species, as *C. eugametos*, where the zygote remains green.

Prior to germination, there is a meiotic division of the fusion nucleus of the zygote. This has been demonstrated both by cytological study and by genetic analysis of the products of germinating zygotes.[1] When a zygote germinates its protoplast usually divides into four uninucleate protoplasts, but there are species where it may divide into 8 (*C. reinhardi* Dang.) or into 16 or 32 protoplasts (*C. intermedia* Chod.). The divided contents of a zygote are extruded after a splitting of the zygote wall. They are without flagella when first extruded but within a few minutes each develops a pair of flagella and swims away (Fig. 8*H–I*). Motile cells formed by a germinating zygote are usually so densely filled with reserve foods that the cell contents are obscured.

FAMILY 2. VOLVOCACEAE

The Volvocaceae include all motile colonial genera in which the cells lie in a disk or a hollow sphere and not in superimposed tiers. The number of cells in a colony is definite, a multiple of two, and there is no increase in number of cells after the juvenile phases of development. In asexual reproduction all or certain specific cells divide simultaneously to form daughter colonies. Sexual reproduction is isogamous, anisogamous, or oögamous. All or only certain cells of a colony may be gametogenic.

The family includes some 10 genera and 30 species, all of them freshwater.

Vegetative cells are always biflagellate, and almost always with a structure like that of *Chlamydomonas*. Cells of all genera have a gelatinous sheath, and abutting sheaths may be distinct from one another or confluent to form a homogeneous colonial matrix. Certain species of one genus (*Volvox*) have conspicuous cytoplasmic strands connecting the cells one to another.

All colonies are **coenobia** (colonies with a definite number of cells arranged in a specific manner). Coenobia of most genera exhibit a definite polarity when swimming through the water, the anterior pole of the ellipsoid or globose colony always being directed forward. There may also be a definite morphological anterior-posterior differentiation, either in size of eyespots at opposite poles of the coenobium or in outline of the colonial envelope. In certain advanced genera all cells toward the anterior end are vegetative and reproductive cells lie toward the posterior pole.

Daughter coenobia are always formed by repeated division of a single cell and according to a definite sequence. All cells of a colony may be

[1] Moewus, 1936, 1938, 1939.

capable of forming daughter coenobia, or the capacity to form them may be restricted to specific cells (**gonidia**) much larger than vegetative cells. Successive divisions in formation of a daughter coenobium are always longitudinal and all cells of each cell generation divide simultaneously. The four cells of the second cell generation are quadrately arranged; the eight of the third cell generation are cruciately arranged and with a tendency to form a curved plate, the **plakea** (Fig. 12, page 40). In all but one genus, the plakea becomes a hollow sphere with a small pore, the **phialopore,** at one pole. Some genera, as *Pandorina,* stop dividing at the 32-celled stage; other genera, as *Eudorina,* do not develop beyond the 64-celled stage. In *Volvox* division may continue until there are many thousands of cells, theoretically a multiple of two. Until fairly late in development of a daughter coenobium the nucleus in each cell lies toward the inner face of the coenobium; later stages have the nuclei toward the outer face of each cell. This change in position is due to the developing coenobium turning itself inside out (inverting) through the phialopore during later stages of development (Fig. 12*H*, page 40).

The three genera described below illustrate the three major evolutionary tendencies in the Volvocaceae. These are: (1) an increase in number of cells in the coenobium; (2) an advance from a condition where all cells are reproductive to one where only certain of them are reproductive; and (3) an advance from isogamy to anisogamy to oögamy.

Pandorina, a genus with three species, is widespread in fresh waters but rarely found in abundance. The coenobia are subspherical to ellipsoidal and have 4, 8, 16, or 32 biflagellate cells embedded within a homogeneous gelatinous matrix (Fig. 9*A*). There may also be an outer colonial sheath of a more watery consistency. The cells are arranged in a hollow sphere within the colonial envelope and in two species lie so close together that they are laterally flattened by mutual compression, but in the third species they are not in lateral contact with one another.[1] Laterally abutting cells are obpyriform and have the two flagella and the eyespot borne on the broad anterior end. The chloroplast is massive and cup-shaped; it may have a smooth outer face and contain a single pyrenoid or its outer face may be longitudinally ridged and it may contain several pyrenoids.

Asexual reproduction is by a simultaneous formation of daughter coenobia by all cells of a coenobium. Prior to reproduction a coenobium ceases moving actively and sinks to the bottom of the pool, and the gelatinous envelope becomes swollen and more watery. Each cell forms a typical plakea and the developing coenobium becomes bowl-shaped instead of a hollow sphere. There is an inversion of the bowl-shaped coenobium to form a sphere in which the phialopore is closed.[2] After inversion, each cell develops a pair of flagella, and the daughter coenobium

[1] Smith, 1931. [2] Morse, 1943; Taft, 1941.

swims through and away from the watery gelatinous envelope of the parent coenobium.

Pandorina is heterothallic, and gametic union is anisogamous but not markedly so. Divisions leading to the formation of gametes are identical with those in asexual reproduction. However, coenobia composed of cells destined to function as gametes are *Eudorina*-like and with a watery gelatinous envelope. These coenobia swim through the water, but sooner or later the individual cells (gametes) escape from the colonial matrix and move about singly.[1] Male gametes are somewhat smaller and swim more actively than female gametes (Fig. 9*C–D*). The quadriflagellate zygote formed by fusion of two gametes remains motile for a short time

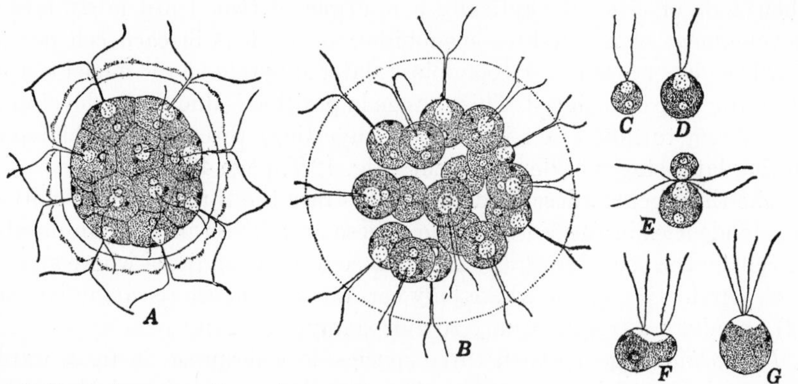

FIG. 9. *Pandorina morum* Bory. *A*, vegetative colony. *B*, colony of female gametes. *C*, male gamete. *D*, female gamete. *E–F*, gametic union. *G*, motile zygote. (× 650.)

before it loses its flagella and secretes a wall. Old zygotes have a smooth wall and a protoplast colored red by "hematochrome." When a zygote germinates the contents are extruded in a vesicle, and the irregularly green and orange protoplast swims away as a single zoospore.[2] Sometimes a germinating zygote produces two or three zoospores. After swimming for a time, a zoospore retracts its flagella, secretes a broad gelatinous envelope, and divides and redivides to form a plakea that develops into a typical coenobium.

Eudorina, a genus with four or five species, is widespread in fresh waters and is sometimes present in abundance in small puddles. Its coenobia are spherical or ovoid and have a homogeneous envelope that may have mamillate projections at the posterior pole.[3] The 16, 32, or 64 cells in a coenobium lie some distance from one another and toward the periphery of the envelope. Frequently the cells are in distinct transverse tiers (Fig. 10*A*). If the coenobia are 32-celled, the anterior and posterior tiers

[1] K. I. Meyer, 1935; N. Pringsheim, 1870; Smith, 1933.
[2] Korshikov, 1923; N. Pringsheim, 1870. [3] Smith, 1931.

contain four cells each, and the three median tiers eight cells each.[1] The individual cells are spherical, biflagellate, and all approximately the same size. The single eyespot lies at the anterior pole of a cell. Certain species have a progressive diminution in size of eyespots from anterior to posterior cells of a coenobium, and eyespots may even be lacking in the lowermost tier of cells. The chloroplasts of cells are cup-shaped, massive, and according to the species contain one or several pyrenoids.[2]

At the time of asexual reproduction all cells of a coenobium divide to form daughter coenobia, but occasionally one or more cells fail to divide. Division to form daughter coenobia is in the plakeal sequence characteris-

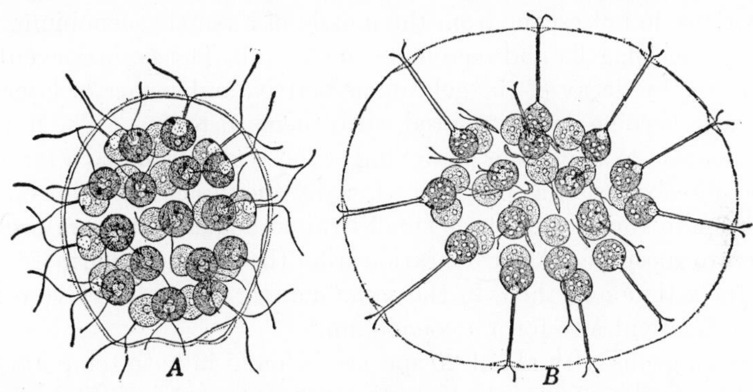

Fig. 10. *A*, vegetative colony of *Eudorina unicocca* G. M. Smith. *B*, female colony of *E. elegans* Ehr. in which there are male gametes swimming within the colonial envelope. (*A*, × 435; *B*, × 235.)

tic of the family and the daughter coenobia escape by swimming directly through the gelatinized envelope of the parent coenobium.

Sometimes a coenobium becomes an amorphous palmelloid mass. Development of such palmella stages is due to gradual desiccation. Within a few minutes after reflooding the palmelloid cells develop flagella and escape as single zooids which develop into coenobia after liberation.[3] Instead of developing into a palmella stage, a coenobium may have its cells losing their flagella and developing into akinetes.[4]

The anisogamous sexual reproduction shows a very close approach to oögamy in that the female gametes are not free-swimming and in that the gametes are dissimilar in shape. According to the species, the coenobia are homothallic or heterothallic. Homothallic species usually have the four anterior cells dividing to form male gametes and the remaining cells functioning as female gametes.[5] Divisions forming male gametes are according to the same sequence as in asexual reproduction and usually continue until there are 64 spindle-shaped male gametes arranged in a flat

[1] Chodat, 1902; Conrad, 1913; Hartmann, 1921; Smith, 1931. [2] Smith, 1931.
[3] Schreiber, 1925. [4] Pocock, 1937.
[5] H. J. Carter, 1858; Iyengar, 1933; K. I. Meyer, 1935.

or curved plate. Heterothallic species have the packets of male gametes escaping as a unit, swimming through the water as a unit, and dissociating into individual gametes when the packet comes near a female colony. Vegetative cells of female coenobia function directly as female gametes and there is no evident change other than a swelling of the gelatinous matrix of a female coenobium.

The male gametes swim directly into the colonial matrix of a female coenobium (Fig. 10*B*) and there fuse with the female gametes. Male gametes have been variously described as having their anterior ends,[1] their posterior ends,[2] and their sides[3] fusing with the female gametes. The zygotes do not escape from the matrix of a female coenobium. They soon lose their flagella and secrete a smooth wall. The zygotes eventually become free by decay of the gelatinous matrix, and sooner or later their protoplasts become deeply colored with "hematochrome." The first step in germination of a zygote is a swelling of the zygote wall and a formation of a sac-like extrusion at one side.[4] Usually the vesicle contains one reddish zoospore and two or three small hyaline bodies which are probably degenerate zoospores. After liberation from the vesicle, a zoospore swims about for a time and then, in the same manner as a vegetative cell, divides and redivides to form a coenobium.

Volvox, a genus with about 20 species, is found in both temporary and permanent fresh-water pools. Sometimes it is present in sufficient abundance to color the water green. *Volvox* usually appears in the spring, increases in abundance, and then abruptly disappears early in the summer. During the remainder of the year it is in a resting zygote condition.

The colonies are spherical to ovoid and with the cells in a single layer just within the periphery of the gelatinous colonial matrix. According to the species, the number of cells may be as low as approximately 500 (512?) or as high as approximately 60,000 (65,536?). Each cell is surrounded by a gelatinous sheath of its own, and the sheaths may be confluent with or distinct from one another. In the latter case, they are angular by mutual compression and usually hexagonal. There is gelatinous material of a more watery consistency internal to the gelatinous sheaths of the cells. Most species have ovoid cells. Some species have the cells joined one to another by conspicuous or delicate cytoplasmic strands (Fig. 11), a connection which becomes established early in development of colonies.[5]

Most of the cells in a colony are vegetative in nature and are incapable of giving rise to new colonies. Each vegetative cell is biflagellate and with the two contractile vacuoles near the base of the flagella, or with two to five contractile vacuoles irregularly distributed in the anterior end of the cell. There is either a cup-shaped or laminate chloroplast toward the

[1] Pocock, 1937. [2] Iyengar, 1937. [3] K. I. Meyer, 1935.
[4] Otrokov, 1875; Schreiber, 1925. [5] Janet, 1912; A. Meyer, 1896; Pocock, 1933*A*.

posterior pole of a cell, and it usually contains but one pyrenoid. Each vegetative cell has a single anteriorly located eyespot, those of cells toward the anterior end of a colony being somewhat larger than those in cells at the posterior end.

Young colonies have all cells alike in size. As a colony grows older certain cells in the posterior half lose their flagella, increase to ten or more times the diameter of vegetative cells, and develop several pyrenoids within their chloroplasts. These enlarged cells are reproductive cells and may be either sexual or asexual. Reproduction is exclusively asexual at

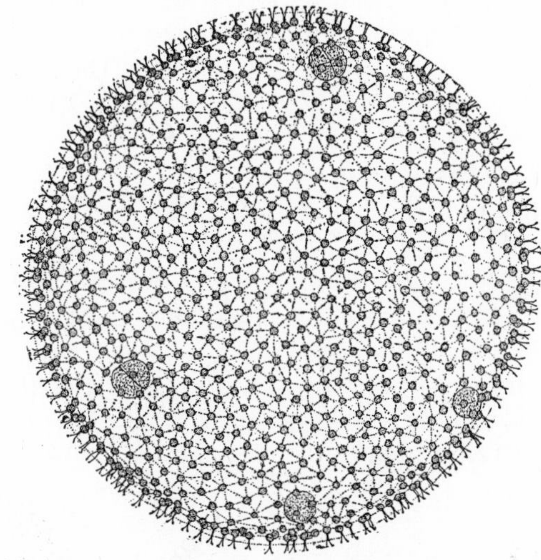

FIG. 11. Colony of *Volvox aureus* Ehr. with daughter colonies at an early stage of development. (× 200.)

the beginning of the growing season and exclusively sexual at the end of the season.

In asexual reproduction, and according to the species, there is a differentiation of 2 to about 50 asexual reproductive cells (**gonidia**) in the posterior half of a colony. A gonidium divides longitudinally and all succeeding divisions are longitudinal and simultaneous (Fig. 12). The 8-celled stage is the usual cruciate plakea, and the 16-celled stage is a hollow sphere with a phialopore at the anterior pole. Simultaneous division continues for several cell generations.[1] In the largest known species (*V. rouseletii* G. S. West) there are 14, 15, or 16 cell generations beyond the two-celled stage.[2] Theoretically this would produce colonies with 16,384 (2^{14}), 32,768 (2^{15}), or 65,536 (2^{16}) cells, but this number is not attained because some cells of the last few cell generations fail to divide. When cell division ceases, the young colony turns itself inside out (Fig. 12*G*) by

[1] Janet, 1923. [2] Pocock, 1933*A*.

invaginating (inverting) through the phialopore.[1] Flagella are developed shortly after inversion, and the daughter colony then revolves slowly within the enlarged gelatinous sac originally containing the gonidium. A daughter colony eventually escapes by moving through a pore-like opening at the free face of the sac.[2]

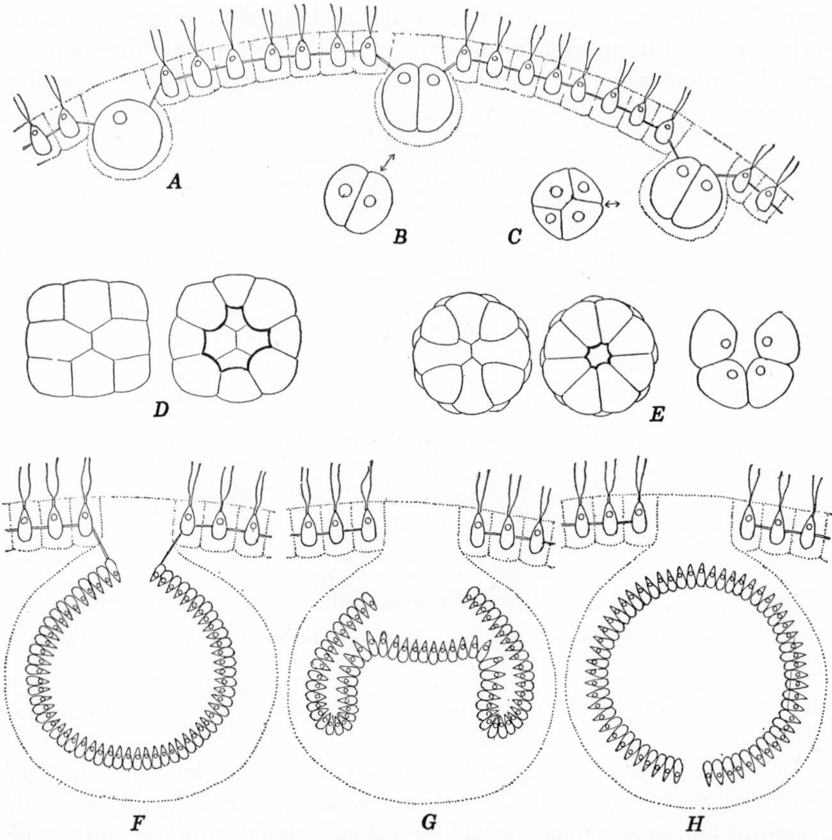

FIG. 12. Diagrams showing stages in development of a gonidium into a daughter colony of *Volvox*. *A*, gonidium. *B–E*, two-, four-, eight-, and sixteen-celled stages of development. *F*, daughter colony just before inversion. *G*, during inversion. *H*, after inversion.

Sexual reproduction is oögamous, and according to the species the colonies are homothallic or heterothallic. Antherozoids are developed from enlarged cells resembling gonidia. Usually there are relatively few of these cells, but in certain species a majority or all cells of a colony may produce antherozoids.[3] According to the species the cell divides to form 16, 32, 64, 128, 256, or 512 fusiform biflagellate antherozoids. Cell divi-

[1] Kuschakewitsch, 1931; Pocock, 1933, 1938; Powers, 1908; Zimmermann, 1925.
[2] Pocock, 1933, 1938. [3] Pocock, 1938; Powers, 1908; Smith, 1944.

sion is in a plakeal sequence and with an inversion to form a bowl-shaped (Fig. 13*A*) or a globose mass of antherozoids.[1] The colony-like mass of antherozoids is liberated as a unit, swims about as a unit, and does not break up into individual antherozoids until it approaches the vicinity of an egg.

Only a small percentage of cells in a colony develop into eggs. These cells enlarge somewhat, lose their flagella, and resemble young gonidia. When fertilization takes place (Fig. 13*B*) the individual antherozoids

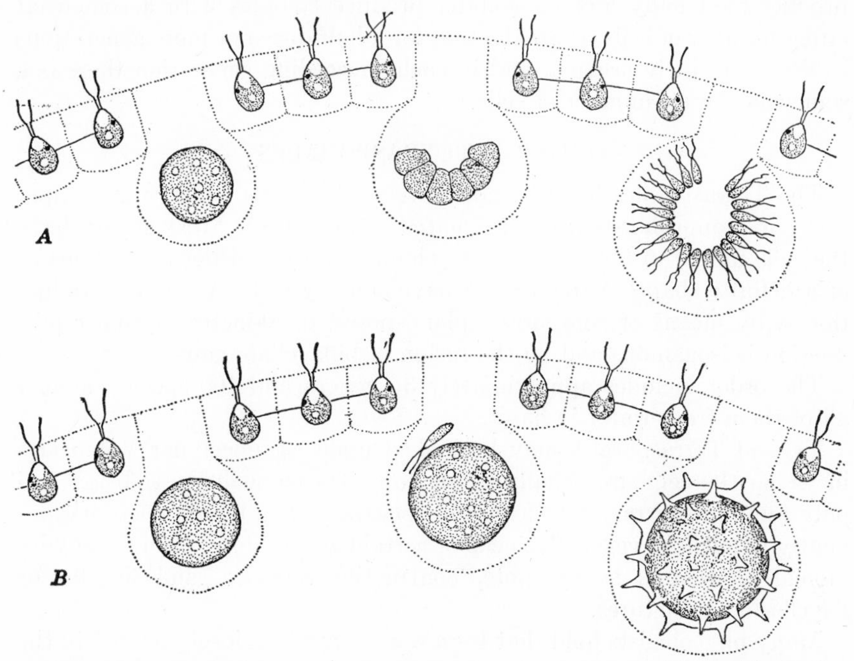

FIG. 13. *Volvox*. *A*, diagram of stages in development of a packet of antherozoids. *B*, diagram of a portion of a colony showing a developing egg, fertilization, and a mature zygote.

swim slowly through the gelatinous sheath around an egg and probably enter it from the side.[2] There may also be a development of unfertilized eggs into parthenospores.[3]

After fertilization, the zygote forms a smooth or stellate thick wall (Fig. 13*B*) and develops sufficient "hematochrome" to color the protoplast an orange red. Zygotes do not germinate until a considerable time after they are liberated from the colony by disintegration of the gelatinous matrix of the colony. Prior to germination there is a meiotic division of the zygote nucleus.[4]

[1] Pocock, 1933, 1933*A*, 1938. [2] Lander, 1910.
[3] Mainx, 1929. [4] Zimmermann, 1921.

When a zygote germinates there is a splitting of the outer wall layer (**exospore**) and an extrusion of the inner wall layer (**endospore**) as a vesicle which surrounds the protoplast. The protoplast may become a biflagellate zoospore, but it rarely escapes from the vesicle and becomes free-swimming.[1] Irrespective of whether or not the protoplast becomes a zoospore, development into a colony is by the same sequence of plakeal stages as in asexual reproduction. The colony thus formed consists of but one or two hundred cells, presumably 128 or 258. This colony always reproduces asexually and its gonidia produce colonies with a somewhat larger number of cells. Reproduction for a half dozen or more generations is also exclusively asexual, and in each succeeding generation there is a somewhat larger number of cells.

ORDER 2. TETRASPORALES

The Tetrasporales have immobile vegetative cells which may temporarily metamorphose into a flagellated motile stage. Most genera have the cells united in nonfilamentous colonies that are either amorphous or of a definite shape. A few genera have solitary cells. Asexual reproduction is by means of zoospores, aplanospores, or akinetes. Sexual reproduction is isogamous and by the fusion of biflagellate gametes.

The order includes approximately 35 genera and 100 species, almost all of them fresh-water in habit.

Typical Tetrasporales may be looked upon as unicellular Volvocales in which the cells are usually in an immobile palmelloid condition and only temporarily revert to a motile condition. The more or less permanently palmelloid vegetative cells of certain genera[2] have such chlamydomonad characters as eyespots, contractile vacuoles, and flagella or flagella-like structures.

Many phycologists hold that these genera are too closely related to the chlamydomonad type to warrant segregation from the Volvocales. They assign them and all other tetrasporaceous algae to the Volvocales and do not recognize the Tetrasporales as a distinct order. However, those who favor this practice admit that the immobility of these primitively organized cells is a step in advance of the temporary immobility found in palmella stages of Chlamydomonadaceae. The tetrasporaceous Chlorophyceae are divided into three[3] or into four[4] families.

Tetraspora is a fresh-water genus with about 20 species. Its cells are spherical to ellipsoidal and united in many-celled colonies by a homogeneous gelatinous matrix. There is a certain tendency for the cells to lie in groups of two or four within the matrix, but in many colonies they

[1] Kirchner, 1883; Metzner, 1945; Pocock, 1933*A*, 1938.
[2] Korshikov, 1926; Lambert, 1930; Pascher, 1927.
[3] Fritsch, 1935. [4] Smith, 1933.

are irregularly scattered. Fully developed colonies of *Tetraspora* are usually several centimeters in diameter (Fig. 14*A–B*). The colonial matrix of most species is of so watery a consistency that the colony breaks in pieces when one attempts to lift it from the water, but in certain species, as *T. cylindrica* (Wahlb.) C.A.Ag., the matrix is tough and firm.

The cells[1] lie toward the periphery of the colonial envelope, and the face toward the exterior of the colony bears two long, immobile, flexible cytoplasmic processes (**pseudocilia**), which may extend only to the

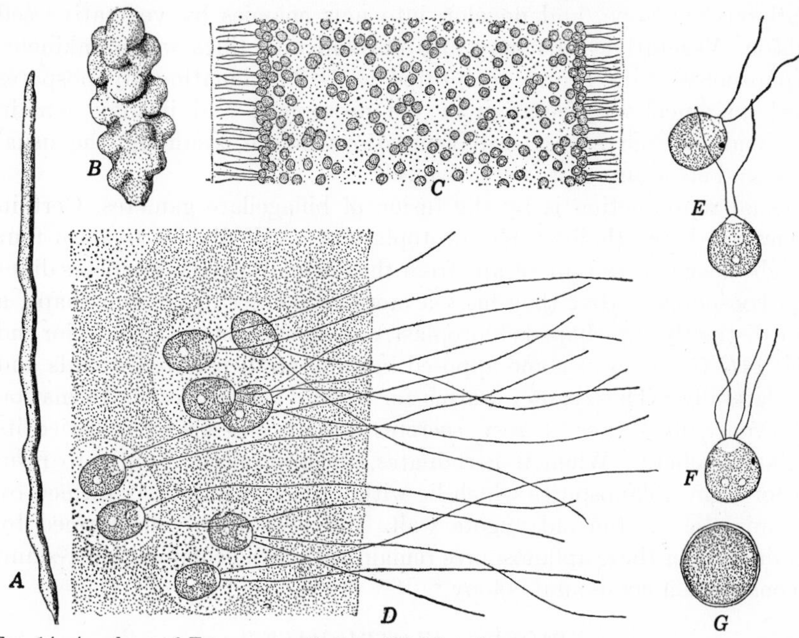

FIG. 14. *A*, colony of *Tetraspora cylindrica* (Wahlb.) C.A.Ag. *B*, colony of *T. lubrica* (Roth) C.A.Ag. *C*, portion of a colony of *T. cylindrica*. *D–G*, *T. gelatinosa* (Vauch.) Desv. *D*, vegetative cells with pseudocilia. *E*, gametes. *F*, motile zygote. *G*, resting zygote. (*A–B*, × ½; *C*, × 155; *D*, × 1,300; *E–G*, × 650.)

surface of the colonial envelope or may extend beyond it (Fig. 14*C*). All species have pseudocilia, but they are not always evident in all colonies of a species. Within the cell are a nucleus and a massive cup-shaped chloroplast containing a single pyrenoid. Cells of old colonies often have the chloroplasts so densely packed with starch that the structure of the chloroplast is obscured.

Growth of a colony is by the cells dividing into two or four daughter cells. Cytokinesis in cells of *Tetraspora* is by means of a cell plate developed on the mitotic spindle.[2] The old parent-cell wall gelatinizes to form a special envelope about the group of daughter cells (Fig. 14*D*).

[1] Klyver, 1929; Schröder, 1902. [2] McAllister, 1913.

The envelope is quite distinct immediately after cell division, but it gradually merges with the colonial matrix as the daughter cells increase in size and become more remote from one another. Colonies may grow to over a meter in length, but they usually become broken in smaller pieces before they attain such a size. At any time in the development of a colony, all or certain of the cells may be metamorphosed into biflagellate zoospores. The zoospores escape from the colonial matrix and swim about for a short time: then they withdraw their flagella, secrete a gelatinous envelope, and develop into new colonies by vegetative cell division. Vegetative cells may also develop into thick-walled akinetes (hypnospores) with brown sculptured walls. Germinating hypnospores have[1] an amoeboid liberation of the protoplast, and it may remain amoeboid through several cell generations before assuming the usual shape and structure of a vegetative cell.

Sexual reproduction is by the fusion of biflagellate gametes. Certain species are heterothallic.[2] The protoplast of a cell divides to form four or eight zoogametes that escape from the colonial matrix. Gametes differ from zoospores in that they have a more pronounced pyriform shape, a more distinctly cup-shaped chloroplast, and an eyespot at the anterior end (Fig. 14*E–G*). They become apposed in pairs at their anterior ends and fuse laterally.[3] The zygote swarms for a short time after its formation but eventually comes to rest, secretes a wall, and grows to twice its original diameter. When it germinates, the protoplast divides to form four or eight aplanospores which lie within a common matrix formed by gelatinization of the old zygote wall. The vegetative cells formed by germination of these aplanospores remain within the common matrix and so constitute a compound colony.[3]

ORDER 3. ULOTRICHALES

The Ulotrichales have uninucleate cells (with the exception of old cells of certain genera) and usually a single parietal laminate chloroplast. The cells are united end to end in simple or branched filaments. Certain branching filamentous genera have their branches apposed in a pseudoparenchymatous mass or are reduced to an irregularly shaped few-celled structure. In one genus (*Protococcus*) the filament is reduced to a single cell. The usual method of asexual reproduction is a formation of bi- or quadriflagellate zoospores, but aplanospores and akinetes are not at all uncommon. Gametic union is found in many genera of the order and may be isogamous, anisogamous, or oögamous.

There are about 80 genera and 430 species. Most of the genera are exclusively fresh-water, but a few have some marine species and a few others are exclusively marine.

[1] Pascher, 1915. [2] Geitler, 1931. [3] Klyver, 1929.

The branching characteristic of a majority of the genera represents a more advanced condition than does the simple filament. Most of the Ulotrichales with a branching thallus have it differentiated into a prostrate and into an erect portion. This **heterotrichous** organization has been held[1] to be a feature of fundamental significance and one warranting segregation of the branching genera in a separate order (the Chaetophorales).

Certain genera, including *Coleochaete* and *Ulothrix,* have been shown to have a life cycle with a multicellular gametophyte alternating with a one-celled diploid phase. This is probably the case with most genera, but it is definitely known that certain genera have an alternation of a multicellular haploid gametophyte and a multicellular diploid sporophyte. This alternation may be isomorphic[2] or heteromorphic.[3]

The Ulotrichales may be divided into two suborders, the *Ulotrichineae* and the *Sphaeropleineae.*

Suborder 1. Ulotrichineae

The Ulotrichineae include the genera in which the cells are uninucleate (at least when young), and in which the majority of genera have a single parietal band-shaped chloroplast. Asexual reproduction is usually by means of zoospores. Sexual reproduction is of widespread occurrence and ranges from isogamy to oögamy.

Families of this order are usually distinguished from one another on the basis of thallus structure and on the method of sexual reproduction. In the families recognized on pages to follow, isogamy and oögamy are held to be characters insufficient for establishment of separate families unless they are supplemented by distinctive features in structure of thallus, wall structure, or chloroplast structure.

Family 1. Ulotrichaceae

The Ulotrichaceae include all the unbranched filamentous genera in which the cells are uninucleate, have a single girdle-shaped chloroplast, and have a cell wall not composed of overlapping **H**-pieces. Almost all genera are known to produce bi- or quadriflagellate zoospores. Asexual reproduction by means of aplanospores or akinetes is not infrequent. Sexual reproduction is known for but few genera, and in all cases thus far recorded is isogamous and with a union of biflagellate gametes.

There are about 15 genera and 120 species, almost all of them freshwater.

Ulothrix, with about 30 species, has a large majority of its species growing in fresh water. Some species, especially *U. zonata* (Weber and Mohr) Kütz., are distinctly cold-water plants; appearing in early spring,

[1] Fritsch, 1916, 1935; Iyengar, 1951. [2] Singh, 1945. [3] Juller, 1937.

disappearing during the summer, and then reappearing in the fall. The cells of *Ulothrix* are united end to end in unbranched filaments of indefinite length (Fig. 15*A*). All cells but the rhizoidal basal one may divide vegetatively or may produce zooids. The cell walls may be thick or thin and homogeneous or stratified. A few species have broad gelatinous sheaths about the filaments, but in most species a sheath is not evident. The cells are always uninucleate and with a single girdle-shaped chloroplast that partially or completely encircles the protoplast. According to the species, the chloroplast extends the whole length of a cell or only a part of its length, and contains one or several pyrenoids.

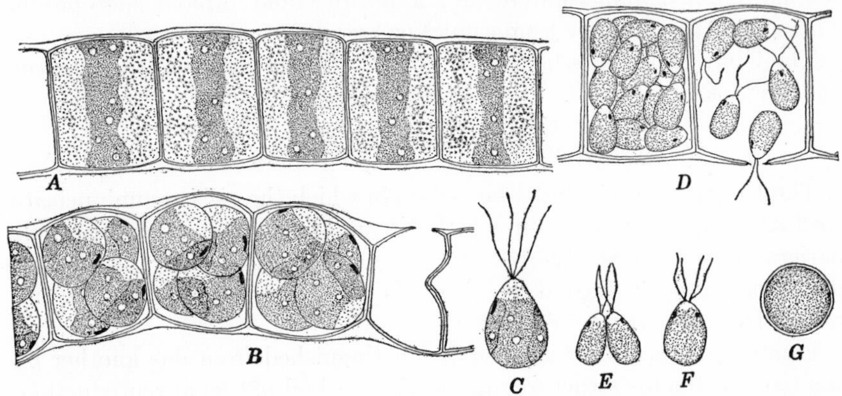

FIG. 15. *Ulothrix zonata* (Weber and Mohr) Kütz. *A*, vegetative cells. *B*, formation of zoospores. *C*, zoospore. *D*, formation and liberation of gametes. *E*, gametic union. *F*, motile zygote. *G*, resting zygote. (× 1,000.)

Vegetative multiplication may be due to an accidental breaking of a filament or, in very rare cases,[1] to its dissociation into many fragments with a few cells each.

All cells but the holdfast may produce zoospores, but those in the distal portion of a filament usually produce them in advance of those in the lower portion. Species with narrow cells produce 1, 2, or 4 zoospores per cell; those with broad cells produce 2, 4, 8, 16, or 32 zoospores in each cell (Fig. 15*B*). The protoplast of a cell about to produce zoospores contracts slightly and becomes filled with reserve food material. If more than one zoospore is to be produced, the nucleus divides and the protoplast cleaves in a plane at right angles to the long axis of the filament. The nucleus in each daughter protoplast may also divide and both protoplasts cleave in a plane perpendicular to that of the first cleavage.[2] Simultaneous bipartition may continue until there are 32 daughter protoplasts. When cleavage ceases, each of the daughter protoplasts is metamorphosed into a quadriflagellate zoospore with a conspicuous eye-

[1] Gross, 1931; Lind, 1932. [2] Cholnoky, 1932; Gross, 1931; Lind, 1932.

spot (Fig. 15*C*). The zoospores are liberated through a pore in the side of the parent-cell wall. The spore mass is usually surrounded by a thin vesicle when first extruded, but this disappears within a minute or two. All zoospores from a filament of a narrow-celled species are alike in size. Filaments of broad-celled species, as *U. zonata*, produce quadriflagellate macro- and microzoospores that differ from each other in size, position of eyespot, and length of swarming period.[1] Zoospores which are not discharged from a parent cell may each secrete a wall and become thin-walled aplanospores. Many of these aplanospores germinate before they are liberated from the parent-cell wall.[2] The protoplast of a vegetative cell may also round up to form a single large thick-walled aplanospore.[3]

Gametes (Fig. 15*D–F*) are formed in the same manner as zoospores, but the number formed is 8, 16, 32, or 64.[4] They are biflagellate, all of the same size, pyriform, and with an eyespot. They fuse in pairs with one another, but fusion only takes place between gametes coming from different filaments.[5] There is no parthenogenetic development of gametes into vegetative filaments.[6] The zygote (Fig. 15*G*) remains motile for a short time and then comes to rest, secretes a thick lamellated wall, and enters upon a resting period during which there is a considerable accumulation of reserve food. The first division of a zygote nucleus is meiotic.[6] The protoplast of a germinating zygote divides into 4 to 14 (16?) daughter protoplasts which develop into aplanospores[7] or into zoospores.[2]

FAMILY 2. MICROSPORACEAE

The Microsporaceae have an unbranched filament in which the cells are uninucleate and contain a single variously lobed chloroplast. The wall of a cell consists of two pieces that are **H**-shaped in optical section.

The single genus *Microspora* has about 15 species. They are all fresh-water, grow in pools and ditches, and are most abundant during early spring.

The walls of a filament are a linear file of segments that are **H**-shaped in optical section. The segments are so articulate that each protoplast is enclosed by the conjoined halves of two successive **H**-pieces (Fig. 16*A*). The **H**-pieces are heavily impregnated with cellulose[8] and sometimes are distinctly stratified. Internal to the **H**-pieces is a very thin layer of cellulose completely encircling the protoplast.[8] At the time of cell division there is a development of a thin layer of cellulose about each daughter protoplast and an intercalation of a short **H**-shaped piece of wall material between the two. This new **H**-piece gradually lengthens

[1] Klebs, 1896; Pascher, 1907. [2] Dodel, 1876. [3] West, 1916.
[4] Dodel, 1876; Gross, 1931; Klebs, 1896; Lind, 1932; Pascher, 1907; West, 1916.
[5] Cholnoky, 1932; Gross, 1931; Lind, 1932. [6] Gross, 1931.
[7] Jörstad, 1919; Klebs, 1896. [8] Tiffany, 1924.

as the two **H**-pieces that formerly enclosed the parent cell pull apart from each other.

The cells are uninucleate and generally with the nucleus lying in a bridge of cytoplasm across the middle of the central vacuole. There is usually so much reserve starch in a cell that but little can be made out concerning structure of the chloroplast. In young, vigorously growing cells, the chloroplast is an irregularly expanded, perforate or reticulate sheet covering both the sides and ends of the protoplast. Pyrenoids are lacking in chloroplasts of *Microspora*.[1]

Asexual reproduction is by the formation of 1, 2, 4, 8, or 16 zoospores within a cell. When more than one zoospore is formed, there is a bipartition of the protoplast after each mitosis.[2] The zoospores may be liber-

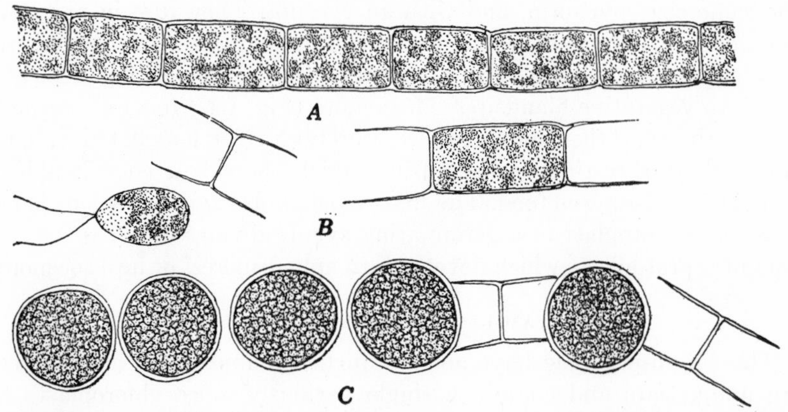

FIG. 16. *Microspora willeana* Wittr. *A*, vegetative cells. *B*, liberation of zoospore. *C*, aplanospores. (× 900.)

ated by a disarticulation of the **H**-pieces of the wall of the parent cell (Fig. 16*B*), or there may be a gelatinization of the sides of the **H**-pieces and a swimming of zoospores through the gelatinized portions. The zoospores are biflagellate, are naked, and have a hyaline anterior end.[3] Quadriflagellate zoospores have been recorded[2] for one species. A zoospore swarms for a short time and then comes to rest and secretes a wall. The germling thus formed may be free-floating, or it may be sessile and affixed by a discoid holdfast. Aplanospores may also be formed. They are usually spherical and are formed singly within a cell (Fig. 16*C*). Germinating aplanospores develop directly into new filaments.[2] Some species also form thick-walled akinetes in abundance. They may contain 2, 4, 8, or 16 nuclei.[2] If they germinate within a few days, there is a direct development into a new filament. If germination is long de-

[1] Lagerheim, 1889; West, 1916. [2] K. Meyer, 1913. [3] Hazen, 1902; West, 1916.

layed, the contents divide into four daughter protoplasts, either before or after escape from the old wall, and each daughter protoplast develops into a new filament.[1]

The single recorded case of gametic union[2] is open to question since there is a possibility that the alga studied was *Tribonema* rather than *Microspora.*

FAMILY 3. CYLINDROCAPSACEAE

The Cylindrocapsaceae have unbranched filaments in which the cells have concentrically stratified walls. They differ from other unbranched Ulotrichales in that their sexual reproduction is oögamous.

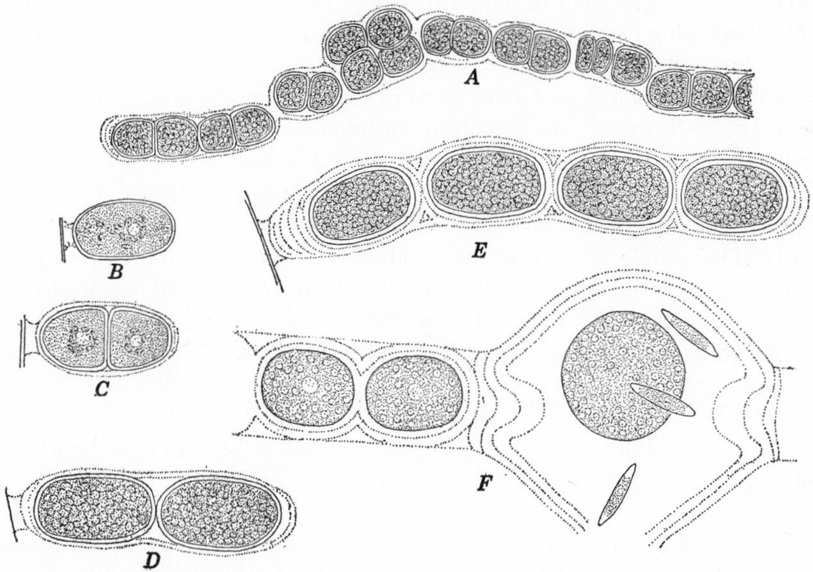

FIG. 17. *A–E*, *Cylindrocapsa geminella* Wolle. *A*, portion of an old filament. *B–E*, early stages in development of a filament. *F*, oögonium of *C. involuta* Reinsch at the time of fertilization. (*F*, *after Cienkowski*, 1876.) (*A*, × 325; *B–E*, × 650; *F*, × 480.)

The single genus, *Cylindrocapsa* (Fig. 17*A*), is fresh-water and has six species. Under certain conditions of growth there is a complete loss of the filamentous organization and a development of palmella stages in which the cells are irregularly arranged. Each protoplast in a filament is enclosed by a cellulose wall[3] which is laid down in concentric strata. The whole filament is surrounded by a tough gelatinous sheath of a pectic nature. In most specimens, it is impossible to make out the structure of the chloroplast, but favorable material shows that there is a single stellate chloroplast with a single pyrenoid.[4]

[1] West, 1916. [2] Steinecke, 1932. [3] Tiffany, 1924. [4] Iyengar, 1939.

Vegetative multiplication is by fragmentation of filaments. Asexual reproduction is by means of zoospores that may be biflagellate[1] or quadriflagellate.[2] Zoospores are formed singly, or in twos or fours, within a cell. Germination stages of zoospores are sessile and affixed to the substratum by a gelatinous holdfast (Fig. 17*B–D*). Cell division in young filaments is transverse and the two daughter cells each develop a wall with several concentric layers.

Sexual reproduction is oögamous and the filaments may be homothallic or heterothallic.[3] Cells developing into sex organs may be distinguished from vegetative cells by their reddish color. In the formation of antherozoids several successive cells in a filament divide longitudinally to form two daughter cells, each of which produces two biflagellate antherozoids. Cells developing into oögonia may lie remote from one another, or several successive cells may develop into oögonia. A cell developing into an oögonium has a considerable increase in size of its protoplast and a swelling of the wall layers. An oögonium contains a single egg and just before fertilization there is a development of a pore at one side of the oögonial wall (Fig. 17*F*). One species[2] resembles nannandrous species of *Oedogonium* in having one-celled sexual plants epiphytic upon vegetative filaments. The female plant produces a single egg, and the male plant produces four quadriflagellate antherozoids. Fertilization in all species takes place within an oögonium. Mature zygotes are spherical and with a smooth thick wall enclosing a bright red protoplast.

FAMILY 4. CHAETOPHORACEAE

The Chaetophoraceae have a branching filamentous thallus in which the branches may be free from one another or laterally adjoined into a pseudoparenchymatous tissue. The cells are uninucleate and usually have a single laminate parietal chloroplast. The terminal portion of a branch may consist of long colorless cells much narrower than other cells. Asexual reproduction may be by means of zoospores, aplanospores, or akinetes. Sexual reproduction is usually isogamous, but it may be anisogamous or oögamous.

There are about 50 genera and 225 species, most of which are freshwater algae.

Stigeoclonium, with some 35 species, is a common fresh-water alga. It grows in standing or flowing water and attached to stones, woodwork, and submerged aquatics. The thallus is heterotrichous and differentiated into a prostrate and an erect portion. The prostrate portion, which attaches the alga to the substratum, is either pseudoparenchymatous or irregularly branched. It bears many erect branches that are sparsely

[1] Cienkowski, 1876. [2] Iyengar, 1939.
[3] Cienkowski, 1876; Iyengar, 1939; Prescott, 1951.

branched, with an alternate or opposite branching, and have the lateral branches attenuated into long multicellular hairs (Fig. 18*A*). The erect branches are often enclosed by a broad gelatinous sheath, but this is of a very watery consistency and not usually evident unless demonstrated by special methods. At times the thallus may develop into a pseudoparenchymatous mass, and it has been shown[1] that development of this palmella stage may be induced in a variety of ways.

Cells of both the filamentous and palmella stages are uninucleate and with a single chloroplast. Larger cells in a filament have a transverse zonate chloroplast with one or more pyrenoids; smaller cells have the chloroplast girdling the whole length of the cell and usually containing but one pyrenoid.

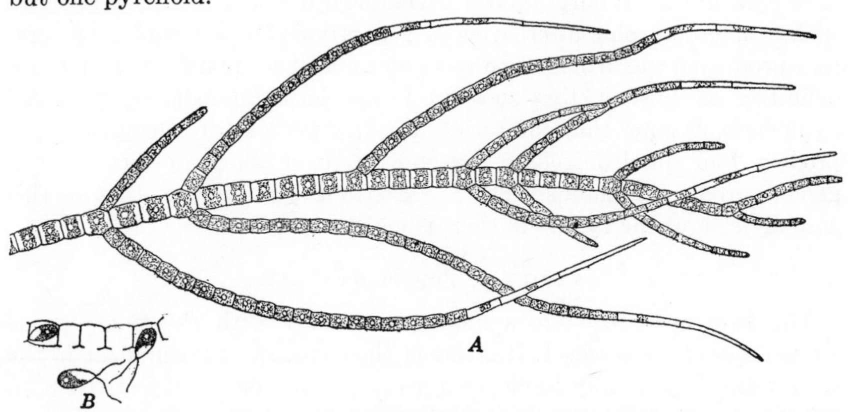

FIG. 18. *A*, vegetative branch of *Stigeoclonium lubricum* (Dillw.) Kütz. *B*, gametes of *S. tenue* (C.A.Ag.) Kütz. (× 400.)

Vegetative multiplication may take place by fragmentation, but fragments from the erect portion do not grow vigorously when severed from the prostrate portion. Zoospore formation is of frequent occurrence in *Stigeoclonium* and one often finds all cells in the smaller branches sporulating a day after collections are brought into the laboratory. Zoospores are quadriflagellate and are generally formed singly within a cell. In some species there is a formation of quadriflagellate swarmers of two sizes. For certain of these species the smaller of the two are also zoosporic in nature[2] and hence quite properly called **microzoospores.** In other cases, the smaller of the two are gametes.[3] After swarming for a time, a zoospore comes to rest with its anterior pole downward and secretes a wall after disappearance of the flagella. According to the species, the one-celled germling grows directly into a vertical filament that later develops the prostrate portion of the thallus from its lowermost cells; or the one-celled germling first grows into a prostrate branching system from which

[1] Livingston, 1900, 1905. [2] Juller, 1937. [3] Godward, 1942.

erect branches arise.[1] Cases are also known where the zoospores become amoeboid and remain amoeboid for some time before developing into a filament.[2] Aplanospores are generally formed singly within a cell and in several successive cells.

Sexual reproduction is isogamous. Some species have a fusion of biflagellate gametes to form a quadriflagellate zygote;[3] others have a fusion of quadriflagellate gametes to form an octoflagellate zygote.[4] After swarming for a time, the motile zygote rounds up, loses its flagella, and secretes a wall. This zygote may germinate within a day or two, or it may enter upon a resting period before germinating. If the zygote germinates within a day or two there is a mitotic division of the zygote nucleus and a development into a short unbranched filament of diploid cells. This species with a heteromorphic alternation of generations has the diploid generation producing quadriflagellate zoospores and it is thought,[3] though not definitely established, that zoospore formation is immediately preceded by meiosis. Zygotes that enter upon a resting period prior to germination produce four quadriflagellate zoospores each of which develops into a gamete-producing thallus.[4] There is a strong presumption that in this case division of the zygote nucleus is meiotic.

FAMILY 5. PROTOCOCCACEAE

The Protococcaceae are a monotypic family with the single genus *Protococcus* (*Pleurococcus*). It is one of the commonest green algae in the world; and is generally found as a green coating on trunks of trees, on brick and stone walls, and on wood. Many other unicellular green algae also grow in such habitats but these should not be considered species of *Protococcus* because they have the ability to form flagellated swarmers.

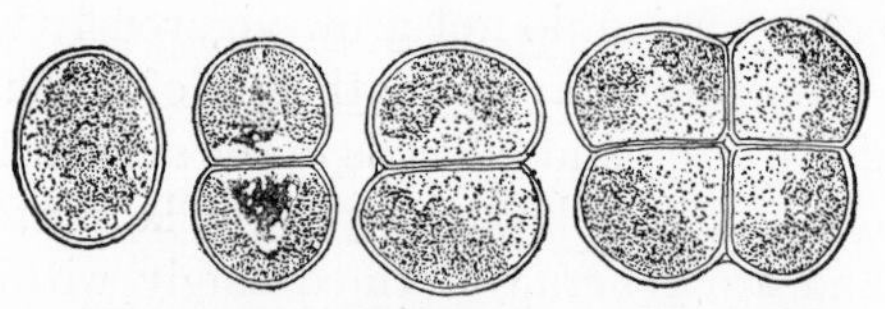

FIG. 19. *Protococcus viridis* C.A.Ag. (× 1,300.)

Solitary cells of *Protococcus* (Fig. 19) are spherical to ellipsoidal and with a fairly thick wall that is without a gelatinous envelope. When solitary cells divide, the two daughter cells may separate from each other and round up, or may remain united in a two-celled colony in which division at right angles to that of the previous plane of division may result in a colony of four or more cells. When the alga grows submerged in water, cell division may continue until there are 50 or more cells in a

[1] Fritsch, 1903; Godward, 1942; Strøm, 1921. [2] Pascher, 1915.
[3] Juller, 1937. [4] Godward, 1942.

colony and there may be a development of a profusely and irregularly branched condition.[1] However, such pseudopleurococcus stages are not always produced when the alga grows submerged in water. Cells of *Protococcus* are uninucleate and have a single parietal laminate chloroplast that is more or less lobed at the margins. The chloroplasts are usually without pyrenoids, but in some instances they have them.

There is no formation of zoospores or gametes, and reproduction is exclusively by division of vegetative cells.

Protococcus is generally interpreted as a reduced form from a branching ulotrichaceous ancestor, and it is thought that the formation of the pseudopleurococcus stage represents a temporary return to the ancestral condition.

FAMILY 6. COLEOCHAETACEAE

Vegetative cells of algae belonging to this family bear long cytoplasmic setae which are partly or wholly surrounded by a gelatinous envelope. All or only certain cells of the thallus may bear these setae. Some members of the family are unicellular, and solitary or gregarious; others are multicellular and with the cells united in branching filaments. The cells are uninucleate and with a single parietal laminate chloroplast. Most genera of the family produce zoospores, and sexual reproduction may be isogamous or oögamous.

The family includes about 10 genera and 25 species, almost all of them fresh-water in habit.

Coleochaete, with about 10 species, is a fresh-water alga that usually grows epiphytically upon other algae or upon submerged aquatics (especially culms of *Typha*), but which may grow endophytically within cell walls of Charales. The cells are joined end to end in branching filaments. Some species have the branches free from one another (Fig. 20*B*); others have the branches laterally apposed to form a pseudoparenchymatous disk (Fig. 20*A*). In all these thalli certain cells bear a single long unbranched cytoplasmic seta whose base is ensheathed by a cylinder of gelatinous material. The development of a seta is due to a blepharoplast that lies immediately beneath a small pore in the cell wall.[2] Cells of *Coleochaete* are uninucleate and with a single laminate chloroplast that partially or wholly encircles the protoplast. There is usually one large pyrenoid within a chloroplast.

Asexual reproduction is by means of biflagellate zoospores that are formed singly within a cell. Isolated cells of a thallus may produce zoospores at any time of the year, but in the spring there is frequently a production of zoospores by every cell in a plant living over from the previous summer. A zoospore escapes by moving in an amoeboid manner

[1] Snow, 1899. [2] Wesley, 1928.

through a pore in the parent-cell wall and then swarms for an hour or so before it comes to rest and secretes a wall.[1] The one-celled germling soon begins to develop into a multicellular thallus, and, when a developing thallus consists of but a few cells only, the cellular arrangement is that characteristic of the species. One or more cells of young developmental

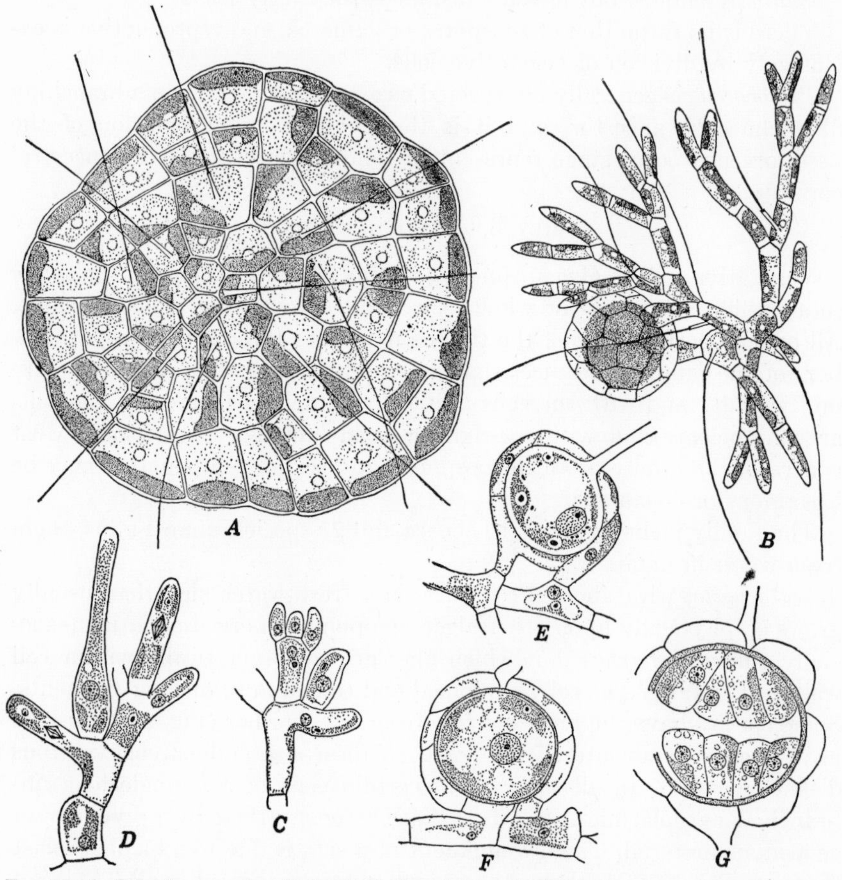

FIG. 20. *A*, *Coleochaete scutata* Bréb. *B–G*, *C. pulvinata* A. Br. *B*, vegetative branch with a spermocarp. *C*, antheridia. *D*, oögonium. *E–F*, young spermocarps. *G*, germinating spermocarp. (*C–G*, *after Oltmanns*, 1898.) (*A*, × 375; *B*, × 110.)

stages bear setae. Aplanospores with fairly thick walls may also be developed singly within a cell.[2]

Most species of *Coleochaete* reproduce sexually, although there are dwarf species that form zoospores only.[3] Sexual reproduction is oögamous, and, according to the species, the plants are heterothallic or

[1] Lambert, 1910; N. Pringsheim, 1860; Wesley, 1930.
[2] Wesley, 1928. [3] Lambert, 1910.

homothallic. In *C. pulvinata* A. Br.[1] and *C. Nitellarum* Jost[2] the antheridia are bluntly conical and are usually borne at the tips of branches (Fig. 20*C*). Antheridia of *C. scutata* Bréb. are developed midway between center and periphery of the discoid thallus.[3] In this species a vegetative cell divides into two daughter cells, one of which, the antheridial mother cell, redivides to form antheridia. Antheridia of *Coleochaete* each produce a single biflagellate antherozoid which may be green or colorless. Oögonia of *C. pulvinata* are formed by a metamorphosis of one-celled lateral branchlets (Fig. 20*D*). The oögonium of this species[1] is a flask-shaped structure with a long colorless neck, the **trichogyne.** Oögonia of *C. scutata* have an inconspicuous trichogyne. They are formed from marginal cells of a thallus. Marginal growth of *C. scutata* continues after differentiation of the oögonia so that they, with their contained zygotes, eventually come to lie some distance in from the thallus margin.

Fertilization takes place by an antherozoid swimming into an oögonium and there uniting with the egg. The zygote remains within the oögonium, secretes a thick wall, and increases greatly in size. At the same time there is an upgrowth of branches from the cell below the oögonium and from neighboring cells to form a parenchymatous layer that more or less completely encloses the oögonium (Fig. 20*E–F*). The oögonium with its ensheathing layer of cells, which soon become reddish brown, is termed a **spermocarp.** The spermocarps remain dormant over winter.[3] The gametes uniting to form a zygote have nuclei of quite different size. But the male gamete nucleus increases greatly in size as it approaches the female nucleus, and, when the two fuse, they are of approximately the same size.[2] Division of the zygote nucleus is meiotic,[4] and each series of nuclear division is followed by a cytokinesis effected by means of a cell plate. Division continues until there are 8 to 32 daughter protoplasts (Fig. 20*G*), and then each of them is metamorphosed into a biflagellate zoospore.[5] The zoospores are liberated by a breaking of the spermocarpic and zygote walls. The liberated zoospores swarm for a short time and then come to rest and develop directly into new thalli.

FAMILY 7. TRENTEPOHLIACEAE

Members of the Trentepohliaceae differ from other Ulotrichineae in that their zoospores and gametes are formed in special cells differing more or less in shape and structure from vegetative cells. These sporangia and gametangia may be terminal or intercalary in position, and solitary or in series. The vegetative cells are united in irregularly branched filaments with a loose or compact branching. The protoplast of a vegetative cell

[1] Oltmanns, 1898. [2] Lewis, 1907. [3] Wesley, 1930.
[4] Allen, 1905. [5] Chodat, 1898; Oltmanns, 1898; N. Pringsheim, 1860.

may contain one or several chloroplasts and is always uninucleate when young. Sexual reproduction is always isogamous.

Typical members of the family, as *Trentepohlia,* have reproductive cells markedly different from vegetative cells, but there are genera in which differences between the two are so slight that it is a question whether they belong to the Trentepohliaceae or Chaetophoraceae.

The family includes some 18 genera and 80 species, a large majority of which are fresh-water algae. Some of them are aquatics; others are aerial and among them are epiphytic species restricted to specific species of trees. Still others of the family are true parasites restricted to specific angiosperms and are parasites of some economic importance.

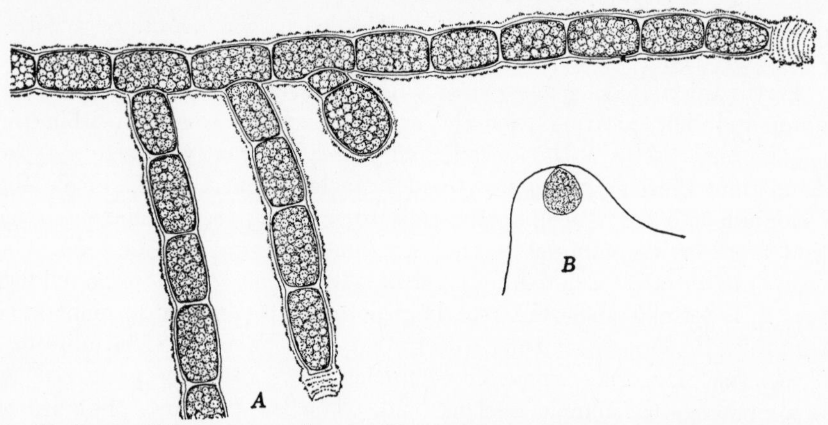

FIG. 21. *Trentepohlia aurea* var. *polycarpa* (Nees and Mont.) Hariot. *A*, portion of a thallus with a gametangium at apex of one lateral branch. *B*, gamete. (*A*, × 325; *B*, × 975.)

Trentepohlia, with about 50 species, is a strictly aerial alga in which the thallus is filamentous and branched (Fig. 21*A*). It is especially abundant in the tropics, but several species grow in temperate and subarctic regions. The alga grows in a felted layer on rocks, or on the leaves and bark of trees. The plant mass is yellowish red to brownish red and quite conspicuous. Sometimes, as on the Monterey Peninsula, California, the alga grows in sufficient abundance to affect the color of the landscape.

The major portion of the plant body may be prostrate and with few short erect branches; or the erect portion may be more extensive than the prostrate portion. Branching of the erect portion may be predominately alternate, opposite, or unilateral. The cells are cylindrical to moniliform and rarely have a length more than twice the breadth. They have lamellated walls composed almost entirely of cellulose.[1] Some species have the wall layers parallel to one another and encircling the cell; other species have the wall layers outwardly and upwardly divergent. In the

[1] West and Hood, 1911.

latter type of wall there is usually a cap of pectose on the terminal cell of each branch. These caps, which are composed of successive transverse lamellae, may become so cumbersome that they impede terminal growth of a branch.[1]

The protoplasts are uninucleate in young cells but may become multinucleate in older ones. There are several parietal chloroplasts in each cell that, according to the species, are discoid, or spiral bands, or combinations of the two.[2] Usually the number and structure of chloroplasts are completely obscured by a "hematochrome" that colors the entire protoplast a deep orange-red. This "hematochrome" is beta-carotene.

Flagellated swarmers are formed in two kinds of special cells; intercalary or terminal cells that remain attached to the thallus, and stalked cells which are always borne terminally and are shed when mature. Both kinds of reproductive cell are often called sporangia, but it is more probable that only the detachable reproductive cells are sporangial in nature. In several,[3] if not all, species the zoospores formed within the sporangia are quadriflagellate. Detachment of a sporangium is due to development of special wall layers between it and the cell below. After becoming detached, sporangia are dispersed as wind-borne spore-like bodies that immediately produce zoospores when moistened.[4] Under certain conditions, the contents of a sporangium become divided into aplanospores before the sporangium becomes detached from the thallus. There may also be a production of akinetes by cells in the prostrate portion of a thallus, and generally in several successive cells.[5] Akinetes have quite thick walls and germinate directly into filaments.

Gametangia may be intercalary or terminal, but in neither case are they shed from the thallus (Fig. 21*A*). They generally differ in shape from sporangia of the same species.[3] The gametes (Fig. 21*B*) are biflagellate and a fusion in pairs has been observed in certain species[6] but has not been found for liberated gametes of other species.[7] In some species the gametes may develop parthenogenetically into filaments;[8] in other species[9] they do not.

Suborder 2. Sphaeropleineae

Because of their multinucleate cells the Sphaeropleaceae, with the single genus *Sphaeroplea*, are frequently ranged alongside the Cladophoraceae. Since other characters are more like those of Ulotrichales it is better to put them in that order. However, the family differs so markedly from

[1] West and Hood, 1911. [2] Geitler, 1923. [3] K. Meyer, 1909, 1936, 1936*A*, 1937.
[4] Gobi, 1871; Karsten, 1891. [5] K. Meyer, 1909.
[6] Karsten, 1891; Wille, 1887. [7] K. Meyer, 1936, 1936*A*, 1937.
[8] K. Meyer, 1936*B*. [9] K. Meyer, 1938.

families assigned to the Ulotrichineae that it is placed in a separate sub-order, the Sphaeropleineae.

Sphaeroplea is a fresh-water genus with five species. It is usually found on periodically inundated ground or in meadows that are flooded at certain times of the year. In such places it may develop to maturity, fruit, and disappear within four or five weeks. *Sphaeroplea* has long cylindrical cells, with a length 15 to 60 times the breadth, which are united end to

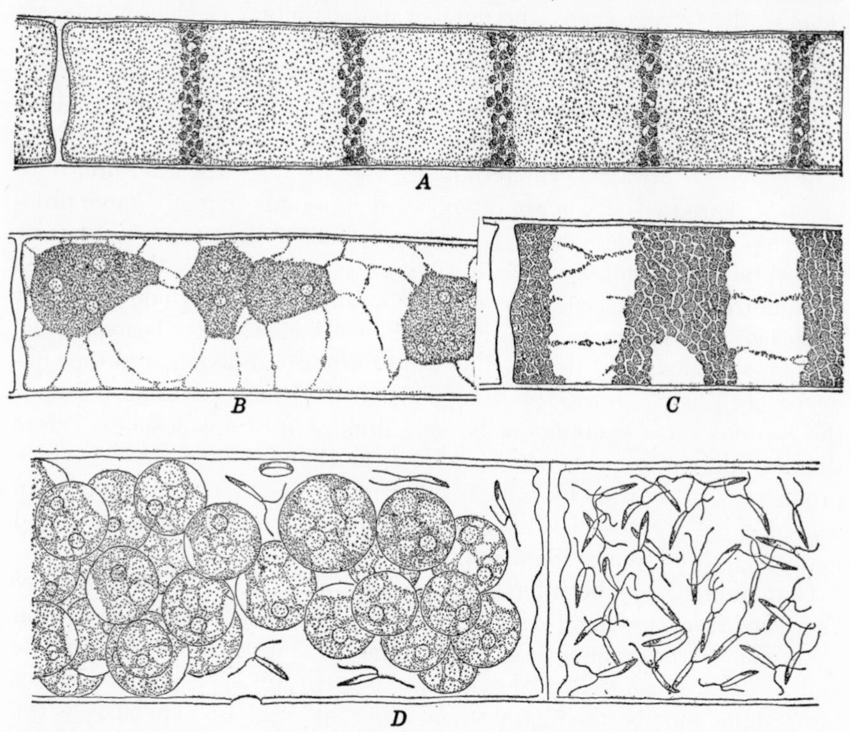

Fig. 22. *A*, portion of a vegetative cell of *Sphaeroplea annulina* (Roth) C.A.Ag. *B–D*, *S. cambrica* Fritsch. *B*, portion of an antheridium early in development of antherozoids. *C*, portion of an antheridium with protoplasm cleaved into small fragments. *D*, portion of an oögonium in which the eggs are being fertilized, and portion of an adjoining mature antheridium. (× 650.)

end in unbranched filaments. Side walls of a cell are relatively thin and without a gelatinous sheath. End walls separating cells one from another are unevenly thickened and sometimes with knob-like projections. A cell contains numerous transverse cytoplasmic septa which are separated from one another by large vacuoles (Fig. 22*A*). Each cytoplasmic septum contains several nuclei, a band-shaped chloroplast with several pyrenoids; or numerous discoid chloroplasts, certain of which contain a pyrenoid. There is a thin layer of cytoplasm between the vacuoles and the side wall of a cell, but chloroplasts are lacking in this portion of the cytoplasm.

Here and there in a cell, a septum develops a vacuole, the enlargement of which divides the septum into two equal parts that become more and more remote from each other as the vacuole increases in size. The resulting increase in length of a cell does not continue indefinitely since, sooner or later, the cell divides transversely into two cells. Growth in length of a filament may continue indefinitely, but usually filaments become accidentally separated into two parts before attaining a length of a few centimeters.

Asexual reproduction is vegetative and by an accidental breaking of filaments. A formation of biflagellate zoospores has been reported[1] but it is very probable that the so-called zoospores are biflagellate female gametes that germinate parthenogenetically.

Sexual reproduction is usually oögamous, but it may be a very advanced type of anisogamy. Eggs and antherozoids are usually produced in separate filaments, but sometimes they are formed in alternate cells of a filament[2] (Fig. 22*D*). *Sphaeroplea* is unique among oögamous Chlorophyceae in that the sex organs are not of distinctive shape. The first step in formation of an antheridial cell is an increase in the number of nuclei, a division of the chloroplasts, and a disappearance of the pyrenoids.[3] There is then a progressive cleavage into angular uninucleate protoplasts, each of which metamorphoses into a naked, spindle-shaped, biflagellate antherozoid[4] (Fig. 22*B–C*). The antherozoids escape singly through small pores in the lateral walls of an antheridial cell.

Cells developing into oögonial cells do not have an increase in the number of nuclei prior to cleavage of the cytoplasm into eggs. The eggs are multinucleate when first formed, but later on there is a degeneration of all nuclei but one. This is not accompanied by a disappearance of the chloroplasts or pyrenoids.[5] The number and size of eggs within an oögonial cell are extremely variable, even in the same species. In most cases the diameter of eggs is more than half that of the oögonial cell, and they lie in a single to double linear series within the cell. More rarely the eggs have a diameter less than a quarter that of an oögonial cell and they lie in multiple longitudinal series (Fig. 23*A–B*). Oögonial cells containing mature eggs have small pores in their walls; and the antherozoids enter through these pores, swim about between the eggs, and eventually unite with them (Fig. 22*D*). In *S. cambrica* Fritsch the oögonial cells at times contain large biflagellate female gametes with contractile vacuoles at the anterior end.[6] They move about sluggishly within the cell for a short time only and then they become immobile and lose their flagella before uniting with antherozoids that have entered the oögonial cell. In *S.*

[1] Rieth, 1952. [2] Rauwenhoff, 1887; Smith, 1933. [3] Klebahn, 1899.
[4] Golenkin, 1899; Klebahn, 1899. [5] Gilbert, 1915; Klebahn, 1899.
[6] Pascher, 1939.

tenuis Fritsch fertilization probably takes place external to the oögonial cell and it is probable that both male and female gametes of this species are motile.[1] Zygotes within an oögonial cell form a thick wall (Fig. 23*C*), with an ornamentation typical for the species, and the protoplast becomes reddish. The zygotes are eventually liberated by decay of walls of oögonial cells but they undergo a resting period of several months before germinating. If conditions for germination continue to be unfavorable, the zygotes may remain viable for several years.

When germination takes place[2] there is usually a division of the protoplast into four zoospores, but one, two, or eight zoospores are sometimes

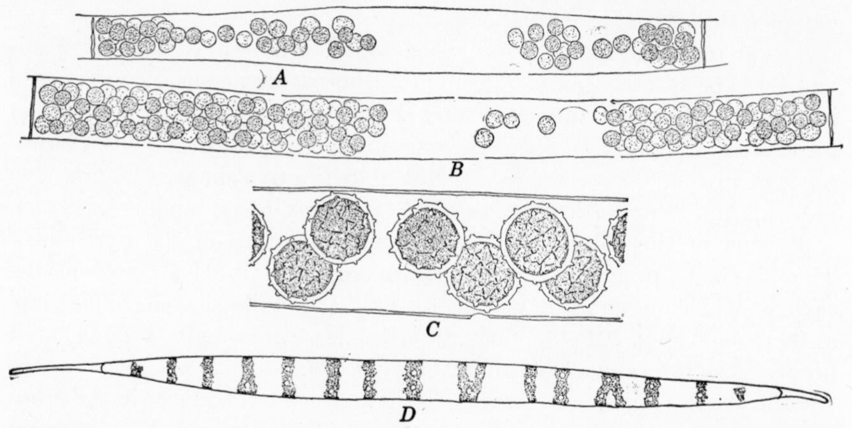

FIG. 23. *A–B*, entire oögonia of *Sphaeroplea cambrica* Fritsch. *C–D*, *S. annulina* (Roth) C.A.Ag. *C*, resting zygotes. *D*, one-celled germling. (*A–B*, × 160; *C*, × 650; *D*, × 352.)

produced. A zoospore is biflagellate and ovoid when first liberated, but shortly before or after it ceases swarming the zoospore becomes spindle-shaped and with greatly attenuated poles. The protoplast of a zoospore secretes a wall soon after swarming ceases, but there is no formation of a holdfast. This free-floating cell elongates to many times its original length and develops many transverse cytoplasmic septa before it divides transversely and begins developing into a filament (Fig. 23*D*).

ORDER 4. ULVALES

The Ulvales have uninucleate cells that divide in two or in three planes to produce parenchymatous thalli that may be expanded sheets, hollow tubes, or solid cylinders. Asexual reproduction is by means of quadriflagellate zoospores. Sexual reproduction is isogamous or anisogamous and by means of biflagellate gametes.

[1] Fritsch, 1929.

[2] Cohn, 1856; Heinricher, 1883; K. Meyer, 1906; Rauwenhoff, 1887.

The order includes 5 or 6 genera and about 125 species. A majority of the species are marine, but certain of them grow in brackish or in fresh waters.

The cell structure of certain genera is so similar to that of Ulotrichales that some phycologists think that differences in vegetative organization do not warrant segregation from the Ulotrichales. In any case, the genera referred to the Ulvaceae are universally recognized as forming a natural family.

FAMILY 1. ULVACEAE

The Ulvaceae have a thallus which is either an expanded sheet one or two cells in thickness, or a hollow cylinder with a wall one cell in thickness, or a ribbon two or more cells broad. The cells are uninucleate and with a single cup-shaped or laminate chloroplast.

Two members of the family (*Enteromorpha*[1] and *Ulva*) are known to have an isomorphic alternation of generations with meiosis just before formation of zoospores by the sporophytic generation. In another genus (*Monostroma*) there is no alternation of generations, all thalli being gametophytic and the zygote germinating to form a number (usually 64) of quadriflagellate zoospores.[2]

Ulva, the sea lettuce, has about 30 species, most of which are exclusively marine. It is a common alga of the mid-tidal zone and it frequently grows in profusion in waters polluted by sewage. A few species grow in brackish water.

The thallus (Fig. 24*A*) is an expanded sheet two cells in thickness and is attached to the substratum by a holdfast composed of rhizoidal outgrowths from the lower cells. As seen in cross section of a thallus (Fig. 24*B*) the cells are isodiametric or vertically elongate to the thallus surface, and their walls are more or less confluent with one another to form a tough gelatinous matrix. Each cell contains a single laminate to cup-shaped chloroplast that lies next to the outer face of the cell. The chloroplast contains a single pyrenoid. The cells are uninucleate and with the nucleus variously located in the interior half of the cell. Cell division may occur anywhere in a thallus, but all divisions are in a plane perpendicular to the thallus surface.

Certain cells in the lower portion of a thallus send out long colorless rhizoids (Fig. 22*C*) that grow down between the two layers of cells and intertwine freely with one another. Near the point of attachment to the substratum, they emerge from the thallus and become closely appressed to one another to form a pseudoparenchymatous holdfast. Emergent portions of rhizoids are transversely septate, multinucleate, and contain

[1] Hartmann, 1929; Kylin, 1930; Ramanathan, 1939.

[2] Moewus, 1938*A*; Schreiber, 1942; Yamada and Saito, 1938.

chlorophyll. The holdfast portion of a thallus is perennial and proliferates new blades each spring.[1]

When *Ulva* is growing in quiet waters of estuaries, it may multiply vegetatively by growth of fragments accidentally detached from a thal-

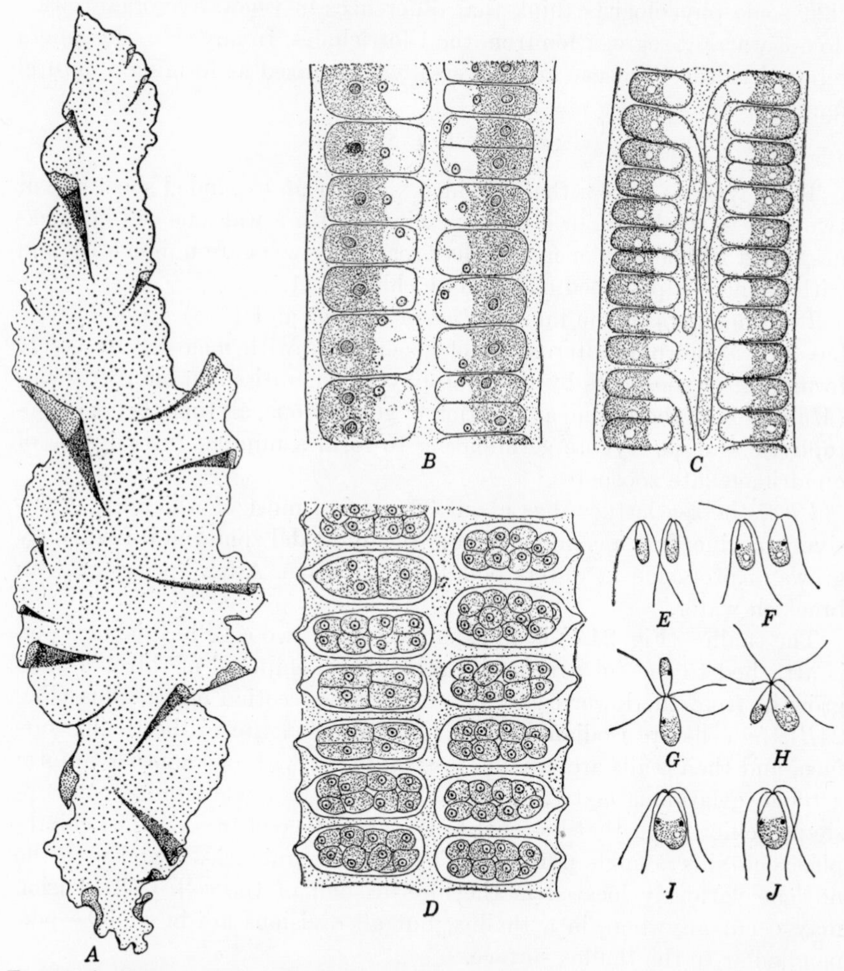

FIG. 24. *A*, thallus of *Ulva stenophylla* Setchell and Gardner. *B–J*, *U. lobata* (Kütz.) S. and G. *B*, vertical section through upper portion of a thallus. *C*, same through basal portion. *D*, formation of gametes. *E*, male gametes. *F*, female gametes. *G–J*, successive stages in union of gametes. (*A*, × ½; *B*, *D–J*, × 975; *C*, × 650.)

lus. There is little vegetative multiplication among individuals growing in the open ocean.

Ulva has an isomorphic alternation of generations, with the gametophyte producing biflagellate gametes and the sporophyte producing quad-

[1] Delf, 1912.

riflagellate zoospores.[1] Along the coast of central California there is a marked biweekly periodicity in liberation of swarmers by both generations; the gametophytes liberating gametes at the beginning of each series of spring tides, and the sporophytes liberating zoospores two to five days later.[2] There is not this marked periodicity along the Atlantic Coast of North America. Liberation of swarmers is at the time when thalli are reflooded by incoming tides and usually during morning tides.[3] The swarmers are often liberated in sufficient quantity to color the water green.

Gametes are produced at the margin of a thallus in a zone 5 to 15 mm. broad, of different color from the vegetative portion, and a zone in which every cell forms gametes. Gametes are formed by repeated bipartition of the protoplast of a cell. In *U. lobata* (Kütz.) S. and G. the first cleavage is always parallel to the thallus surface and the second in a plane perpendicular to the first (Fig. 24*D*). The pyrenoid persists in one daughter protoplast of the first division but usually disappears before the second cleavage takes place. Cleavage continues until there are 32 or 64 daughter protoplasts each of which metamorphoses into a biflagellate gamete. Prior to cleavage of the protoplast each cell develops a beak-like outgrowth at its outer face and it extends to the thallus surface.[2] The tip of this outgrowth eventually becomes the pore through which gametes are liberated. All species investigated have been found to be heterothallic and in one of them it has been shown[4] that there is a genotypic segregation of sex at the time zoospores are formed. Most species are isogamous but at least three species, including *U. lobata* (Fig. 24*E–F*), are known to be anisogamous. In these species[2] it is possible to distinguish between male and female gametophytes by differences in color of the fertile portion. The zygote resulting from fusion of gametes is quadriflagellate (Fig. 24*I–J*). It swarms for a short time only, and then comes to rest, loses its flagella, and secretes a wall. Germination follows within a day or two and division of the zygote nucleus is mitotic.[5] Of the two daughter cells formed by division of a zygote, one develops into a rhizoid and the other eventually develops into a blade. The first divisions in development of a blade are all transverse and result in a filament of several cells, after which cell divisions are both vertical and transverse. In certain species there may be a parthenogenetic development of gametes into gametophytes;[6] but in other species, including *U. lobata*, a gamete that has failed to fuse with another gamete does not divide and disintegrates within a few days.

[1] Føyn, 1929, 1934*A*; Moewus, 1938*A*; Smith, 1947; Yamada and Saito, 1938.
[2] Smith, 1947. [3] Føyn, 1929; Miyake and Kunieda, 1931; Smith, 1947.
[4] Føyn, 1934*A*. [5] Føyn, 1929, 1934*A*.
[6] Føyn, 1934*A*; Moewus, 1938*A*; Yamada and Saito, 1938.

Stages in formation of zoospores by a sporophyte resemble those in formation of gametes except that the first two nuclear divisions are meiotic.[1] Liberation of zoospores is similar to liberation of gametes, and stages in development of a zoospore into a gametophyte are identical with those of development of a zygote into a sporophyte.

FAMILY 2. SCHIZOMERIDACEAE

Mature thalli of Schizomeridaceae are solid cylinders several cells in diameter. The single genus, *Schizomeris*, is a fresh-water alga with two or three species. *Schizomeris* is sometimes placed in the Ulotrichales but the organization of the thallus is more like that of Ulvales.

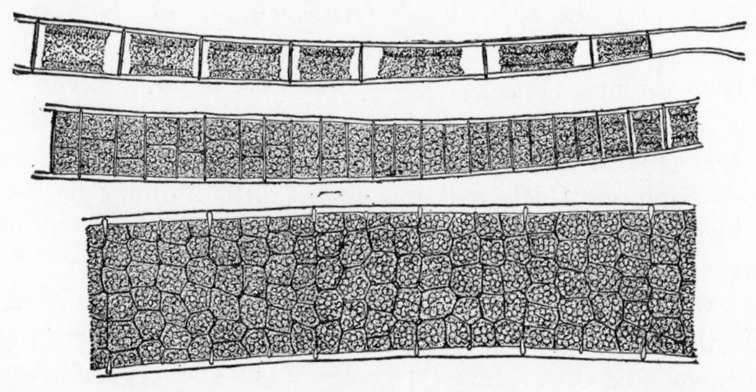

FIG. 25. *Schizomeris liebleinii* Kütz. Portions of a thallus at three different levels. (× 325.)

During early stages of development, a thallus of *Schizomeris* is an unbranched uniseriate filament with an acuminate distal cell and a somewhat elongate basal cell terminating in a discoid holdfast. At this stage of development it resembles one of the Ulotrichaceae. Later on in its development there are vertical divisions at right angles to each other in all cells excepting those toward the base. Continued vertical and transverse division results in a thallus that is a solid cylinder of approximately cubical cells (Fig. 25). The cylinder may have parallel sides, or it may be constricted at infrequent and irregular intervals. Cells of the early filamentous stage have fairly thick lateral walls and are separated from one another by "ring-like" transverse walls.[2] These rings persist after vertical division begins, and they delimit each portion of the mature thallus derived from a single cell of the filamentous stage (Fig. 25). Chloroplasts of the filamentous stage are ulotrichoid and encircle about two-thirds of the protoplasts. They usually contain several pyrenoids. Cells of the mature cylindrical portion have more massive chloroplasts which fill most of the protoplasts. In one species[3] the chloroplast in older cells may be

[1] Føyn, 1929, 1934*A*. [2] Watson and Tilden, 1930. [3] Fritsch and Rich, 1924.

greatly lobed or broken up into several chloroplasts each with a single pyrenoid.

Vegetative multiplication may take place by a fragmentation of old thalli. The region where breaks occur is almost always a constricted portion of a thallus and fragmentation may be due to a disintegration of the transverse ring of wall material persisting from the filamentous stage. Asexual reproduction is by means of quadriflagellate zoospores formed by cells in the upper part of a thallus. Most[1] of those who have observed liberation of zoospores record a breaking down of the cross walls in the region of zoospore formation and an escape of zoospores through the thallus apex; but a liberation of zoospores by a gelatinization of the lateral walls has also been reported.[2]

ORDER 5. SCHIZOGONIALES (PRASIOLALES)

Thalli of Schizogoniales may be either filamentous, or sheet-like plates, or solid cylinders. They are composed of uninucleate cells, each with a single stellate chloroplast. Flagellated reproductive cells are not formed by members of the order, and reproduction is by means of either aplanospores or akinetes.

There are 2 or 3 genera and about 25 species, some fresh-water, others marine. There is but one family, the Schizogoniaceae (Prasiolaceae). The distinctiveness of this family is universally recognized but some phycologists think that it does not merit ordinal rank and should be placed among the Ulotrichales.

Prasiola is the most widely distributed member of the order. There are approximately 20 species, some of which are marine and others freshwater. Certain species grow only where the substratum is rich in soluble nitrogenous compounds, and most of the marine species are restricted to the spray zone of rocks covered with the droppings of sea birds.

The adult thallus of *Prasiola* is an expanded sheet one cell in thickness and with the cells tending to lie in groups of four (Fig. 26*A–B*). The tetrads, in turn, lie in larger more or less rectangular groups separated from one another by narrow or broad intervening spaces. Attachment to the substratum may be by rhizoidal outgrowths from the thallus margin or by means of a thickened stipe. The first cell divisions in development of a thallus are always transverse and result in a simple filament. The filamentous stage may at times be falsely branched because of death of one or two cells and a growth of adjoining portions through the sheath investing the filament.[3] The juvenile phase may persist indefinitely; or, as a result of vertical and transverse divisions, a filament may become

[1] Hazen, 1902; Wolle, 1887; Wood, 1872. [2] Korshikov, 1927.
[3] Brand, 1914; Gay, 1891; Wille, 1901.

either a ribbon two to a few cells broad or an expanded sheet about as broad as long.

Cells of vigorously growing thalli have a single stellate chloroplast with a pyrenoid at the center (Fig. 26*C*). The cells are uninucleate, with the nucleus excentric in position.

Vegetative multiplication may take place at the filamentous or at the adult stage. Multiplication at the filamentous stage is by a fragmentation into segments containing one to four cells,[1] or by a dissociation into spherical cells which readily separate from one another.[2] Vegetative multiplication of adult thalli is by abscission of small proliferous shoots.

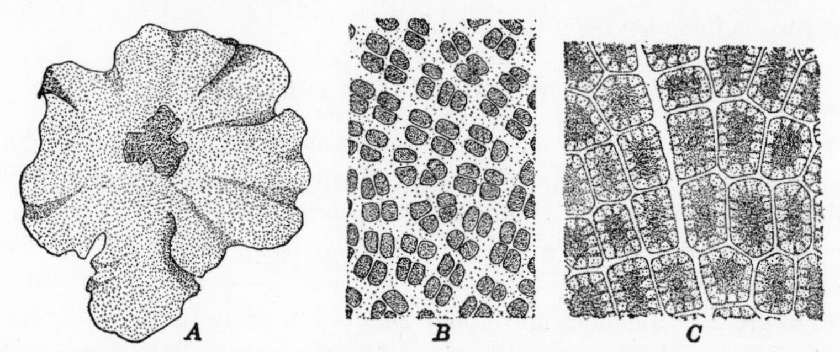

Fig. 26. *A–B*, *Prasiola mexicana* J.G.Ag. *A*, thallus. *B*, portion of a thallus. *C*, portion of a thallus of *P. meridionalis* Setchell and Gardner, showing structure of cells. (*A*, × ½; *B*, × 485; *C*, × 975.)

Asexual reproduction is by metamorphosis of a vegetative cell into an akinete. The akinetes are liberated by a softening of the thallus matrix. They may develop directly into new thalli, or they may become aplanosporangia which contain several aplanospores.[3] The supposed production of biflagellate gametes reported for *Prasiola*[4] has never been confirmed.

ORDER 6. CLADOPHORALES

The Cladophorales have multinucleate cylindrical cells united end to end in simple or branched filaments. The chloroplast is a reticulate sheet encircling the protoplast and with a pyrenoid at many intersections of the reticulum. In some cases connecting strands between intersections are so delicate that the cell seems to have numerous discoid chloroplasts. Asexual reproduction is by means of quadriflagellate zoospores, aplanospores, or akinetes. Sexual reproduction is isogamous or anisogamous.

The order includes about 12 genera and 350 species. Some genera are exclusively marine, others exclusively fresh-water, and still others with both marine and fresh-water species.

[1] Gay, 1891; Wille, 1901. [2] Borzi, 1895; Gay, 1891.
[3] Wille, 1901, 1906. [4] Yabe, 1932.

All genera are placed in a single family, the Cladophoraceae. The validity of the Cladophoraceae is universally recognized but there is disagreement as to whether or not they should be placed in a separate order (see page 29).

Two members of the order (*Chaetomorpha*[1] and *Cladophora*) are known to have an isomorphic alternation of generations. *Urospora* does not have an alternation of generations[2] and there is a strong presumption[3] that the same holds for *Spongomorpha*.

Cladophora, with some 160 species, is unusual in that some species are marine and others are fresh-water. Its cylindrical cells have a length three to twenty times the breadth and are united end to end in freely branched

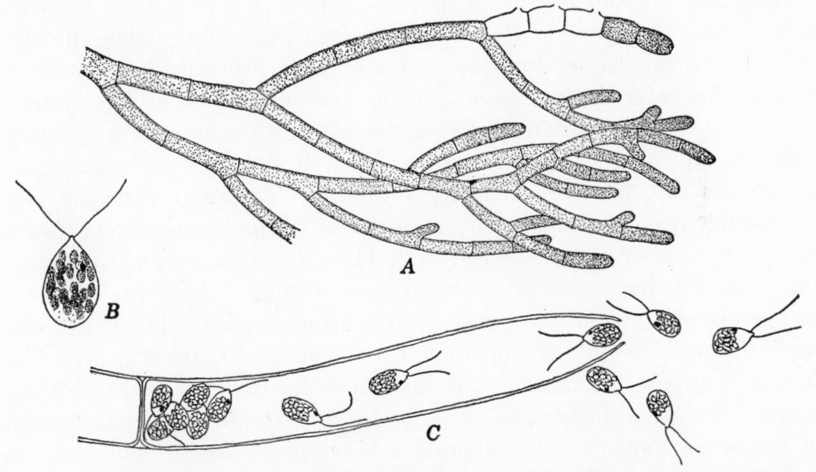

FIG. 27. *A–B*, *Cladophora glomerata* (L.) Kütz. *A*, portion of a thallus. *B*, gamete. *C*, liberation of gametes of *C. kuetzingianum* Grun. (*A*, × 40; *B*, × 600; *C*, × 325.)

filaments (Fig. 27*A*). The branching is usually lateral, but at times appears to be dichotomous because of a pushing aside (evection[4]) of a branch producing a lateral branch. Branches originate as lateral outgrowths from the upper end of a cell and are usually formed only from cells near the apex of a filament. Thalli of *Cladophora* are usually sessile and attached to the substratum by fairly long rhizoidal branches, some of which arise adventitiously from cells near the base of a thallus. Many species of *Cladophora* are perennial, the thallus dying back to the prostrate rhizoidal system whose cells are densely filled with food reserves. In the following growing season certain of these cells give rise to new erect branches.

The cells have thick stratified walls consisting of an inner cellulose layer, a median pectic zone, and an outer layer of some insoluble sub-

[1] Hartmann, 1929. [2] Jorde, 1933. [3] Smith, 1947*A*. [4] Brand, 1901.

stance that has been thought[1] to be chitin. Internal to the wall is a layer of cytoplasm and internal to this is a large central vacuole. A single reticulate sheet-like chloroplast encircles the outer portion of the cytoplasm, and there is a pyrenoid at many intersections of the reticulum. The cells are always multinucleate and with the nuclei lying internal to the chloroplast.

All critically investigated species have been shown[2] to have an isomorphic alternation of generations; the sporophytes producing quadriflagellate zoospores and the gametophytes producing biflagellate gametes. Zoospore formation is restricted to vigorously growing cells near the tips of branches. There is a period of active nuclear division just prior to zoospore formation and in certain species the divisions have been shown to be meiotic.[3] *C. glomerata* (L.) Kütz. is atypical in that nuclear divisions immediately preceding formation of zoospores are mitotic, meiosis occurring just before formation of gametes.[4] After completion of the nuclear divisions there is a progressive cleavage into uninucleate protoplasts by means of a progressive vacuolization.[5] Each uninucleate protoplast metamorphoses into a quadriflagellate zoospore. Coincident with the cytoplasmic cleavage there is a development of a small lens-shaped area at or near the upper end of the cell wall. The gelatinization and bursting of this area produce a small circular pore through which the zoospores escape. Liberation of zoospores from marine species takes place when thalli are reflooded by the incoming tide. Along the coast of central California, zoospore formation and liberation in *C. trichotoma* (C.A.Ag.) Kütz. take place during the spring tides, but the beginning and ending of the period during which liberation takes place are not so sharply defined as in species of *Ulva* growing in the same locality (see page 63). Germination takes place soon after the zoospore ceases swarming. The one-celled germling secretes a wall, elongates vertically, becomes multinucleate, and then divides transversely into two daughter cells, the lower of which is rhizoidal.

Gamete formation is similar to zoospore formation but, except for *C. glomerata*, the nuclear divisions immediately preceding formation of gametes are mitotic. The gametes are biflagellate (Fig. 27*B*–*C*) and the mechanism of their liberation is similar to that of zoospores. *C. trichotoma* also has a biweekly liberation of gametes but, different from *Ulva*, both gametophytes and sporophytes liberate swarmers on the same days. All species thus far investigated are isogamous and strictly heterothallic. Certain species have a disintegration of gametes which have not fused to form a zygote; other species have a parthenogenetic germination of gametes that fail to unite with other gametes.

[1] Wurdack, 1923. [2] Føyn, 1929, 1934; Schussnig, 1928, 1930, 1931.
[3] Føyn, 1934; Schussnig, 1928, 1930*B*. [4] List, 1930. [5] Czempyrek, 1930.

Division of the zygote nucleus is mitotic and the zygote germinates within a day or two after being formed by a union of two gametes.

ORDER 7. OEDOGONIALES

The Oedogoniales have cylindrical uninucleate cells united end to end in simple or branched filaments. Cell division is of a unique type and has a distinctive annular splitting of the lateral cell wall. Motile reproductive cells differ from most other Chlorophyceae in that they have a transverse whorl of flagella. Asexual reproduction is usually by zoospores formed singly within a cell, but it may also be by means of akinetes. Sexual reproduction is always oögamous.

There are 3 genera and approximately 350 species, all fresh-water in habit. These are placed in a single family, the Oedogoniaceae.

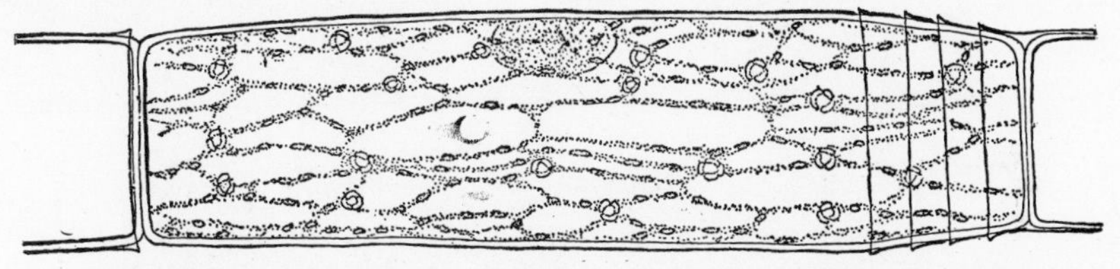

FIG. 28. Vegetative cell of *Oedogonium crassum* (Hass.) Wittr. (× 485.)

Oedogonium, with some 285 species, is the only genus of the family in which the filaments are unbranched. It is a submerged aquatic and is of frequent occurrence in permanent and semipermanent fresh-water pools and ponds. All species are sessile when young, and usually epiphytic upon leaves and stems of submerged vascular plants or epiphytic upon the larger filamentous green algae. The basal cell is always modified to form a holdfast, and the distal cell is usually broadly rounded or acuminate. Intercalary cells of a filament have an apical-basal polarity, and this is maintained even when upper portions of filaments have broken away and continued growth as free-floating plants.

The cells are cylindrical and with fairly thick rigid walls. The lateral wall of a cell consists of an inner cellulose layer, a median pectic zone, and an outer layer that is thought[1] to be chitinous. Lateral walls of certain cells of every filament have one or more transverse striae at the distal end. They constitute the so-called **apical cap** (Fig. 28). The chloroplast is a reticulate sheet extending from pole to pole of a cell and completely encircling the protoplast. According to the species, the strands of the reticulum are broad or narrow, but in either case the majority of strands are parallel to the long axis of the cell (Fig. 28). The pyrenoids, of which there are usually many in a chloroplast, lie at the intersections of the reticulum. Each pyrenoid is surrounded by a sheath of starch

[1] Wurdack, 1923.

plates. Starch plates formed by pyrenoids may migrate to and accumulate in the strands of the reticulum until the reticulate nature of the chloroplast is completely obscured by this "stroma" starch. The single nucleus usually lies midway between the ends of a protoplast and just internal to the chloroplast. It is of large size, is biscuit-shaped, has a well-defined chromatin-linin network and one or more nucleoli.

Cell division is terminal or intercalary and may take place in any cell but the basal one. Prior to cell division, there is an upward migration of the nucleus until it lies about two-thirds the distance from the proximal end. After elongating somewhat, the nucleus divides mitotically. This generally takes place during the night. During the prophases of mitosis,

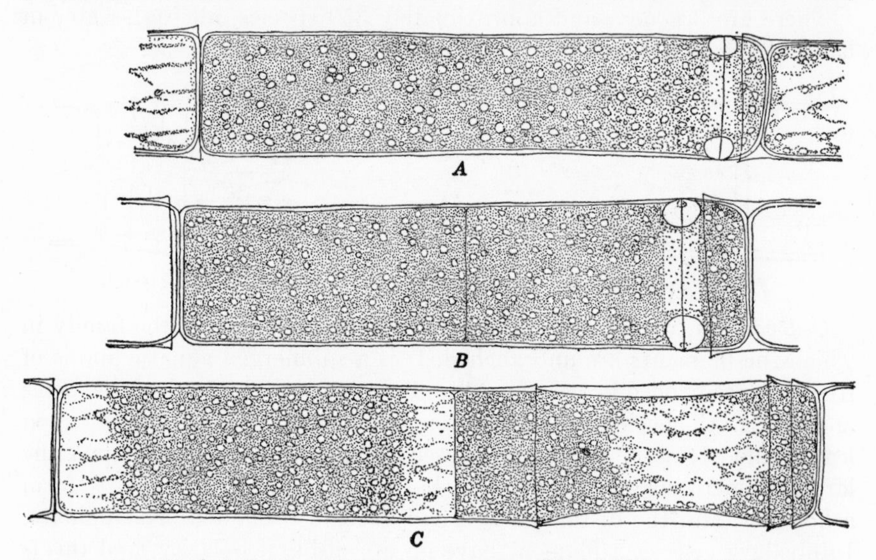

Fig. 29. Cell division of *Oedogonium crassum* (Hass.) Wittr. (× 485.)

there is an appearance of a ring of wall material that completely encircles the inner face of the lateral wall just below the distal end of the cell.[1] The ring, which is thought[2] to consist of hemicellulose, increases in thickness until it is several times thicker than the rest of the lateral wall (Fig. 29*A*). There is next a formation of a small groove completely encircling the portion of the ring adjoining the lateral wall. A transverse rent then appears in the portion of the lateral wall external to the groove. Mitosis is completed by the time that the ring is fully developed, and, shortly after the two daughter nuclei are reconstructed, there is a transverse cytokinesis of the protoplast by an annular furrowing of the plasma

[1] Hirn, 1900; Kraskovits, 1905; Kretschmer, 1930; Ohashi, 1930; N. Pringsheim, 1858; Steinecke, 1929; Strasburger, 1880; Tuttle, 1910; van Wisselingh, 1908, 1908*A*.

[2] Steinecke, 1929.

membrane midway between the ends of the cell (Fig. 29*B*). There is no elongation of the cell during these stages of division, but, after transverse division of the protoplast, each daughter protoplast elongates to about the same length as that of the parent protoplast. This elongation takes but a short time and is often completed within 15 minutes. The lower daughter protoplast elongates until its distal end is level with, or slightly above, the former level of the hemicellulose ring. The wall lateral to this protoplast is therefore the side wall of the old parent cell. Meanwhile, the upper daughter protoplast has been elongating to about the same

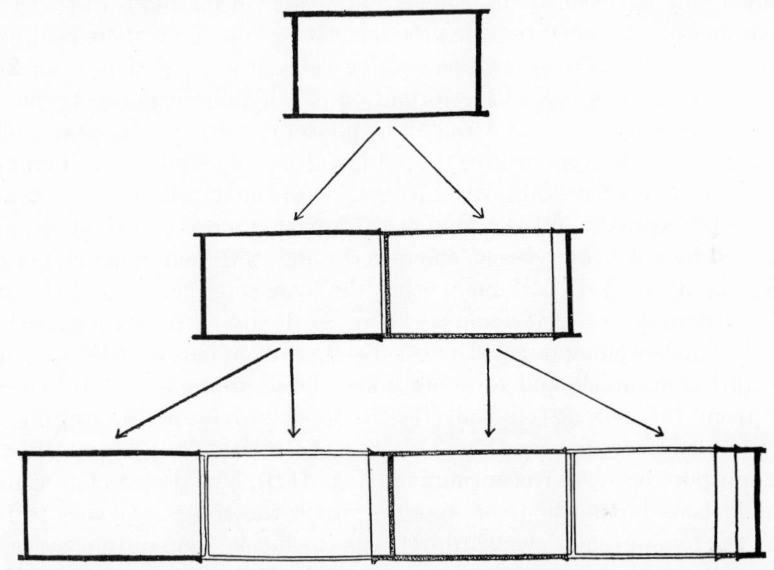

FIG. 30. Diagram showing the distribution of mother-cell walls to daughter cells in *Oedogonium*. Walls of the first cell generation are shaded black, those of the second generation are in stipple, and those of the third generation are unshaded.

extent. The wall lateral to this protoplast is formed by a vertical stretching of the hemicellulose ring (Fig. 29*C*), except for the persistent portion of the parent-cell wall at the upper end—the apical cap. After the daughter protoplasts have completed their elongation, there is a secretion of a transverse wall which separates them from each other. Some phycologists describing cell division in *Oedogonium* hold[1] that the transverse wall is formed immediately after cytokinesis and that it is pushed upward as the lower daughter protoplast elongates.

Division of every cell in a filament and repeated division of the daughter cells would result in alternate cells with and without caps. Cells with one, two, three, or more caps would also have a definite disposition with respect to one another (Fig. 30). This theoretical condition rarely ob-

[1] Strasburger, 1880.

tains in nature, and frequently the repeated division of the distal daughter cell results in a filament in which a cell with several apical caps lies above several successive cells without caps. In some species the terminal cell is the only one with apical caps.

Vegetative multiplication by an accidental breaking of filaments is of common occurrence, especially among species growing in free-floating masses. All species may produce zoospores, and their production is stimulated by an increase in the amount of carbon dioxide in the surrounding water.[1] Zoospores are formed singly within a cell. They are usually formed only by recently divided cells and their formation is restricted to the upper of two daughter cells, the one with a cap. Thus there is at least one sterile cell between two successive cells producing zoospores. Zoospore formation begins with a formation of a hyaline region between the nucleus and the cell wall.[2] A ring of blepharoplast granules appears about the margin of the hyaline area, and it is quite probable that each granule gives rise to one flagellum. After formation of the flagella the lateral wall breaks transversely in the region of the apical cap and the zoospore, surrounded by a delicate vesicle, emerges through the open upper end of the cell (Fig. 31*A–C*). It is thought[3] that the transverse splitting of the wall and pushing out of vesicle and zoospore result from a pressure caused by imbibitional swelling of gelatinous substances secreted by the protoplast. Liberation of vesicle and zoospore takes about 10 minutes. After emerging from the parent-cell wall the zoospore swims around within the vesicle for a few minutes (Fig. 31*C*) but the vesicle soon disappears and the zoospore becomes free-swimming (Fig. 31*D*). The period of swarming usually lasts but an hour or so, after which the zoospore comes to rest with the hyaline end downward, retracts its flagella, and develops a holdfast that attaches it to the substratum (Fig. 31*E*). The type of holdfast developed depends upon both the species concerned and the nature of the substratum. Species with a rhizoidal holdfast have been shown[4] to form a simple holdfast if the substratum is smooth and to form a more or less branched one if the substratum is rough. A zoospore secretes a wall shortly after it becomes sessile, but the wall differs from that enclosing other vegetative cells in that it lacks a superficial layer of chitinous material.[5]

Sessile one-celled germlings of most species divide transversely by means of an apical ring similar to that in an ordinary cell division.[6] Division of the distal cell and the division and redivision of its daughter

[1] Gussewa, 1927, 1930.

[2] Gussewa, 1927, 1930; Hirn, 1900; Kretschmer, 1930; Ohashi, 1930; Strasburger, 1892.

[3] Steinecke, 1929. [4] Peirce and Randolph, 1905.

[5] Tiffany, 1924. [6] Fritsch, 1902; Wille, 1887*A*.

cells result in a many-celled filament; the basal cell formed by the first division does not divide again (Fig. 31*F*). Sessile one-celled germlings of a few species are hemispherical and do not form a ring at the time of the first division. Division of these germlings begins[1] with the protrusion of a cylindrical outgrowth from the upper portion. When the cylinder has attained a certain length, there is a transverse division of the protoplast at the juncture of cylinder and hemisphere and a formation of a cross wall between the two.

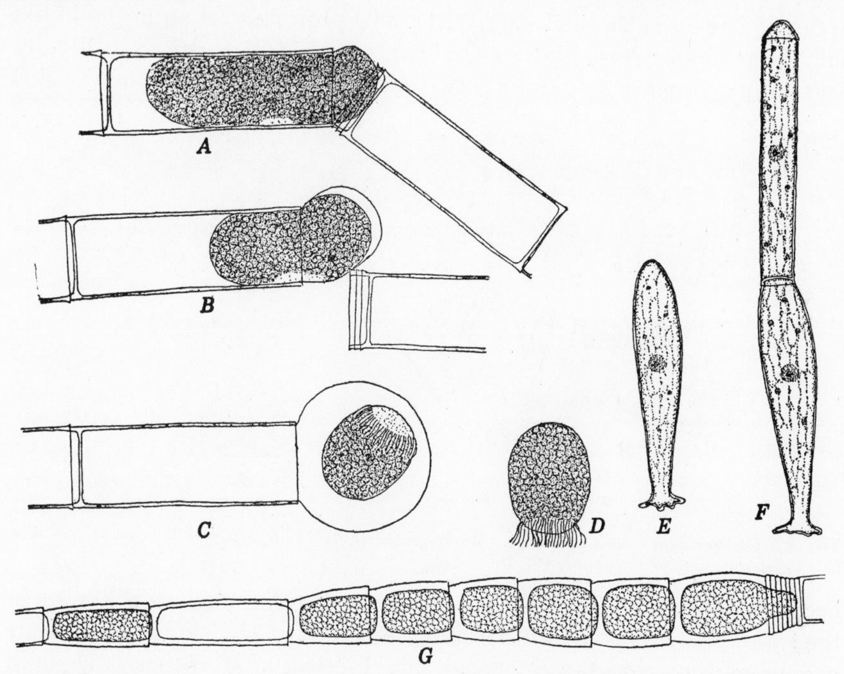

Fig. 31. *Oedogonium* spp. *A–C*, liberation of zoospore. *D*, zoospore. *E–F*, germlings. *G*, akinetes. (× 325.)

Oedogonium may also form akinetes.[2] They are formed in chains of 10 to 40 and in inflated cells resembling oögonia (Fig. 31*G*). Their protoplasts are rich in reserve starch and a reddish-orange oil. Akinetes germinate directly into new filaments.

Sexual reproduction is oögamous. It is of frequent occurrence when filaments are growing in standing water but is infrequent if they are in flowing water. Each species produces sex organs at rather definite seasons of the year. As a rule, species with small cells have a short vegetative phase and fruit early in the growing season, whereas those with large cells have a longer vegetative period and fruit later in the growing season.[3]

[1] Fritsch, 1904. [2] Wille, 1883. [3] Tiffany, 1930; Tiffany and Transeau, 1927.

Sexual reproduction may be **macrandrous,** with antheridia produced in filaments of normal size; or **nannandrous,** with the antheridia produced by special dwarf male filaments. Macrandrous species may be homothallic or heterothallic. Their antheridia are either terminal or intercalary and are produced by division of an **antheridial mother cell.** This division is quite similar to that of a vegetative cell, except that the upper cell, which is the **antheridium,** is much shorter than the sister cell.[1] The lower sister cell may, in turn, divide repeatedly and so give rise to a series of 2 to 40 antheridia (Fig. 32*A*). The protoplast of an antheridium may be metamorphosed into a single antherozoid, but usually it divides vertically or transversely to form two daughter protoplasts, each of which

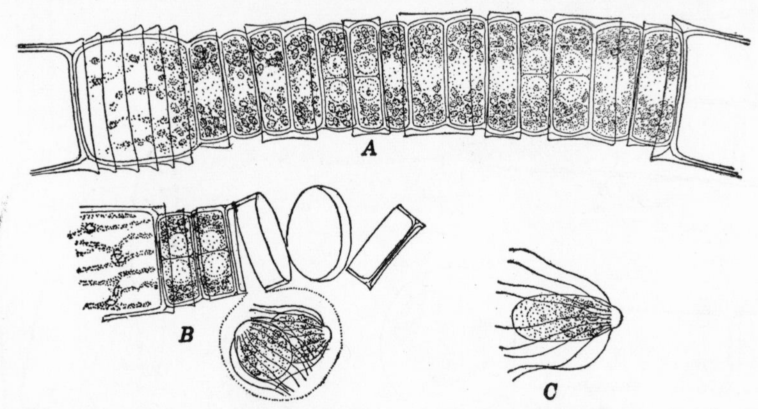

FIG. 32. *Oedogonium crassum* (Hass.) Wittr. *A*, antheridia. *B*, liberation of antherozoids. *C*, free-swimming antherozoid. (× 485.)

becomes an antherozoid. Division of the antheridial nucleus is always in the transverse axis of the antheridium, but the two nuclei may come to lie one above the other before cytokinesis. Liberation of antherozoids is in the same manner as that of zoospores, and the antherozoids are likewise surrounded by a vesicle when first liberated (Fig. 32*B*). Except for the smaller size and fewer flagella, antherozoids of most species are like zoospores, but those of some species[2] have flagella longer than the body of the antherozoid (Fig. 32*B*, *C*).

Oögonia of macrandrous species are formed by transverse division of an **oögonial mother cell** that may be terminal or intercalary in position. The distal daughter cell always matures into an oögonium (Fig. 33). Hence, oögonia always have one or more caps at the upper end. The lower daughter cell, the **suffultory cell,** may remain undivided, or it may function as an oögonial mother cell. In the former case the oögonia are solitary; in the latter they are in series of two or more. Each oögonium

[1] Gussewa, 1930; Ohashi, 1930. [2] Smith, 1933; Spessard, 1930.

becomes more or less rounded and has a diameter greater than that of vegetative cells of the filament. As it approaches maturity, there is a formation of a small pore or a formation of a transverse crack in the oögonial wall. The shape and position of this opening are quite characteristic for a species and are characters of diagnostic importance in separating species from one another. The protoplast within an oögonium metamorphoses into a single egg. The nucleus is centrally located within

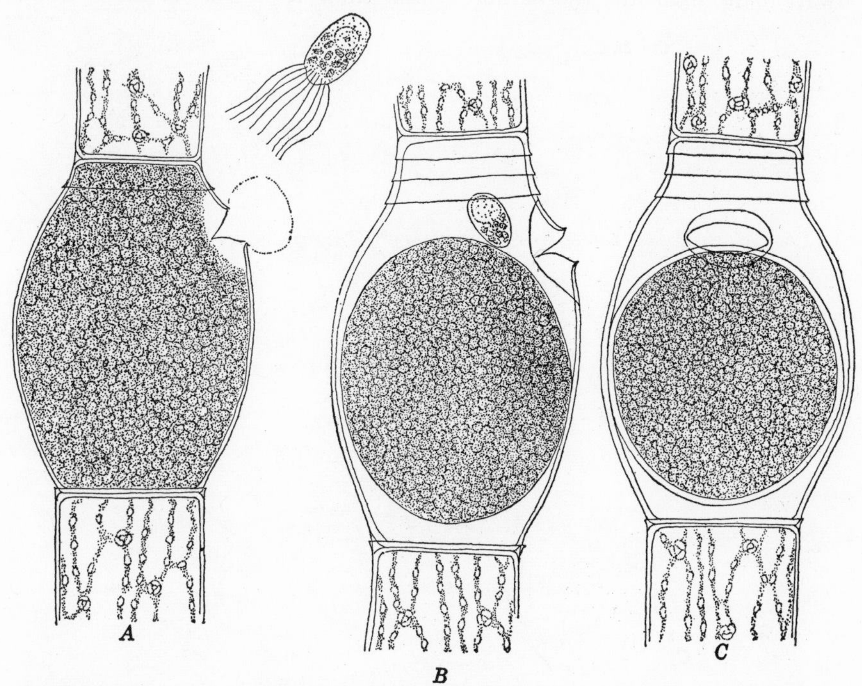

Fig. 33. Oögonia of a macrandrous species of *Oedogonium*, *O. crassum* (Hass.) Wittr. *A*, with egg ready for fertilization. *B*, just after fertilization; the antherozoid within the oögonium is probably a supernumerary one. *C*, zygote after the beginning of wall formation. (× 485.)

a developing egg,[1] but shortly before fertilization it migrates to the egg periphery just within the opening in the oögonial wall. Eggs ready for fertilization retract slightly from the oögonial wall and develop a hyaline receptive spot external to the nucleus.

The dwarf male filaments of nannandrous species are produced by the germination of special zoospores (**androspores**) that are produced within **androsporangia.** Androsporangia (Fig. 34*A*) are quite similar in appearance to the antheridia of macrandrous species. If a nannandrous species is one with androsporangia and oögonia borne on the same filament, it is

[1] Klebahn, 1892; Ohashi, 1930.

gynandrosporous; if the two are borne on separate filaments, the species is **idioandrosporous.** Androsporangia, similar to antheridia, are produced by unequal division of a mother cell. Only one androspore is formed within an androsporangium,[1] and, when it is first liberated, it is surrounded by a vesicle. After the vesicle disappears, the androspore swims freely in all directions until it comes in the vicinity of an oögonium or a developing oögonium. It then becomes affixed and germinates to form a dwarf male filament—the **nannandrium.** Androspores of certain species,

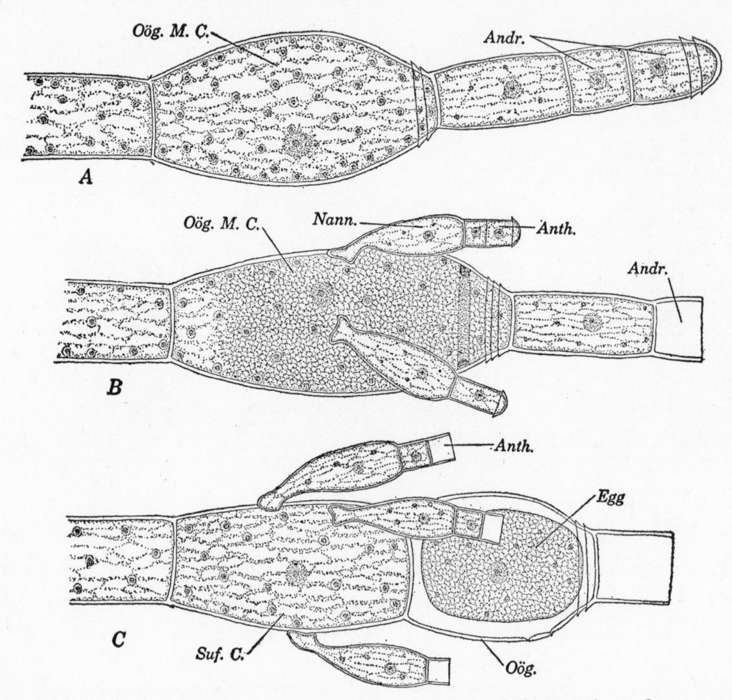

Fig. 34. Sexual reproduction of a nannandrous species of *Oedogonium*, *O. concatenatum* (Hass.) Wittr. (*Andr.*, androsporangium; *Anth.*, antheridium; *Nann.*, nannandrium; *Oög.*, oögonium; *Oög. M.C.*, oögonial mother cell; *Suf. C*, suffultory cell.) (× 325.)

as *O. concatenatum* (Hass.) Wittr., come to rest upon oögonial mother cells not yet divided into oögonium and suffultory cell (Fig. 34*B–C*). These species regularly bear their nannandria upon the suffultory cell. Other species usually liberate androspores after division of the oögonial mother cell, and their nannandria may be perched upon either oögonium or suffultory cell. One-celled germlings of nannandria are, except for their smaller size, quite like germlings developed from zoospores. One-celled germlings of most species function as antheridial mother cells and cut off one or more antheridia at their apices (Fig. 34*B*). The lower portion of

[1] Hirn, 1900; Tiffany, 1930.

the antheridial mother cell is never completely used up in the formation of antheridia and persists as a stipe supporting the antheridia. The protoplast of each antheridium divides to form two antherozoids, each with an apical crown of flagella.[1]

It is generally agreed that nannandrous species have been evolved from macrandrous ones. Some phycologists think that this has been brought about by a gradual reduction in size of male filaments of heterothallic macrandrous species. The occurrence of macrandrous species with somewhat smaller male filaments[2] and the precocious formation of antheridia by young filaments of heterothallic species[3] are held to be evidence for this. The similarity in structure and development of androsporangia and macrandrous antheridia indicates, however, that androsporangia have been evolved from antheridia. Androspores are, in a sense, macrandrous antherozoids that always develop parthenogenetically,[4] but which still retain sufficient of their gametic nature to swim to, and germinate upon, oögonia or cells related to them.

Oögonial development of nannandrous species is identical with that of macrandrous species.

Fertilization[5] in both nannandrous and macrandrous species is by the antherozoid swimming through the opening in the oögonial wall and entering the egg at the hyaline receptive spot (Fig. 33*A–B*). The male and female nuclei unite with each other in a resting condition and their fusion takes place soon after entrance of the antherozoid.[6] The zygote, which is somewhat retracted from the oögonial wall and of a different shape, begins to secrete a wall as soon as it is formed (Fig. 33*C*). Walls of mature zygotes are usually composed of three layers, but some species have a wall with two layers only. The layer outside the innermost may be smooth, but more often it is ornamented with pits, scrobiculations, reticulations, or costae. The color of the protoplast in a ripening zygote changes from green to a reddish brown, largely because of an accumulation of a reddish oil.

Some species have a regular development of unfertilized eggs into parthenospores; other species have a disintegration of eggs that are not fertilized. Parthenospores have a zygote-like wall, but they may be distinguished from zygotes by the fact that they completely fill the oögonial cavity and are of the same shape as the oögonium.[7]

The zygote is eventually liberated from the filament by a decay of the oögonial wall. It usually undergoes a further period of rest before germinating, and this may regularly last for a year or more.[7] During the ripening there is a meiotic division of the zygote nucleus to form four

[1] Hirn, 1900; Tiffany, 1930. [2] Hirn, 1900; West, 1912. [3] Fritsch, 1902*A*.
[4] Schaffner, 1927. [5] Hirn, 1900; Klebahn, 1892; Ohashi, 1930.
[6] Gussewa, 1930; Klebahn, 1892; Ohashi, 1930. [7] Mainx, 1931.

haploid nuclei.[1] Shortly before germination the protoplast becomes green and divides to form four daughter protoplasts, each of which becomes a zoospore.[2] The zoospores lie within a common vesicle when first liberated by a bursting of the zygote wall, but the vesicle soon disappears. The swarming and subsequent development of zoospores into filaments are identical with those of zoospores produced by vegetative cells. In some macrandrous heterothallic species it has been shown[3] that two of the four zoospores develop into male filaments and the other two into female filaments.

ORDER 8. ZYGNEMATALES

The Zygnematales (Conjugales) differ from all other Chlorophyceae in that their gametes are amoeboid and without flagella. Sexual reproduction is always isogamous.

The order includes some 40 genera and 3,000 species, all fresh-water in habit.

The cells may be solitary or united end to end in unbranched filaments. The cell wall is generally composed of two layers, a cellulose layer next to the protoplast and an outer layer of pectic material. The chloroplasts are of three general types: peripheral spirally twisted bands extending the length of a cell, an axial plate extending the length of a cell, or two stellate chloroplasts axial to each other. There are many modifications of the last-named type in the Desmidiaceae, and many members of this family have "stellate" chloroplasts from which either the rays or the central mass have disappeared.

None of the Zygnematales forms asexual reproductive bodies. All genera reproduce sexually by a fusion of amoeboid aplanogametes. Aplanogametes are formed singly within a cell, and in most genera all of the protoplast is used in production of an aplanogamete. Gametic union may be through a tubular connection established between two cells, or the aplanogametes may escape from their enclosing walls at the time they fuse with each other. The zygote (frequently called a **zygospore**) develops a thick wall and enters upon a period of rest before germinating. The fact that all cytologically investigated species[4] have a meiotic division of the zygote nucleus seems to justify the assumption that vegetative cells of all Zygnematales are haploid. Depending upon the genus, a germinating zygote gives rise to one, two, or four new plants.

Some phycologists divide the Zygnematales into two families, one containing the truly filamentous genera, the other containing the unicellular

[1] Gussewa, 1930; Mainx, 1931.

[2] Gussewa, 1930; Jurányi, 1873; Mainx, 1931; N. Pringsheim, 1858.

[3] Mainx, 1931.

[4] Kauffmann, 1914; Kurssanow, 1911; Potthoff, 1927; Tröndle, 1911.

genera and their derivatives (collectively known as the **desmids**). Other phycologists recognize two series among the desmids and give each the rank of a family.

FAMILY 1. ZYGNEMATACEAE

The Zygnemataceae have cylindrical cells that are permanently united in unbranched filaments. The cell walls are without pores. The protoplast may contain either one to several peripheral spiral ribbon-shaped chloroplasts, or a single axial laminate chloroplast, or two axial stellate chloroplasts. Union of two aplanogametes is usually by establishment of a tubular connection (**conjugation tube**) between two cells, but in rare cases gametic union may be through an opening in the wall between two adjacent cells.

According to the most recent monograph of the family[1] there are 13 genera and 533 species.

The well-known *Spirogyra* is a member of the family. Another widely distributed member is *Zygnema*, a genus with some 95 species. It has cells with two stellate chloroplasts, but one may not be certain that any vegetative filament with such cells is *Zygnema*, because cells of certain other Zygnemataceae also have two stellate chloroplasts. The cells of *Zygnema* are cylindrical and usually with a length not more than twice the breadth. Lateral walls of filaments of *Zygnema* have a thick pectose layer,[2] and there is never a refolding (replication) of transverse walls as is found in certain species of *Spirogyra*. Most filaments have all cells alike, but occasionally[3] certain cells of a filament develop rhizoid-like outgrowths (**haptera**).

The two stellate chloroplasts lie axial to each other and in the longitudinal axis of a cell (Fig. 35*A*). A chloroplast has numerous delicate to massive strands extending to the plasma membrane and has a single large pyrenoid at its center. The cells are uninucleate, with the nucleus embedded in a broad strand of cytoplasm connecting the two chloroplasts.

Division of a nucleus usually begins early in the evening and is completed by midnight. Cell division follows shortly after nuclear division. It is transverse and due to an annular furrowing of the plasma membrane in a zone midway between the ends of a cell. In cell division each daughter cell receives one of the chloroplasts of the parent cell. The nucleus of a recently divided daughter cell lies lateral to the chloroplast and midway between the poles of the cell (Fig. 35*B*). Later on there is a division of the chloroplast, accompanied by a division of the pyrenoid and a migration of the nucleus to a position midway between the two daughter chloroplasts.[4]

[1] Transeau, 1951. [2] Tiffany, 1924. [3] Borge, 1894; Iyengar, 1923.
[4] Escoyez, 1907; Merriam, 1906.

Cell division increases the number of cells in a filament but does not result in a direct increase in number of filaments. *Zygnema* may reproduce vegetatively by an accidental severing of filaments, and the rapid increase in number of them when the alga is growing in quiet water shows that this is an efficient method of reproduction. In very rare cases there is a vegetative multiplication by disjunction into individual cells or into

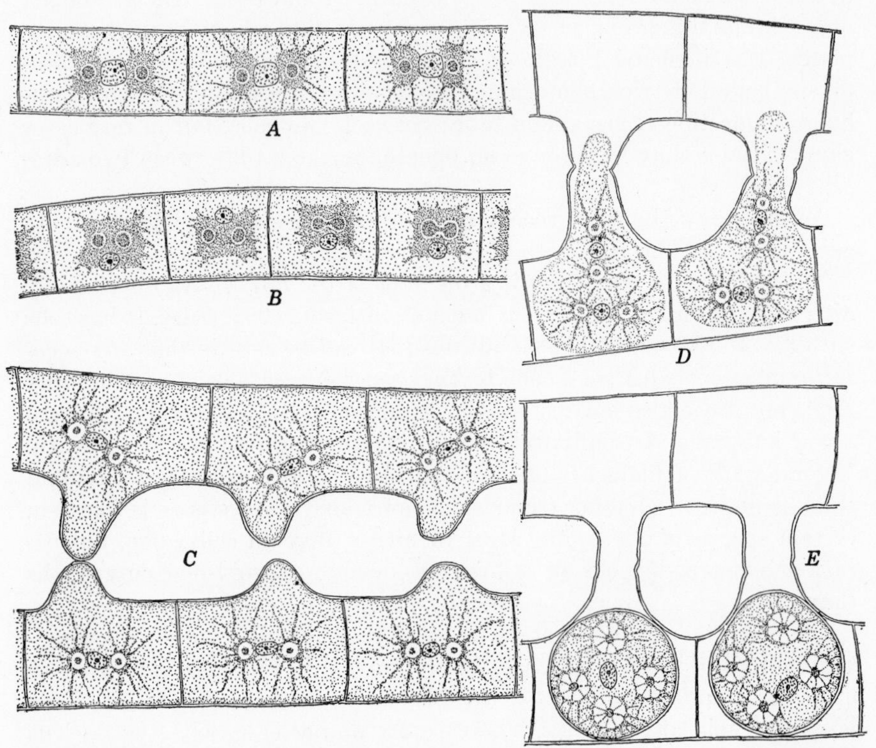

FIG. 35. *Zygnema* spp. *A*, mature vegetative cells. *B*, recently divided cells. *C–E*, stages in sexual reproduction. (× 430.)

fragments with a few cells each. One terrestrial species has been reported[1] as forming thick-walled resting cells. Such thick-walled cells of Zygnemataceae are usually called "akinetes," but they are not strictly comparable to the akinetes of Ulotrichales and other Chlorophyceae because there is not a true spore wall fused with the wall of the vegetative cell.

Cells of *Zygnema* may also have a rounding up of the protoplast and a secretion of a thick wall about the retracted protoplast. For any given species, the structure and ornamentation of the special walls surrounding these bodies are identical with wall structure of zygotes. It is therefore much more fitting to term them **parthenospores** or **azygotes** (azygospores)

[1] de Puymaly, 1922*A*.

than to call them aplanospores. The gametic nature of parthenospores is clearly evident in conjugating filaments when they result from the failure of gametes to unite with one another. Practically all collections of fruiting *Zygnema* contain one or more parthenospores of this nature. A few species regularly form parthenospores in greater number than zygotes, or form parthenospores only.

There is a marked seasonal periodicity of sexual reproduction and each species usually fruits at a definite time of the year. Most species fruit in the spring. The time of fruiting of *Spirogyra* has been shown[1] to be directly correlated with the ratio between the surface and volume of the cell, and the same is thought to be true for *Zygnema*. Vegetative cells of *Zygnema* function directly as gametangia, and each cell produces a single nonflagellate gamete. All cells of a filament are potentially capable of producing gametes, and at the time of fruiting there is a simultaneous production of gametes by all or almost all cells of a filament. At the time of gametic union the gametangia are connected in pairs by a conjugation tube. The tubular connection may be established between cells of different filaments (**scalariform conjugation**) or between adjoining cells of the same filament (**lateral conjugation**). Conjugation of *Zygnema* is usually scalariform.

Scalariform conjugation begins with an approximation of two filaments so that they lie side by side throughout their entire length. Small dome-shaped protuberances next grow toward each other from opposed pairs of cells, and each protuberance elongates until it becomes a short cylindrical outgrowth (Fig. 35*C*). The cylindrical outgrowths from opposite cells come in contact; the wall of each is digested at the point of mutual contact; and with the establishment of the opening the two outgrowths become a conjugation tube. In some species both gametes become amoeboid and migrate into the conjugation tube where they fuse with each other to form the zygote. In other species one of the gametes (the male) is actively amoeboid, and the other (the female) is passive. Gametic union in such species takes place in the female gametangium (Fig. 35*D*). Sexual differentiation in these species may be recognized at a relatively early stage of conjugation because of the earlier shrinkage of the male protoplast and its rotation so that the two chloroplasts stand perpendicular to the developing conjugation tube.

Union of the two gamete nuclei in a zygote may take place at once or may be delayed for a time (Fig. 35*E*). The four chloroplasts persist for a time, but there is an eventual disintegration of the two lying in the short axis of the zygote,[2] and it is very probable that the degenerating chloroplasts were contributed by the male gamete (Fig. 36*C–D*). Development of a wall about a zygote begins quite early, but it does not become

[1] Transeau, 1916. [2] Kurssanow, 1911.

fully developed for several weeks. A mature wall consists of a thin inner layer of cellulose, a thin outer layer of cellulose or pectose, and a thick median layer of cellulose that may be more or less chitinized.[1] The coloration and ornamentation characteristic of a zygote of a particular species are usually developed in the median wall layer. The zygotes are eventually liberated by a decay of the gametangial or the conjugation tube walls. They rarely germinate as soon as they appear to be mature; and it is very probable that in the majority of species there is no germination until the spring following their formation.

Prior to germination there is a meiotic division of the zygote nucleus[2] (Fig. 36). Three of the resultant haploid nuclei degenerate; the fourth remains unchanged until the zygote germinates (Fig. 36*D–F*). At the

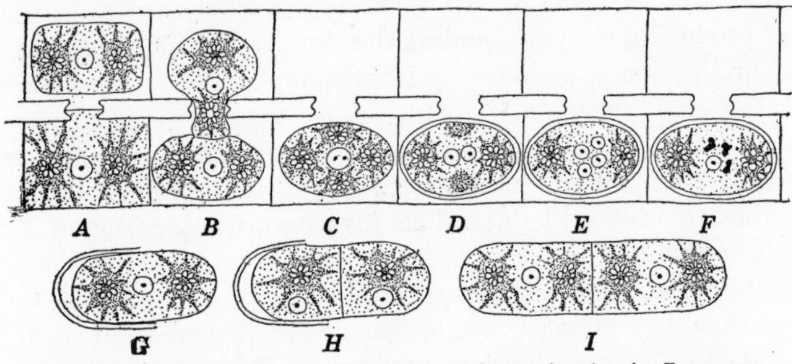

FIG. 36. Diagram of zygote formation and germination in *Zygnema*.

time of germination there is a rupture of the two outermost zygote wall layers. The protoplast, still surrounded by the innermost wall layer, may escape from the outer layers (Fig. 36*G–I*) or only partially escape from them.[3] In either case it divides transversely, and the two daughter cells divide and redivide to form a filament.

FAMILY 2. MESOTAENIACEAE

The Mesotaeniaceae, the "saccoderm" desmids, have uninucleate cells of various shape, and they may be solitary or united in simple filaments. The cell walls are without pores, and dividing cells do not have the regeneration of a new "half cell" that is found in "placoderm" desmids. Conjugation is generally by means of a definite conjugation tube.

The family includes 7 genera and about 75 species. All species are fresh-water in habit, and most of them are restricted to soft waters.

Cell walls of Mesotaeniaceae (Fig. 37) are unsegmented, without pores, and never impregnated with iron compounds.[4] Most genera have a wall composed of two concentric layers, but some have one with three layers.

[1] Tiffany, 1924. [2] Kurssanow, 1911. [3] DeBary, 1858; Kurssanow, 1911.
[4] Höfler, 1926; Lütkemüller, 1902.

The innermost layer consists almost wholly of cellulose and the outermost almost wholly of pectose. The gelatinous pectic layer may be quite broad, and in some cases sheaths of cells are confluent with one another to produce an amorphous mucilaginous mass containing many cells.

Chloroplasts of Mesotaeniaceae are of the same three types that are found in the Zygnemataceae.[1] Cells of the three types have their nuclei localized as in the corresponding types among the Zygnemataceae.

The meager accounts of cell division among Mesotaeniaceae[2] indicate that it is identical with that of Zygnemataceae. Increase in length seems to take place throughout the entire length of the daughter cells and not, as in Desmidiaceae, by the formation of a new semicell. Cell division is

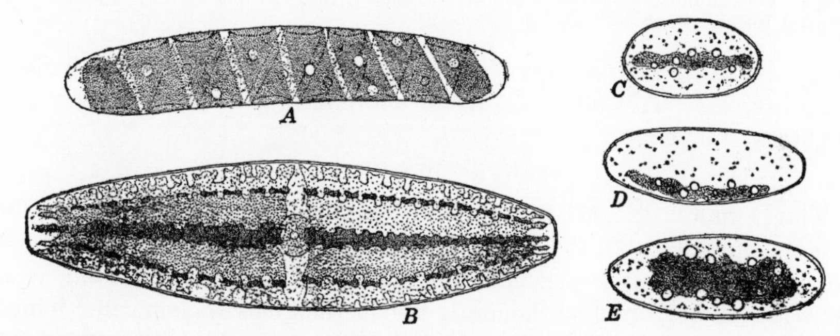

FIG. 37. Vegetative cells of various Mesotaeniaceae. *A*, *Spirotaenia condensata* Bréb. *B*, *Netrium digitus* (Ehr.) Itz. and Rothe. *C–E*, *Mesotaenium greyii* var. *breve* W. West. (*A–B*, × 400; *C–E*, × 485.)

usually followed by an immediate separation of the daughter cells as a result of disintegration of the middle lamella between them. In at least two of the genera the cells usually remain united end to end for several cell generations, but such filaments readily dissociate into single cells when disturbed.

Conjugation has been recorded for all genera. In some genera it is of frequent occurrence; in others it is infrequent. The process is initiated by two cells becoming enveloped by a common gelatinous sheath. The pair of cells may lie parallel to, or at right angles with, each other. Conjugation is usually between fully mature cells, but in *Netrium*[3] it takes place between recently divided ones. Most species establish a conjugation tube similar to that of Zygnemataceae, and those with a conjugation tube have the zygote formed in the tube.

Zygotes of Mesotaeniaceae have a thick wall and usually one composed of three layers. However, these zygotes do not have the elaborate sculpturing and spinescence so often found in those of Desmidiaceae.

[1] Nellie Carter, 1919*A*, 1920*A*.

[2] DeBary, 1858; Kauffmann, 1914; West, 1915.

[3] Potthoff, 1928.

Two genera have been shown[1] to have a meiotic division of the nucleus in a ripening zygote and a formation of four functional nuclei. One genus[2] has the fusion nucleus dividing meiotically to form two functional and two nonfunctional nuclei (Fig. 38). The nuclear divisions are followed,

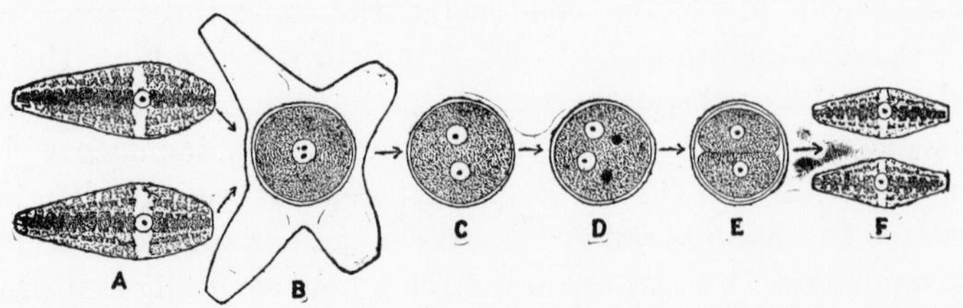

Fig. 38. Diagram of the formation and germination of the zygote of *Netrium digitus* (Ehr.) Itz. and Rothe. (*Diagram based upon Potthoff*, 1928.)

respectively, by a division of the protoplast into four or into two daughter protoplasts. This may take place before or after rupture of the outer zygote wall layers.

FAMILY 3. DESMIDIACEAE

The Desmidiaceae, the "placoderm" desmids, have cells which may be solitary, united end to end in filamentous colonies, or united in amorphous colonies. In all but two genera the cells have an evident median constriction (**sinus**), dividing them into two distinct halves (**semicells**) joined together by a connecting zone (the **isthmus**). Cells of various genera are diverse in form, but all of them have walls that are transversely segmented and with vertical pores. Conjugating cells usually have their protoplasts escaping from the surrounding walls as they unite to form a zygote.

There are 23 genera and some 2,500 species, all fresh-water. Desmidiaceae are found sparingly intermingled with free-floating algae everywhere, but collections rich in species and in number of individuals are usually made only when the waters have a pH of 5 to 6. Most genera are immediately recognizable because their cells are transversely constricted into two symmetrical halves. Generic distinctions are based entirely upon shape and structure of vegetative cells (Fig. 39). Specific distinctions are based in part upon cell shape and in part upon ornamentation of the cell wall. In many genera the cell must be examined in both front and vertical view before the species can be determined with accuracy.

Walls of all Desmidiaceae have three concentric layers. The innermost layer is thin and composed entirely of cellulose; the median layer is somewhat thicker and has a substratum of cellulose that is impregnated with pectic compounds; the outer layer is a gelatinous sheath of pectose

[1] Kauffmann, 1914; Potthoff, 1928. [2] Potthoff, 1928.

that may be narrow or very broad. The two inner layers are perforated by vertical pores[1] that are usually arranged in a definite pattern. Pores may be present on all parts of a wall except the isthmus, or they may be localized in definite parts of each semicell. The pores are filled with a pectic material that is often of a tougher consistency than, and extends into, the watery sheath of pectic material. Sometimes the gelatinous

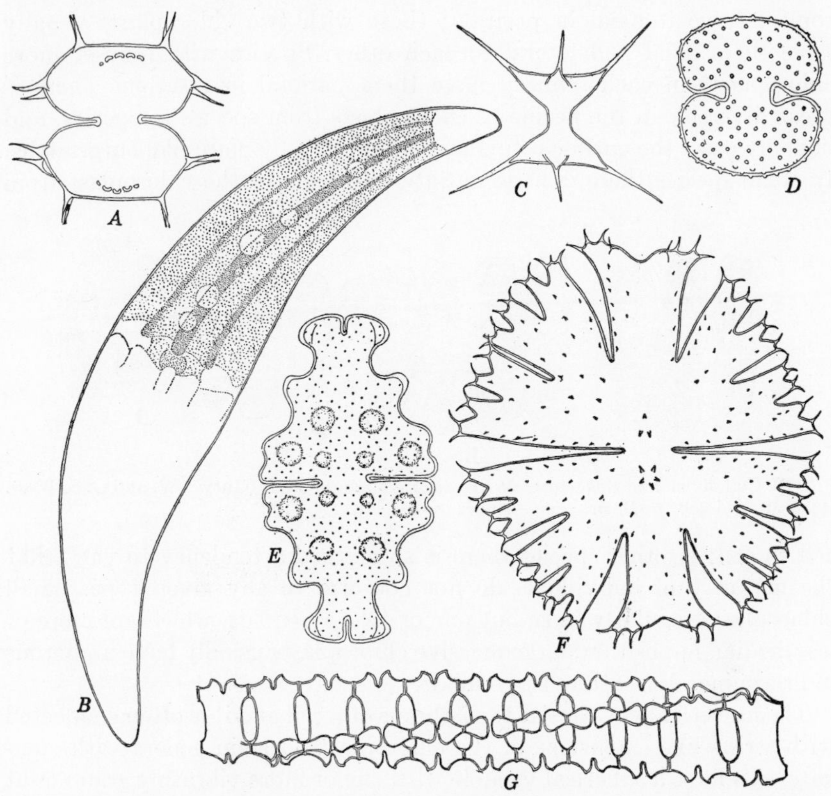

FIG. 39. Vegetative cells of various Desmidiaceae. *A*, *Xanthidium antilopaeum* var. *polymazum* Nordst. *B*, *Closterium moniliforme* (Bory) Ehr. *C*, *Staurastrum curvatum* W. West. *D*, *Cosmarium reniforme* (Ralfs) Arch. *E*, *Euastrum affine* Ralfs. *F*, *Micrasterias apiculata* (Ehr.) Menegh. *G*, *Desmidium aptogonum* Bréb. (× 400.)

material extending through the pores is evident in living cells, but more often it is evident only when the walls have been stained with special reagents.[1] Many Desmidiaceae have brown cell walls because of an impregnation with iron salts. The salts are localized chiefly in the median layer, and they may be uniformly distributed over the entire layer or restricted to certain portions of it.[2] Many Desmidiaceae move over the

[1] Lütkemüller, 1902. [2] Höfler, 1926.

bottom and toward the side when they are placed in an aquarium. Movement is in a series of jerks, and it has been shown[1] to be intimately connected with a localized secretion of gelatinous material through pores at one end of the cell.

In the vast majority of Desmidiaceae there is at least one chloroplast in each semicell.[2] A few species with very small cells have a single chloroplast extending the entire length of the cell. Semicells with one chloroplast have it axial in position; those with two chloroplasts usually have them axial and lateral to each other. Species with four or more chloroplasts in each semicell have them parietal in position. There is great diversity in the profile of chloroplasts from species to species, and in many cases the outline is further complicated by plate-like outgrowths. In some species there is little variation in form of the chloroplast from

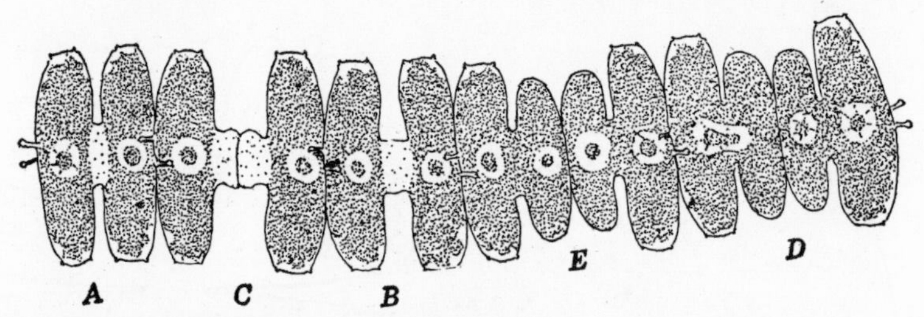

FIG. 40. Cell division in *Sphaerozosma aubertianum* var. *archerii* (Gutw.) W. and G. S. West. *A*, undivided cell. *B–E*, successive stages in division. (× 730.)

cell to cell; in other species there is so marked a tendency to vary that the majority of individuals do not conform to any given type. Small chloroplasts regularly have but one or two pyrenoids, which are more or less median in position; large massive chloroplasts usually have numerous indiscriminately scattered pyrenoids.

The nucleus always lies at the isthmus of a cell and it is often connected with string-like extensions of the chloroplast. Certain genera with elongate cells have a spherical vacuole with one or more vibrating granules at each pole of the cells. The granules have been shown[3] to be crystals of gypsum, and it has been held[4] that they function as statoliths.

In genera with a conspicuous isthmus, the cell division following nuclear division begins with an elongation of the isthmus. The cell then divides transversely at the elongated isthmus, after which the portion of the isthmus attached to each semicell enlarges to form a new semicell (Fig. 40). Division of the chloroplast or chloroplasts in each of the original semicells takes place during the development of new semicells. New

[1] Klebs, 1885; Kol, 1927; Schröder, 1902.
[2] Nellie Carter, 1919*A*, 1919*B*, 1920, 1920*A*.
[3] Fischer, 1884. [4] Steinecke, 1926.

pyrenoids may be formed by division of those present in a chloroplast,[1] or they may be formed *de novo*.[2] Occasionally there is a complete or incomplete failure of cell division as the isthmus starts to elongate. Continued enlargement of this undivided isthmus results in a monstrous cell in which an abnormally shaped structure is intercalated between two semicells.

Aplanospores have been recorded for a few species, but most of the so-called aplanospores are parthenospores. Possibly the spore-like bodies formed in cells of one genus[3] are true aplanospores since their shape is not the same as that of zygotes.

Zygotes (Fig. 41) have been described for many species, but they are of infrequent occurrence and one is rarely fortunate enough to collect

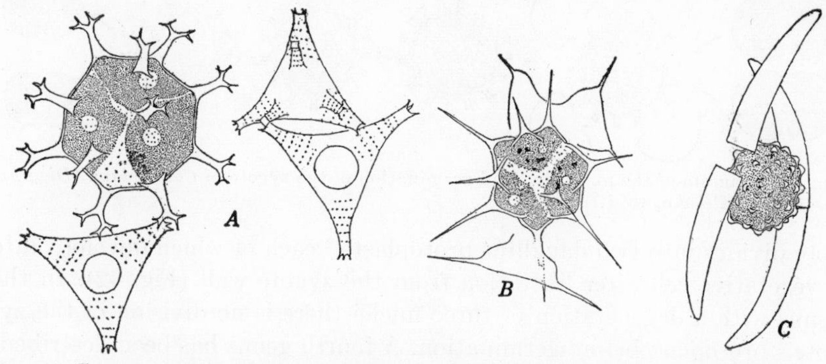

Fig. 41. Zygotes of Desmidiaceae. *A*, *Staurastrum fucigerum* Bréb. *B*, *Arthrodesmus incus* var. *extensus* Anderss. *C*, *Closterium calosporum* Wittr. (*A*, *C*, × 300; *B*, × 600.)

material rich in fruiting specimens. Conjugation usually takes place between fully mature cells, but sometimes it is only between recently divided ones in which the new semicells have not attained their full size. In some cases the newly divided conjugating cells are sister cells. Conjugation of solitary free-floating species takes place between two cells that lie within a common gelatinous envelope. All but four or five species form a single zygote within the common gelatinous envelope. The four or five exceptional species form twin zygotes, and in certain cases this has been shown to be due to conjugation in pairs between four young daughter cells lying within a common envelope. Almost all unicellular species have the two cells within an envelope breaking open at the isthmus and both protoplasts moving out from the cell walls and meeting midway between the two. A few unicellular[4] and filamentous[5] species develop a conjugation tube and generally have the zygote formed in the

[1] Acton, 1916. [2] Nellie Carter, 1919*A*. [3] Roy and Bissett, 1893–1894.
[4] Scherffel, 1928. [5] Nellie Carter, 1923.

tube. Zygotes of Desmidiaceae have a wall composed of three layers. The outermost layer often develops spines or warts distinctive of the species.

Gametic union (Fig. 42) is followed by a fusion of the two nuclei. Species with a single chloroplast contributed by each gamete have one chloroplast disintegrating as the zygote matures;[1] those with two chloroplasts from each gamete have two chloroplasts disintegrating.[2] Three genera have been shown[3] to have two successive divisions of the fusion nucleus followed by a disintegration of either two or three of the four nuclei. Division of the zygote nucleus has been shown to be meiotic in one of the genera,[1] and the same is probably true of the others. In the genus where two nuclei disintegrate the protoplast of a germinating zy-

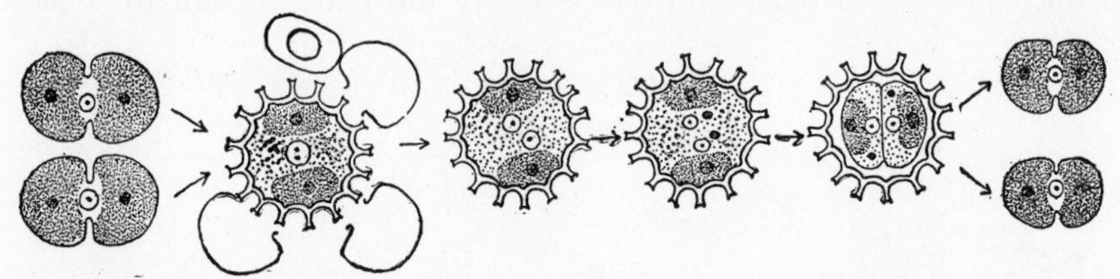

Fig. 42. Diagram of the formation and germination of the zygote of *Cosmarium*. (*Diagram based upon Klebahn*, 1891.)

gote divides into two daughter protoplasts,[2] each of which develops into a vegetative cell after liberation from the zygote wall (Fig. 42). In the genus with a degeneration of three nuclei there is no division of the zygote's protoplast before germination. A fourth genus has been described[4] as having a formation of four nuclei within a ripening zygote and a production of one, two, three, or four cells by a germinating zygote.

ORDER 9. CHLOROCOCCALES

Cells of Chlorococcales may be solitary, or they may be united in nonfilamentous colonies with either a definite or an indefinite number of cells. Cells may be uninucleate or multinucleate, but in neither case do they divide vegetatively. Asexual reproduction is by means of zoospores or aplanospores that are frequently autospores. Sexual reproduction, when present, is isogamous, anisogamous, or oögamous.

The order includes about 100 genera and 800 species. Almost all the species are fresh-water, and many of them are found only in the plankton of ponds and lakes.

The primary feature of the order is the lack of vegetative cell division. The Chlorococcales constitute an evolutionary line derived directly from unicellular Volvocales and one giving rise to more elaborate forms in

[1] Potthoff, 1927. [2] Klebahn, 1891. [3] Klebahn, 1891; Potthoff, 1927.
[4] Turner, 1922.

which there is no vegetative division of the cells (Fig. 6, page 27). The only divisions in protoplasts of Chlorococcales are those immediately preceding the formation of zoospores, autospores, gametes, or other reproductive bodies. Loss of ability to divide vegetatively has not always been accompanied by loss of ability of the nuclei to divide, and there are several multinucleate (coenocytic) Chlorococcales with a definite or an indefinite number of nuclei. The formation of colonies by certain genera is due either to an apposition of all zoospores or aplanospores (autospores) liberated from a parent cell, or is due to cells developed from spores remaining within a common matrix produced by gelatinization of the parent-cell walls.

The Chlorococcales are variously divided into seven or into nine families. Certain of them (Hydrodictyaceae and Scenedesmaceae) are natural; others (as the Oöcystaceae and Chlorococcaceae) are more or less artificial, and members of a family have little in common aside from the method of reproduction.

FAMILY 1. CHLOROCOCCACEAE

The Chlorococcaceae include the zoosporic unicellular genera in which the cells are more or less globose and apparently haploid. The cells are usually uninucleate. Chloroplasts are of various shapes from genus to genus. Asexual reproduction is by means of zoospores (sometimes also by aplanospores) that separate from one another after liberation. Sexual reproduction is isogamous and by a fusion of zoogametes.

The family includes about 10 genera and 50 species, all fresh-water.

The type genus, *Chlorococcum*, is a subaerial alga that sometimes grows in abundance on damp soil or brickwork. The cells may be solitary, or they may be gregarious and either in a pulverent mass or embedded in a gelatinous matrix. One of the features distinguishing this genus from most other unicellular globose green algae is the striking variation in size of vegetative cells of any given species (Fig. 43*A–C*). Young cells are thin-walled and spherical or somewhat compressed. Old cells have thick walls, often irregular in outline because of local button-like thickenings. Chloroplasts of young cells are parietal massive cups, completely filling the cell except for a small hyaline area at one side. They contain a single pyrenoid. Old cells have a diffuse chloroplast that generally contains many starch grains and sometimes droplets of oil. The cells are uninucleate until shortly before reproduction.[1]

There is never an increase in the number of cells by vegetative division, and all formation of new cells is due to a germination of zoospores or aplanospores. Reproduction by means of zoospores may take place

[1] Bold, 1931; Bristol, 1919.

at almost any stage in the enlargement of a cell.[1] Small cells usually form 8 to 16 zoospores; large cells produce many zoospores (Fig. 43*D–E*). The cells are multinucleate at the time of reproduction, and there is a progressive cleavage into uninucleate protoplasts by an inward furrowing of the plasma membrane.[2] Each uninucleate protoplast is metamorphosed into a zoospore, and the zoospores are liberated through an aperture in the parent-cell wall. The zoospores (Fig. 43*F*) are ellipsoidal and biflagellate, and with an eyespot and a cup-shaped chloroplast. Uninucleate protoplasts formed by progressive cleavage may develop into aplanospores instead of into zoospores. The parent-cell wall may burst as the aplanospores begin to enlarge into vegetative cells, and most of the enlargement takes place after the aplanospores are liberated,[2] or the aplano-

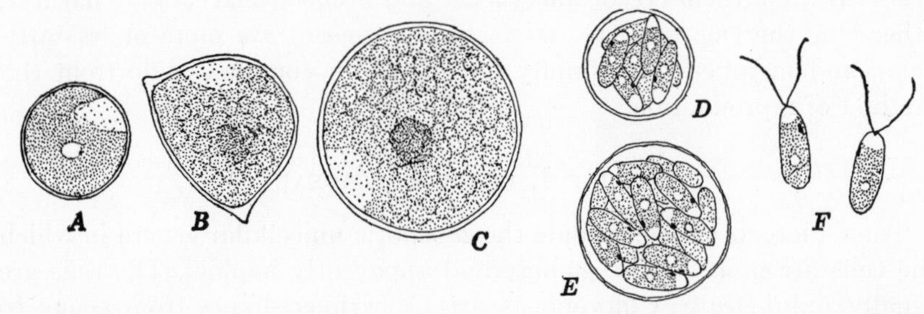

FIG. 43. *Chlorococcum humicola* (Nag.) Rab. *A–C*, vegetative cells. *D–E*, cells containing zoospores. *F*, zoospores. (× 800.)

spores may remain within the old parent-cell wall until the latter gelatinizes. This results in a palmella stage. Cells of palmella stages divide to form two or four naked daughter cells that become flagellated and function as gametes.[3]

Sexual reproduction is also by means of biflagellate gametes formed by division of protoplasts of ordinary vegetative cells.[4] These gametes are formed in the same manner as zoospores.

Trebouxia is found both in the thalli of lichens and as a free-living aerial alga. Many species have been described, but those found in a majority of lichens cannot be distinguished morphologically from *T. cladoniae* (Chod.) G. M. Smith. *Trebouxia* is not the only unicellular green alga in lichens,[5] but it is the one most often encountered. The cells are usually spherical, but they may be ovoid or pyriform. The cell walls are always thin, and they never have the irregular thickenings that are found in walls of *Chlorococcum*. *Trebouxia* differs from the great majority of genera in the family in having a massive centrally located chloroplast that extends nearly to the plasma membrane (Fig. 44*A–C*).

[1] Artari, 1892; Bristol, 1919. [2] Bold, 1931. [3] Bristol, 1919.
[4] de Puymaly, 1924. [5] Chodat, 1913.

The outline of the chloroplast is usually irregular and lobed. There is a single pyrenoid at the center of a chloroplast. The single nucleus of a cell lies at one side of the chloroplast and just within the plasma membrane.

There is never a multiplication by vegetative cell division. Reproduction by means of zoospores has been repeatedly observed[1] when the alga is growing in a liquid medium. It is very probable that zoospores are also formed under natural conditions during rainy periods. The zoospores are subspherical to subellipsoidal, are biflagellate, and have a chloroplast at the posterior end. Liberation of zoospores is through an opening at one side of the parent-cell wall, and they may escape singly through the opening or be extruded in a mass.[2] In most cases asexual

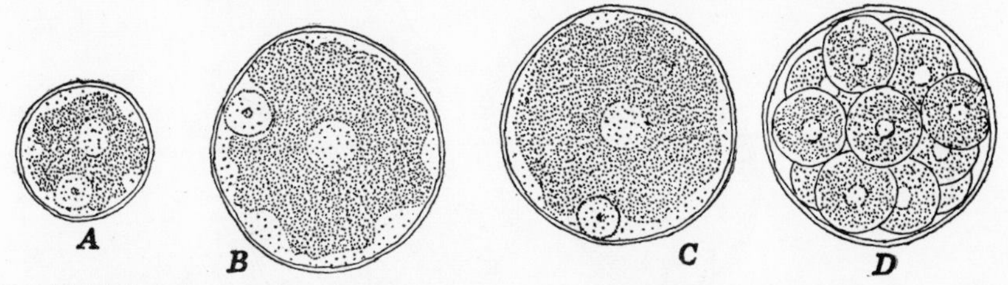

FIG. 44. *Trebouxia cladoniae* (Chod.) G. M. Smith. *A–C*, vegetative cells. *D*, a cell containing autospores. (× 1,950.)

reproduction is by means of autospores (Fig. 44*D*) instead of zoospores. Eight to a hundred or more of them are produced within a cell, and they may be liberated from the parent-cell wall soon after their formation or they may be retained within the wall until they have grown to a size equal to that of adult vegetative cells.

Sexual reproduction is by the fusion of biflagellate gametes that may be of equal or unequal size.[2]

FAMILY 2. ENDOSPHAERACEAE

The Endosphaeraceae are unicellular and generally with large irregularly shaped cells. Most of them grow endophytically within tissues of marine algae, mosses, or angiosperms. Their chloroplasts may be parietal or central in position and with one or many pyrenoids. One genus is strictly parasitic and is without chloroplasts or pyrenoids. Reproduction is by means of biflagellate zooids.

The family includes about 4 genera and 20 species.

In some species there is always a fusion of the zooids in pairs;[3] in other species there is never a fusion;[4] in still other species there may

[1] Chodat, 1913; Famintzin, 1914; Famintzin and Boranetzky, 1867; Jaag, 1929.
[2] Jaag, 1929. [3] Gardner, 1917; Klebs, 1881. [4] Bristol, 1917; Reichardt, 1927.

or may not be a fusion to form a zygote.[1] Although our knowledge of these algae is still too fragmentary to warrant a definite statement, it is not impossible that all zooids are gametic in nature. If this is true, the cases where the swarmers germinate directly into vegetative cells must be interpreted as parthenogenesis rather than as an asexual reproduction by means of zoospores. There is also the possibility that all species with gametic union are similar to *Chlorochytrium lemnae* Cohn and have diploid vegetative cells.

Chlorochytrium, with about 10 species, grows endophytically in other plants. Fresh-water species grow within tissues of mosses and angiosperms. Marine species grow within tissues of various membranous or expanded Rhodophyceae. The cells of *Chlorochytrium* are irregularly

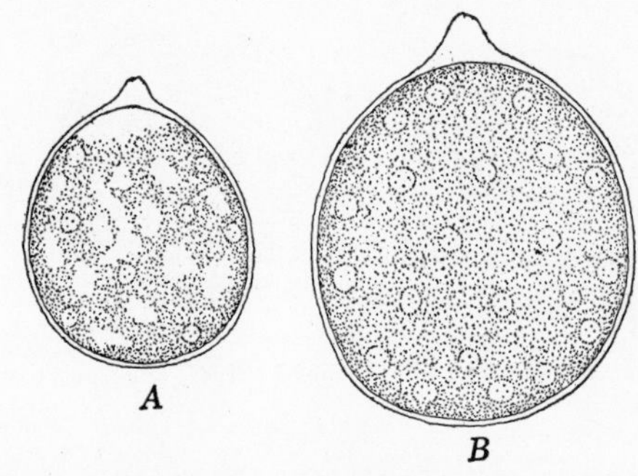

FIG. 45. *Chlorochytrium inclusum* Kjellm. (× 440.)

globose or ellipsoidal (Fig. 45). Walls of mature cells may be thick and stratified, or relatively thin and homogeneous. Either type of wall may have localized lamellated thickenings. Chloroplasts of young cells are parietal and cup-shaped,[2] but, as the cell increases in size, the chloroplasts come to fill the entire cell. A chloroplast may have a smooth surface, or it may have[3] numerous radial projections. Young cells of *C. Lemnae* Cohn are uninucleate. As the cell grows in size, the nucleus increases in volume but does not divide.[4] Reproduction is preceded by a repeated series of simultaneous nuclear divisions in which the first is reductional.[4] There is a transverse cytokinesis after the first nuclear division and a further bipartition after each mitosis. Nuclear division and cytokinesis may continue until 256 uninucleate protoplasts are formed. These uninucleate protoplasts are then metamorphosed into biflagellate gametes that escape from the old parent-cell wall. The gametes fuse in pairs[5] to form a quadriflagellate zygote that swarms for

[1] Griggs, 1912; Klebs, 1881. [2] Cohn, 1872. [3] Bristol, 1920.
[4] Kurssanow and Schemakhanova, 1927.
[5] Cohn, 1872; Gardner, 1917; Kurssanow and Schemakhanova, 1927.

a short time and then settles down upon the host, loses its flagella, and secretes a wall. Fusion of the two gamete nuclei may be completed before secretion of the zygote wall.[1] The side of the zygote next to the host soon sends out a tubular protrusion that grows between the host cells and enlarges at the distal end.[2] The entire protoplast of the zygote moves into the enlarged end of the protrusion and there develops into a large vegetative cell.

FAMILY 3. CHARACIACEAE

The Characiaceae have sessile elongate cells that may be solitary or joined to one another in radiate colonies. The cells are usually multinucleate, although sometimes they are uninucleate. Most genera have a single parietal laminate chloroplast containing one or more pyrenoids. One genus has cells without chloroplasts. Asexual reproduction is usually by means of zoospores, but it may be by means of aplanospores. Sexual reproduction is by a fusion of biflagellate gametes that may be of equal or unequal size.

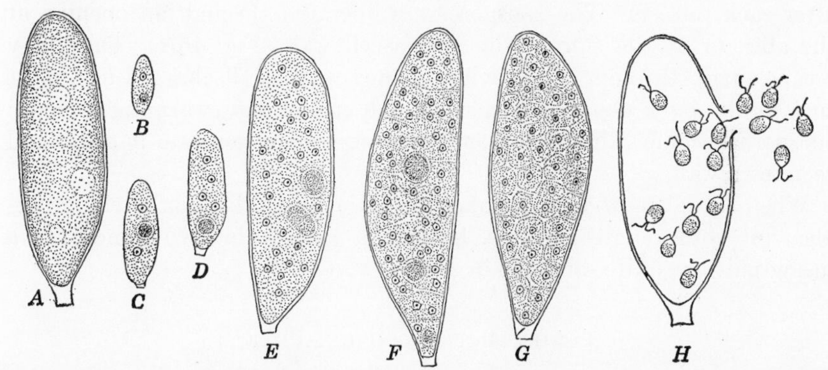

FIG. 46. *Characium sieboldii* A. Br. *A*, mature cell. *B–E*, stages in development from uninucleate to multinucleate condition. *F–G*, stages in progressive cleavage. *H*, liberation of zoospores. (*A*, *H*, *from living material; B–G, from stained preparations.*) (× 1,900.)

There are about 6 genera and 55 species, almost all of which are fresh-water.

Characium, a genus with about 40 species, usually grows upon other algae, submerged angiosperms, or various aquatic animals; but it may grow upon submerged woodwork or stones. The cells may be subspherical or ovoid, but more often they are elongated and fusiform or cylindrical. They are sessile and usually attached to the substratum by a more or less elongate stipe expanded into a small disk at the point of attachment to the substratum (Fig. 46*A*). The cells may grow isolated from

[1] Kurssanow and Schemakhanova, 1927. [2] Cohn, 1872.

one another, or they may be present in such abundance that they form a continuous stratum.

Young cells are uninucleate and with a parietal laminate chloroplast. As a cell grows older there may be a repeated nuclear division (Fig. 46*B–E*) until 16, 32, 64, or 128 are present in the cell,[1] or the cell may remain uninucleate until just before reproduction.[2] Old cells frequently have a diffuse chloroplast containing more than one pyrenoid.

Asexual reproduction is by division of the protoplast into 8, 16, 32, 64, 128, or more biflagellate zoospores (Fig. 46*F–G*). Multinucleate cells have a progressive cleavage of the cell contents into uninucleate protoplasts.[1] Cells that are uninucleate at maturity have a repeated division of the nuclei just before reproduction and a division of the protoplast after each mitosis.[2] The zoospores are liberated through an opening at the apex or at the side of the parent-cell wall (Fig. 46*H*). They may escape singly through the opening or they may be discharged in a mass surrounded by a delicate vesicle. At the end of the swarming period a zoospore becomes affixed to some firm object, retracts its flagella, and secretes a wall.

When sexual reproduction takes place there is a division of the protoplast into biflagellate gametes. In certain species the two gametes of a fusing pair are quite different in size.[3]

FAMILY 4. PROTOSIPHONACEAE

The Protosiphonaceae have solitary, spherical to tubular, multinucleate cells in which one side may be prolonged into a colorless rhizoidal process. The cells may contain a single reticulate or perforate chloroplast, or may contain many small parietal chloroplasts. Some genera produce zoospores. Others form biflagellate gametes only.

The family includes five genera, each with a single species. One is marine; the others are fresh-water.

Certain phycologists[4] consider the family a member of the Siphonales rather than a member of the Chlorococcales. This certainly does not hold for *Protosiphon* since it has been shown[5] to lack the distinctive xanthophylls found in Siphonales.

Protosiphon, with the single species *P. botryoides* (Kutz.) Klebs, is usually found growing on drying muddy banks of streams and ponds, or on bare damp soil. It generally grows intermingled with *Botrydium*, an alga quite similar in appearance. *Protosiphon* may be distinguished from *Botrydium* by testing for starch since *Botrydium* always lacks it. *Protosiphon*

[1] Smith, 1916. [2] Nellie Carter, 1919*C*. [3] Schiller, 1924.

[4] Bold, 1933; Fritsch, 1935; Setchell and Gardner, 1920; West, 1916.

[5] Strain, 1951.

is a unicellular coenocytic alga. Young plants are short erect cylinders with rounded ends and with the lower portion colorless; older plants have a broadly expanded, globose, aerial portion that is subtended by a narrow, colorless, simple or branched rhizoid which grows into the soil (Fig. 47*A*). The aerial portion contains a single large parietal chloroplast with several irregularly shaped perforations. Chloroplasts of mature cells contain several pyrenoids each surrounded by starch platelets. Internal to the chloroplast is a large central vacuole.

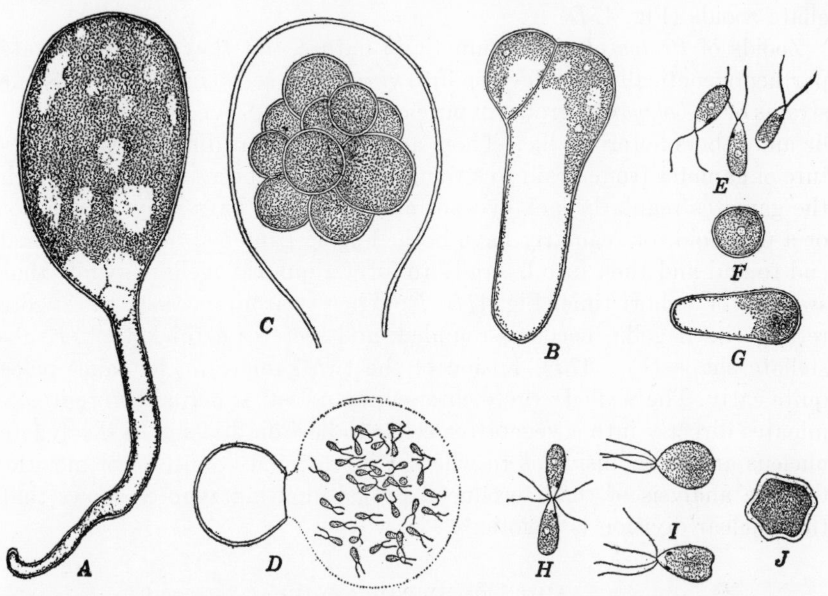

FIG. 47. *Protosiphon botryoides* (Kütz.) Klebs. *A*, mature vegetative cell. *B*, young cell cutting off a proliferation. *C*, aplanospores. *D*, germination of an aplanospore. *E*, gametes. *F–G*, parthenogenetic germination of gametes. *H*, gametic union. *I*, motile zygotes. *J*, mature zygote. (*A*, *C–D*, × 230; *B*, *E–J*, × 650.)

Juvenile cells may multiply vegetatively[1] by sending out proliferous outgrowths and cutting off the proliferations by transverse septa (Fig. 47*B*).

Flooding of plants growing on damp soil is followed by a division of the entire protoplast into zooids.[2] The formation of zooids begins with an extrusion of water from the protoplast and its shrinking away from the cell wall. There then follows a progressive cleavage into uninucleate protoplasts as a result of an inward growth of furrows from the plasma and vacuolar membranes.[3] Each uninucleate protoplast is usually meta-

[1] Bold, 1933; Klebs, 1896.

[2] Bold, 1933; Klebs, 1896; Rostafiński and Woronin, 1877.

[3] Bold, 1933.

morphosed into a biflagellate zooid, but it may develop into a uninucleate aplanospore.

Thalli growing upon drying soil or in strongly illuminated places have the protoplast dividing to form a few or many multinucleate spore-like bodies (Fig. 47*C*). There is great variation in the size of these bodies formed within a single thallus. These aplanospores or "coenocysts" are produced by an inward furrowing of the plasma membrane.[1] The coenocytic aplanospores may develop directly into vegetative cells, but more frequently there is a progressive cleavage of their contents into biflagellate zooids (Fig. 47*D*).

Zooids of *Protosiphon* are gametic in nature, but they may germinate parthenogenetically and develop into vegetative cells (Fig. 47*E–G*). Some strains of *P. botryoides* grown in pure culture have proved to be homothallic and others heterothallic.[2] There are also constant differences in structure of gametes from strain to strain. Strains have been isolated[2] in which the gametes regularly lack eyespot and pyrenoid, have only an eyespot or a pyrenoid, or regularly have both. Fusing gametes[3] become apposed end to end and then fuse laterally to form a quadriflagellate zygote that swarms for a short time (Fig. 47*H–I*). When swarming ceases, the zygote retracts its flagella, becomes rounded, and secretes a thick wall of substellate shape (Fig. 47*J*). Fusion of the two gamete nuclei takes place quite early. The walled zygote enters upon a resting period before it germinates directly into a vegetative cell. Studies[1] on division of the zygote nucleus are inconclusive as to whether its division is mitotic or meiotic. Genetic analysis of thalli produced by germinating zygotes shows that this nuclear division is meiotic.[2]

FAMILY 5. HYDRODICTYACEAE

The Hydrodictyaceae have their cells united in free-floating colonies (coenobia) that are formed by an apposition of zoospores at the end of the swarming period. The swarming may take place within a gelatinous vesicle extruded from the parent cell, or the swarming zoospores may not escape from the parent-cell wall. Sexual reproduction is isogamous and by a union of zoogametes.

The family includes 4 genera and about 40 species, all fresh-water.

Pediastrum, with some 30 species, is a widely distributed alga that grows free-floating in pools, ditches, and the plankton of lakes. It rarely occurs in abundance. The coenobia have 2, 4, 8, 16, 32, 64, or 128 polygonal cells arranged in a stellate plate one cell in thickness (Fig. 48*A*). If a coenobium has 16 or more cells, there is a tendency for the cells to be in concentric rings and to have a definite number in each ring. The oc-

[1] Bold, 1933. [2] Moewus, 1935. [3] Bold, 1933; Klebs, 1896.

currence or nonoccurrence of this regularity of arrangement is determined by factors affecting the extent to which zoospores swarm at the time a colony is formed.[1] Peripheral cells of a colony often differ in shape from interior cells. Peripheral cells may have one, two, or three processes; interior cells may or may not have them. Cell walls may be smooth, granulate, or finely reticulate. Walls of plankton species sometimes have long tufts of gelatinous bristles. Young cells have a single parietal chloroplast with one pyrenoid; old cells have a diffuse chloroplast that may contain more than one pyrenoid. Young cells are uninucleate; old cells may be bi- or quadrinucleate.[2]

Every cell in a colony (coenobium) is capable of giving rise to biflagellate zoospores, but there is rarely a simultaneous production of zoospores

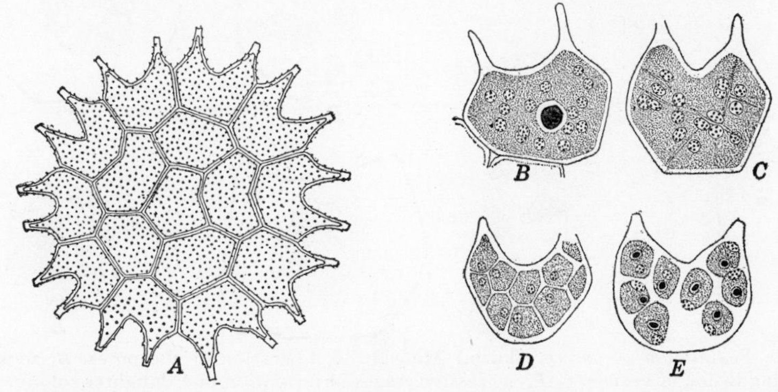

FIG. 48. *Pediastrum boryanum* (Turp.) Menegh. *A*, sixteen-celled colony. *B*, a cell just before cleavage into zoospores. *C*, progressive cleavage. *D–E*, after the completion of cleavage. (*A*, × 500; *B–E*, × 1,000.)

by all cells of a colony. The zoospores are produced during the night and are liberated shortly after daybreak. During the night before reproduction, there is a two- or a fourfold increase in the number of nuclei (Fig. 48*B*), followed by a progressive cleavage (Fig. 48*C–E*) of the coenocyte into uninucleate protoplasts that are metamorphosed into zoospores.[2] The zoospores produced by a cell are surrounded by a vesicle as they escape from the old cell wall, and the vesicle persists throughout the period of swarming and for a short time after the new colony is formed.[3] The number of zoospores is dependent upon the physiological condition of the parent cell. For example, cells in a 16-celled colony may produce 4- or 8-celled daughter colonies, or they may produce daughter colonies with 32 or 64 cells. At the time zoospores are liberated, there is a sudden slit-like rupturing of the outer layer of the parent-cell wall and an extrusion

[1] Harper, 1916, 1918, 1918*A*. [2] Smith, 1916*A*.
[3] Askenasy, 1888; Braun, 1851; Smith, 1916*A*.

of the spore mass surrounded by a sac-like vesicle (Fig. 49*A*). The vesicle is derived from the inner wall layer of the parent cell.[1] The zoospores swim freely and actively within the vesicle for the first three or four minutes following extrusion; after this they tend to arrange themselves in a flat plate (Fig. 49*B–D*) and to have their motion restricted to a writhing and twitching. Coincident with slowing down of movement, the zoospores begin to take on the shape of a vegetative cell, and cell walls are formed within a few minutes after swarming ceases.

In very rare cases the entire protoplast of a cell develops into a thick-walled aplanospore. These aplanospores (hypnospores) are extremely re-

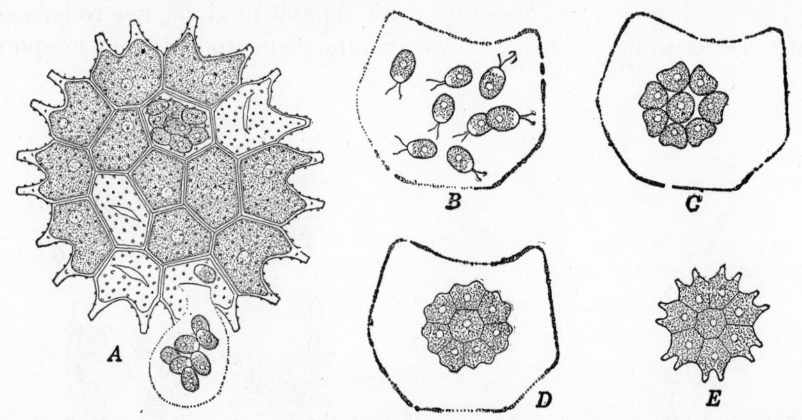

FIG. 49. *Pediastrum boryanum* (Turp.) Menegh. *A*, liberation of zoospores. *B*, zoospores swarming inside of vesicle. *C–E*, successive stages in formation of a daughter colony. (*B–D* drawn at approximately 10-minute intervals.) (*A*, × 500; *B–E*, × 1,000.)

sistant to adverse conditions and have been known[2] to germinate after 12 years' desiccation.

Pediastrum also produces biflagellate gametes that are formed in the same manner as zoospores.[3] They are spindle-shaped instead of ovoid and fuse in pairs to form a spherical zygote. After the zygotes have increased greatly in size (Fig. 50*A*), their protoplasts divide to form a considerable number of biflagellate zoospores.[4] The zoospores are liberated through a large opening at one side of the zygote wall, and they swim freely in all directions after liberation (Fig. 50*B–C*). Upon coming to rest they develop into solitary angular cells (Fig. 50*D*). These "polyeders" also increase greatly in size before their protoplasts divide to form zoospores. Zoospores produced by polyeders are surrounded by a vesicle when liberated.[5] They remain within the vesicle and become apposed to one another to form a vegetative colony, just as in asexual reproduction (Fig. 50*E–F*).

[1] Harper, 1918. [2] Strøm, 1921*A*. [3] Askenasy, 1888.
[4] Palik, 1933. [5] Askenasy, 1888; Palik, 1933.

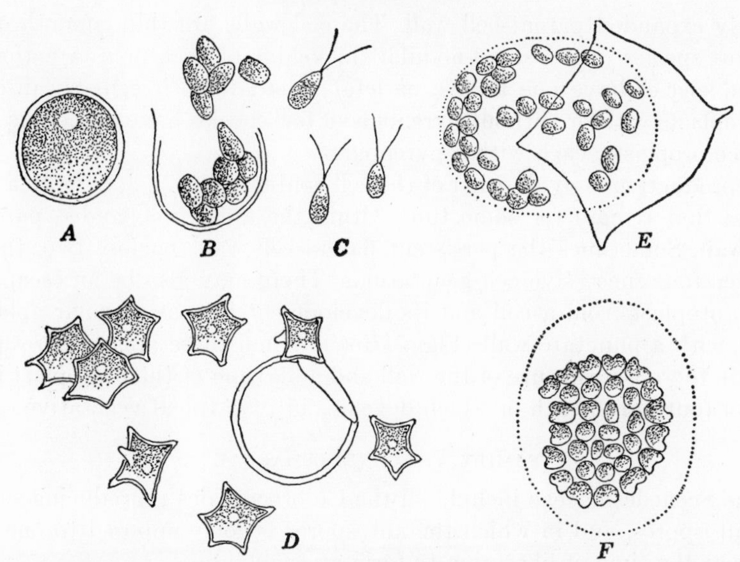

FIG. 50. *Pediastrum boryanum* (Turp.) Menegh. *A*, zygote. *B*, germinating zygote. *C*, zoospores from germination of zygote. *D*, empty zygote and polyeders. *E–F*, germination of polyeder. (*After Palik*, 1933.) (*A–B*, × 495; *C*, × 750; *D*, × 800; *E–F*, × 525.)

FAMILY 6. OÖCYSTACEAE

The Oöcystaceae include all the Chlorococcales forming autospores (see page 21) and in which the cells are solitary or are aggregated in colonies with an indefinite number of cells. There is no other method of reproduction than a formation of autospores or aplanospores.

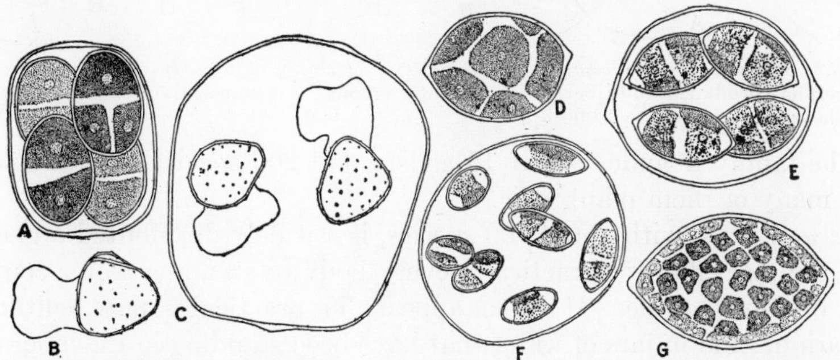

FIG. 51. *A–C*, *Oöcystis borgei* Snow. *D*, *O. crassa* Wittr. *E*, *O. lacustris* Chod. *F*, *O. parva* W. and G. S. West. *G*, *O. eremosphaeria* G. M. Smith. (× 666.)

The family includes about 45 genera and 350 species. All species are fresh-water, and many of them are known only from the plankton.

Oöcystis (Fig. 51), a genus with about 30 species, has ellipsoidal to cylindrical cells. Its cells are free-floating and usually solitary. At times there are 2, 4, 8, or 16 cells surrounded by a partially gelatinized and greatly expanded parent-cell wall. The cell walls are thin, smooth, and in most species with a small nodular thickening at each pole. A majority of the species have one to five parietal, laminate to irregularly discoid chloroplasts with or without pyrenoids; a few species have numerous discoid chloroplasts, each with a pyrenoid.

Reproduction is by division of the cell contents into 2, 4, 8, or 16 autospores that remain for some time within the greatly expanded parent-cell wall. Sometimes the persistent parent-cell walls enclose two, three, or even four successive cell generations. There may also be an escape of the protoplast from a cell and its development into an angular aplanospore with a punctate wall (Fig. 51*B–C*). When these aplanospores germinate there is a rupture of the wall and a division of the protoplast into two or four parts, each of which develops into a typical vegetative cell.

FAMILY 7. SCENEDESMACEAE

The Scenedesmaceae include all the Chlorococcales reproducing solely by autospores, and in which the autospores become apposed to one another at the time of liberation to form a coenobium.

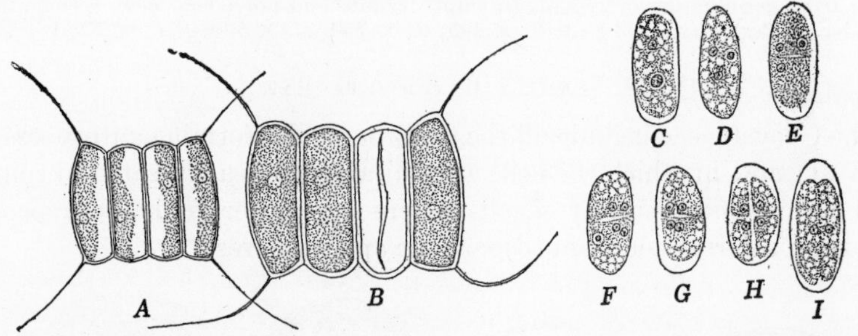

FIG. 52. *Scenedesmus quadricauda* (Turp.) Bréb. *A*, young colony. *B*, old colony in which one cell has produced and liberated a daughter colony. *C–I*, successive stages in formation of a daughter colony. (× 1,000.)

The family includes about 15 genera and 200 species, all fresh-water and many of them planktonic.

Scenedesmus, with about 100 species, is a widely distributed organism, and the algal flora of practically every body of standing water contains one or more species. It often appears in practically pure culture in aquariums and in jars of water that have been standing in the laboratory for some time. The colony (coenobium) of *Scenedesmus* is a flat, rarely curved, plate of ellipsoidal to fusiform cells arranged in a single to double series with their long axes parallel to one another. The number of cells in a coenobium is always a multiple of two; usually 4 or 8, although sometimes 16 or 32. According to the species, the cell wall is smooth, corrugated, granulate, or spicate and is with or without terminal or lateral teeth or spines. Young cells have a single longitudinal laminate chloroplast containing one pyrenoid; chloroplasts of old cells usually fill the entire cell cavity (Fig. 52*A–B*). There is but one nucleus.

Each cell in a colony is capable of giving rise to a daughter colony, but there is rarely a simultaneous formation of daughter colonies by all cells in a colony. The number of cells in a daughter colony is partially dependent upon the physiological condition of the parent cell and may be smaller or greater than the number of cells in the colony to which the parent cell belongs. The protoplast of a cell about to form a daughter colony divides transversely, and the two daughter protoplasts divide vertically (Fig. 52*C–I*). This may be followed by one or two additional series of vertical divisions.[1] The last generation of daughter protoplasts become autospores that remain laterally united to one another after their liberation by a longitudinal rupture of the parent-cell wall.

ORDER 10. SIPHONALES

Thalli of members of this order consist of a single multinucleate cell which is generally a branched tube capable of indefinite growth. The thallus of certain genera is amorphous. That of other genera has the branches definitely arranged upon an axis or has them intertwined to form a thallus of definite macroscopic form. Relatively few members of the order produce zoospores or aplanospores. Almost all of them produce gametes, either in undifferentiated branches or in special gametangia. Sexual reproduction is isogamous, anisogamous, or oögamous.

The order includes about 50 genera and 400 species, most of which are marine and found in tropical or subtropical seas.

In addition to the vegetative structure there are other features separating the Siphonales from other green algae. They contain two distinctive xanthophylls (siphonein and siphonoxanthin) not found in other Chlorophyceae.[2] Vegetative cells of all species thus far investigated have been found to have diploid nuclei, and it is not impossible that this is characteristic for the entire order.

The order is divided either into four or into five families. These may be ranged in an ascending series according to complexity of vegetative structure or according to increased complexity of gametangia and type of gametic union.

FAMILY 1. BRYOPSIDACEAE

Thalli of Bryopsidaceae are unseptate and differentiated into a prostrate rhizome-like portion and an erect pinnately branched portion. Zoospores are unknown, but there may be an asexual reproduction by abscission of pinnules. Sexual reproduction is anisogamous, and the gametes are produced in pinnules of the erect branches or in outgrowths from them.

[1] Smith, 1914. [2] Strain, 1949, 1951.

There are but 2 genera: *Bryopsis* with about 30 species, and *Pseudobryopsis* with 2 species. Both genera are marine.

Most species of *Bryopsis* are found in warm seas, but a few of them grow in cold waters. The genus is widely distributed along both coasts of this country, but nowhere along either of them is it a common alga. The rhizome-like portion of the thallus appears to be perennial; it is uncertain whether the erect branches are annual or perennial. The erect axes are pinnately branched, and the pinnules may also be pinnately branched (Fig. 53*A*). Most species have the pinnules in two vertical rows along the erect axis, but some of them have pinnules arising on all sides of an axis. Since there is a continual abscission of fully developed pinnules, the lower half of an axis is generally devoid of appendages.

Internal to the cell wall is a layer of cytoplasm containing many nuclei and many small disciform to spindle-shaped chloroplasts, each usually with a single pyrenoid (Fig. 53*C*). There is a large central vacuole internal to the cytoplasm. Vacuoles within pinnules are described[1] as continuous with that within the axis, but this is not true for the commonest Pacific Coast species, *B. corticulans* Setchell. The protoplasm within an old pinnule becomes separated from that within the axis by a broad gelatinous transverse wall. In *B. plumosa* (Huds.) C.A.Ag. this has been described[2] as arising through an ingrowth of the pinnule wall where it adjoins the axis. In *B. corticulans* there seems to be a transverse cleavage of the protoplasm at the base of a pinnule and a secretion of a gelatinous cross wall between the two newly formed plasma membranes. Later on, additional wall layers, similar in chemical composition to the lateral walls, are laid down on either face of the gelatinous wall (Fig. 53*E*). Sooner or later after formation of the cross wall, there is an abscission of the pinnule. In *B. corticulans* there is a conspicuous development of rhizoidal outgrowths at the pinnule base before this abscission takes place (Fig. 53*B*). Pinnules shed from an axis frequently develop into new thalli if conditions are favorable.

Sexual reproduction is anisogamous, and the gametes are biflagellate. On the Monterey Peninsula, California, *Bryopsis* fruits abundantly during the spring and only occasionally during the summer. The same appears to be true for plants growing in European waters, since all investigators describing sexual reproduction[3] collected their material during the spring. Male and female gametes are produced upon separate plants. They are formed within unmodified pinnules separated from the main axis by a transverse wall. Occasionally there is also a formation of gametes within the axis. Fruiting male plants are macroscopically recognizable because

[1] Fritsch, 1935. [2] Mirande, 1913.
[3] Mirande, 1913; N. Pringsheim, 1871; Zinnecker, 1935.

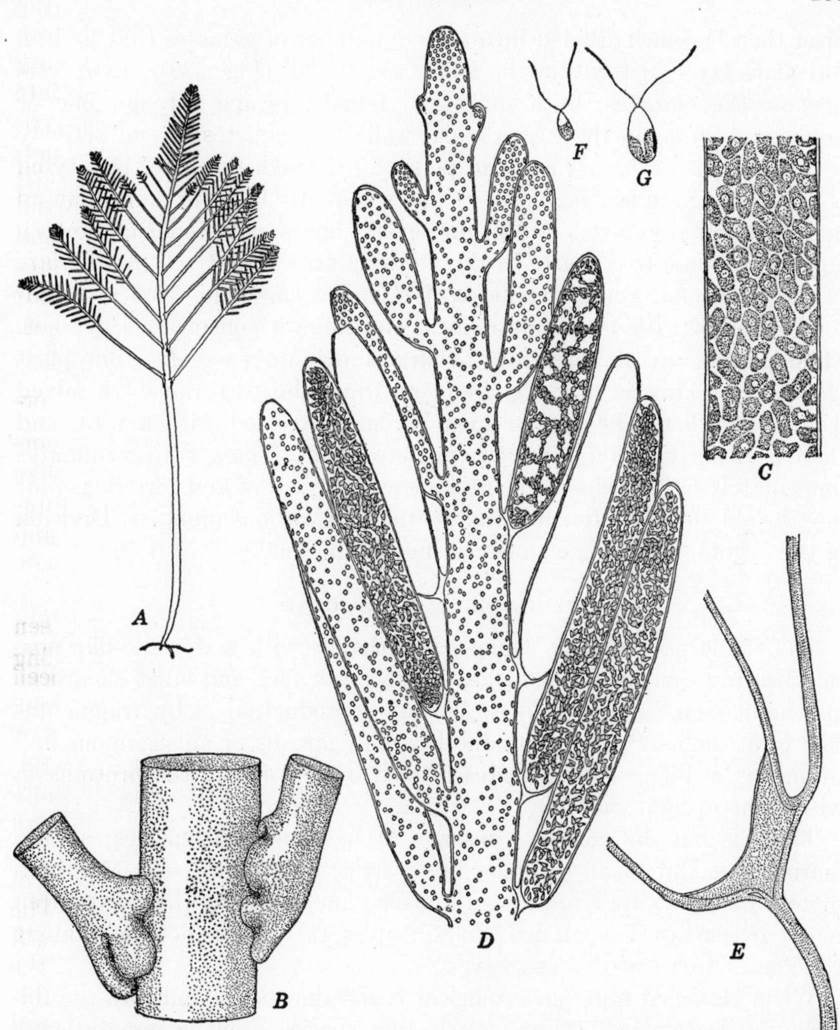

FIG. 53. *Bryopsis corticulans* Setchell. *A*, portion of a thallus. *B*, basal portion of pinnules showing rhizoidal outgrowths after formation of cross walls. *C*, chloroplasts within a pinnule. *D*, apex of a female plant with empty gametangia and gametangia containing gametes. *E*, cross wall at base of a gametangium. *F*, male gamete. *G*, female gamete. (*A*, natural size; *B*, × 21; *C*, *E*, × 325; *D*, × 42; *F–G*, × 650.)

of the yellowish color of the fertile pinnae (gametangia), and female plants because of the dark-green color of their gametangia.

Conversion of a pinnule into a gametangium begins with a formation of a basal transverse wall. This is formed in the same manner as are those of old vegetative pinnae. An increase in the number of nuclei follows, and it has been shown[1] that nuclear division is meiotic. The proto-

[1] Zinnecker, 1935.

plast then becomes divided into a large number of gametes that lie in a reticulate layer just within the gametangial wall (Fig. 53*D*). In *B. corticulans* the gametes, both male and female, escape through one or more small pores in the gametangial wall. The gametes swarm actively within the gametangium and escape singly through the pore. Emptying of a gametangium is a slow process and frequently lasts for more than an hour. Liberated gametes swarm for several hours, and under laboratory conditions those freed early in the morning are still actively motile late in the afternoon. Female gametes of *B. corticulans* (Fig. 53*G*) are pyriform, usually with two chloroplasts, and have a conspicuous eyespot. Male gametes are about a third as large and contain a single chloroplast (Fig. 53*F*). Gametic union is frequent when the two kinds are mixed with each other. The zygote soon becomes invested with a wall, and there is an early fusion of the two gamete nuclei.[1] The zygote germinates immediately but development into a new plant is slow and germlings four months old are but a few millimeters tall and without pinnules. Division of the zygote nucleus is equational, not reductional.[1]

FAMILY 2. CAULERPACEAE

The Caulerpaceae have a one-celled thallus with a rhizome-like portion bearing root-like appendages on its lower face and erect shoot-like appendages on its upper face. Asexual reproduction is by fragmentation of a thallus. Sexual reproduction is isogamous or anisogamous and by means of biflagellate gametes formed by division of the protoplasm within the upright shoots.

There is but one genus, *Caulerpa.* It has about 60 species; all are marine and almost all of them are restricted to warm seas. Approximately 15 species are known from Florida,[2] and several of them have been found growing at a depth of 75 to 80 meters. *Caulerpa* is not found along the Pacific Coast of this country.

When classified upon an ecological basis[3] the species fall into the following three classes: (1) mud-collecting species growing epiphytically upon roots of mangroves, (2) sand- and mud-bottom species that may grow in shallow or in deep water, and (3) rock and coral-reef species.

The one-celled thallus of *Caulerpa* has a size and an external form comparable to that of a vascular plant with a creeping stolon. The rhizome-like portion of a thallus and the root-like rhizoids are much the same from species to species. There is great variation in form of the erect branches—the "leafy shoots"; and species have been named for the resemblance of their leafy shoots to cacti, to yews, to mosses, and to lycopods (Fig. 54). Mechanical support of the erect shoots is due to turgor and to thickness of the cell wall; not, as in certain other Siphona-

[1] Zinnecker, 1935. [2] Taylor, 1928. [3] Børgesen, 1907.

les, to an interweaving of branches or to an impregnation with lime. A thallus is without transverse walls, but there are numerous transverse and longitudinal rods (**trabeculae**) of callose and pectic materials (Fig. 55*A*). The function of the trabeculae is uncertain. Possibly they are mechanical supports that increase the rigidity of a plant. The multinucleate layer of cytoplasm internal to the wall contains many disciform chloroplasts without pyrenoids.

Vegetative multiplication is effected by a fragmentation of the thallus or by an abscission of proliferous shoots.

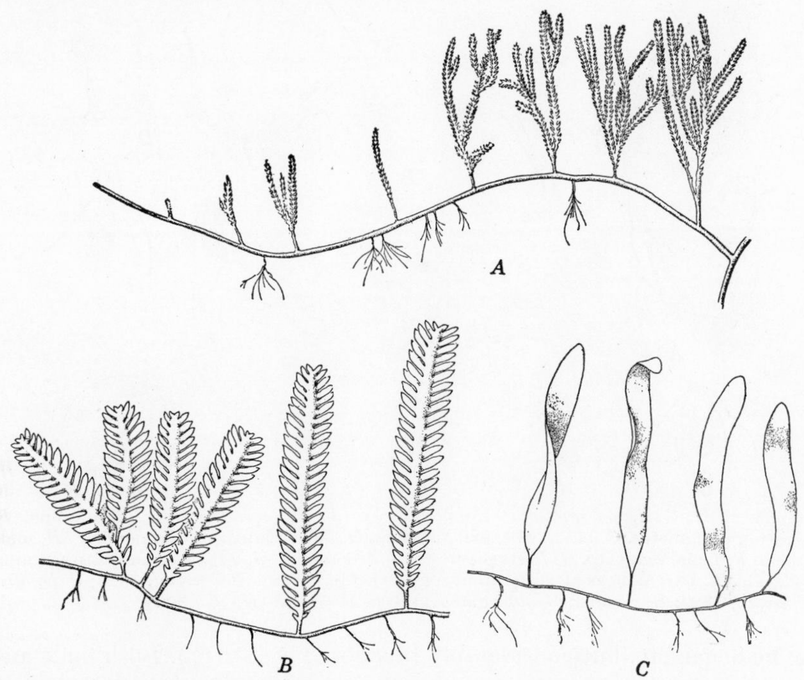

FIG. 54. *A*, *Caulerpa cupressoides* (West) C.A.Ag. *B*, *C. crassifolia* (C.A.Ag.) J.G.Ag. *C*, *C. prolifera* (Forsk.) Lamx. (× ½.)

Several species are known[1] to produce biflagellate gametes, and when growing in the Mediterranean *C. prolifera* (Fosk.) Lamx. fruits during the autumn.[2] The production of gametes may be restricted to the foliar portions (phylloids) of a thallus, or it may take place in the stolons. Just prior to the formation of gametes there is a meiotic division of nuclei in the fertile area,[3] and after being formed the gametes lie in reticulate masses within the thallus. Gamete formation is accompanied by a devel-

[1] Dostal, 1928, 1929; Ernst, 1931; Iyengar, 1933*A*, 1940; Miyake and Kunieda, 1937; Schussnig, 1929, 1939.

[2] Dostal, 1928, 1929; Schussnig, 1929, 1939.

[3] Schussnig, 1939.

opment of numerous papillate outgrowths upon the surface of the fertile portion of a thallus. These are the **extrusion papillae** through which the gametes escape (Fig. 55*C–D*). Gametes escape through the extrusion papillae shortly after daybreak—sometimes in such quantity[1] that small green clouds appear in the water surrounding the fertile portion of a plant. Most species are heterothallic but one species has been found[2] to be homothallic. All species in which sexual reproduction has been observed are anisogamous, with the female gamete only slightly longer than

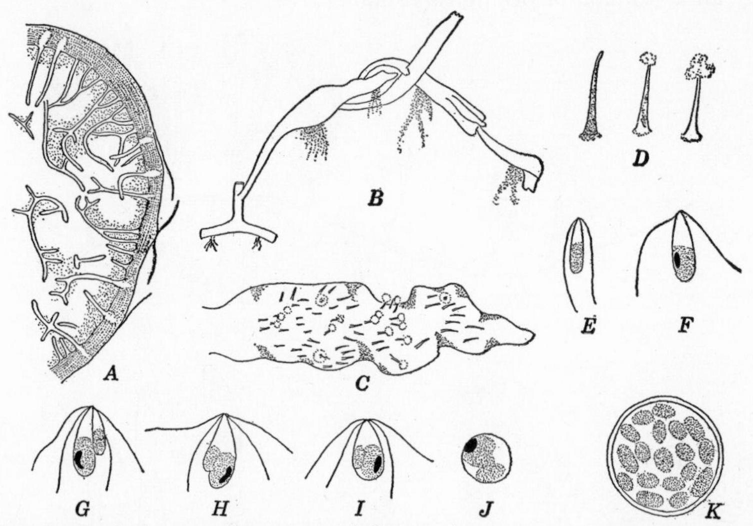

FIG. 55. *A–D*, *Caulerpa prolifera* (Forsk.) Lamx. *A*, transverse section of a stolon. *B*, liberation of gametes. *C*, blade with exit papillae. *D*, development of exit papillae. *E*, male gamete. *F*, female gamete. *G–I*, stages in union of gametes. *J*, zygote after disappearance of flagella. *K*, two months after germination of zygote. (*A–B*, *after Dostal*, 1929; *C–D*, *after Schussnig*, 1929; *E–K*, *after Miyake and Kunieda*, 1937.) (*E–K*, × 1,300.)

the male gamete, but considerably broader (Fig. 55*E–F*). Both male and female gametes are pyriform, biflagellate, and have a single chloroplast and a conspicuous eyespot. Fruiting of a thallus is followed by a disintegration and disappearance of the fertile portion. The zygote soon loses its flagella, becomes spherical, and secretes a wall. In germinating, the spherical zygote enlarges (Fig. 55*K*) and the number of chloroplasts increases to 30 or more.[3] Its further development has not been followed.

FAMILY 3. HALICYSTIDACEAE

The Halicystidaceae differ from other Siphonales in that there is only a plasma membrane between the gametangium and the vegetative portion of a thallus.

[1] Dostal, 1929. [2] Iyengar, 1940. [3] Miyake and Kunieda, 1937.

The single genus, *Halicystis*, is a marine algae with three or four species. It is widespread, although not common, along the Pacific Coast of this country and has been collected at the Dry Tortugas, Florida. The Pacific Coast species, *H. ovalis* (Lyngb.) Aresch., grows epiphytically upon calcareous Rhodophyceae, especially *Lithophyllum* and *Lithothamnion*.

The thallus is differentiated into a short erect colorless rhizome and a large globose green vesicle a centimeter or more in diameter (Fig. 56*A*).

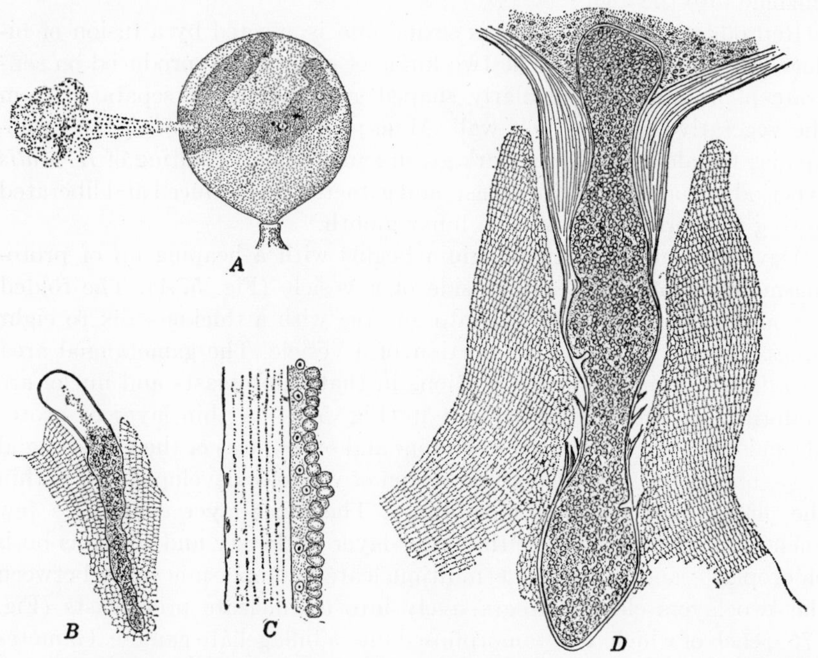

Fig. 56. *Halicystis ovalis* (Lyngb.) Aresch. *A*, fertile mature plant liberating gametes. *B*, juvenile plant. *C*, vertical section of a portion of a vesicle. *D*, old rhizome with a cross wall at the juncture with vesicle. (*A*, × 3; *B*, *D*, × 80; *C*, × 650.)

The rhizome grows directly downward into the substratum, the vesicle stands above it. The vesicle has a thick wall with many concentric layers.[1] Within the wall is a layer of protoplasm, and internal to this is a large central vacuole. At the inner face of the protoplasm are many small disciform chloroplasts without pyrenoids. The nuclei lie external to the chloroplasts (Fig. 56*C*). The wall of a rhizome is thinner than that of a vesicle, but it has many peg-like ingrowths. The rhizome is more or less completely filled with a multinucleate mass of cytoplasm containing many starch grains.

[1] Hollenberg. 1935.

Thalli of *H. ovalis* are perennial; shedding their vesicles in the autumn and regenerating new ones each spring.[1] Late in the summer there is a formation of a cross wall at the juncture of vesicle and rhizome. Shortly afterward there is a development of a transverse line of abscission across the basal region of the wall of the vesicle (Fig. 56*D*), which is followed by an abscission of the vesicle. The persistent rhizome becomes more deeply embedded in the substratum from year to year. This is due to an upgrowth of the host alga rather than to a downward growth of the rhizome into the alga.[2]

Reproduction of *Halicystis* is sexual and is effected by a fusion of biflagellate anisogametes.[3] The two kinds of gametes are produced on separate plants and in irregularly shaped gametangia not separated from the vegetative portion by a wall. Male plants have yellowish-tan gametangia; female plants have dark green gametangia.[1] Fruiting of *H. ovalis* is periodic along the Pacific Coast, and gametes are produced and liberated during the spring tides of each lunar month.[4]

Development of a gametangium begins with a heaping up of protoplasm in radiate folds at one side of a vesicle (Fig. 57*A*). The folded region gradually smooths out into an area with a thickness six to eight times[2] that of a vegetative portion of a vesicle. The gametangial area also differs from vegetative portions in that chloroplasts and nuclei are uniformly distributed throughout it (Fig. 57*B*). A thin layer of protoplasm is then cut off on both the inner and outer faces of the gametangial area. This is effected by a lateral fusion of vacuoles developed just within the plasma and vacuolar membranes. The inner layer contains a few nuclei but no chloroplasts: the outer layer is thicker and contains both chloroplasts and nuclei. The multinucleate protoplasmic mass between the two layers cleaves progressively into uninucleate protoplasts (Fig. 57*C*), each of which is metamorphosed into a biflagellate gamete. Gametes within a gametangial area of a male plant are small, pyriform, with a single chloroplast (Fig. 57*D*). Those of female plants are somewhat larger and contain several chloroplasts (Fig. 57*E*). Gametogenesis is accompanied by a localized gelatinization of several small areas in the cell wall external to the gametangium. These become the pores through which the gametes are discharged.

The gametes are forcibly and suddenly ejected shortly after daybreak.[3] Discharge of gametes from plants growing in aquariums may be delayed for two or three hours by keeping them in a dark room and then bringing them into the light. Discharge takes place within three or four minutes after plants are brought into daylight. The gametes are discharged in a green jet that extends from 20 to 40 mm. from an exit

[1] Hollenberg, 1935; Kuckuck, 1907. [2] Hollenberg, 1935.
[3] Hollenberg, 1935; Smith, 1930. [4] Hollenberg, 1936.

pore (Fig. 56*A*). The jet disperses within a few seconds and much like a puff of smoke. Discharge may be in a continuous stream or in several intermittent puffs. Intermittent discharge may be through the same pore, or each successive jet may be through a different pore.

Gametic union follows immediately after discharge and a fusing pair have their anterior poles apposed to each other (Fig. 57*F*). The flagella disappear shortly after the gametes become apposed, and the zygote soon becomes spherical and secretes a wall. There is an immediate germination

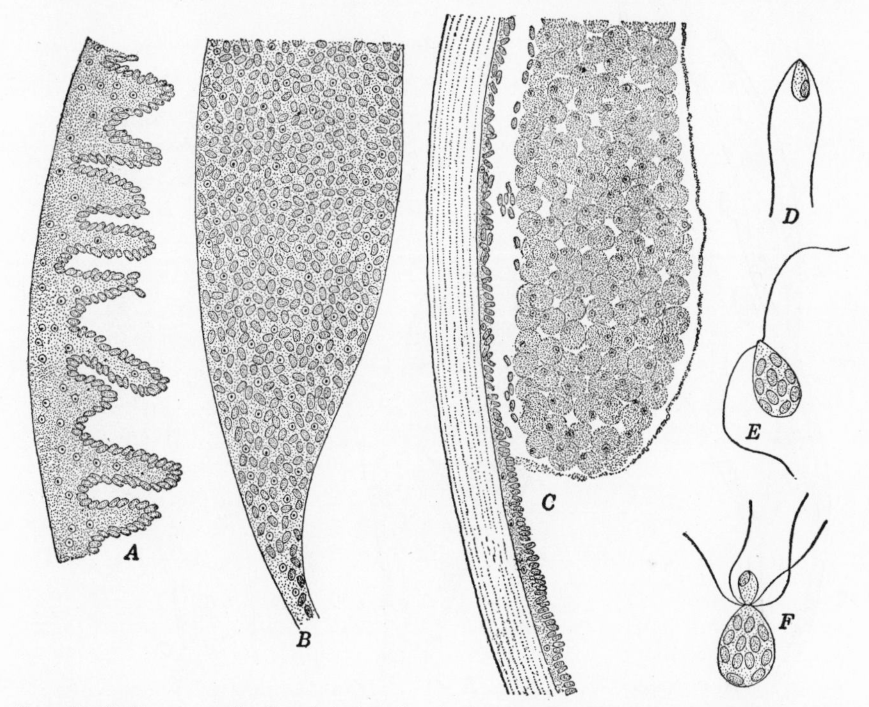

FIG. 57. *Halicystis ovalis* (Lyngb.) Aresch. *A–C*, successive stages in development of a gametangium. *D*, male gamete. *E*, female gamete. *F*, union of gametes. (× 650.)

of a zygote, and within a week the germ tube grows to a length four to six times the diameter of the zygote.[1] The germ tube eventually becomes a branched prostrate filament bearing short erect branches. The first cultural studies[1] seemed to indicate that the prostrate filamentous stage eventually gives rise to the vesicle typical of *Halicystis*. Later studies seem to indicate that this is not the case. In a study[2] of the alga known as *Derbesia marina* (Lyngb.) Kjellm. it was found that zoospores of *Derbesia* gave rise to unseptate filaments with localized nodular thickenings which eventually developed into characteristic *Halicystis* vesicles

[1] Hollenberg, 1935. [2] Kornmann, 1938.

that produced typical fertile areas. Still later,[1] cultures started from zygotes of *Halicystis* were shown to develop into "*Derbesia*" thalli which produced sporangia and zoospores at the end of two months. Thus, there seems to be a justification for thinking that *Halicystis* and *Derbesia* are alternate phases or generations of the same alga.

"*Derbesia*" is a unicellular, freely branched, tubular coenocyte differentiated into a densely interwoven basal portion and a tuft-like erect

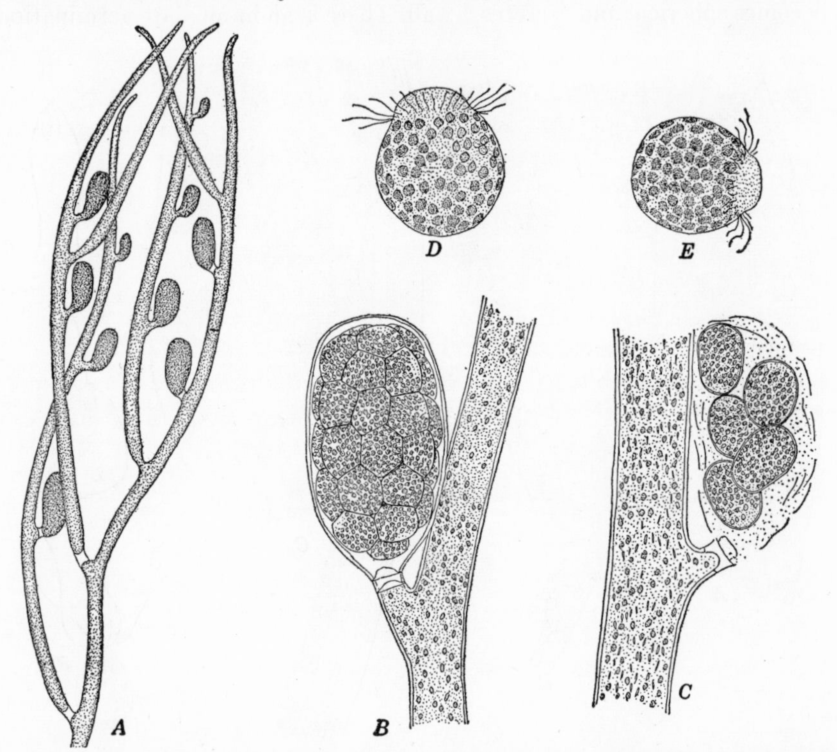

FIG. 58. *Derbesia marina* (Lyngb.) Kjellm., an alga which is now considered the sporophytic generation of *Halicystis ovalis* (Lyngb.) Aresch. *A*, portion of a fertile thallus. *B*, sporangium containing zoospores. *C*, sporangium containing aplanospores. *D–E*, zoospores. (*A*, × 30; *B–C*, × 325; *D–E*, × 650.)

portion. Branching of the erect portion is frequently dichotomous and sometimes with an unequal elongation of the dichotomies that results in a distinctly monopodial branching (Fig. 58*A*). Older branches may have the protoplasm separated from the protoplast of the remainder of the filament by broad transverse septa. These develop as localized annular thickenings on the inner face of lateral walls.[2]

There is a thin layer of cytoplasm just within the cell wall, and internal to this is a large central vacuole. At the inner face of the cytoplasm are

[1] Feldmann, 1950. [2] Mirande, 1913.

many small chloroplasts which, according to the species, are disciform or spindle-shaped and with or without pyrenoids.

The zoospores are produced within sporangia borne laterally upon the erect filaments. Very young sporangia look like initials of branches; but they soon become ovoid, globose, or pyriform and elongate but little. When the sporangia are about half grown there is a formation of a transverse basal septum by an annular ingrowth of the lateral wall. Developing sporangia have been described[1] as containing thousands of nuclei, but in "*Derbesia marina*" as found along the Pacific Coast of North America there are not more than 200 to 300 of them. Certain of the nuclei degenerate; the others enlarge to four to six times their original diameter. There is a progressive cleavage of the sporangial contents into uninucleate protoplasts by an inward furrowing of the plasma membrane. Each protoplast is metamorphosed into an ovoid *Oedogonium*-like zoospore (Fig. 58*D–E*) with a transverse whorl of flagella at one pole. The flagella are produced by a ring-shaped blepharoplast just within the plasma membrane.[1] A sporangium contains 10 to 50 zoospores (Fig. 58*B*), and they are liberated by an irregular rupture of the sporangial wall. The zoospores swarm actively for several hours; then they come to rest, withdraw their flagella, secrete a wall, and germinate. Occasionally there may be a secretion of walls around zoospores with unopened sporangia. These aplanospores are liberated by a disintegration of the sporangial wall (Fig. 58*C*).

If the foregoing interpretation is correct, *Halicystis* has an alternation of generations (or phases) in which a unicellular multinucleate gametophyte alternates with a unicellular multinucleate tubular sporophyte. The nuclear cycle has not been followed so that it is impossible to say whether or not meiosis immediately precedes gametogenesis, as in certain Siphonales, or whether it immediately precedes sporogenesis. The fact that the zoospores of the *Derbesia* stage germinate into branched tubular thalli that may produce either sporangia or globular thickenings that develop into the *Halicystis* stage suggests[2] that meiosis immediately precedes gametogenesis.

FAMILY 4. CODIACEAE

The Codiaceae have freely branched tubular thalli in which the branches are interwoven to form a plant body of definite macroscopic form. Reproduction is sexual, anisogamous, and with the gametes produced in gametangia of distinctive form.

The family includes some 16 genera and 120 species. All species are marine, and a very large majority of them are restricted to warm seas.

[1] Davis, 1908. [2] Feldmann, 1950.

Codium, a genus with about 50 species, is primarily tropical and subtropical. It is found along the entire Pacific Coast of this country and as far north as North Carolina on the Atlantic Coast. The much-branched tubular thallus may have the branches interwoven into a prostrate cushion-like mass, into a spherical mass, or into a crustose prostrate portion bearing several erect shoots that are generally cylindrical and dichotomously branched (Fig. 59*A*). Erect portions of the thallus have an axial

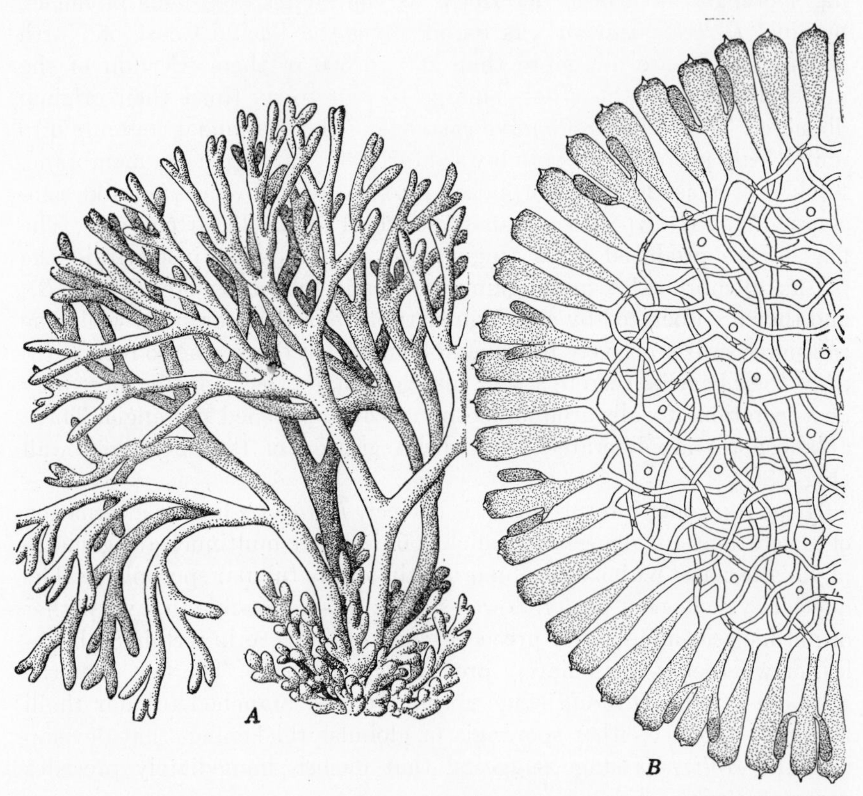

Fig. 59. *Codium fragile* (Suring.) Hariot. *A*, thallus. *B*, diagrammatic transverse section of a thallus branch. (*A*, × ½; *B*, × 21.)

core of densely interwoven colorless filaments from which arise lateral branchlets, the **utricles,** that lie in a palisade-like layer surrounding the central axial core (Fig. 59*B*). Each utricle has a large central vacuole and a fairly thick layer of cytoplasm between the vacuole and the cell wall. The chloroplasts, which are disciform and without pyrenoids, lie just within the plasma membrane, and most of them are at the distal end of a utricle (Fig. 60*A*). The nuclei are minute, numerous, and lie internal to the chloroplasts. Filaments of the axial core become blocked off here and there by an annular ingrowth of the cell wall. These thick transverse septa are especially numerous near the bases of utricles.

Reproduction of *Codium* is sexual and the club-shaped gametangia are developed laterally upon the utricles. Two gametangia are usually formed upon a utricle, but development of them is not simultaneous. Some species are dioecious; others are monoecious. Most species fruit throughout the year but most abundantly during the summer.

Gametangial development begins with the outgrowth of a tubular projection at one side of a utricle. A developing gametangium is solidly filled with cytoplasm in which the nuclei are evenly distributed, and the chloroplasts tend to aggregate at the distal end. When a gametangium is about two-thirds developed, there is an annular thickening of the wall at its base. This completely separates the gametangial protoplast from that in the utricle. Some of the nuclei within a gametangium degenerate; others enlarge and divide meiotically into four daughter nuclei.[1] Beginning at the basal end, there is next a progressive cleavage into uninucleate protoplasts. Female gametangia contain a few hundred uninucleate protoplasts, male gametangia a few thousand. Each uninucleate protoplast then metamorphoses into a biflagellate gamete. Male gametes are pyriform and contain one or two chloroplasts; female gametes are also pyriform, several times larger, and contain many chloroplasts (Fig. 60*E–F*). Male and female gametangia may be distinguished from each other even before the gametes are formed because of the golden brown color of the former and the dark green color of the latter.

On the Monterey Peninsula, California, *C. fragile* (Suring.) Hariot grows in the intertidal zone and discharges its gametes when thalli are reflooded by the incoming tide. Discharge of gametes seems to be due to an imbibitional swelling of inner layers of the gametangial wall. Discharge begins[2] with a rupture of the lid-like apical portion of the gametangial wall. There is next an extrusion of a gelatinous mass of much the same size and shape as the gametangium.[1] There is an axial canal within the gelatinous mass, and the gametes exude rapidly through this canal and accumulate at its free end (Fig. 60*B–D*). Movement of gametes through the canal is purely passive and is due to hydrostatic pressure within the gametangium. The passive nature of gametes during discharge is shown by their lack of flagella and, in the case of female gametes, by their being squeezed to a narrower diameter while being ejected through the canal. Ejection of gametes is rapid and usually takes less than a minute. Flagella become evident on gametes that have been discharged through the canal and within a minute or two the lashing back and forth

[1] Schussnig, 1930, 1950; Williams, 1925.

[2] Berthold in Oltmanns, 1922; Smith, 1930.

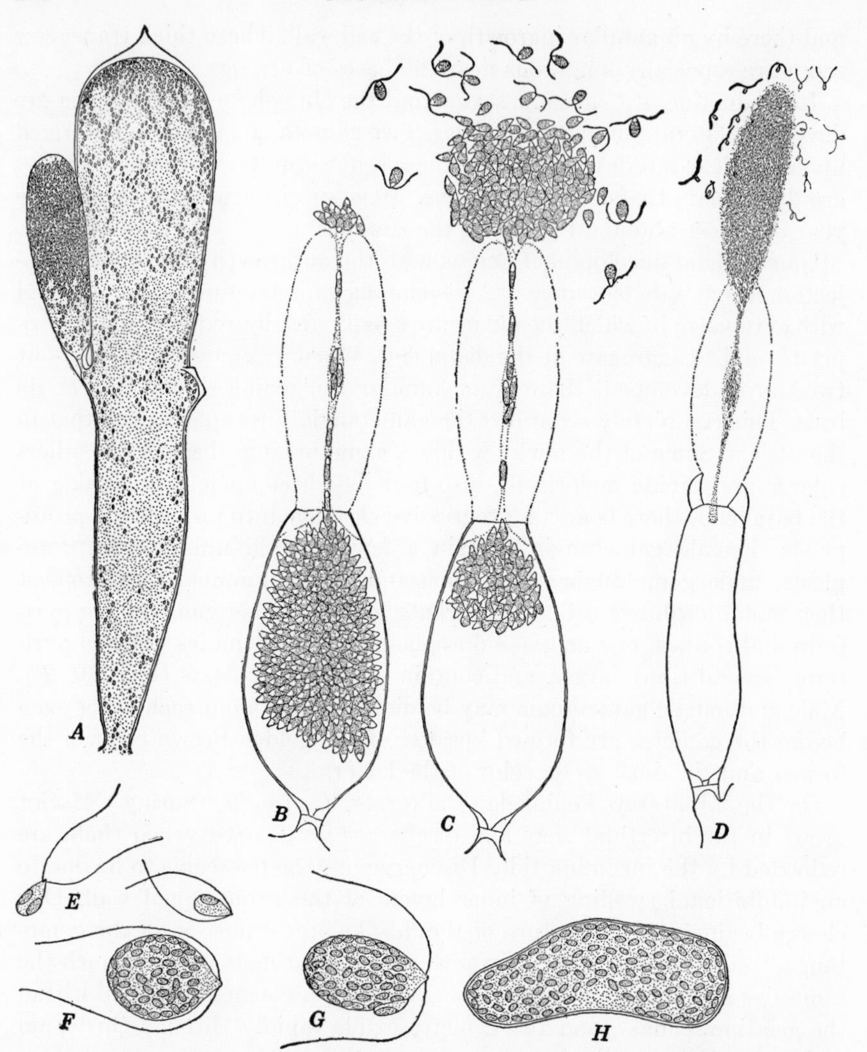

FIG. 60. *Codium fragile* (Suring.) Hariot. *A*, utricle with a young female gametangium. *B–C*, female gametangia liberating gametes. *D*, male gametangium liberating gametes. *E*, male gametes. *F*, female gamete. *G*, after union of male gamete with a female gamete. *H*, germination of zygote. (*A*, × 100; *B–C*, × 175; *D*, × 150; *E–H*, × 600.)

of its flagella propels a gamete away from the heap accumulating at the mouth of the canal (Fig. 60*C*).

Gametic union takes place while both gametes are actively motile. A male gamete becomes applied to the side of a female gamete, loses its flagella, and gradually fuses with the female gamete[1] (Fig. 60*G*). Flagella of the female gamete persist for a time after gametic union, but they soon

[1] Berthold in Oltmanns, 1922; Smith, 1930.

disappear and the zygote assumes a spherical shape and secretes a wall. There is an immediate germination of a zygote, but development is slow and the length of tubular germlings three weeks old is but four or five times the diameter of a zygote. Somewhat older germlings are longer and sparingly branched.[1] Eventually certain branches of this protonema-like stage enlarge greatly and become the first-formed utricles.[2] Additional utricles are formed as growth continues, and there is gradually the assumption of the organization characteristic of the adult thallus of the species.

FAMILY 5. DICHOTOMOSIPHONACEAE

The tubular coenocytic thalli of members of this family are dichotomously branched and organized into an amorphous felty layer. Sexual reproduction is oögamous.

Until recently all oögamous siphonaceous, apparently green algae were placed in the family Vaucheriaceae. Later, *Vaucheria*, the type genus of the Vaucheriaceae, was shown[3] to be a member of the Xanthophyceae; *Dichotomosiphon* was shown[4] to be a member of the Chlorophyceae and made the type of the monogeneric family Dichotomosiphonaceae.

Dichotomosiphon has but two species, the fresh-water *D. tuberosus* (A. Br.) Ernst and the marine *D. pusillus* Collins. *D. tuberosus* grows in lakes with a rich organic silty bottom and down to where the water is 20 meters deep. The thalli frequently grow with the major portion buried in the bottom deposits and with only the tips of the branches extending above the deposits.[5]

The thallus of *Dichotomosiphon* is a dichotomously branched tubular coenocyte constricted at each dichotomy and with constrictions between the dichotomies (Fig. 61*A*). The entire thallus, except for colorless rhizoidal branches at the base, contains numerous lens-shaped chloroplasts without pyrenoids and generally without starch. In addition to the chloroplasts there are leucoplasts containing granules of starch.[6] The cell wall is said[4] to lack cellulose.

Asexual reproduction is by means of large tuberous akinetes and is the only method of reproduction when the alga grows where the water is more than 2 meters deep.[7] The akinetes (Fig. 61*B*) are generally borne in catenate series and at the ends of rhizoid-like branches. They are densely packed with starch and may or may not be set off from the remainder of the thallus by transverse septa. Akinetes germinate directly into new thalli.[7]

[1] Berthold in Oltmanns, 1922. [2] Tobler, 1911. [3] Chadefaud, 1945.
[4] Feldmann, 1946. [5] Prescott, 1951.
[6] Chadefaud and Rossat, 1947; Feldmann, 1946. [7] Ernst, 1902.

Sexual reproduction is oögamous and thalli producing sex organs are rarely found at a depth greater than 2 meters. *Dichotomosiphon* is homothallic and with the sex organs borne terminally on di-, tri-, or tetrachotomously branched curved ends of filaments. An antheridium (Fig. 61*D*) is conical and is of the same diameter as the branch bearing it. Antheridia are separated from the remainder of the thallus by transverse walls. The protoplast of an antheridium divides into a large number of minute biflagellate antherozoids that are liberated by an apical rupture

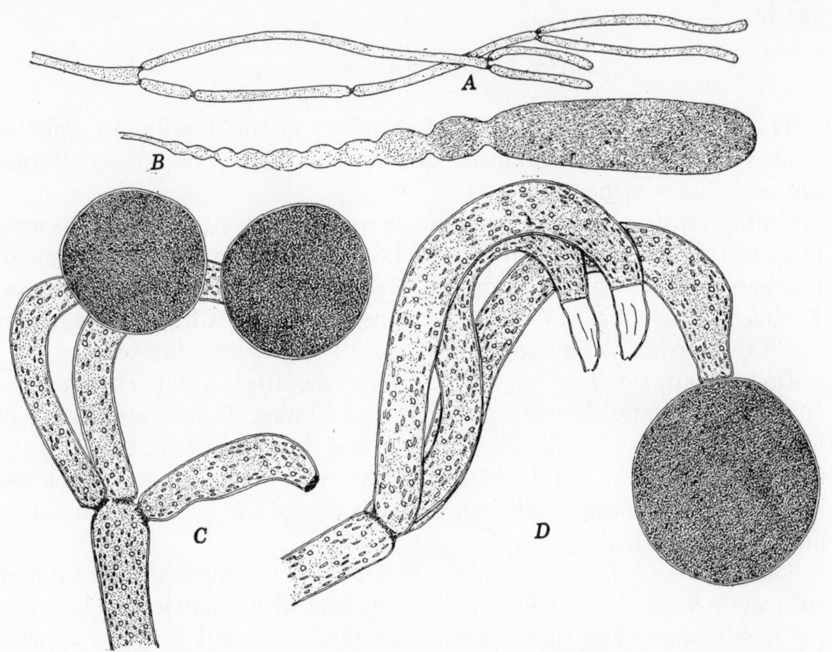

Fig. 61. *Dichotomosiphon tuberosus* (A. Br.) Ernst. *A*, vegetative portion of a thallus. *B*, portion of thallus with akinetes. *C–D*, sex organs. (*A–B*, × 6; *C–D*, × 325.)

of the antheridial wall.[1] An oögonium is spherical and with a diameter four or five times that of the branch on which it is borne. Just before fertilization, an oögonium develops a small beak-like opening at its apex. Mature zygotes have a smooth thick wall surrounding a protoplast densely packed with starch, and are retained within the oögonium for a considerable time after fertilization (Fig. 61*C–D*).

ORDER 11. SIPHONOCLADALES

The Siphonocladales have multicellular thalli attached to the substratum by a system of rhizoids. The cells are multinucleate, with reticulate chloroplasts, and divide in the distinctive manner known as **segregative cell division.** Asexual reproduction is by means of quadriflagellate zoo-

[1] Ernst, 1902.

spores. Sexual reproduction is usually isogamous but it may be oögamous.

The order includes about 18 genera and 150 species; all of them marine and usually restricted to tropical and subtropical seas.

Phycologists[1] who include all multicellular green algae with multinucleate cells in the order usually divide it into three families (Valoniaceae, Dasycladaceae, Cladophoraceae) in which the Valoniaceae are divided into four subfamilies. Those[2] who place the Dasycladaceae and Cladophoraceae in other orders usually elevate the four subfamilies of the Valoniaceae to the rank of families.

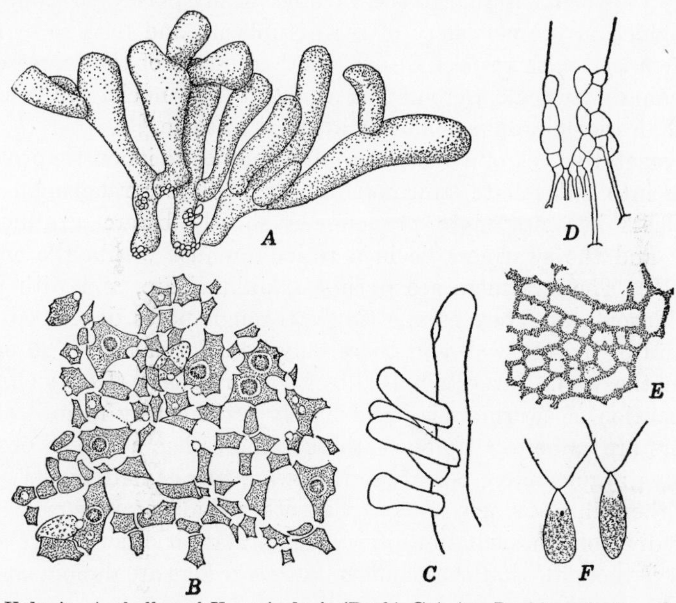

Fig. 62. *Valonia*. *A*, thallus of *V. utricularis* (Roth) C.A.Ag. *B*, chloroplasts and nuclei of *V. macrophysa* Kütz. *C*, apex of *V. utricularis* forming new cells by segregative cell division. *D*, base of *V. aegagropila* C.A.Ag. forming rhizoids by segregative cell division. *E*, reticulum of zooids in a cell of *V. macrophysa*. *F*, zooids of *V. macrophysa*. (*A–E*, *after Kuckuck*, 1907; *F*, *after Famintzin*, 1860.) (*A*, *C*, × 2; *B*, × 600; *D–E*, × 12.)

Valonia (Fig. 62), a genus with about 18 species, is found in tropical and subtropical seas and in the Mediterranean. A young plant consists of a bladder-like multinucleate primary cell which is attached to the substratum by small unicellular holdfast cells that are formed by what has been called[3] **segregative cell division.** Segregative division begins with a differentiation of a dense lens-shaped mass of protoplasm at a local area in the cell, and this is followed by a formation of a wall between the mass and the remainder of the protoplasm. The small lens-shaped cell thus differentiated then elongates into a holdfast cell (Fig. 62*D*). In *V. ven-*

[1] Fritsch, 1935; Printz, 1927; Taylor, 1942.

[2] Børgesen, 1925; Egerod, 1952; Feldmann, 1938. [3] Børgesen, 1913.

tricosa J.G.Ag., a species extensively studied by cellular physiologists, there is generally no division of the cell except for formation of rhizoidal holdfast cells, and the primary cell may become 3 or more centimeters in diameter. Primary cells of most other species, by segregative division, cut off small lens-shaped cells at the upper end, and these grow to approximately the same size and shape as the primary cell (Fig. 62*A*, *C*). The resultant mass of more or less club-shaped cells may lie in a palisade-like cushion over 20 cm. broad.

A mature cell has a conspicuous central vacuole and a relatively thick layer of cytoplasm external to the vacuole. Many polygonal chloroplasts lie embedded in the periphery of the cytoplasm[1] and tend to be reticulately arranged with respect to one another. Most of the larger chloroplasts contain a single pyrenoid (Fig. 62*B*). The nuclei are somewhat larger than the chloroplasts and lie internal to them.

Any vegetative cell of a *Valonia* thallus may have its entire protoplast dividing into biflagellate swarmers. The reticulate arrangement of the chloroplasts becomes more pronounced shortly before swarmers are formed[2] and the swarmers lie in a reticulum just within the cell wall (Fig. 62*F*). The swarmers are pyriform, uninucleate, and with two or three chloroplasts. They escape singly through pores developed in the distal end of the cell wall and there may be a formation of 20 or more pores in the wall.[1] In certain thalli of *V. utricularis* (Roth) C.A. Ag., the formation of swarmers is immediately preceded by meiosis and the swarmers are gametes.[3] Union of these gametes has not been observed, but young zygotes have been found showing two gamete nuclei or a fusion of them into a single nucleus.[4] In other thalli of *V. utricularis* the nuclear divisions immediately preceding formation of swarmers are mitotic. It is thought[4] that these biflagellate swarmers are diploid zoospores which develop directly into new thalli.

Two other Siphonocladales (*Anadyomene*[5] and *Microdictyon*[6]) have an isomorphic alternation of generations. The gametophytes are heterothallic, and gametes produced by them are isogamous. The sporophytes produce quadriflagellate zoospores and in the case of *Microdictyon* it has been shown[6] that meiosis immediately precedes formation of zoospores.

ORDER 12. DASYCLADALES

Thalli of Dasycladales have an erect central axis bearing whorls of branches from top to bottom or only at the upper end. The thalli have a single diploid nucleus until well along in development and then it divides

[1] Kuckuck, 1907. [2] Famintzin, 1860; Kuckuck, 1907.
[3] Schechner-Fries, 1934; Schussnig, 1938. [4] Schechner-Fries, 1934.
[5] Iyengar and Ramanathan, 1940. [6] Iyengar and Ramanathan, 1941.

amitotically to form many nuclei. All whorls of branches may be fertile, or some whorls may be fertile and others sterile. Reproduction is sexual and with lateral branches bearing gametangia whose contents divide to form one or more operculate cysts. Meiotic division of nuclei within cysts is followed by a formation of biflagellate gametes. The zygote grows directly into a new thallus.

There are about seven genera with living species, all marine and limited to warm waters. These are placed in a single family, the Dasycladaceae.

Thalli of many genera are heavily encrusted with lime. Calcareous petrefactions and cases of these encrusted species may remain after death and decay of the plant. Many such petrefactions and casts have been found in limestone rocks, and the geological record for these fossil Dasycladaceae extends back to the Ordovician.[1] The distinctive arrangement of lateral appendages in these fossil algae, often called *Siphonae verticullatae*, shows that they are Dasycladaceae. Genera from the Carboniferous and earlier periods have their appendages irregularly distributed along the central axis. Those with whorled (verticillate) appendages (Fig. 63) are known from the Triassic onward.

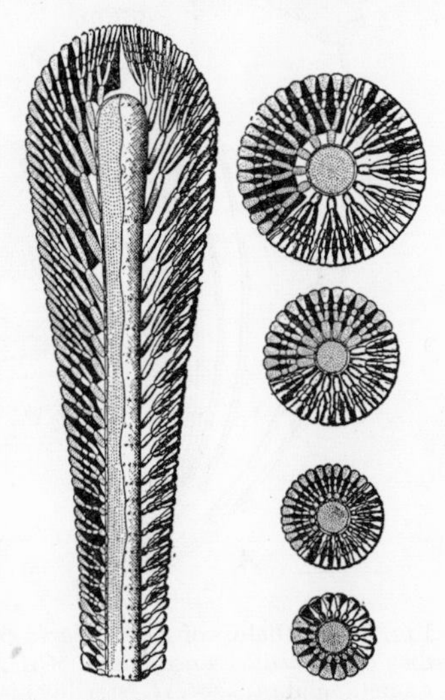

FIG. 63. Reconstruction of *Palaeodasycladus mediterraneus* Pia. (*From Pia*, 1920.) (× 8.)

Acetabularia, the mermaid's wineglass, is a genus with some 20 species. A mature thallus (Fig. 64*A*) is strongly calcified and has an erect unbranched axis that terminates in a single transverse whorl or more than one transverse whorl of gametangial rays. Mature thalli of smaller species may be 2 to 5 mm. tall and with a fertile cap 1 to 3 mm. in diameter; those of certain large species may be 9 to 10 cm. tall and with a cap 1 cm. in diameter.

Development of a zygote into a thallus begins two to three days after gametic union. The germinating zygote develops into a short tube with a definite polarity. One pole grows erect and becomes the axis of the thallus; the other pole becomes the rhizoidal system attaching the thallus to the substratum. Growth is at a rapid rate, and within two or three weeks there may be a formation of a transverse whorl of sterile hairs just below the elongating apex of the axis.[2] As the apex of the axis elongates two or three successive whorls of sterile hairs are formed above the first. Beginning with the first-formed there is eventually a shedding of each

[1] Pia, 1927. [2] Hammerling, 1931.

whorl of hairs, each hair leaving a scar on the axis to mark its former position (Fig. 65*D–I*).

Growth of a thallus terminates with the formation of one or more fertile disks at the thallus apex. According to the species, the gametangial rays of a fertile disk are laterally adjoined or stand free from one another. On the upper face and near the base each ray bears a coronal knob, the coronal knobs jointly comprising the **corona superior.** In many cases the coronal knobs bear sterile hairs. Some species also have a **corona inferior** below the gametangial rays (Fig. 64*B*).

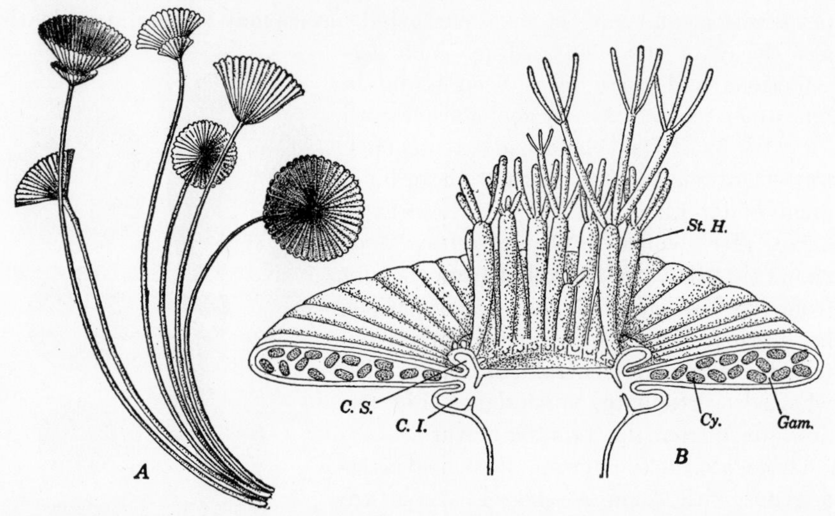

Fig. 64. *A*, thallus of *Acetabularia crenulata* Lamx. *B*, diagram of a vertical section of fertile disk of *A. mediterranea* Lamx. (*C.I.*, corona inferior; *C.S.*, corona superior; *Cy.*, cysts; *Gam.*, gametangial rays; *St. H.*, sterile hairs.) (*B, based upon Oltmanns*, 1922.) (*A*, × 1½; *B*, × 8.)

One remarkable feature in the development of *Acetabularia* is the fact that the zygote nucleus does not divide until the fertile whorl has grown to full size.[1] The same holds for other critically examined genera of the order.[2] The zygote nucleus, the so-called primary nucleus, remains near the base of the axis and enlarges to about twenty times its original diameter. Then it divides amitotically into a number of nuclei which may then divide mitotically.[3] Streaming of cytoplasm carries the nuclei up to the thallus apex, and eventually most of them migrate into the gametangial rays. Regeneration and transplant experiments show[4] that development of sterile hairs and gametangial rays is due to a production of formative substances associated with the primary nucleus; and that division of the primary nucleus is, in turn, stimulated by the presence of a fully grown fertile portion.

[1] Hammerling, 1931, 1934, 1944; K. L. Schulze, 1939. [2] Hammerling, 1944.
[3] K. L. Schulze, 1939. [4] Hammerling, 1934*A*, 1934*B*, 1934*C*, 1936, 1939.

The multinucleate protoplast of each gametangial ray divides into uninucleate protoplasts that round up and secrete a wall which differentiates a definite lid. These cysts enlarge to many times their original size and there is a repeated series of nuclear divisions in which the last series is meiotic.[1] In the Mediterranean, cysts are formed during the summer but principally in July. Cysts of *A. mediterranea* Lamx. are strongly calcified and do not germinate until the following spring; those of *A. wettsteinii* Schussnig are faintly calcified and may germinate within a few days after they are mature.[2] In germination there is a division of the cyst's protoplast into a thousand or more biflagellate pyriform isogametes. Liberation of gametes from a cyst is through a circular pore formed by an open-

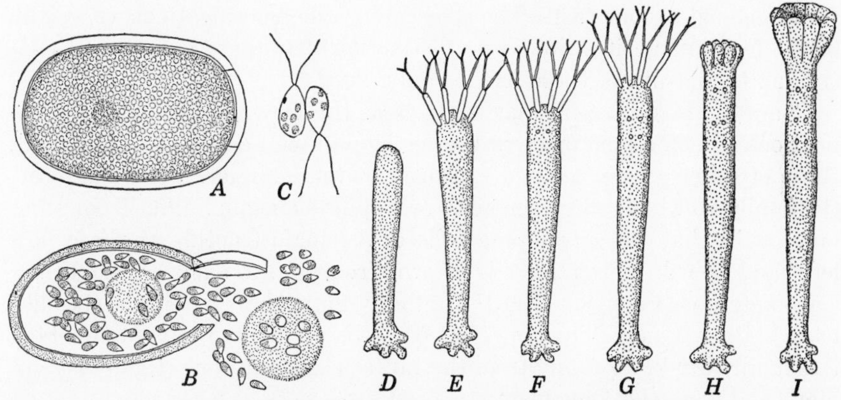

Fig. 65. *A–C*, *Acetabularia mediterranea* Lamx. *A*, resting cyst. *B*, germinating cyst. *C*, gametes. *D–I*, diagram of stages in development of thallus of *Acetabularia* sp. *D*, before formation of sterile hairs. *E–G*, formation and shedding of successive whorls of sterile hairs. *H–I*, early and somewhat later stage in formation of fertile disk. (*A–C*, *after DeBary and Strasburger*, 1877; *D–I*, *based upon Egerod*, 1952.)

ing of the lid portion of the cyst wall (Fig. 65*A–B*). A thallus is homothallic in the sense that it produces gametes of both sexes, but it is thought[3] that all gametes from any one cyst are of the same sex. Instances of parthenogenesis have been noted among gametes that have not fused with another gamete to form a zygote.

CLASS 2. CHAROPHYCEAE

The Charophyceae, familiarly known as stoneworts, have an erect branched thallus differentiated into a regular succession of nodes and internodes. Each node bears a whorl of branches of limited growth (the "leaves"), but branches capable of unlimited growth may arise axillary to the "leaves." Many members of the class are heavily calcified. Sexual reproduction is oögamous. The oögonia are one-celled, surrounded by a

[1] K. L. Schulze, 1939. [2] Hammerling, 1934. [3] Hammerling, 1934, 1944.

sheath of sterile cells, and are always borne upon the "leaves." The antheridia are one-celled, united in uniseriate branched filaments, of which several are surrounded by a common spherical envelope composed of eight cells. Envelopes surrounding antheridia are always borne on the "leaves."

Classification. All members of the class are placed in a single order, the *Charales;* and this, in turn, is divided into four families. All living genera are referred to the family *Characeae* with 6 genera and about 250 living species. There are also Characeae known only as fossils. The remaining families are all fossil. The calcareous material accumulating around a thallus may remain intact after death of a plant and decay of the organic remains, and many fossil stoneworts have been described from such calcareous casts. The structure of the fructifications, especially of the female fructification, is so distinctive that there is no doubt concerning the nature of these fossil plants.

Charales are known from as far back as the Devonian.[1] Female fructifications of some genera have the enveloping cells arranged in a spiral; those of other genera are not arranged in this manner. The Characeae, the family to which all present-day charophytes belong, differ from other families in that the enveloping cells of a female fructification are in a left-hand spiral. This family is known from as far back as the Upper Carboniferous (Pennsylvanian). Another family, the Trochiliscaceae, also has a spirally twisted envelope, but one twisted to the right. Members of this family are known only from the Lower Carboniferous (the Mississippian) and from the Devonian.

Occurrence. Most present-day stoneworts grow submerged in fresh water and upon muddy or sandy bottoms of pools and ponds. A few species grow in brackish water. When growing in fresh-water ponds the Charophyceae frequently are in extensive subaquatic meadows that extend to a considerable distance below the surface of the water. The stoneworts thrive best in clear hard waters, but aerated water is not essential. Many species, especially those of *Chara*, become encrusted with lime, and the continued presence of the alga from year to year may result in the deposition of considerable marl upon the bottom of the pond or lake.

Vegetative Structure. The thallus of Charophyceae is an erect branched axis attached to the substratum by multicellular rhizoids. The rhizoids are uniseriately branched, and with or without a differentiation into nodes and internodes (Fig. 71*F*). The axis always has an *Equisteum*-like differentiation into nodes and internodes (Fig. 66*A*). Each node bears a whorl of several branches (the "leaves") that cease to grow after they have attained a certain length. The leaves may be simple or branched, and with or without a differentiation into nodes and internodes.

[1] Peck, 1946.

In some genera, as *Nitella*, an internode of the axis consists of a single cell, many times longer than broad. In other genera, as *Chara*, a majority of the species have each internodal cell ensheathed (corticated) by a layer of vertically elongated cells of much smaller diameter. The ensheathing layer (**cortex**) of an internode is always one cell in thickness.

Terminal growth of an axis is initiated by a single dome-shaped **apical cell** which cuts off derivatives at its posterior face (Fig. 66*B*). Each derivative cut off by an apical cell divides transversely into two daughter

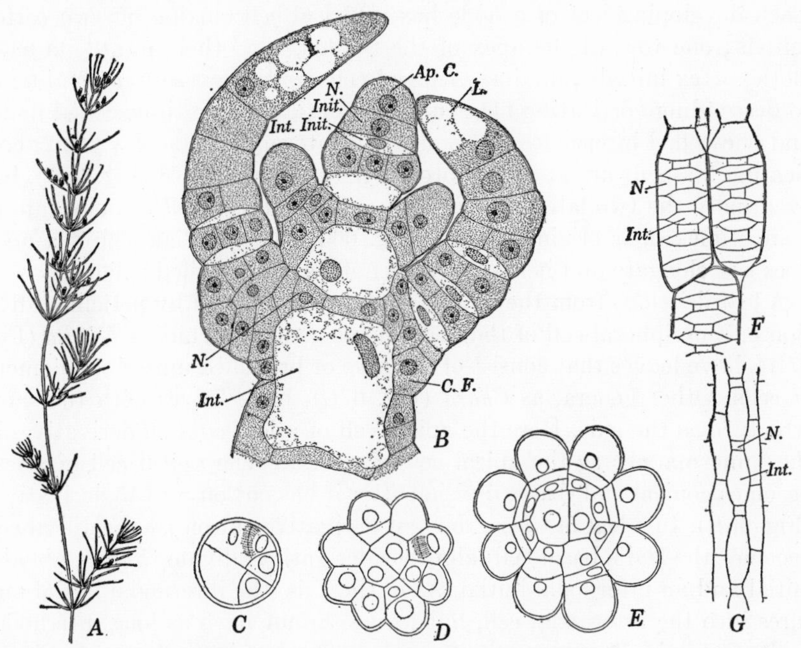

FIG. 66. *Chara* sp. *A*, thallus. *B*, vertical section of thallus apex. *C–E*, transverse sections of second, third, and fourth nodes. *F*, young corticating filaments. *G*, portion of a mature corticating filament. (*Ap. C.*, apical cell; *C.F.*, corticating filament; *Int.*, internode; *Int. Init.*, internodal initial; *L.*, leaf; *N.*, node; *N. Init.*, nodal initial.) (*A*, × ⅔; *B*, × 210; *C–F*, × 145; *G*, × 105.)

cells. The upper daughter cell is the **nodal initial** and the lower is the **internodal initial.** The internodal initial remains undivided, elongates to many times its original length, and matures into the single axial cell comprising an internode. The nodal initial divides vertically and asymmetrically into two daughter cells that also divide vertically and in a plane intersecting the first plane of division (Fig. 66*C*). Succeeding divisions are also vertical and in planes intersecting the preceding plane of division.[1] The nodal tissue produced by these divisions consists of two cen-

[1] Giesenhagen, 1896, 1897, 1899.

tral cells surrounded by a ring of 6 to 20 peripheral cells (Fig. 66*D*). The central cells may remain undivided or may divide vertically two or three times. All the peripheral cells divide periclinally. Of the two cells produced by periclinal division of a peripheral cell, the outer is the initial of a leaf, and the inner contributes to the tissue of the node. The inner cell contributing to tissue of the node may remain undivided or it may divide vertically (Fig. 66*E*).

Among species with corticated internodes, half of the corticating tissue is derived from the node above, and the other half from the node below. Each developing leaf of a node has its basal cell cutting off two **cortex initials**; one toward the apex of the thallus, the other toward its base. Both cortex initials function as apical cells and give rise to ascending or to descending corticating filaments differentiated into three-celled nodes and one-celled internodes. All nodal and internodal cells of a young corticating filament are at first approximately the same size (Fig. 66*F*), but eventually the two lateral nodal cells and the internodal cell elongate to many times their original length (Fig. 66*G*). The median cell of a node does not elongate and it may or may not form one-celled spines.

A leaf develops from the outer daughter cell formed by periclinal division of a peripheral cell of the node. Some genera, including *Nitella* (Fig. 67*A*), have leaves that consist of a simple or branched uniseriate filament of cells. Other genera, as *Chara* (Fig. 67*C*), have leaves with the same structure as the axis. Here the apical cell of a leaf cuts off derivatives in the same manner as the apical cell of an axis. The apical cell of a leaf becomes conical and ceases division after it has cut off 5 to 15 derivatives (Fig. 66*B*). In a leaf of *Chara* the first derivative cut off by the apical cell becomes the leaf's basal cell; all other derivatives divide to form a nodal initial and an internodal initial. As in the axis, the internodal initial matures into the internodal cell, but leaves do not have as long internodes as does an axis. Development of the node of a leaf is similar to that in an axis, except that there is but one central cell. Peripheral cells at the node of a leaf never give rise to leaves, but they may mature into one-celled spine-like structures. A node of a leaf may form corticating tissue in the same manner as does the node of an axis, or the cortex initials of a leaf may elongate without dividing.

Cell Structure. Cells near a branch apex are without conspicuous vacuoles and are uninucleate. Greatly enlarged cells of mature regions, as those of an internode, have a large central vacuole and many have a few large irregularly shaped nuclei because of nuclear division by constriction[1] (amitosis). The cytoplasm external to the central vacuole contains many small ellipsoidal chloroplasts that lie in longitudinal, spirally

[1] Sundaralingam, 1948.

twisted, parallel series. The portion of the cytoplasm next to the central vacuole streams continuously in a longitudinal direction, and there are ascending and descending longitudinal streams laterally separated from one another by a motionless streak of cytoplasm without chloroplasts.

Asexual Reproduction. None of the Charales produces zoospores, but many of them regularly produce asexual reproductive bodies of a vegetative nature. Vegetative propagation may be effected by: (1) star-shaped aggregates of cell developed from the lower nodes, and frequently called **amylum stars** because they are densely filled with starch; (2) bulbils developed upon rhizoids; and (3) protonema-like outgrowths from a node.

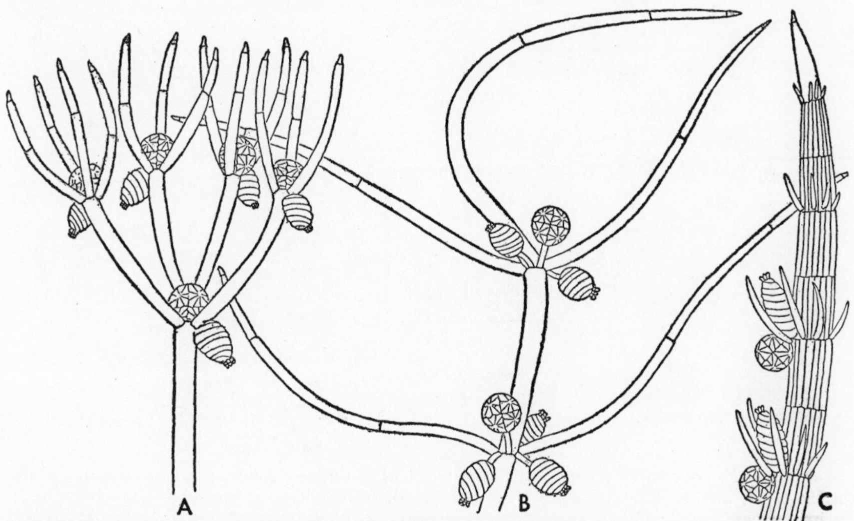

FIG. 67. Fertile leaves of Characeae. *A*, *Nitella gracilis* (J. E. Smith) C.A.Ag. *B*, *Tolypella prolifera* (Ziz.) van Leonh. *C*, *Chara intermedia* A.Br.

Sexual Reproduction. All genera reproduce sexually and oögamously. The male and female fructifications are usually called, respectively, antheridia and oögonia; but these names are inappropriate because the structures so designated include both a sex organ (or organs) and an enveloping multicellular sheath derived from cells below the sex organ. According to the old terminology,[1] the male fructification is a **globule** and the female is a **nucule.** These names are more appropriate since they do not imply that the entire fructification is a sex organ.

The vast majority of species are homothallic, and only relatively few are heterothallic. Globules and nucules are borne on the nodes of leaves. Homothallic species bear the two at the same node and the manner in which they are borne is characteristic of a genus. There may be only one

[1] Sachs, 1875.

globule and one nucule at a node, and regularly with the globule above the nucule as in *Nitella* (Fig. 67*A*), or regularly with the nucule above the globule as in *Chara* (Fig. 67*C*). Leaf nodes of other genera have a single organ of one kind adjoined by more than one reproductive organ of the other kind. Examples of this are *Tolypella* where several nucules flank a single globule (Fig. 67*B*) or *Lychnothamnus* where a single nucule is flanked on either side by a globule.

Chara may be taken as illustrative of the manner in which the reproductive organs develop. Here, a single superficial nodal cell on the adaxial side of a leaf ultimately gives rise to both the globule and the nucule

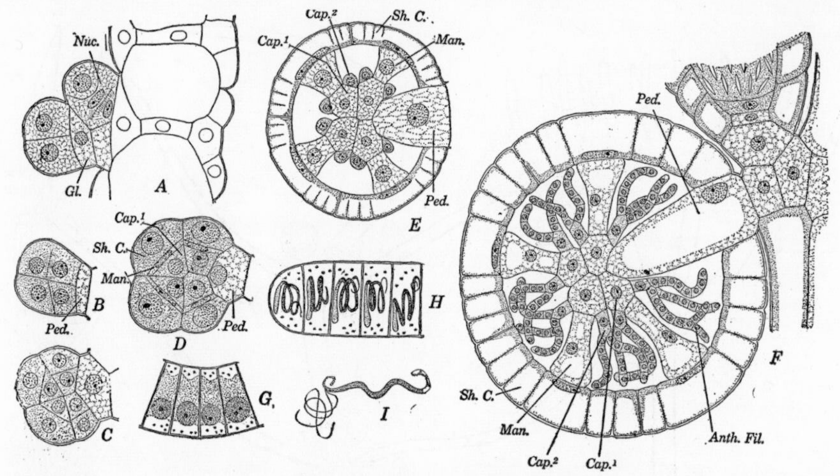

Fig. 68. *A–F*, successive stages in development of globule of *Chara* sp. *G–I*, *Chara foetida* A.Br. *G–H*, antheridial filaments. *I*, antherozoid. (*Anth. Fil.*, antheridial filament; *Cap.*[1], primary capitulum; *Cap.*[2], secondary capitulum; *Gl.*, globule; *Man.*, manubrium; *Nuc.*, nucule; *Ped.*, pedicel; *Sh. C.*, shield cell.) (*G–I, after Belajeff*, 1894.) (*A–D*, × 210; *E–F*, × 145; *G–H*, × 575; *I*, × 290.)

borne at a node. One cell derived from this superficial cell is the initial cell of the globule; another is the initial cell of the nucule.

Development of a globule begins with a transverse division of the initial cell. The lower daughter cell does not divide again and becomes the **pedicel cell** of the globule. The upper daughter cell forms four quadrately arranged cells (Fig. 68*A*) by two successive divisions, and each of these four cells then divides transversely (Fig. 68*B*). Each cell of the octad divides periclinally (Fig. 68*C*) and the eight outer daughter cells thus produced also divide periclinally. The outer of the three cells derived from each octad cell is a **shield cell,** the median is a handle cell or **manubrium** and the innermost is a **primary capitulum cell** (Fig. 68*D*). Maturing shield cells expand laterally and as a result cavities appear within the developing globule. The manubria enlarge radially as the cavities enlarge, but the primary capitulum cells remain apposed to one another at the center of the globule (Fig. 68*E*). There is also an upward enlargement of the pedicel cell toward the interior of the globule (Fig. 68*E–F*). The outer periclinal wall of each maturing shield cell develops radial ingrowths which incompletely divide them into a number of compartments. Hence the outer layer of a maturing globule seems to be many cells in perimeter when viewed in cross section (Fig. 68*F*). Mature globules are a bright orange or red because of a change in color of chloroplasts within the shield cells.

Each primary capitulum cell within a globule cuts off six **secondary capitulum cells** and these may or may not cut off tertiary or quaternary capitulum cells.[1] The secondary capitulum cells usually cut off the initials of **antheridial filaments,** but such initials may also be produced upon primary, tertiary, or quaternary capitulum cells. An antheridial initial develops into an antheridial filament that may be branched or unbranched (Fig. 68*F*). The number of cells in a filament varies greatly, and even in the same species it may range from 5 to 50 or more.[1] Each cell of a fully developed antheridial filament is an **antheridium** whose protoplast matures into a single **antherozoid.** The nucleus of a metamorphosing protoplast moves toward the side wall, elongates, and becomes spirally coiled (Fig. 68*G–H*). Meanwhile, there has been a differentiation of a spirally coiled blepharoplast that causes a differentiation of the two long flagella borne just back from the anterior end of the coiled antherozoid (Fig. 68*I*). When the antherozoids are mature, the shield cells of a globule separate from each other and expose the antheridial filaments and the manubrium to which they are attached. A manubrium with its attached capitular cells and antheridial filaments resembles a many-thonged whip. Soon after the antheridial filaments are exposed, there is an escape of each antherozoid through a pore in the antheridial wall. Liberation of antherozoids generally takes place in the morning and their swarming may continue until evening.

A globule has been interpreted[2] as a metamorphosed branch in which the terminal cell divides into octants. Each octant consists of a one-celled basal node (the shield cell), an internode (the manubrium), and an upper nodal cell (the primary capitular cell). The filamentous outgrowths (antheridial filaments) from the upper node are not differentiated into nodes and internodes.

The initial cell of a nucule divides to form a row of three cells. The terminal cell of the row is an **oögonial mother cell** which eventually elongates vertically and divides transversely into a short **stalk cell** and a vertically elongate **oögonium** containing a single **egg** (Fig. 69*E*). The

[1] Karling, 1927. [2] Goebel, 1930.

lower cell of the row does not divide and enlarges to form the **pedicel** subtending the nucule (Fig. 69*B–F*). The median cell of the row of three divides vertically to form five **sheath initials** encircling a single **central cell.** Even before vertical elongation of the oögonial mother cell, there is an upgrowth of the five sheath initials so that they encircle the oögonial mother cell (Fig. 69*C*). Each of the five sheath initials soon divides transversely. The five cells of the upper tier are the **corona cells** of a nucule and the five cells of the lower tier are the **tube cells** (Fig. 69*E–F*). The corona cells elongate but little and mature into the **corona** capping a mature nucule. The tube cells elongate to many times their original length

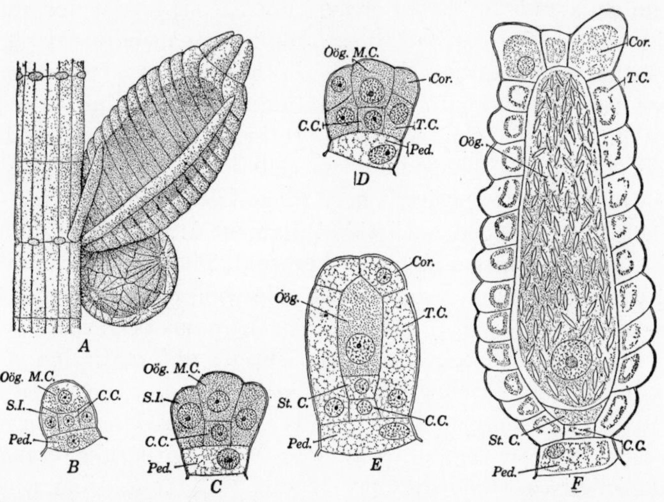

FIG. 69. *Chara* sp. *A*, portion of a leaf bearing a mature nucule and globule. *B–F*, successive stages in development of a nucule. (*Cor.*, corona; *C.C.*, central cell; *Oög.*, oögonium; *Oög.M.C.*, oögonial mother cell; *Ped.*, pedicel; *S.I.*, sheath initial; *St.C.*, stalk cell; *T.C.*, tube cell.) (*A*, × 50; *B–E*, × 210; *F*, × 145.)

and become spirally twisted about the oögonium (Fig. 69*A*). In certain genera, including *Nitella*, the corona consists of two tiers and has five cells in each tier.

When a nucule is mature the spirally twisted tube cells separate from one another just below the corona to make five small angular slits[1] (Fig. 70*A*). Antherozoids swim through these openings in the sheath of a nucule, swim to the oögonium, and penetrate its gelatinized wall. Male gamete nuclei have been observed[2] within the egg of *Nitella*, and it is thought that in *Chara* there is the same union of one of them with the nucleus at the base of the egg.

The Zygote and Its Germination. The zygote secretes a thick wall and the inner periclinal walls of tube cells also become thickened (Fig. 70*B*).

[1] DeBary, 1871. [2] Goetz, 1899.

Other portions of walls of a sheath decay, leaving the persisting portions of walls of tube cells projecting like the threads of a screw (Fig. 70*C*). The zygote, with the surrounding remains of the sheath, falls to the bottom of the pool and there germinates after a period of weeks or months. Prior to germination, the zygote nucleus migrates to the apical pole of a zygote and there divides[1] into four daughter nuclei (Fig. 71*A*). This division into four nuclei suggests that division is meiotic. Evidence confirming this supposition is found in the absence of meiosis prior to the formation of gametes.[2] According to such an interpretation the thallus of

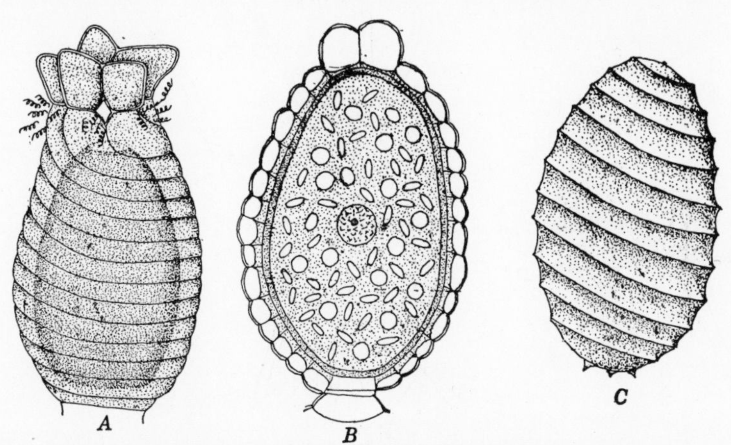

FIG. 70. *A*, entrance of antherozoids into nucule of *Chara foetida* A.Br. *B–C*, *Chara* sp. *B*, longitudinal section of nucule after formation of zygote wall and thickening of inner face of walls of tube cells. *C*, surface view of nucule after disappearance of corona and outer face of walls of tube cells. (*A*, *after DeBary*, 1871.) (*A*, × 70; *B–C*, × 85.)

Charales is gametophytic and the zygote is the only diploid cell in the life cycle.

Germination begins with an asymmetrical division of the zygote into a small lenticular distal cell with one nucleus, and a large basal cell containing the other three nuclei (Fig. 71*B*). The lenticular cell, after becoming exposed by a cracking of the zygote wall, divides vertically into a **rhizoidal initial** and a **protonematal initial** (Fig. 71*C–D*). The large three-nucleate cell remains undivided and its nuclei eventually disintegrate. The rhizoidal initial develops into a colorless filamentous **rhizoid** differentiated into nodes and internodes, and a rhizoid with a whorl of secondary rhizoids at each node.[3] The protonematal initial develops into a green filament (the **primary protonema**), also differentiated into nodes and internodes (Fig. 71*E*). Appendages produced by the lowermost node

[1] Oehlker, 1916. [2] Lindenbein, 1927; Sundaralingam, 1948.
[3] DeBary, 1875.

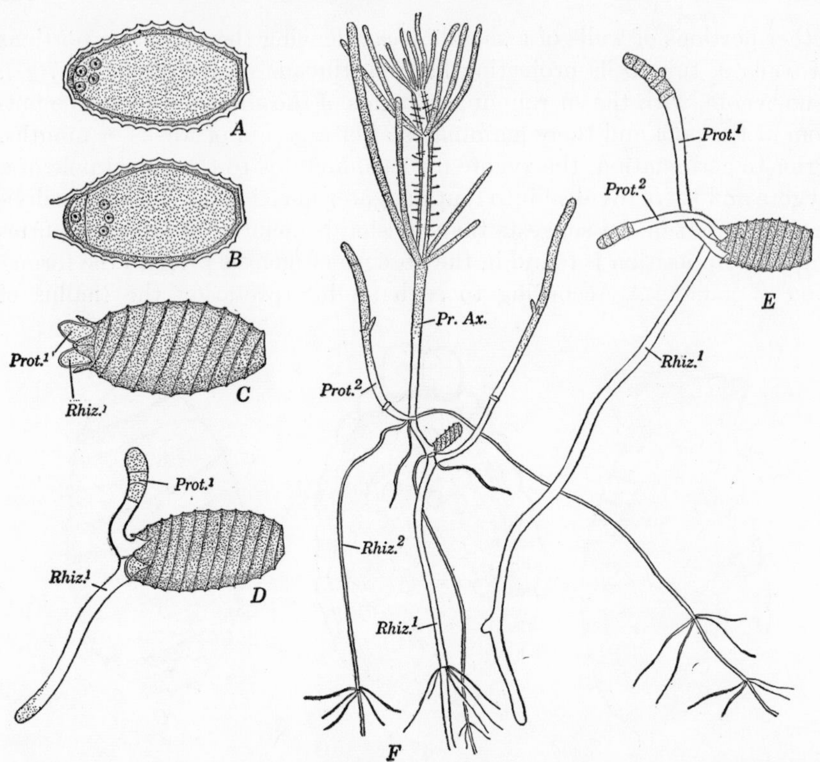

FIG. 71. *A–B*, *Chara foetida* A.Br.; *C–F*, *Chara crinata* Wallr. *A–B*, diagrams of longitudinal sections of germinating zygotes. *C–D*, surface views of germinating zygotes. *E*, germling at protonematal stage. *F*, young plant after primary axis formed by a secondary protonema has begun formation of nodes and internodes. (*Pr. Ax.*, primary axis; *Prot.*¹, primary protonema; *Prot.*², secondary protonema; *Rhiz.*¹, primary rhizoid; *Rhiz.*², secondary rhizoid.) (*A–B, based upon Oehlkers*, 1916; *C–F, after DeBary*, 1875.) (*A–B*, × 45; *C–D*, × 50; *E*, × 25; *F*, × 4.)

of a primary protonema become either rhizoids or secondary protonemata. The second node of a primary protonema bears a whorl of appendages (Fig. 71*F*). All but one of them are simple green filaments; the remaining appendage develops into a typical axis in which growth is as in an adult plant.

Bibliography

Acton, Elizabeth. **1916**. *Ann. Bot.* **30**: 379–382. 1 pl. 4 figs. [Desmidiaceae.]
Allen, C. E. **1905**. *Ber. Deutsch. Bot. Ges.* **23**: 285–292. 1 pl. [*Coleochaete.*]
Artari, A. **1892**. *Bull. Soc. Imp. Nat. Moscou N.S.* **6**: 222–263. 3 pl. [*Chlorococcum.*]
Askenasy, E. **1888**. *Ber. Deutsch. Bot. Ges.* **6**: 127–138. 1 pl. [*Pediastrum.*]
Belajeff, W. **1894**. *Flora* **79**: 1–48. 1 pl. [Spermatogenesis, *Chara.*]
Blackman, F. F. **1900**. *Ann. Bot.* **14**: 647–688. 2 figs. [Evolution of algae.]
Blackman, F. F., and A. G. Tansley. **1902**. *New Phytol.* **1**: 17–24, 47–48, 67–72, 89–96, 114–120, 133–144, 163–168, 189–192, 213–220, 233–244. [Classification of green algae.]

Bohlin, K. **1901.** Utkast till de gröna Algernas och Arkegoniaternas Fylogenie. Upsala. 43 pp.

Bold, H. C. **1931.** *Bull. Torrey Bot. Club* **57:** 577–604. 5 pl. 5 figs. [*Chlorococcum.*]

1933. *Ibid.* **60:** 241–299. 10 pl. 7 figs. [*Protosiphon.*]

Borge, O. **1894.** Über die Rhizoidenbildung bei einigen fadenförmigen Chlorophyceen. Upsala. 61 pp. 2 pl.

Børgesen, F. **1907.** *Kgl. Danske Videnskab. Selskab. Skr.* **7** ser. *Naturvidensk-Math.* Afd. 4: 340–391. 31 figs. [Ecology of *Caulerpa.*]

1913. *Dansk Bot. Arkv.* **1:** 1–158. 126 figs. [Marine algae Danish West Indies.]

1925. *Kgl. Danske Videnskab. Selskab. Skr. Biol. Meddel.* **5,** No. 3: 1–123. 49 figs. [Canary Island algae.]

1939. *Danish Scientific Investigations in Iran* **1:** 47–140. 43 figs. [Siphonocladales.]

Borzi, A. **1895.** Studi algologici. Fasc. 2. pp. 121–378. 22 pl.

Brand, F. **1901.** *Beih. Bot. Centralbl.* **10:** 481–521. 10 figs. [*Cladophora.*]

1914. *Hedwigia* **54:** 295–310. 1 fig. [*Prasiola.*]

Braun, A. **1851.** Betrachtungen über die Erscheinung der Verjüngung in der Natur. Leipzig. 363 pp. 3 pl.

Bristol, B. Muriel. **1917.** *Ann. Bot.* **31:** 107–126. 2 pl. 2 figs. [*Chlorochytrium.*]

1919. *Jour. Linn. Soc. Bot. London* **44:** 473–482. 2 pl. [*Chlorococcum.*]

1920. *Ibid.* **45:** 1–28. 3 pl. 1 fig. [*Chlorochytrium.*]

Carter, H. J. **1858.** *Ann. and Mag. Nat. Hist.* 3 ser. **2:** 237–253. 1 pl. [*Eudorina.*]

Carter, Nellie. **1919.** *Ann. Bot.* **33:** 467–478. 1 pl. 2 figs. [*Cladophora.*]

1919A. *Ibid.* **33:** 215–254. 5 pl. [Chloroplasts of desmids.]

1919B. *Ibid.* **33:** 295–304. 2 pl. 1 fig. [Chloroplasts of desmids.]

1919C. *New Phytol.* **18:** 177–186. 3 figs. [*Characium.*]

1920. *Ann. Bot.* **34:** 265–285. 4 pl. 2 figs. [Chloroplasts of desmids.]

1920A. *Ibid.* **34:** 303–319. 3 pl. [Chloroplasts of desmids.]

1923. Vol. 5 of W. West and G. S. West, a monograph of the British Desmidiaceae. London. 300 pp. 39 pl.

Chadefaud, M. **1945.** *Bull. Soc. Bot. France* **92:** 47–50. [Vaucheriaceae.]

Chadefaud, M., and H. Rossat. **1947.** *Compt. Rend. Acad. Sci. Paris* **225:** 765–766. 2 figs. [*Dichotosiphon.*]

Chodat, R. **1898.** *Bull. Herb. Boiss.* **6:** 431–476. 2 pl. 15 figs. [*Coleochaete.*]

1902. *Matér. pour la Flore Crypt. Suisse* **1,** Fasc. 3: 1–373. 264 figs. [Algae of Switzerland.]

1913. *Ibid.* **4,** Fasc. 2: 1–266. 9 pl. 201 figs. [*Trebouxia.*]

Cholnoky, B. von. **1930.** *Zeitschr. Bot.* **22:** 545–585. 42 figs. [*Cladophora.*]

1932. *Beih. Bot. Centralbl.* **49:** 221–238. 27 figs. [*Ulothrix.*]

Cienkowski, L. **1876.** *Bull. Acad. Imp. Sci. St. Pétersbourg* **21:** 531–572. 2 pl. [*Cylindrocapsa.*]

Cohn, F. **1856.** *Ann. Sci. Nat. Bot.* 4 ser. **5:** 187–208. 2 pl. [*Sphaeroplea.*]

1872. *Beitr. Biol. Pflanzen* **1**[2]: 87–106. 1 pl. [*Chlorochytrium.*]

Conrad, W. **1913.** *Rec. Inst. Leo Errera* **9:** 321–343. 13 figs. [*Eudorina.*]

Czempyrek, Hanna. **1930.** *Arch. Protistenk.* **72:** 433–452. 10 figs. [*Cladophora.*]

Czurda, V. **1928.** *Beih. Bot. Centralbl.* **45:** 97–270. [Pyrenoid.]

Davis, B. M. **1908.** *Ann. Bot.* **22:** 1–20. 2 pl. [*Derbesia.*]

DeBary, A. **1858.** Untersuchungen über die Familie der Conjugaten. Leipzig. 91 pp. 8 pl.

1871. *Monatsber. Akad. Wiss. Berlin* **1871:** 227–240. 1 pl. [Fertilization in *Chara.*]

1875. *Bot. Zeitg.* **33:** 377–385, 393–401, 409–420. 2 pl. [Germination in *Chara.*]

DeBary, A., and E. Strasburger. **1877.** *Ibid.* **35:** 713–743, 745–758. 1 pl. 1 fig. [*Acetabularia.*]

Debski, B. **1898.** *Jahrb. Wiss. Bot.* **32:** 635–670. 2 pl. [Nucule of *Chara.*]
Delf, E. Marion. **1912.** *Ann. Bot.* **26:** 403–408. 1 pl. 3 figs. [*Ulva.*]
Dodel, A. **1876.** *Jahrb. Wiss. Bot.* **10:** 417–550. 8 pl. [*Ulothrix.*]
Dostal, R. **1928.** *Planta* **5:** 622–634. 3 figs. [*Caulerpa.*]
1929. *Ibid.* **8:** 84–139. 16 figs. [*Caulerpa.*]
Egerod, Lois E. **1952.** *Univ. Calif. Publ. Bot.* **25:** 325–454. 13 pl. 23 figs. [Siphonocladales, Dasycladales.]
Elliott, A. M. **1934.** *Arch. Protistenk.* **82:** 250–272. 2 pl. 7 figs. [Neuromotor apparatus.]
Entz, G. **1918.** *Ibid.* **38:** 324–354. 2 pl. 5 figs. [Neuromotor apparatus.]
Ernst, A. **1902.** *Beih. Bot. Centralbl.* **13:** 115–148. 5 pl. [*Dichotomosiphon.*]
1904. *Ibid.* **16:** 199–236. 3 pl. [Codiaceae.]
1931. *Planta.* **15:** 459–494. 1 pl. [*Caulerpa.*]
Escoyez, E. **1907.** *Cellule* **24:** 355–366. 1 pl. [*Zygnema.*]
Famintzin, A. **1860.** *Bot. Zeitg.* **18:** 341–344. 1 pl. [*Valonia.*]
1914. *Ber. Deutsch. Bot. Ges.* **32:** 218–222. [*Trebouxia.*]
Famintzin, A., and J. Boranetzky. **1867.** *Ann. Sci. Nat. Bot.* 5 ser. **8:** 137–144. 1 pl. [*Trebouxia.*]
Feldmann, J. **1938.** *Rev. Gen. Bot.* **50:** 571–598. 5 figs. [Siphonocladales.]
1946. *Compt. Rend. Acad. Sci. Paris* **222:** 752–753 [Chloroplasts of *Dichotomosiphon.*]
1950. *Ibid.* **230:** 322–323. [*Halicystis.*]
Fischer, A. **1884.** *Jahrb. Wiss. Bot.* **14:** 135–184. 2 pl. [Desmidiaceae.]
Føyn, B. **1929.** *Ber. Deutsch. Bot. Ges.* **47:** 495–506. 2 figs. [*Cladophora, Ulva.*]
1934. *Arch. Protistenk.* **83:** 1–56. 5 pl. 18 figs. [*Cladophora.*]
1934A. *Ibid.* **83:** 154–177. 13 figs. [*Ulva.*]
Fritsch, F. E. **1902.** *Ann. Bot.* **16:** 412–417. 1 fig. [Germination of zoospore, *Oedogonium.*]
1902A. *Ibid.* **16:** 467–485. 3 figs. [Dwarf males, *Oedogonium.*]
1903. *Beih. Bot. Centralbl.* **13:** 368–387. 2 pl. [*Stigeoclonium.*]
1904. *Ann. Bot.* **18:** 648–653. 1 fig. [Germination of zoospore, *Oedogonium.*]
1916. *New Phytol.* **15:** 233–250. 2 figs. [Evolution of algae.]
1929. *Ann. Bot.* **43:** 1–26. 8 figs. [*Sphaeroplea.*]
1935. The structure and reproduction of the algae. Cambridge. Vol. 1. 791 pp. 243 figs.
1944. *Bot. Rev.* **10:** 233–277. [Classification of algae.]
1947. *Jour. Indian Bot. Soc. Iyengar Commemorative Vol.* Pp. 28–48. 5 figs. [Siphonocladales.]
Fritsch, F. E., and Florence Rich. **1924.** *Trans. Roy. Soc. S. Africa* **11:** 297–398. 31 figs. [Algae from Natal.]
Gardner, N. L. **1917.** *Univ. Calif. Publ. Bot.* **6:** 377–416. 5 pl. [*Chlorochytrium.*]
Gay, F. **1891.** Recherches sur le développement et la classification de quelques algues vertes. Paris. 116 pp. 15 pl.
Geitler, L. **1923.** *Oesterr. Bot. Zeitschr.* **72:** 76–83. 5 figs. [*Trentepohlia.*]
1926. *Arch. Protistenk.* **56:** 128–144. 8 figs. [Pyrenoid.]
1931. *Biol. Zentralbl.* **51:** 173–187. 5 figs. [*Tetraspora.*]
Giesenhagen, K. **1896.** *Flora* **82:** 381–433. 1 pl. 25 figs. [Thallus structure, *Chara.*]
1897. *Ibid.* **83:** 160–202. 1 pl. 17 figs. [Thallus structure, *Chara.*]
1898. *Ibid.* **85:** 19–64. 2 pl. 17 figs. [Thallus structure, *Chara.*]
Gilbert, E. M. **1915.** *Science* N.S. **41:** 183. [*Sphaeroplea.*]
Gobi, C. **1871.** *Bull. Acad. Imp. Sci. St. Pétersbourg Mélanges Biol.* **8:** 339–362. 1 pl. [*Trentepohlia.*]
Godward, M. B. **1942.** *New Phytol.* **41:** 293–300. 2 pl. 6 figs. [*Stigeoclonium.*]

Goebel, K. **1882.** Grundzüge der Systematik und speciellen Pflanzenmorphologie. Leipzig, 550 pp. 407 figs.
1930. Flora **124:** 491–498. 3 figs. [Globules of *Chara.*]
Goetz, G. **1899.** *Bot. Zeitg.* **57:** 1–13. 1 pl. 3 figs. [Nucule of *Chara.*]
Golenkin, M. **1899.** *Bull. Soc. Imp. Nat. Moscou* **13:** 343–361. 1 pl. [*Sphaeroplea.*]
Goroschankin, J. **1905.** *Flora* **94:** 420–423. 1 pl. [*Chlamydomonas.*]
Griggs, R. F. **1912.** *Bot. Gaz.* **53:** 127–173. 6 pl. [Endosphaeraceae.]
Gross, Ilse. **1931.** *Arch. Protistenk.* **73:** 206–234. 20 figs. [*Ulothrix.*]
Gussewa, K. A. **1927.** *Arch. Russ. Protistol.* **6:** 31–48. 1 pl. 2 figs. [*Oedogonium.*]
1930. *Planta* **12:** 293–326. 54 figs. [*Oedogonium.*]
Hammerling, J. **1931.** *Biol. Zentralbl.* **51:** 633–647. 6 figs. [*Acetabularia.*]
1934. *Arch. Protistenk.* **83:** 57–97. 3 figs. [*Acetabularia.*]
1934A. *Biol. Zentralbl.* **54:** 650–665. 6 figs. [*Acetabularia.*]
1934B. *Roux' Arch. f. Entwicklungsmech.* **131:** 1–81. 30 figs. [*Acetabularia.*]
1934C. *Ibid.* **132:** 424–462. 10 figs. [*Acetabularia.*]
1936. *Zool. Jahrb. Abt. Allg. Zool.* **56:** 440–486. 5 figs. [*Acetabularia.*]
1939. *Biol. Zentralbl.* **59:** 158–193. 12 figs. [*Acetabularia.*]
1944. *Arch. Protistenk.* **97:** 7–56. 1 pl. [Dasycladales.]
Harper, R. A. **1916.** *Mem. New York Bot. Garden* **6:** 91–104. 2 figs. [*Pediastrum.*]
1918. *Proc. Amer. Phil. Soc.* **57:** 375–439. 2 pl. 35 figs. [*Pediastrum.*]
1918A. *Mem. Torrey Bot. Club* **17:** 210–240. 27 figs. [*Pediastrum.*]
Hartmann, M. **1921.** *Arch. Protistenk.* **43:** 223–286. 2 pl. 7 figs. [*Eudorina.*]
1929. *Ber. Deutsch. Bot. Ges.* **47:** 485–494. 1 fig. [Ulvaceae, Cladophoraceae.]
Hartshorne, J. E. **1953.** *New Phytol.* **52:** 292–297. 1 fig. [Eyespot.]
Hazen, T. E. **1902.** *Mem. Torrey Bot. Club* **11:** 135–250. 23 pl. [Ulotrichales.]
Heinricher, E. **1883.** *Ber. Deutsch. Bot. Ges.* **1:** 433–450. 1 pl. [*Sphaeroplea.*]
Hirn, K. E. **1900.** *Acta. Soc. Sci. Fennicae* **27:** 1–394. 64 pl. 27 figs. [*Oedogonium.*]
Höfler, K. **1926.** *Sitzungsber. Akad. Wiss. Wien* (Math.-Nat. Kl.) **135[1]:** 103–166. 1 pl. [Cell wall, Desmidiaceae.]
Hollenberg, G. J. **1935.** *Amer. Jour. Bot.* **22:** 782–812. 4 pl. 5 figs. [*Halicystis.*]
1936. *Ibid.* **23:** 1–3. 1 fig. [*Halicystis.*]
Iyengar, M. O. P. **1923.** *Jour. Indian Bot. Soc.* **2:** 1–9. 4 pl. [Zygnemataceae.]
1933. *Jour. Linn. Soc. Bot. London* **49:** 323–373. 1 pl. 10 figs. [Volvocaceae.]
1933A. *Jour. Indian Bot. Soc.* **12:** 325. [*Caulerpa.*]
1937. *Ibid.* **16:** 111–118. 1 pl. 15 figs. [*Eudorina.*]
1939. *Current Science* **8:** 216–217. 5 figs. [*Cylindrocapsa.*]
1940. *Jour. Indian Bot. Soc.* **18:** 191–194. 9 figs. [*Caulerpa.*]
1951. Chlorophyta. In G. M. Smith (editor), Manual of Phycology. Waltham, Mass. pp. 21–67. 17 figs.
Iyengar, M. O. P., and K. R. Ramanathan. **1940.** *Jour. Indian Bot. Soc.* **19:** 175–176. [Siphonocladales.]
1941. *Ibid.* **20:** 157–159. 1 pl. 9 figs. [Siphonocladales.]
Jaag, O. **1929.** Recherches expérimentales sur les gonidies des lichens appartenant aux genres Parmelia et Cladonia. Geneva. 128 pp. 6 pl. 5 figs.
Janet, C. **1912.** Le Volvox. Limoges. 151 pp. 15 figs.
1923. Le Volvox. Troisième mémoire. Paris. 179 pp. 17 pl.
Jorde, Ingerid. **1933.** *Ibid.* **73:** 1–19. 1 pl. 5 figs. [Life cycles.]
Jörstadt, I. **1919.** *Nyt. Mag. Naturvidenskab.* **51:** 61–68. 1 pl. [*Ulothrix.*]
Juller, E. **1937.** *Arch. Protistenk.* **89:** 55–93. 21 figs. [*Stigeoclonium.*]
Jurányi, L. **1873.** *Jahrb. Wiss. Bot.* **9:** 1–35, 3 pl. [*Oedogonium.*]
Karling, J. S. **1927.** *Bull. Torrey Bot. Club* **54:** 187–230. 5 pl. 13 figs. [Globule of *Chara.*]

Karsten, G. **1891.** *Ann. Jard. Bot. Buitenzorg* **10:** 1–66. 6 pl. [*Trentepohlia.*]
Kater, J. M. **1925.** *Biol. Bull.* **49:** 213–236. 3 pl. [Neuromotor apparatus.]
1929. *Univ. Calif. Pul. Zool.* **33:** 125–168. 6 pl. 7 figs. [*Chlamydomonas.*]
Kauffmann, H. **1914.** *Zeitschr. Bot.* **6:** 721–774. 1 pl. 4 figs. [Mesotaeniaceae.]
Kirchner, O. **1883.** *Beitr. Biol. Pflanzen* **3:** 95–103. 1 pl. [*Volvox.*]
Klebahn, H. **1891.** *Jahrb. Wiss. Bot.* **22:** 415–443. 2 pl. [Desmidiaceae.]
1892. *Ibid.* **24:** 235–267. 1 pl. [Gametogenesis, *Oedogonium.*]
1899. *Schwendener Festschr.* pp. 81–103. 1 pl. [*Sphaeroplea.*]
Klebs, G. **1881.** *Bot. Zeitg.* **39:** 249–257. 265–272, 281–290, 297–308, 313–319, 329–336. 2 pl. [Endosphaeraceae.]
1885. *Biol. Centralbl.* **5:** 353–367. [Desmidiaceae.]
1895. Die Bedingungen der Fortpflanzung bei einigen Algen und Pilzen. Jena. 543 pp. 3 pl. 15 figs.
Klyver, F. D. **1929.** *Arch. Protistenk.* **66:** 290–296. 1 pl. [*Tetraspora.*]
Kol, E. **1927.** *Folia Cryptogamica Szeged* **1:** 435–442. 2 pl. [Desmidiaceae.]
Kornmann, P. **1938.** *Planta* **28:** 464–470. 4 figs. [*Halicystis.*]
Korshikov, A. A. **1923.** *Arch. Russ. Protistol.* **2:** 179–194. 1 pl. [*Pandorina.*]
1926. *Arch. Protistenk.* **55:** 439–503. 9 pl. 15 figs. [Tetrasporales.]
1927. *Arch. Russ. Protistol.* **6:** 71–82. 2 pl. 4 figs. [*Schizomeris.*]
Kraskovits, G. **1905.** *Sitzungsber. Akad. Wiss. Wien.* (Math.-Nat. Kl.) **114**[1]: 237–274. 3 pl. 11 figs. [Cell division, *Oedogonium.*]
Kretschmer, Hirta. **1930.** *Arch. Protistenk.* **71:** 101–138. 2 pl. 16 figs. [*Oedogonium.*]
Kuckuck, P. **1907.** *Bot. Zeitg.* **65:** 139–185. 2 pl. 25 figs. [*Halicystis, Valonia.*]
Kurssanow, L. **1911.** *Flora* **104:** 65–84. 4 pl. [*Zygnema.*]
Kurssanow, L. J., and N. M. Schemakhanova. **1927.** *Arch. Russ. Protistol.* **6:** 131–146. 2 pl. 2 figs. [*Chlorochytrium.*]
Kuschakewitsch. S. **1931.** *Arch. Protistenk.* **73:** 323–330. 1 pl. 14 figs. [*Volvox.*]
Kylin, H. **1930.** *Bot. Notiser* **1930:** 417–420. [*Prasiola.*]
Lagerheim, G. **1889.** *Flora* **72:** 179–210. 2 pl. [*Microspora.*]
1892. *Ber. Deutsch. Bot. Ges.* **10:** 366–374. 1 pl. [*Prasiola.*]
Lambert, F. D. **1910.** *Tufts College Studies.* Scientific ser. **3:** 61–68. 1 pl. [*Coleochaete.*]
1930. *Zeitschr. Bot.* **23:** 227–244. 4 figs. [Tetrasporales.]
Lander, Caroline A. **1929.** *Bot. Gaz.* **87:** 431–436. 1 pl. [*Volvox.*]
Lewis, I. F. **1907.** *Johns Hopkins Univ. Circ.* **195:** 201–209 (29–30). [*Coleochaete.*]
Lind, Edna M. **1932.** *Ann. Bot.* **46:** 711–725. 2 pl. 12 figs. [*Ulothrix.*]
Lindenbein, W. **1927.** *Planta* **4:** 437–466. 22 figs. [*Chara.*]
List, Hedwig. **1930.** *Arch. Protistenk.* **72:** 453–481. 7 figs. [*Cladophora.*]
Livingston, B. E. **1900.** *Bot. Gaz.* **30:** 289–317. 2 pl. [*Stigeoclonium.*]
1905. *Bull. Torrey Bot. Club* **32:** 1–34. 17 figs. [*Stigeoclonium.*]
Lütkemüller, J. **1902.** *Beitr. Biol. Pflanzen* **8:** 347–414. 3 pl. [Cell wall, Desmidiaceae.]
Lutman, B. F. **1910.** *Bot. Gaz.* **49:** 241–255. 2 pl. [Pyrenoid.]
1911. *Ibid.* **51:** 401–430. 2 pl. 1 fig. [Desmidiaceae.]
McAllister, F. **1913.** *Ann. Bot.* **27:** 681–696. 1 pl. [*Tetraspora.*]
1931. *Amer. Jour. Bot.* **18:** 838–853. 2 pl. [Cell division.]
Mainx, F. **1927.** *Arch. Protistenk.* **57:** 1–13. 1 pl. 1 fig. [Cell division.]
1929. *Ibid.* **67:** 205–214. [*Volvox.*]
1931. *Zeitschr. Bot.* **24:** 481–527. 1 pl. 13 figs. [*Oedogonium.*]
Mast, S. O. **1916.** *Jour. Exper. Zool.* **20:** 1–17, 6 figs. [Eyespot.]
1928. *Arch. Protistenk.* **60:** 197–220. 1 pl. 4 figs. [Eyespot.]
Merriam, Mabel L. **1906.** *Bot. Gaz.* **41:** 43–53. 2 pl. [*Zygnema.*]
Metzner, J. **1945.** *Bull. Torreu Bot. Club* **72:** 86–113, 121–136. 120 figs. [*Volvox.*]

Meyer, A. **1896.** *Bot. Zeitg.* **54:** 187–217. 1 pl. 7 figs. [*Volvox.*]
Meyer, K. **1906.** *Bull. Soc. Imp. Nat. Moscou* N.S. **19:** 60–84. 2 pl. [*Sphaeroplea.*]
1909. *Bot. Zeitg.* **67:** 25–43. 2 pl. 2 figs. [*Trentepohlia.*]
1913. *Ber. Deutsch. Bot. Ges.* **31:** 441–448. 1 pl. [*Microspora.*]
1936. *Bull. Soc. Nat. Moscou* **45:** 315–321. 20 figs. [*Trentepohlia.*]
1936A. *Ibid.* **45:** 425–432. 17 figs. [*Trentepohlia.*]
1936B. *Ibid.* **45:** 95–103. 43 figs. [*Trentepohlia.*]
1937. *Ibid.* **46:** 101–110. 33 figs. [*Trentepohlia.*]
1938. *Ibid.* **47:** 64–68. 11 figs. [*Trentepohlia.*]
Meyer, K. I. **1935.** *Beih. Bot. Centralbl.* **53:** 421–426 [*Pandorina, Eudorina.*]
Mirande, R. **1913.** *Ann. Sci. Nat. Bot.* 9 ser. **18:** 147–264. 47 figs. [Cell wall, Siphonales.]
Miyake, K., and H. Kunieda. **1931.** *Jour. Coll. Agr. Imp. Univ. Tokyo* **11:** 341–357. [*Ulva.*]
1937. *Cytologia* **8:** 205–207. 11 figs. [*Caulerpa.*]
Moewus, F. **1933.** *Arch. Protistenk.* **80:** 469–526. 8 figs. [*Chlamydomonas, Protosiphon.*]
1935. *Ibid.* **86:** 1–57. 5 figs. [*Protosiphon.*]
1935A. *Zeitschr. Indukt. Abstamm. u. Vererb.* **69:** 374–417. 12 figs. [Unicellular Volvocales.]
1936. *Ber. Deutsch. Bot. Ges.* **54:** (45)–(57). 1 pl. 3 figs. [*Chlamydomonas.*]
1938. *Biol. Zentralbl.* **58:** 516–536. [*Chlamydomonas.*]
1938A. *Arch. Protistenk.* **91:** 357–441. 25 figs. [*Ulva.*]
1939. *Biol. Zentralbl.* **59:** 40–58. [*Chlamydomonas.*]
1944. *Beitr. Biol. Pflanzen* **27:** 297–338. [Unicellular Volvocales.]
Morse, D. C. **1943.** *Trans. Amer. Microsc. Soc.* **62:** 24–26. [*Pandorina.*]
Oehlkers, F. **1916.** *Ber. Deutsch. Bot. Ges.* **34:** 223–227. 1 fig. [Zygote of *Chara.*]
Ohashi, H. **1930.** *Bot. Gaz.* **90:** 177–197. 3 pl. 21 figs. [*Oedogonium.*]
Oltmanns, F. **1898.** *Flora* **85:** 1–14. 2 pl. [*Coleochaete.*]
1922. Morphologie und Biologie der Algen. 2 Aufl. Bd. 1. Jena. 459 pp. 287 figs.
Otrokov, P. **1875.** *Nachtr. d. kais. Ges. d. Liebh. d. Naturw. u. Anthropol. usw.* 10 pp. (Ref. Schreiber, 1925.) [*Eudorina.*]
Owen, H. M. **1949.** *Trans. Amer. Microsc. Soc.* **68:** 261–274. 3 pl. [Structure of flagella.]
Palik, P. **1933.** *Arch. Protistenk.* **79:** 234–238, 10 figs. [*Pediastrum.*]
Papenfuss, G. F. **1951.** *Svensk. Bot. Tidsskr.* **45:** 4–11. 2 figs. [Classification of algae.]
Pascher, A. **1907.** *Bibliotheca Bot.* **15.** Heft 67: 1–116. 8 pl. [Zoospores of *Stigeoclonium.*]
1915. *Ber. Deutsch. Bot. Ges.* **33:** 427–442. 1 pl. [Amoeboid stages of zoospores.]
1916. *Ibid.* **34:** 228–242. 5 figs. [*Chlamydomonas.*]
1918. *Ibid.* **36:** 352–359. 13 figs. [Amoeboid stages of zoospores.]
1927. Volvocales. In A. Pascher, Die Süsswasserflora Deutschlands, Österreichs und der Schweiz. Heft 4. Chlorophyceae. I. 506 pp. 451 figs.
1929. *Arch. Protistenk.* **68:** 261–304. 21 figs. [Multiflagellate zoospores.]
1931. *Beih. Bot. Centralbl.* **48:** 466–480. 10 figs. [Unicellular Volvocales.]
1931A. *Jahrb. Wiss. Bot.* **75:** 551–580. 10 figs. [*Chlamydomonas.*]
1939. *Beih. Bot. Centralbl.* **59:** 188–213. 22 figs. [*Sphaeroplea.*]
Peck, R. E. **1946.** *Amer. Midland Nat.* **36:** 275–278. 6 figs. [Fossil Charophyceae.]
Peirce, G. J., and Flora A. Randolph. **1905.** *Bot. Gaz.* **40:** 321–350. 27 figs. [Zoospores, *Oedogonium.*]
Petersen, J. B. **1929.** *Bot. Tidskr.* **40:** 373–389. 1 pl. [Structure of flagella.]
Pia, J. **1920.** *Abhandl. Zool.-Bot. Ges. Wien.* **11,** Heft 2: 1–263. 8 pl. 26 figs. [Fossil Dasycladales.]
1927. Thallophyta. In M. Hirmer, Handbuch der Paläobotanik. Bd. 1. Munich. pp. 31–136. 116 figs.

Pocock, M. A. **1933.** *Ann. South African Mus.* **16:** 473–521. 13 pl. 7 figs. [*Volvox.*]
1933A. *Ibid.* **16:** 523–646. 12 pl. 10 figs. [*Volvox.*]
1937. *Proc. Linn. Soc. London* **1937:** 55–58 [*Eudorina.*]
1938. *Jour. Queckett Microsc. Club.* ser. IV. **1:** 1–25. 4 pl. 3 figs. [*Volvox.*]
Potthoff, H. **1927.** *Planta* **4:** 261–283. 1 pl. 14 figs. [Meiosis, Zygnematales.]
1928. *Ber. Deutsch. Bot. Ges.* **46:** 667–673. 3 figs. [Zygnematales.]
Powers, J. H. **1908.** *Trans. Amer. Microsc. Soc.* **28:** 141–175. 4 pl. [*Volvox.*]
Prescott, G. W. **1951.** Algae of the western Great Lakes area. Bloomfield Hills, Mich. 946 pp. 136 pl.
Pringsheim, E. G. **1937.** *Cytologia. Fujii Jubilee Volume.* Pp. 234–255. (Eyespot.)
Pringsheim, N. **1858.** *Jahrb. Wiss. Bot.* **1:** 11–81. 6 pl. [*Oedogonium.*]
1860. *Ibid.* **2:** 1–38. 6 pl. [*Coleochaete.*]
1870. *Monatsber. Akad. Wiss. Berlin* **1869:** 721–738. 1 pl. [*Pandorina.*]
1871. *Ibid.* **1871:** 240–255. 1 pl. [*Bryopsis.*]
Printz, H. **1927.** Chlorophyceae. In A. Engler and K. Prantl, Die natürlichen Pflanzenfamilien. 2d ed. Bd. 3. 463 pp. 366 figs.
Puymaly, A. de. **1922.** *Compt. Rend. Acad. Sci. Paris* **175:** 1229–1231. [*Zygnema.*]
1924. *Rev. Algologique* **1:** 107–114. [*Chlorococcum.*]
Ramanathan, K. R. **1939.** *Ann. Bot.* N.S. **3:** 375–398. 74 figs. [Ulvales.]
Rauwenhoff, N. W. P. **1887.** *Arch. Néerland. Sci. Exactes et Nat.* **22:** 91–144. 2 pl. [*Sphaeroplea.*]
Reichardt, A. **1927.** *Arch. Protistenk.* **59:** 301–338. 4 pl. 9 figs. [Endosphaeraceae.]
Rieth, A. **1952.** *Flora* **139:** 28–38. 7 figs. [*Sphaeroplea.*]
Rostafiński, J., and M. Woronin. **1877.** *Bot. Zeitg.* **35:** 649–671. 5 pl. [*Protosiphon.*]
Roy, J., and P. Bissett. **1893–1894.** *Ann. Scottish Nat. Hist.* **1893:** 106–111, 170–180, 237–245. 1 pl. **1894:** 40–46, 100–105, 167–178, 241–256. 3 pl. [Desmidiaceae.]
Sachs, J. **1875.** Text-book of botany, morphological and physiological. Translated by A. W. Bennett. Oxford. 858 pp. 461 figs.
Schaffner, J. H. **1927.** *Bull. Torrey Bot. Club* **54:** 619–629. [Dwarf males, *Oedogonium.*]
Schechner-Fries, Margarete. **1934.** *Oesterr. Bot. Zeitschr.* **83:** 241–254. 3 figs. [*Valonia.*]
Scherffel, A. **1928.** *Arch. Protistenk.* **62:** 167–176. 1 pl. 3 figs. [Desmidiaceae.]
Schiller, J. **1907.** *Sitzungsber. Akad. Wiss. Wien* (Math.-Nat. Kl.) **116**[1]**:** 1691–1716. 2 pl. [*Ulva.*]
1924. *Oesterr. Bot. Zeitschr.* **73:** 14–23. 1 pl. [*Characium.*]
Schmidt, O. C. **1923.** *Bibliotheca Bot.* **23,** Heft 91: 1–67. 44 figs. [*Codium.*]
Schreiber, E. **1925.** *Zeitschr. Bot.* **17:** 336–376. 1 pl. 2 figs. [Volvocales.]
1942. *Planta* **32:** 414–417. 1 fig. [Ulvales.]
Schröder, B. **1902.** *Verhandl. Naturh.-Med. Ver. Heidelberg* N.F. **7:** 139–196. 2 pl. [*Tetraspora.*]
Schulze, B. **1927.** *Arch. Protistenk.* **58:** 508–576. 2 pl. 28 figs. [Volvocales.]
Schulze, K. L. **1939.** *Ibid.* **92:** 179–225. 2 pl. 20 figs. [*Acetabularia.*]
Schussnig, B. **1928.** *Oesterr. Bot. Zeitschr.* **77:** 62–67. 4 figs. [*Cladophora.*]
1929. *Ibid.* **78:** 1–8. 5 figs. [*Caulerpa.*]
1929A. *Ber. Deutsch. Bot. Ges.* **47:** 266–274. [*Acetabularia.*]
1930. *Oesterr. Bot. Zeitschr.* **79:** 58–77. [Meiosis in *Codium.*]
1930A. *Ibid.* **79:** 323–332. [Nuclear cycles.]
1930B. *Ibid.* **79:** 273–278. 4 figs. [*Cladophora.*]
1930C. *Ibid.* **79:** 333–339. 4 figs. [*Acetabularia.*]
1931. *Planta* **13:** 474–528. 18 figs. [*Cladophora.*]
1938. *Ibid.* **28:** 43–59. 3 figs. [*Valonia.*]

1939. *Bot. Notiser* **1939:** 75–96. 6 figs. [*Caulerpa.*]
1950. *Svensk. Bot. Tidsskr.* **44:** 55–71. [*Codium.*]
Setchell, W. A., and N. L. Gardner. **1920.** *Univ. Calif. Publ. Bot.* **8:** 139–374. 25 pl. [Marine algae of Pacific Coast.]
Singh, R. N. **1945.** *New Phytol.* **44:** 118–129. 49 figs. [Isomorphic alternation.]
Smith, G. M. **1914.** *Arch. Protistenk.* **32:** 278–297. 2 pl. [*Scenedesmus.*]
1916. *Ann. Bot.* **30:** 459–466. 1 pl. 2 figs. [*Characium.*]
1916A. *Ibid.* **30:** 467–479. 1 pl. 4 figs. [*Pediastrum.*]
1930. Contributions to marine biology, lectures and symposia given at the Hopkins Marine Station Dec. 20–21, 1929. Stanford, Calif. Pp. 222–233. 3 figs. [*Codium, Halicystis.*]
1931. *Bull. Torrey Bot. Club* **57:** 359–370. 2 pl. [Volvocales.]
1933. The fresh-water algae of the United States. New York. 716 pp. 449 figs.
1938. Cryptogamic botany. Vol. 1. New York. 545 pp. 299 figs.
1944. *Trans. Amer. Microsc. Soc.* **63:** 265–310. 45 figs. [*Volvox.*]
1947. *Amer. Jour. Bot.* **34:** 80–87. 38 figs. [*Ulva.*]
1947A. *Jour. Indian Bot. Soc. Iyengar Commemorative Vol.* Pp. 201–208. 5 figs. [Cladophoraceae.]
1950. The fresh-water algae of the United States. 2d ed. New York. 719 pp. 559 figs.
Snow, Julia W. **1899.** *Ann. Bot.* **13:** 189–195. 1 pl. [*Protococcus.*]
Solms-Laubach, H. **1894.** *Trans. Linn. Soc. Bot.* 2 ser. **5:** 1–39. 4 pl. [*Acetabularia.*]
Spessard, E. A. **1930.** *Bot. Gaz.* **89:** 385–393. 11 figs. [Gametogenesis in *Oedogonium.*]
Steinecke, F. **1926.** *Bot. Arch.* **14:** 312–318. 23 figs. [Desmidiaceae.]
1929. *Ibid.* **24:** 391–403. 2 figs. [*Oedogonium.*]
1932. *Ibid.* **34:** 216–229. 5 figs. [*Microspora.*]
Strain, H. H. **1949.** In J. Frank and W. E. Loomis, Photosynthesis in plants. Ames, Iowa, Pp. 133–178. [Pigments.]
1951. The pigments of algae. In G. M. Smith (editor), Manual of phycology. Waltham, Mass. Pp. 243–262. [Pigments.]
Strasburger, E. **1880.** Zellbildung und Zelltheilung. 3d ed. Jena. 392 pp. 14 pl.
1892. *Histol. Beitr.* **4:** 47–158. 1 pl. [Zoospores, gametes.]
Strehlow, K. **1929.** *Zeitschr. Bot.* **21:** 625–692. 17 figs. [Volvocales.]
Strøm, K. M. **1921.** *Nyt. Mag. Naturvidenskab.* **59:** 9–11. 1 pl. (*p.p.*) [*Stigeoclonium.*]
1921A. *Ibid.* **59:** 11–12. 1 pl. (*p.p.*) [*Pediastrum.*]
Sundaralingam, V. S. **1948.** *Jour. Indian Bot. Soc. Iyengar Commemorative Vol.* Pp. 289–303. 44 figs. [Cytology of *Chara.*]
Taft, C. E. **1941.** *Trans. Amer. Microsc. Soc.* **60:** 327–328 [*Pandorina.*]
Taylor, W. R. **1928.** *Carnegie Inst. Wash. Publ.* **379:** 1–219. 37 pl. [Marine algae of Florida.]
1942. Allan Hancock Atlantic expedition. Report 2. 193 pp. 20 pl.
Thuret, G. **1850.** *Ann. Sci. Nat. Bot.* 3 ser. **14:** 214–260. 16 pl. [*Codium.*]
Tiffany, L. H. **1924.** *Ohio Jour. Sci.* **24:** 65–98. 1 pl. [Cell wall.]
1930. The Oedogoniaceae. Columbus, Ohio. 188 pp. 64 pl.
Tiffany, L. H., and E. N. Transeau. **1927.** *Trans. Amer. Microsc. Soc.* **46:** 166–174. 3 figs. [Periodicity in *Oedogonium.*]
Timberlake, H. G. **1901.** *Ann. Bot.* **15:** 619–635. 1 pl. [Pyrenoid.]
1902. *Trans. Wis. Acad.* **13:** 486–522. 2 pl. [Zoospores.]
Tobler, F. **1911.** *Flora* **103:** 78–87. 3 figs. [*Codium.*]
Transeau, E. N. **1913.** *Trans. Amer. Microsc. Soc.* **32:** 31–40. 8 figs. [Periodicity.]
1916. *Amer. Jour. Bot.* **3:** 121–133. 3 figs. [Periodicity.]

1951. The Zygnemataceae. Columbus, Ohio. 327 pp. 41 pl. 6 figs.
Tröndle, A. **1911.** *Zeitschr. Bot.* **3:** 593–619. 1 pl. 20 figs. [*Spirogyra.*]
Turner, C. **1922.** *Proc. Linn. Soc. London* **1922:** 59–63. 1 pl. [Desmidiaceae.]
Tuttle, A. H. **1910.** *Jour. Exper. Zool.* **9:** 143–157. 18 figs. [Mitosis, *Oedogonium.*]
Uspenskaja, W. J. **1930.** *Zeitschr. Bot.* **22:** 337–393. 12 figs. [Zoospore formation.]
Vlk, W. **1938.** *Arch. Protistenk.* **90:** 448–488. 1 pl. 12 figs. [Flagella.]
1939. Reprint from *Lotos* Vol. 87. 15 pp. 8 figs. [Pyrenoid.]
Watson, Jeanette B., and Josephine E. Tilden. **1930.** *Trans. Amer. Microsc. Soc.* **49:** 160–167. 1 pl. [*Schizomeris.*]
Wesley, Ophelia C. **1928.** *Bot. Gaz.* **86:** 1–31. 2 pl. 41 figs. [*Coleochaete.*
1930. *Ibid.* **89:** 180–191. 2 pl. [*Coleochaete.*]
West, G. S. **1912.** *Jour. Botany* **50:** 321–325. 1 fig. [Dwarf males, *Oedogonium.*]
1915. *Ibid.* **53:** 78–81. 2 figs. [Mesotaeniaceae.]
1916. Algae. Vol. 1. Cambridge. 475 pp. 271 figs.
West, G. S., and F. E. Fritsch. **1927.** A treatise on the British fresh-water algae. New and rev. ed. Cambridge. 534 pp. 207 figs.
West, G. S., and Olive E. Hood. **1911.** *New Phytol.* **10:** 241–248. 6 figs. [*Trentepohlia.*]
Wettstein, F. von. **1921.** *Sitzungsber. Akad. Wiss. Wien* (Math.-Nat. Kl.) **130**^{1}**:** 3–20. [Cell walls.]
Wille, N. **1883.** *Bot. Centralbl.* **16:** 215–219. [Akinetes, aplanospores.]
1887. *Jahrb. Wiss. Bot.* **18:** 426–434. 1 pl. [*Trentepohlia.*]
1887A. *Ibid.* **18:** 443–454. 2 pl. [*Oedogonium.*]
1901. *Videnskab. Selsk. Skr. Christiana* (Math.-Nat. Kl.) **1900**^{6}**:** 13–18. 1 pl. [*Prasiola.*]
1903. *Nyt. Mag. Naturvidenskab.* **41:** 109–162. 2 pl. [*Chlamydomonas.*]
1906. *Videnskab. Selsk. Skr. Christiana* (Math.-Nat. Kl.) **1906**^{3}**:** 1–12. 1 pl. [*Prasiola.*]
Williams, May M. **1925.** *Proc. Linn. Soc. New South Wales* **50:** 98–111. 42 figs. [*Codium.*]
Wisselingh, C. van. **1908.** *Beih. Bot. Centralbl.* **23:** 137–156. 1 pl. [*Oedogonium.*]
1908A. *Ibid.* **23:** 157–190. 4 pl. [*Oedogonium.*]
1913. *Verslag. K. Akad. Wetenschap. Amsterdam* **16:** 11–19. [*Zygnema.*]
Wolle, F. **1887.** Fresh-water algae of the United States. Bethlehem, Pa. 364 pp. 210 pl.
Wood, H. C. **1872.** *Smithsonian Contributions to Knowledge* **19,** No. 241: 1–262. 21 pl. [Algae of N. America.]
Wurdack, Mary E. **1923.** *Ohio Jour. Sci.* **23:** 181–191. [Cell wall.]
Yabe, Y. **1932.** *Sci. Rept. Tokyo Bunrika Daigaku* Sec. *B.* **1:** 39–40. 1 pl. [*Prasiola.*]
Yamada, Y., and E. Saito. **1938.** *Papers Inst. Algol. Res. Hokkaido Imp. Univ.* **2:** 35–51. 1 pl. 12 figs. [Ulvales.]
Zimmermann, W. **1921.** *Jahrb. Wiss. Bot.* **60:** 256–294. 1 pl. 2 figs. [*Volvox.*]
1925. *Naturwissensch.* **13:** 397–402. 3 figs. [*Volvox.*]
Zinnecker, Emmi. **1935.** *Oesterr. Bot. Zeitschr.* **84:** 53–72. 6 figs. [*Bryopsis.*

CHAPTER 3

EUGLENOPHYTA

The euglenoid algae are a series primarily composed of motile unicellular forms and in which there has been an evolution of immobile multicellular forms but with no types higher than palmelloid colonies. The protoplasts may be colorless or with pigments localized in grass-green chloroplasts. Chloroplasts contain the same chlorophylls as Chlorophyta, contain beta-carotene only, and contain at least one xanthophyll not found in Chlorophyta (see Table I, page 4). Food reserves consist of **paramylum** (an insoluble carbohydrate related to starch) and fats. Motile cells may be uni-, bi-, or triflagellate. Flagella are always anterior and with the lower end inserted at the base of an interior chamber (reservoir) connected with the exterior of the cell by a narrow gullet. Reproduction is generally by cell division. Thick-walled resting stages (cysts) are known for several genera. Sexual reproduction has not been demonstrated beyond all doubt for the group.

There are about 25 genera and 450 species, almost all of which are found in fresh waters.

The relationships between Euglenophyta and other algal series are obscure. Certain similarities in pigmentation suggest a relationship to the Chlorophyta, but the organization of the protoplast of motile cells of the two is so different that it is better to follow the usual practice and accord the euglenoid series a rank equal to that of the chrysophycean, dinoflagellate, and volvocine (chlorophycean) series.

The first formal recognition[1] of the euglenoids as a division (Euglenophyta) of the plant kingdom divides them into two classes, each with a single order. A more logical treatment seems to be that of placing them in a single class (*Euglenophyceae*) with two orders.

ORDER 1. EUGLENALES

The Euglenales include all the Euglenophyceae in which the flagellated motile cell is the dominant phase in the life cycle. The cells are always

[1] Pascher, 1931.

solitary and never united in colonies. All but one of the genera of the Euglenophyceae are referred to this order.

Occurrence. Euglenales are most often found in small pools rich in organic matter. The pigmented forms, especially *Euglena*, are frequently present in sufficient abundance to color the water. The saprophytic colorless forms are rarely present in quantity, and they grow most abundantly where a considerable amount of putrefaction is taking place. Some euglenoids grow on damp mud along the banks of rivers, estuaries, or salt marshes, and here they may be present in sufficient abundance to color the mud.[1] Members of the order found in unusual habitats include the

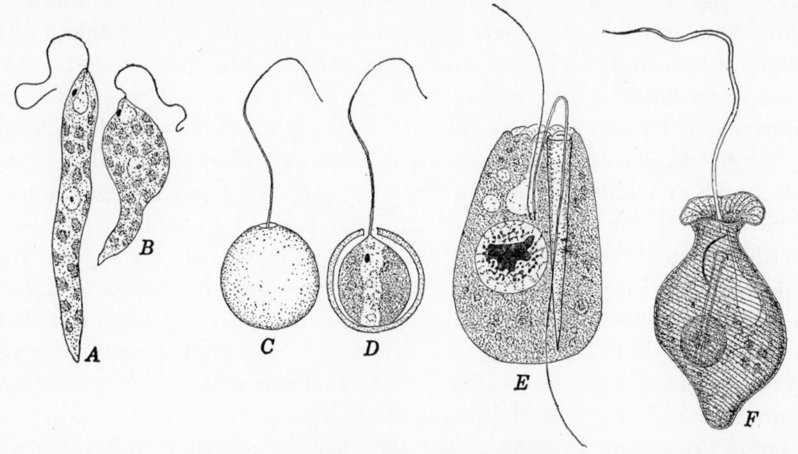

Fig. 72. Euglenales. *A–B*, *Euglena intermedia* (Klebs) Schmitz; *C*, *D*, surface view and optical section of *Trachelomonas volvocina* Ehr. *E*, diagrammatic ventral view of *Entosiphon sulcatum* (Duj.) Stein; *F*, *Urceolus cyclostomus* (Stein) Meresch. (*E*, *based upon Lackey*, 1929; *F*, *after Senn*, 1900.) (*A–B*, × 325; *C–D*, × 650; *F*, × 1,000.)

Euglena that has been found[2] to be one of the organisms causing green snow, and those genera which grow parasitically in the intestinal tracts of amphibia.

Cell Shape. The exterior portion of the cytoplasm is always differentiated into a **periplast,** and one that is frequently longitudinally striate or punctate. The periplast may be so rigid that the cells have a fixed shape, or it may be so flexible that the shape of a cell is constantly changing as it swims through the water. Cells with a flexible periplast are more or less elongated and approximately circular in transverse section; those with a firm periplast may be radially symmetrical or markedly compressed.

A few genera have the protoplast surrounded by an envelope (**lorica**) that stands free from the protoplast (Fig. 72*C–D*). The lorica is always

[1] Jahn, 1946. [2] Kiener, 1944.

open at the anterior end and the flagellum or flagella project through the open end. A lorica is composed of a firm gelatinous substance without any trace of cellulose.[1] It is colorless and transparent when first formed; later it frequently becomes impregnated with iron compounds that make it opaque and yellow to dark brown in color. The shape and ornamentation of the lorica are characteristic for any given species and the chief characters in differentiating species within genera having a lorica.

Cell Structure. Although cells of several genera have chloroplasts, those of the majority of genera do not. When present, there are usually numerous discoid to band-shaped chloroplasts within a cell. Certain species of *Euglena*, a genus with chloroplasts, may also produce a red pigment (euglenarhodone) which may be present in such quantity as to obscure the cell contents. Euglenarhodone is a ketonic carotenoid.[2] When *Euglena* is grown in darkness on a suitable organic substratum there is a disappearance of the chloroplasts but these reappear if the culture is returned to light. Under exceptional conditions *Euglena* may give rise to colorless (apochlorotic) races whose cells are apochlorotic even when grown in light.[3] Apochlorotic races of *Euglena* have also been induced by treating cells with streptomycin in light.[4]

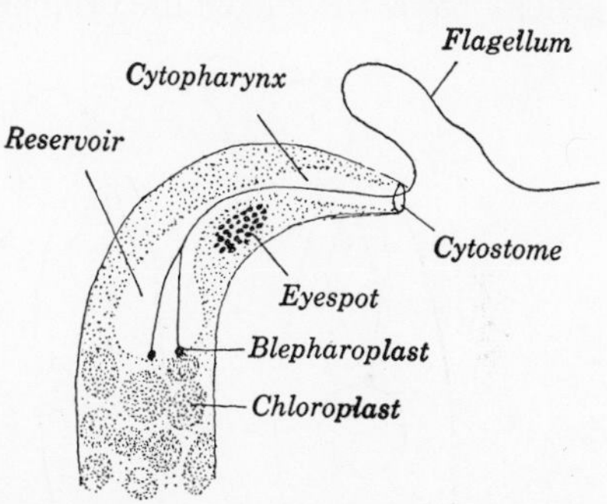

FIG. 73. Apex of cell of *Euglena intermedia* (Klebs) Schmitz. (*Slightly modified from Krichenbauer*, 1938.)

Irrespective of the mode of nutrition, the food reserve accumulating within cells is **paramylum,** an insoluble carbohydrate which is laid down in the shape of disks, rings, rods, or spherical granules, and these sometimes become relatively large. Paramylum is a polysaccharid with the same empirical formula as starch, but one that does not respond to the usual tests for starch. Paramylum granules resemble starch grains in that they appear to be concentrically stratified, but the apparent stratification has been held to be due to a helical twisting of elongate micellae of paramylum rather than to a deposition of paramylum in concentric layers.[5]

The anterior end of a cell (Fig. 73) is a **cytostome** (a differentiated portion of the periplast) and beneath the cytostome is a flask-shaped **gullet.** The gullet consists of a narrow neck, the **cytopharynx,** and an enlarged posterior portion, the **reservoir.** The reservoir is adjoined by one or more **contractile vacuoles** in which the interval between cystole and diastole

[1] Klebs, 1883. [2] Strain, 1951. [3] Pringsheim, 1948.
[4] Provasoli, Hutner, and Schatz, 1948. [5] Heidt, 1937.

usually is but a few seconds.[1] Certain genera have **rod organs (pharyngeal rods)** adjacent to the gullet. They lie parallel to the long axis of the gullet and with their lower extremities level with the base of the reservoir or extending to the posterior end of a cell (Fig. 72*E–F*). Some genera with rod organs seem[2] to have them terminating beneath a cytostome entirely distinct from the gullet. The function of the rod organs has been thought[3] to be that of a trichite which serves as a supporting organ when the cytostome is distended in the ingestion of solid food.

Flagella of Euglenales are inserted in the base of the reservoir and project through the cytopharynx and cytostome (Fig. 73). Uniflagellate genera have the flagellum projecting forward. Some biflagellate genera

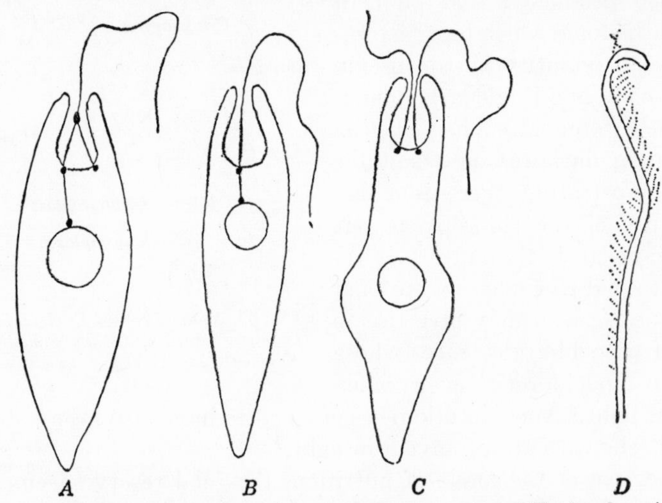

Fig. 74. *A–C*, diagrams of flagella and neuromotor apparatus of Euglenales. *A*, *Euglena*. *B*, *Astasia*. *C*, *Distigma*. *D*, mastigonemes on flagellum of *Urceolus cyclostomus* (Stein) Meresch. (*A*, *based upon Hall and Jahn*, 1929; *B*, *based upon Hall and Powell*, 1927; *C*, *based upon Lackey*, 1934; *D*, *after Vlk*, 1938.)

have both flagella of equal length and projecting forward; but more genera have flagella of unequal length, one projecting forward and the other trailing (Fig. 72*E*). Flagella of Euglenales are of the so-called tinsel type in which there are delicate hair-like appendages along the length of the flagellum. These appendages are usually called cilia but since they are not comparable to cilia of protozoa the term **mastigoneme** has been proposed.[4] Studies[5] of euglenoid flagella by means of special staining techniques, dark-field illumination, and the electron microscope show that all flagella are similar in structure. A flagellum (Fig. 74*D*) consists

[1] Günther, 1928; Hall and Powell, 1928.

[2] V. E. Brown, 1930; Lackey, 1929; Rhodes, 1926.

[3] Hall and Powell, 1927; Rhodes, 1926; Schaeffer, 1918.

[4] Deflandre, 1934.

[5] H. P. Brown, 1945; Deflandre, 1934; Petersen, 1929; Pitelka, 1949; Vlk, 1938.

of either one or two central filaments (**axonemes**) surrounded by a sheath bearing a vertical row of mastigonemes. A majority of the genera investigated have been shown[1] to have a neuromotor apparatus of the blepharoplast-rhizoplast-centriole type (Fig. 74*A–C*.) Some of the uniflagellate genera have the flagellum bifurcating within the reservoir and each fork terminating in a blepharoplast. One of the blepharoplasts is connected to an extranuclear centriole by a delicate rhizoplast; the other is without a rhizoplast. Other uniflagellate genera do not have a bifurcation of the flagellum, but they may have a granular swelling some distance above the blepharoplast. Biflagellate genera do not have a forking of either flagellum, but there may be a granular swelling above each blepharoplast.

The pigmented Euglenales and apochlorotic forms immediately derived from them have an eyespot near the anterior end of the cell. Other

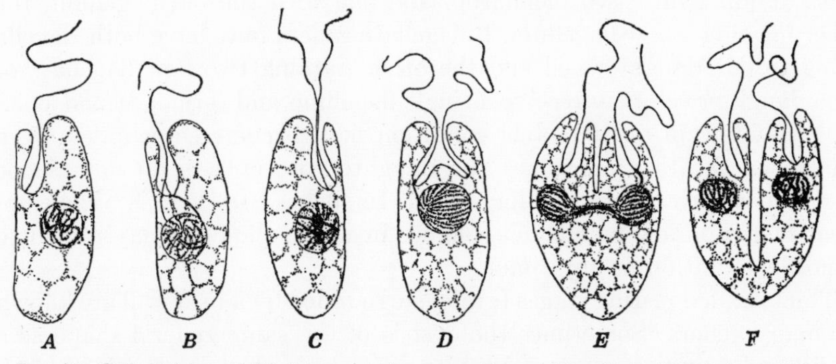

FIG. 75. Cell division of *Rhabdomonas incurvum* Fres. (*After Hall*, 1923.) (× 1,400.)

colorless Euglenales have no eyespots. The eyespot (Fig. 73) consists of numerous reddish granules arranged in a concavo-convex matrix.[2] The eyespot is an organelle concerned in phototactic responses of motile cells and it is thought that orientation of waving of a flagellum is controlled by the eyespot shading its basal swelling. Eyespots of daughter cells are formed by bipartition of the eyespot of the parent cell instead of being formed *de novo*.[3]

The nucleus of a euglenoid cell is a prominent structure and one easily recognized without staining. All Euglenales are uninucleate under normal conditions, but a cell may become multinucleate if cytokinesis is inhibited.[4] The nucleus has one or more centrally located endosomes, a definite nuclear membrane, and numerous irregularly shaped chromatin

[1] Baker, 1926: Hall, 1923; Hall and Jahn, 1929; Hall and Powell, 1927.
[2] Mast, 1928; Wager, 1900. [3] Baker, 1926; Günther, 1928; Gojdics, 1934.
[4] Krichenbauer, 1938; Mainx, 1928.

granules between endosome and the nuclear membrane. Resting nuclei lie near the center of a cell, but those about to divide may move toward the anterior end of a cell. The chromatic material of a dividing nucleus becomes organized into a definite number of chromosomes that lie with their long axes perpendicular to the plane of nuclear division (Fig. 75). The chromosomes are enclosed by the nuclear membrane throughout mitosis, and mitotic separation is accompanied by a bipartition of the endosome or endosomes.[1]

Asexual Reproduction. Multiplication is by cell division and it may take place while cells are actively motile or after they have come to rest. Genera with a lorica have the protoplast dividing within the lorica. One of the daughter protoplasts remains within the old lorica; the other escapes and secretes a new lorica. Division of motile cells is longitudinal and begins at the anterior end. Uniflagellate genera have the blepharoplast dividing into two blepharoplasts; one with the old flagellum, the other forming a new flagellum. Biflagellate genera may have both flagella going to one daughter cell and the other forming two new flagella;[2] or each daughter cell may receive a single flagellum and form a second one.[3] Cells dividing in an immobile condition may become surrounded by a gelatinous sheath. Sometimes the daughter protoplasts do not escape from the sheath before dividing again. In such cases there is a development of temporary palmelloid colonies in which the cells may return to a motile condition at any time.

Thick-walled resting stages (cysts) surrounded by a firm wall are known for many genera. Sometimes the cyst is of the same general shape as a motile cell, but more often it is quite different in shape and either spherical or polygonal. Protoplasts of cysts may produce a considerable amount of euglenarhodone and become a deep red. Germinating cysts usually have the protoplast escaping from the wall and developing into a single motile cell.

Sexual Reproduction. A gametic union of vegetative cells has been described for a few euglenoids[4] but all the supposed cases are considered extremely dubious. Autogamy (the fusion of two sister nuclei in a cell) has been described for *Phacus*.[5] Reported cases of autogamy must always be scrutinized with care because stained stages in separation of two daughter nuclei may be arranged in such a sequence that they are misinterpreted as a fusion of two nuclei. In *Phacus*, as in other Euglenales, nuclear division is in a plane at right angles to the long axis of a cell. Binucleate cells with the two nuclei in the long axis of the cell and the finding of uninucleate cells with large nuclei and two endosomes are given as evidence for autogamy. Nuclear fusion in *Phacus* is followed by

[1] See Jahn, 1946, for references to mitosis. [2] Lackey, 1929. [3] Loefer, 1931.
[4] Berliner, 1909; Dobell, 1908; Haase, 1910. [5] Krichenbauer, 1938.

a meiotic division into four daughter nuclei and a quadripartition into four uninucleate daughter protoplasts.

Classification. Several systems[1] for the classification of Euglenales stress the mode of nutrition and group them in three families according to their holophytic, saphrophytic, or holozoic nutrition. Such a classification is arbitrary because there are certain genera, as *Euglena*, in which some species have chloroplasts and others lack them. The best basis for a differentiation into families seems to be the finer cytological structure, especially that of bifurcation and granulation of flagella.[2] The taxonomic significance of the pharyngeal rod apparatus is less certain. Some euglenophiles[3] place great emphasis on this structure; others[4] hold that it is one of minor importance. In any case, only three or four families are recognizable within the order.

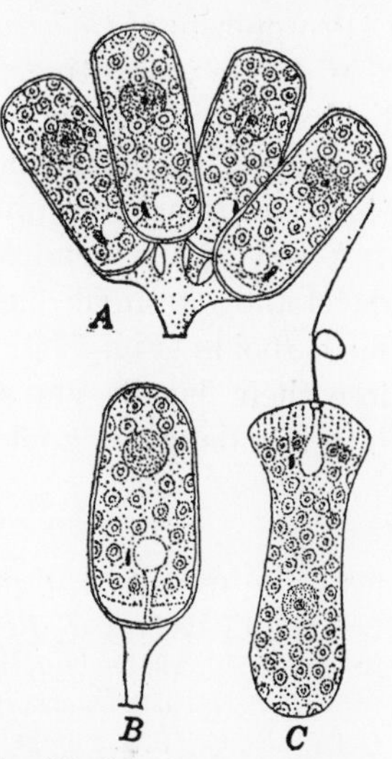

FIG. 76. *Colacium calvum* Stein. (*After Stein*, 1878.)

ORDER 2. COLACIALES (EUGLENOCAPSALES)

The Colaciales have immobile cells permanently encapsulated within a wall and united in amorphous or dendroid palmelloid colonies. There may be a temporary formation of naked uniflagellate stages.

The single genus, *Colacium*, is epizoic upon copepods, rotifers, and other members of the fresh-water zooplankton. There are but two species.

Cells of *Colacium* (Fig. 76) are surrounded by a gelatinous envelope and are affixed, with the anterior pole downward, by means of gelatinous stalks, to the host. The stalks are the result of a greater secretion of gelatinous material at the anterior end of a cell. When cell division takes place, each of the two daughter cells secretes a stalk of its own, and they remain attached to the stalk of the parent cell. Repeated cell division results in a dendroid colony in which the cells are borne at the extremities of a repeatedly branched gelatinous-stalk system.

The cells of dendroid colonies are ovoid or subcylindrical. They contain numerous discoid chloroplasts, with or without pyrenoids. There is a single large nucleus toward the upper end of a protoplast. The lower portion of a protoplast, the morphologically anterior end, contains a con-

[1] Klebs, 1892; Lemmermann, 1913; Senn, 1900.
[2] Hall and Jahn, 1929; Lackey, 1934.
[3] V. E. Brown, 1930; Rhodes, 1926. [4] Hall and Jahn, 1929.

spicuous gullet and an eyespot. Flagella are not evident in protoplasts of dendroid colonies.[1]

Cells grown in culture on agar slants are globose and surrounded by an envelope that is without a stalk.[2] Their daughter cells may separate from each other immediately following cell division, or the two may remain within the parent-cell envelope. Repeated division of cells within a common envelope may continue until there is an amorphous palmelloid colony of 20 or more cells. Palmelloid cells are ordinarily uninucleate, but they may become larger than usual and two- to eight-nucleate.

Protoplasts of *Colacium* may also develop into naked amoeboid stages that divide vegetatively.[3] There may also be a formation of naked amoeboid stages with four to eight nuclei.[2] The only known method of reproduction in these plasmodial stages is a budding off of uninucleate portions and a metamorphosis of them into uniflagellate swarmers.

A cell of the dendroid or palmelloid stage may have its protoplast developing a single flagellum and escaping as a free-swimming zooid.[4] Such zooids (Fig. 76*C*) usually swarm for a short time only before they lose their flagella and secrete walls. In rare cases[5] a zooid may divide into two daughter zooids while in a motile condition.

Bibliography

Baker, W. B. **1926.** *Biol. Bull.* **51:** 321–362. 2 pl. 2 figs. [Euglenales.]

Berliner, E. **1909.** *Arch. Protistenk.* **15:** 297–325. 2 pl. [Euglenales.]

Brown, H. P. **1945.** *Ohio Jour. Sci.* **45:** 247–301. 12 pl. 22 figs. [Flagella.]

Brown, V. E. **1930.** *Quart. Jour. Microsc. Sci.* N.S. **73:** 403–419. 3 pl. 1 fig. [Euglenales.]

Deflandre, G. **1934.** *Compt. Rend. Acad. Sci. Paris* **198:** 497–499. 4 figs. [Flagella.]

Dobell, C. C. **1908.** *Quart. Jour. Microsc. Sci.* N.S. **52:** 75–120. 2 pl. 3 figs. [Euglenales.]

Gojdics, Mary. **1934.** *Trans. Amer. Microsc. Soc.* **53:** 299–310. 3 pl. [*Euglena.*]

Günther, F. **1928.** *Arch. Protistenk.* **60:** 511–590. 3 pl. 5 figs. [Euglenales.]

Haase, Gertrude. **1910.** *Ibid.* **20:** 47–59. 3 pl. [Euglenales.]

Hall, R. P. **1923.** *Univ. Calif. Publ. Zool.* **20:** 447–476. 2 pl. 2 figs. [Euglenales.]

Hall, R. P., and T. L. Jahn. **1929.** *Trans. Amer. Microsc. Soc.* **48:** 388–405. 3 pl. 2 figs. [Euglenales.]

Hall, R. P., and W. N. Powell. **1927.** *Ibid.* **46:** 155–165. 1 pl. 2 figs. [Euglenales.]

1928. *Biol. Bull.* **54:** 36–64. 2 pl. 3 figs. [Euglenales.]

Heidt, K. **1937.** *Arch. Protistenk.* **88:** 127–142. 14 figs. [Euglenales.]

Jahn, T. L. **1946.** *Quart. Rev. Biol.* **21:** 246–274. 6 figs. [Euglenophyta.]

Johnson, D. F. **1934.** *Arch. Protistenk.* **83:** 241–263. 20 figs. 3 pl. [*Colacium.*]

Kiener, W. **1944.** *Proc. Neb. Acad. Sci. 54th Annual Meeting.* p. 12. [Green snow.]

Klebs, G. **1883.** *Untersuch. Bot. Inst. Tübingen* **1:** 233–361. 2 pl. [Euglenales.]

1892. *Zeitschr. Wiss. Zool.* **55:** 353–445. 6 pl. [Euglenales.]

Krichenbauer, H. **1938.** *Arch. Protistenk.* **90:** 88–122. 18 figs. [Autogamy.]

Lackey, J. B. **1929.** *Ibid.* **66:** 175–200. 24 figs. [Euglenales.]

1934. *Biol. Bull.* **67:** 145–162. 26 figs. [Euglenales.]

[1] Stein, 1878. [2] Johnson, 1934. [3] Schiller, 1924.
[4] Johnson, 1934; Stein, 1878. [5] Johnson, 1934; Schiller, 1924.

Lemmermann, E. **1913.** Eugleninae. In A. Pascher, Die Süsswasserflora Deutschlands, Österreichs und der Schweiz. Heft 2, Flagellatae 2. Pp. 115–174. 198 figs.
Loefer, J. B. **1931.** *Arch. Protistenk.* **74:** 449–470. 3 pl. 3 figs. [Euglenales.]
Mainx, J. B. **1928.** *Ibid.* **60:** 305–354. 1 pl. 8 figs. [Euglenales.]
1928A. *Ibid.* **60:** 355–414. [Euglenales.]
Mast, S. O. **1928.** *Ibid.* **60:** 197–220. 1 pl. 4 figs. [Eyespot.]
Pascher, A. **1931.** *Beih. Bot. Centralbl.* **48:** 317–332. [Classification.]
Petersen, J. B. **1929.** *Bot. Tidsskr.* **40:** 373–389. 1 pl. [Flagella.]
Pitelka, Dorothy R. **1949.** *Univ. Calif. Publ. Zool.* **53:** 377–430. 11 pl. 3 figs. [Flagella.]
Pringsheim, E. G. **1948.** *New Phytol.* **47:** 52–87. 13 figs. [Apochlorotic Euglenales.]
Provasoli, L., S. H. Hutner, and A. Schatz. **1948.** *Proc. Soc. Exper. Biol. and Med.* **69:** 279–282. [Apochlorotic Euglenales.]
Rhodes, R. C. **1926.** *Anat. Record* **34:** 152–153. [Euglenales.]
Schaeffer, A. A. **1918.** *Trans. Amer. Microsc. Soc.* **37:** 177–182. 1 pl. [Euglenales.]
Schiller, J. **1924.** *Oesterr. Bot. Zeitschr.* **73:** 5–14. 11 figs. [*Colacium.*]
Senn, G. **1900.** Flagellata. In A. Engler and K. Prantl, Die natürlichen Pflanzenfamilien. Teil 1, Abt. 1A. Pp. 93–188. 78 figs.
Stein, F. **1878.** Der Organismus der Infusionsthiere. Bd. 3. Hälfte 1. Leipzig. 154 pp. 24 pl.
Strain, H. H. **1951.** The pigments of algae. In G. M. Smith (editor), Manual of phycology. Waltham, Mass. Pp. 243–262.
Vlk, W. **1938.** *Arch. Protistenk.* **90:** 448–488. 1 pl. 12 figs. [Flagella.]
Wager, H. **1900.** *Jour. Linn. Soc. Zool. London* **27:** 463–481. 1 pl. [Eyespot.]

CHAPTER 4

PYRROPHYTA

Members of this division have their pigments localized in chromatophores which are usually greenish tan to golden brown. The pigments are chlorophyll *a*, chlorophyll *c*, beta-carotene, and four xanthophylls, three of which are found only in members of this division (see Table I, page 4). Photosynthetic reserves generally accumulate as starch or starch-like compounds, but they may also accumulate as oils. The nucleus is distinctive in that the chromatin lies in numerous bead-like strands. Cell walls, when present, generally contain cellulose. The great majority of genera have distinctive asymmetrical motile cells, the motile cells being biflagellate and with the flagella morphologically unlike. Asexual reproduction may be by cell division or by means of zoospores or aplanospores. Sexual reproduction is found in but two or three genera.

For a long time all known genera were unicellular biflagellate organisms whose affinities were thought to be with the protozoa. Later, there was a discovery of a few truly algal unicellular and colonial types which are obviously related to the motile forms previously referred to the Protozoa.

Certain characters in common to the motile forms known as dinoflagellates, desmokonts, and cryptomonads were first pointed out by Pascher.[1] Chief among these are two flagella unlike in movement and shape, and the formation of starch by brown chromatophores. Later, Pascher[2] named the three groups of organisms the Dinophyceae, the Desmokontae, and the Cryptophyceae; and called the combined groups the Pyrrophyta. The relationships of Cryptophyceae to the other Pyrrophyta have been questioned.[3] Chief among arguments for excluding the Cryptophyceae from the Pyrrophyta are the markedly different structure of their nuclei and the presence of a gullet in motile forms. On this account it is better to consider the Cryptophyceae an algal group of uncertain systematic position than to assign them to the Pyrrophyta. As thus restricted, the Pyrrophyta may be divided into two classes, the *Desmophyceae* and the *Dinophyceae*.

[1] Pascher, 1911. [2] Pascher, 1914.

[3] Fritsch, 1935; Graham, 1951; Pringsheim, 1944; Smith, 1950.

CLASS 1. DESMOPHYCEAE (DESMOKONTAE)

Motile genera assigned to the Desmophyceae differ in three respects from those of Dinophyceae. The two flagella are borne at the cell apex; the cell is without a transverse furrow; and the cell wall, when present, is vertically divided into two halves (valves) that are without subdivision into definitely arranged plates. The protoplast contains brownish chromatophores and granules of starch.

There are about 6 genera and 30 species, all rare organisms and most of them marine. The dinophysid dinoflagellates (see page 158) have been included among the Desmophyceae[1] because their walls are vertically

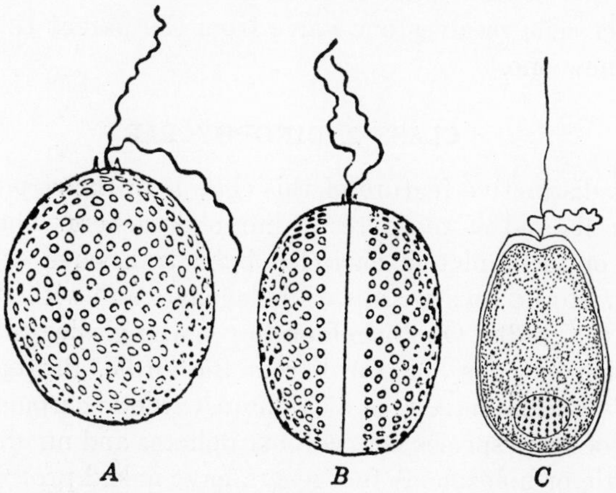

FIG. 77. *Exuviaella marina* Cienk. *A–B*, surface views from front and side. *C*, optical section. (*A–B, from Schütt*, 1896; *C, after Klebs*, 1884.) (*A–B*, × 600; *C*, × 300.)

divided into two halves. However, the dinophysid flagellates are to be referred to the Dinophyceae because each half of the wall is composed of a series of definitely arranged plates just as in the "armored" dinoflagellates.

Some of the Desmophyceae are motile and with or without cell walls; others are without flagella and have a wall. On the basis of the presence or absence of a cell wall the motile genera have been segregated into two orders and the immobile genera have been placed in a third order.[2]

Exuviaella (Fig. 77), a marine genus with about 10 species, is among the best-known members of the class. Its cells are compressed and with the protoplast surrounded by a cellulose wall composed of two longitudinally apposed valves. Each valve may be smooth, or with many small pores irregularly distributed over all the surface except the margin. *Exuviaella* is biflagellate and with the two flagella projecting through a

[1] Fritsch, 1935; Pascher, 1927, 1931. [2] Pascher, 1927, 1931.

circular pore at the anterior end of a cell. One of the flagella projects vertically outward from the pore and its lashing propels the cell through the water.[1] The other flagellum stands at right angles to the propulsive flagellum (Fig. 77). Its movement is undulatory and causes a rotation of a cell as it moves through the water.

The protoplast contains two brownish, laminate, vertically elongate chromatophores that are with or without pyrenoids. Reserve foods accumulate both in the chromatophores and in the cytoplasm. They include minute granules, probably of a starch-like nature, and small droplets of oil. There may be conspicuous noncontractile vacuoles in the upper half of a cell. The single nucleus lies toward the posterior end of a cell.

Reproduction of *Exuviaella* is by longitudinal bipartition. Each of the two daughter cells receives one valve from the parent cell and secretes an entirely new one.

CLASS 2. DINOPHYCEAE

The most distinctive feature of this class is in the structure of motile vegetative cells and of zoospores of immobile genera. These are always completely or incompletely encircled by a transverse or spiral groove (the **girdle**). Motile cells are always biflagellate and with the two flagella inserted in the girdle. One flagellum lies in the girdle and encircles the cell; the other extends backward from the girdle. Protoplasts of most members of the class have brownish photosynthetic chromatophores; but protoplasts of some species lack chromatophores and nutrition of the cell is saprophytic or holozoic. A few genera have naked protoplasts, but the great majority have cellulose walls that may be homogeneous or may consist of a definite number of articulated plates. Food reserves are stored as starch or as oil.

Asexual reproduction of motile unicellular genera is by cell division and that of unicellular and multicellular immobile genera is by zoospores or autospores. Sexual reproduction, known for but a couple of genera, is isogamous, and is either by a fusion of zoogametes or aplanogametes.

There are about 120 genera and 1,000 species.

Occurrence. The great majority of Dinophyceae are motile unicellular flagellates (*dinoflagellates*). Most dinoflagellates are to be found in the plankton of the ocean, especially that of warmer portions. Fresh-water dinoflagellates are most abundant in pools, ditches, and small lakes with considerable vegetation. They are not uncommon in plankton catches from large lakes, but rarely occur in abundance. Some of the fresh-water species thrive best in hard waters; others are found in greatest numbers in soft waters.[2]

[1] Klebs, 1884, 1912; Schütt, 1890. [2] Höll, 1928.

The nonflagellated genera (*phytodinads*) are rare organisms and those occurring in fresh waters are usually epiphytic upon the coarser filamentous Chlorophyceae. The parasitic forms, of which there are several genera, are found within and upon various animals.[1]

The Cell Wall. A majority of the dinoflagellates and all phytodinads have definite walls. Walls of most species contain cellulose but there are certain species that do not seem to have cellulose in their walls.[2] The cell wall may consist of a single layer; or it may be differentiated into two layers, the outer of cellulose, the inner of unknown chemical composition.[3]

Phytodinads and a few dinoflagellates have homogeneous walls. The great majority of dinoflagellates have walls composed of definite plates (Fig. 83) whose number and arrangement are important in classifying these so-called "armored" dinoflagellates.

Structure of the Protoplast. Chromatophores of Dinophyceae lie at the periphery of the protoplast and vary in shape from species to species. A majority of species have more than one rod-shaped, discoid, or irregularly band-shaped chromatophore within a cell; but cells of certain species[4] have a single stellate axial chromatophore with numerous radiating processes. Many species have pyrenoids that may lie within the chromatophores or external to them. The yellow-brown color of chromatophores is due in large part to a predominance of specific xanthophylls found only in Pyrrophyta (see Table I, page 4).

Cells of Dinophyceae store their photosynthetic reserves as starch or as oil. As a general rule,[5] the chief food reserve of fresh-water species is starch and that of marine species is oil. In some cases starch formation is associated with pyrenoids; in other cases there are no pyrenoids, and starch is deposited either in the chromatophores or in the cytoplasm. Dinoflagellates with chromatophores may also ingest solid foods, and this holozoic method of nutrition may be fully as important a source of food as is photosynthesis. Nutrition of species without chromatophores may be holozoic or saprophytic. Diatoms and protozoa are among the most easily ingested foods, and in some cases[6] the ingested organism may be about half the size of the dinoflagellate.

Many dinoflagellates and the zoospores of most phytodinads have a large eyespot of simple structure. In one family of marine forms[7] there is a definite ocellus composed of two parts, a refractive lens and a surrounding pigment mass.

Motile cells are always biflagellate and with the flagella inserted in the girdle. The two flagella always differ morphologically and in their method

[1] Chatton, 1920. [2] Schilling, 1891. [3] Mangin, 1907, 1911.
[4] Geitler, 1926. [5] Killian, 1924; Klebs, 1912.
[6] Hofeneder, 1930; Woloszyńska, 1917. [7] Kofoid and Swezy, 1921.

of movement. The flagellum which lies within the grooves and encircles the cells transversely is usually, if not always, ribbon-like and moves in a spiral or undulatory manner. The other flagellum extends backward from the point of insertion. It is of the whiplash type[1] and waves in broad curves or with an active vibration at the distal end. Two genera have been shown[2] to have a neuromotor apparatus of the blepharoplast-rhizoplast-centriole type associated with the flagella.

Protoplasts of motile cells also contain **pulsules** that bear a superficial resemblance to contractile vacuoles but they have a distinct membrane and are noncontractile. There are usually two pulsules, but sometimes there are more or less evanescent accessory ones.[3] Pulsules are concerned

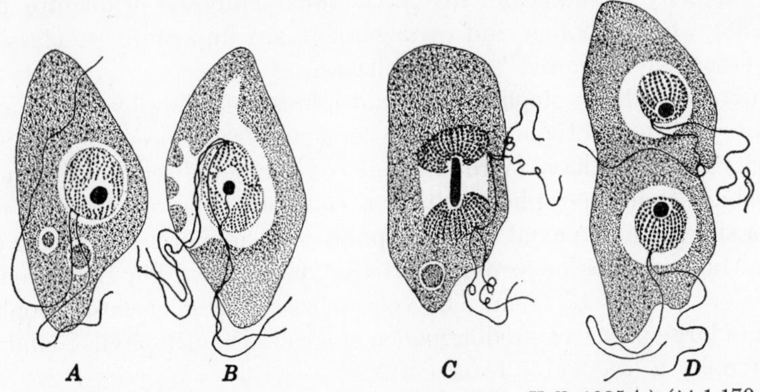

Fig. 78. Cell division of *Oxyrrhis marina* Duj. (*After Hall*, 1925*A*.) (× 1,170.)

with the intake of fluids into the protoplast and not, as might be supposed, with the discharge of liquids.[4]

All the dinoflagellates are uninucleate and with a relatively large centrally located nucleus. A nucleus has a conspicuous endosome and the chromatin is in parallel, straight, or spirally arranged moniliform threads.[5] Nuclear division is mitotic and with or without a persistence of the nuclear membrane during mitosis (Fig. 78).

Asexual Reproduction. Dinoflagellates usually multiply by cell division. This may take place while the cells are actively motile or after they have come to rest. In the division of certain "armored" dinoflagellates each daughter cell receives a predetermined portion of the parent-cell wall (see page 157). In the division of other "armored" dinoflagellates the protoplast escapes from the parent-cell wall, divides, and the daughter protoplasts form entirely new walls. There are also dinoflagellates

[1] Vlk, 1938. [2] Hall, 1925, 1925*A*.
[3] Kofoid and Swezy, 1921. [4] Kofoid, 1909.
[5] Entz, 1921; Hall, 1925, 1925*A*; Kofoid and Swezy, 1921; Köhler-Wieder, 1937.

where the protoplast within the wall divides into two naked daughter protoplasts that do not form walls until after liberation from the parent-cell wall.[1]

Asexual reproduction of phytodinads is by means of zoospores, aplanospores, or autospores. Both the filamentous genera and certain of the coccoid genera have the protoplast dividing to form two, four, or eight naked gymnodinoid zoospores that are liberated through a pore in the parent-cell wall (Fig. 88) or are liberated by a gelatinization of the parent-cell wall.

As is the case with Chlorophyceae and Xanthophyceae, division of the protoplast of a cell may be followed by a formation of aplanospores instead of zoospores. Aplanospores of Dinophyceae are usually globose, but

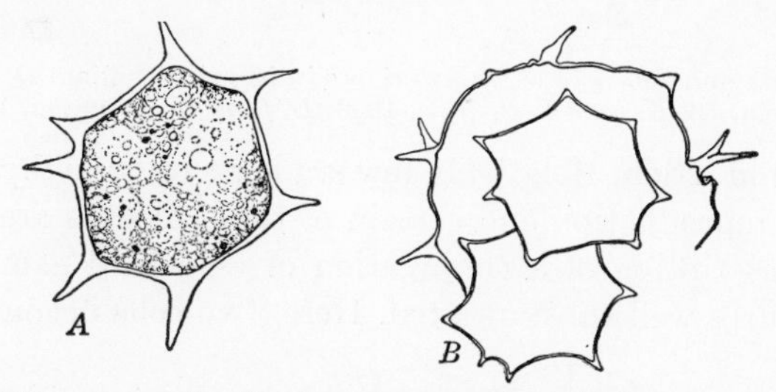

FIG. 79. *Dinastridium sexangulare* Pascher. *A*, vegetative cell. *B*, autospores. (*From Pascher*, 1927.)

in some cases they have a complicated outline and one quite unlike that of the vegetative cell. In many of the Dinococcales the aplanospores are of the same distinctive shape as the vegetative cell (Fig. 79). Such aplanospores are autospores.

The so-called cysts of dinoflagellates are comparable to aplanospores of phytodinads and other algae. Fresh-water dinoflagellates may form aplanospores at any time, but they usually form them in greatest abundance at the close of an active vegetative period.[2] A periodic formation of aplanospores has also been observed in a dinoflagellate grown in culture.[1] Most dinoflagellates have the entire protoplast rounding up to form a single aplanospore, but cases have been reported[3] of a formation of two aplanospores. Formation of aplanospores may take place within the parent-cell wall, or the protoplast may escape from the wall before it rounds up and secretes a new thick wall. A majority of dinoflagellates produce globose aplanospores, but certain of them form angular or lunate ones. The protoplast of a germinating aplanospore may develop directly into a gymnodinoid zoospore (Fig. 80*A–C*), or it may divide to form two such

[1] Diwald, 1937. [2] West, 1909. [3] Klebs, 1912.

zoospores. Zoospores may be liberated by a splitting[1] or by a gelatinization[2] of the aplanospore wall.

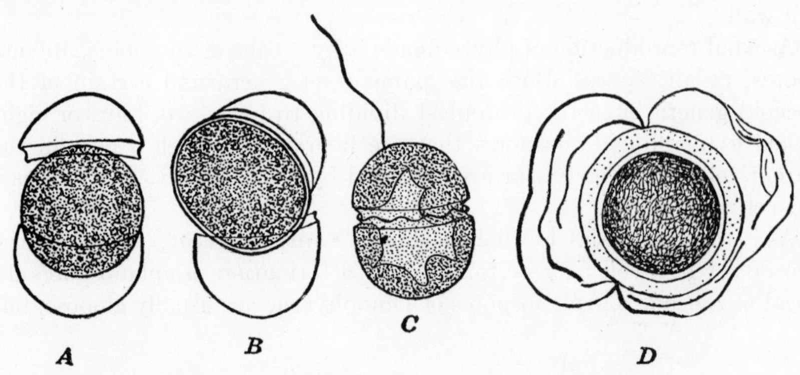

FIG. 80. *A–C*, cysts and zoospore of *Glenodinium uliginosum* Schilling. *D*, cyst of *Hemidinium nasutum* Stein. (*A–C, from G. S. West*, 1909; *D, from Woloszyńska*, 1925.)

Sexual Reproduction. Relatively few students of Dinophyceae have recorded sexual reproduction and certain of these records are open to suspicion. The description of a conjugation of amoeboid gametes in *Ceratium*[3] seems fairly well substantiated. Here, two cells become apposed to

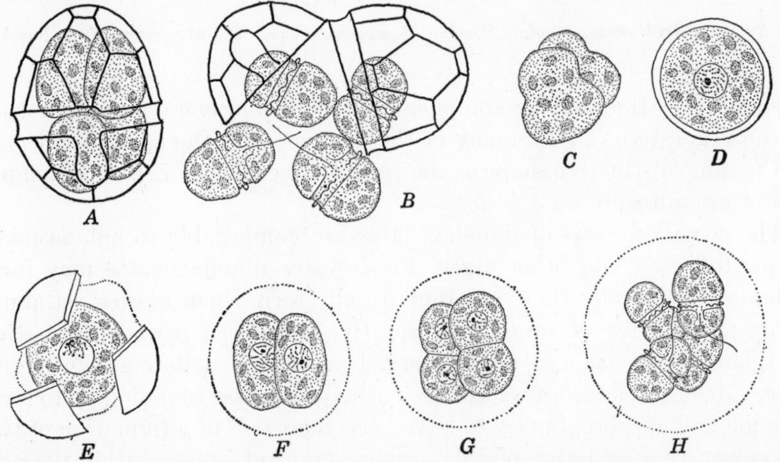

FIG. 81. Diagrams of sexual reproduction and zygote germination of *Glenodinium lubiniensiforme* Diwald. *A–B*, formation and liberation of gametes. *C*, union of gametes. *D*, zygote. *E–H*, germination of zygote. (*Diagrams based upon Diwald*, 1937.)

each other and establish a conjugation tube in which the two protoplasts unite to form a zygote. A union of motile gametes has been described for *Glenodinium*. This dinoflagellate was grown in culture and found to be heterothallic and to have a union of gametes only when the two came

[1] Diwald, 1937; West, 1909. [2] Woloszyńska, 1925. [3] Zederbauer, 1904.

from clones of opposite sex.[1] The protoplast of a cell divides to form four *Gymnodinium*-like gametes which are liberated by a transverse rupture at the girdle of the parent-cell wall (Fig. 81*A–B*). The gametes unite to form an immobile globose zygote that soon secretes a wall. Zygotes must ripen for at least 10 days before germinating. In germination (Fig. 81*E–H*) there is a splitting of the zygote wall and an extrusion of the uninucleate protoplast within it. The zygote nucleus divides meiotically and two successive bipartitions of the protoplast result in four uninucleate protoplasts which develop flagella. These cells are *Gymnodinium*-like for a short time and then they secrete walls.

Classification. Evolution of Dinophyceae from a motile unicellular ancestor has paralleled that in Chlorophyceae, Xanthophyceae, and Chrysophyceae, and certain of the types in these classes have their counterpart among the Dinophyceae. Thus, the Dinophyceae can be segregated into orders homologous with those in the classes just mentioned. Differences among the dinoflagellates warrant the recognition of more than one order but there is disagreement[2] concerning the number that should be recognized. The phytodinads have been divided[3] into four orders. The names given these four orders by Pascher are not in accord with Article 27 of the International Code of Botanical Nomenclature, which states that "The name of an order is taken from that of its type family." Despite their illegality, Pascher's ordinal names are universally used by phycologists.

ORDER 1. GYMNODINIALES

The Gymnodiniales typically have cells without walls, but the cell has such a firm periplast that it is rigid and with a fixed shape. Vegetative cells are always motile and with the characteristic dinophycean flagella.

There are some 25 genera and 300 species, the great majority of which are marine.

Cells of Gymnodiniales are circular, oval, or subrhomboidal in front view; and circular to narrowly ellipsoidal in vertical view. The surface of naked cells may be smooth or longitudinally striated. A few fresh-water species have been described[4] as having a delicate wall composed of a large and indefinite number of small hexagonal platelets. All species have a transverse furrow (girdle), that is, a descending left-wound spiral, with the ends more or less widely separated from each other. The separated ends of a girdle are connected to each other by a vertical furrow (**sulcus**) that may project beyond the upper or lower ends of a girdle (Fig. 82). The flagella are inserted in the sulcus. The transverse flagellum is always

[1] Diwald, 1937.
[2] Graham, 1951; Kofoid and Swezy, 1921; Lindemann, 1928; Schiller, 1931–1937.
[3] Pascher, 1927, 1931. [4] Woloszyńska, 1917.

inserted at the level of the upper end of the girdle; the longitudinal flagellum is variable in insertion, although usually below the level of the lower end of the girdle.

Most species have numerous discoid or bacilliform chromatophores but several species lack them.[1] The chromatophores are usually a golden brown, but they may be green, blue-green, or blue. Coloration of Gymnodiniales is not due entirely to chromatophores since the cytoplasm may also be tinged with colors covering nearly the whole range of the spectrum.

Reproduction is usually by cell division and may take place while the cells are motile or immobile. The plane of division is generally vertical, but it may be transverse. Gymnodiniales may also form "resting cysts" that are comparable to the aplanospores of Chlorophyceae. The cysts are globose and surrounded by a definite wall. The entire protoplast of a cell generally develops into a single cyst, although it may divide to form two cysts.[2] The protoplast of a germinating cyst may develop into a single zoospore, or it may divide to form two or more zoospores. These may be liberated immediately or retained for some time within the gelatinized wall.

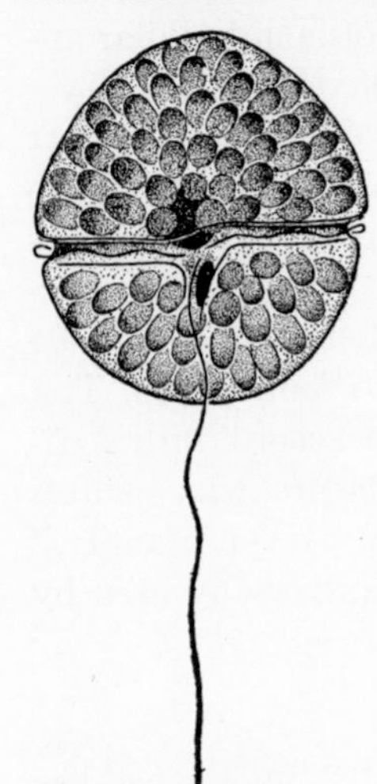

FIG. 82. *Gymnodinium neglectum* (Schilling) Lindem. (*From Thompson*, 1947.) (× 1,060.)

ORDER 2. PERIDINIALES

The Peridiniales include the dinoflagellates with a wall composed of a definite number of plates arranged in a specific manner, and in which the entire wall is never vertically separated into two halves or valves.

There are about 60 genera and 500 species, almost all of which are marine organisms. Most species have solitary cells but some species do not have a separation of daughter cells after division and so have the cells united end to end in a linear series.

The transverse girdle of a cell wall divides it into an upper part (the **epitheca**) and a lower part (the **hypotheca**), each with the plates in transverse bands or series (Fig. 83). Plates in the uppermost series of an epitheca have been called[3] **apical plates,** and those adjoining the girdle called **precingular plates.** Some genera have an incomplete band of **anterior intercalary plates** between the apical and precingular series. In the hypotheca there is a series of **postcingular plates** next to the girdle and either one or two **antapical plates** below them. Some genera have a single

[1] Kofoid and Swezy, 1921. [2] Klebs, 1912. [3] Kofoid, 1907, 1909.

posterior intercalary plate between the two series. Many genera have a thin membranous **ventral plate** intercalated in the girdle region and extending into or through the pre- and postcingular series. The so-called ventral plate is really a series of small plates, and the girdle is also made up of a series of small curved plates.

Each of the two flagella emerges through a small pore in the region of the ventral plate. One is band-like and lies within the groove of the girdle; the other is straight, of the whiplash type, and extends toward the posterior end of a cell.

The protoplasts are uninucleate and almost always have many golden brown chromatophores that form starch as the reserve carbohydrate. In spite of the fact that the protoplast is surrounded by a wall, the photo-

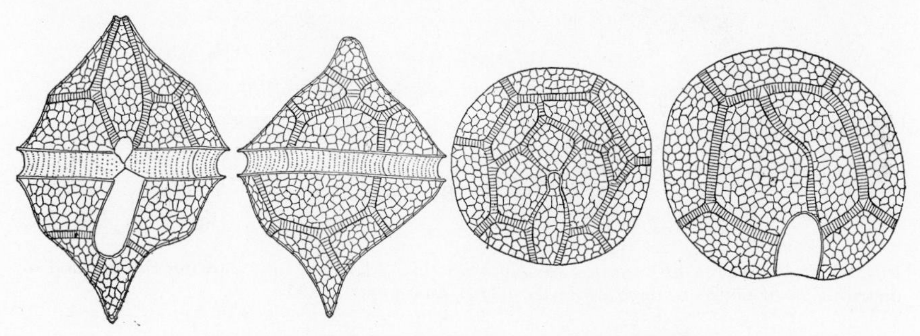

FIG. 83. *Peridinium wisconsinense* Eddy. (× 650.)

synthetic activities of chromatophores may be supplemented by a holozoic nutrition in which solid foods are ingested. The method by which Peridiniales ingest solid food is not fully known, but it probably takes place by means of pseudopodia extruded through the ventral plate region.[1]

Reproduction of Peridiniales is usually by a cell dividing into two daughter cells. This may take place either while the cells are actively motile or after they have come to rest. The plane of division is always more or less oblique and each daughter cell may receive only a portion of the parent-cell wall, or the daughter cells may escape from the old wall and develop entirely new walls. In the former case the parent-cell wall breaks in a specific manner and in such a fashion as to distribute specific epi- and hypothecal plates to each daughter cell (Fig. 84). After separation of the daughter cells there is a reciprocal formation of plates not derived from the parent-cell wall. A formation of aplanospores ("cysts") is known for several of the genera (Fig. 80).

The sexual reproduction found in *Ceratium* and in *Glenodinium*, both members of the Peridiniales, has already been described.

[1] Hofeneder, 1930.

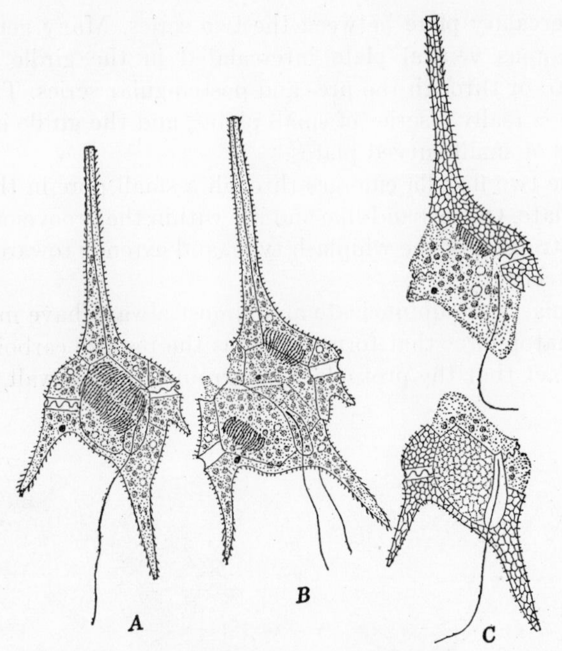

Fig. 84. Cell division of *Ceratium hirundinella* (O.F.M.) Schrank, showing the method of distribution of plates to daughter cells. (*After Lauterborn*, 1895.)

ORDER 3. DINOPHYSIDALES

The Dinophysidales are dinoflagellates with a wall composed of a definite number of plates arranged in a specific manner and with a wall that is vertically differentiated into two apposed halves (valves).

There are about 10 genera and 150 species, all marine and almost all of them plankton organisms.

The Dinophysidales have been referred[1] to the Desmophyceae because the wall was thought to consist of two valves without a differentiation into plates. Both valves of a wall are now known[2] to consist of a specific number of plates arranged in a definite manner.

Dinophysidales resemble Peridiniales in that a transverse girdle divides the wall into epi- and hypotheca but differ from them in that the epithecal portion is small and the hypothecal is very large. Dinophysidales also differ from Peridiniales in that there is regularly a development of conspicuous transverse wings by margins of epi- and hypotheca abutting on the girdle (Fig. 85). There may also be a conspicuous development of wings on the vertical zigzag saggital line (**suture**) where the two valves are apposed to each other. The wings have been con-

[1] Fritsch, 1935; Pascher, 1931.

[2] Kofoid, 1926; Kofoid and Skogsberg, 1928; Tai and Skogsberg, 1934.

sidered[1] upturned margins of plates. Wings along the suture may be restricted to the ventral face of a cell (that bearing the flagella), or they may be upon both dorsal and ventral faces.

The wall always consists of 17 plates.[1] The epitheca is composed of five plates; a small symmetrical pair, a large symmetrical pair, and a single small asymmetrical **pore plate.** The girdle consists of two symmetrical pairs; one large, the other small. The hypotheca consists of eight plates; two symmetrical pairs, one very large and the other small,

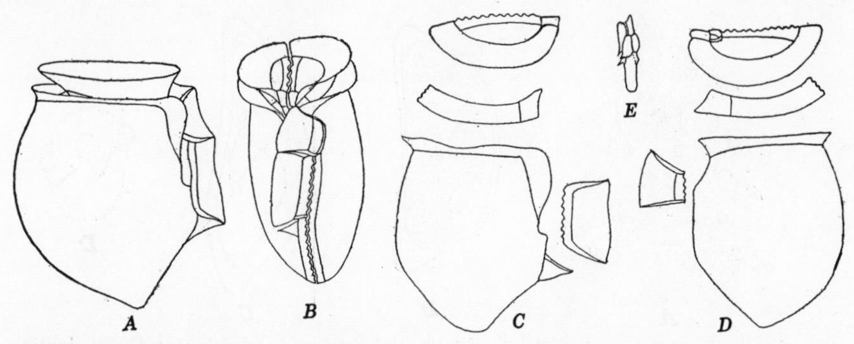

FIG. 85. *Dinophysis acuta* Ehr. *A*, side view. *B*, ventral view. *C*, disarticulated plates of left-hand valve. *D*, disarticulated plates from right-hand valve. *E*, sulcal plates. (*Based upon Tai and Skogsberg*, 1934.)

and an asymmetrical group of four small platelets that lie in the longitudinal furrow (**sulcus**).

The arrangement of the flagella and the structure of the protoplast are as in the Peridiniales.

Reproduction is by longitudinal division. Each daughter protoplast receives one of the valves of the parent-cell wall and forms an entirely new half wall.

ORDER 4. RHIZODINIALES

The Rhizodiniales are Dinophyceae in which the vegetative cells are naked and amoeboid. The single known representative, *Dinamoebidium varians* Pascher,[2] is marine.

Dinamoebidium (Fig. 86) is an organism in which vegetative cells are permanently amoeboid, not temporarily so, as in certain Peridiniales. The protoplasts are without chromatophores but have a conspicuous nucleus. Amoeboid movement of cells is vigorous and due to a sending forth of plump pseudopodia somewhat shorter than those of *Amoeba proteus*. The nutrition of *Dinamoebidium* is holozoic, and its cells frequently contain unicellular algae and protozoa (Fig. 86*A*).

Vegetative division of the amoeboid stage has never been observed,[2] but a formation of temporary cysts takes place quite frequently. An

[1] Tai and Skogsberg, 1934. [2] Pascher, 1915.

amoeboid protoplast becomes spindle-shaped and secretes a gelatinous wall with a thickened cap at either pole (Fig. 86*B*). The encysted protoplast soon divides transversely, and each of the daughter protoplasts redivides once or twice. Cessation of division is followed by a metamorphosis of each daughter protoplast into a naked *Gymnodinium*-like zoospore with a single transverse flagellum (Fig. 86*C–D*). The zoospores are liberated by a softening of one pole of the enclosing cyst wall. Their shape changes continually as they swim about through the water. Swarming rarely lasts

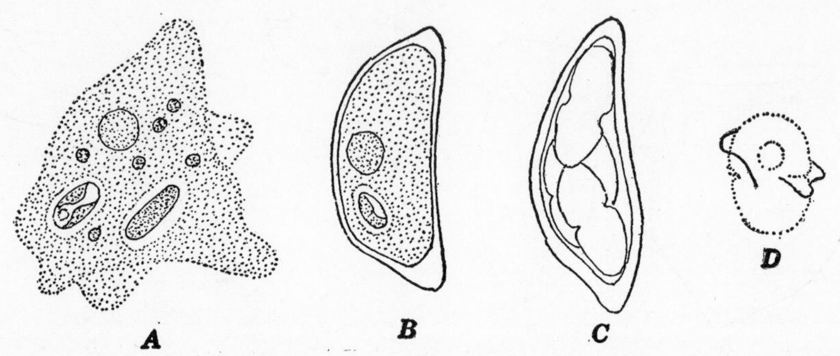

Fig. 86. *Dinamoebidium varians* Pascher. *A*, amoeboid stage. *B*, resting cyst. *C*, germinating cyst. *D*, zoospore from a germinating cyst. (*After Pascher*, 1915.)

for more than 15 minutes; then the zoospores retract their flagella and become amoeboid.

ORDER 5. DINOCAPSALES

The Dinocapsales are palmelloid Dinophyceae with a temporary motile gymnodinoid stage. The order corresponds to the Tetrasporales of Chlorophyceae, Heterocapsales of Xanthophyceae, and Chrysocapsales of Chrysophyceae.[1]

For a long time *Gloeodinium* was the only known member of the order. Recently *Urococcus insignis* (Hass.) Kütz., a palmelloid alga usually placed in the Chlorophyceae, has been placed[2] among the Dinocapsales because of its gymnodinoid zoospores.

Gloeodinium, with the single species *G. montanum* Klebs, is a freshwater alga and has usually been found in peaty marshes. Its large, subspherical, nonflagellated cells are united in packets of two, four, or eight cells surrounded by a homogeneous or concentrically stratified gelatinous envelope (Fig. 87). The cells are uninucleate and contain many small brownish chromatophores that are sometimes radially arranged.[3] The protoplasts contain considerable starch and frequently a single large red globule of oil.

[1] Pascher, 1927. [2] R. H. Thompson in Smith, 1950.
[3] Killian, 1924; Klebs, 1912; Thompson, 1949.

A cell divides into two daughter cells that are retained within the parent-cell envelope for a considerable time, and often until one or both cells have divided. Such colonies rarely develop beyond the eight-celled stage. Reproduction may also be by means of naked gymnodinoid zoospores and this occurs most frequently in late summer.[1] They escape through a rent in the parent-cell wall.

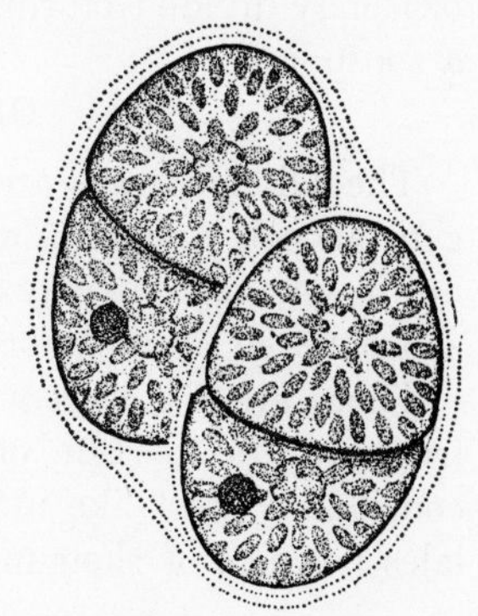

FIG. 87. *Gloeodinium montanum* Klebs. (*From Thompson*, 1949.) (× 725.)

ORDER 6. DINOTRICHALES

The Dinotrichales are Dinophyceae in which the cells are immobile, more or less cylindrical, and joined end to end in branching filaments.

There are two genera, each with a single species.[2] Filaments of one genus (*Dinothrix*, Fig. 88*A*) are of the same diameter throughout; those of the other genus (*Dinoclonium*, Fig. 88*B*) are gradually attenuated toward the branch apices. Cell walls of Dinotrichales are stratified and contain cellulose. The protoplast of a cell contains many small disciform chromatophores with a typical dinophycean color. Food reserves are stored either as starch or as oil. Increase in length of a filament is due to

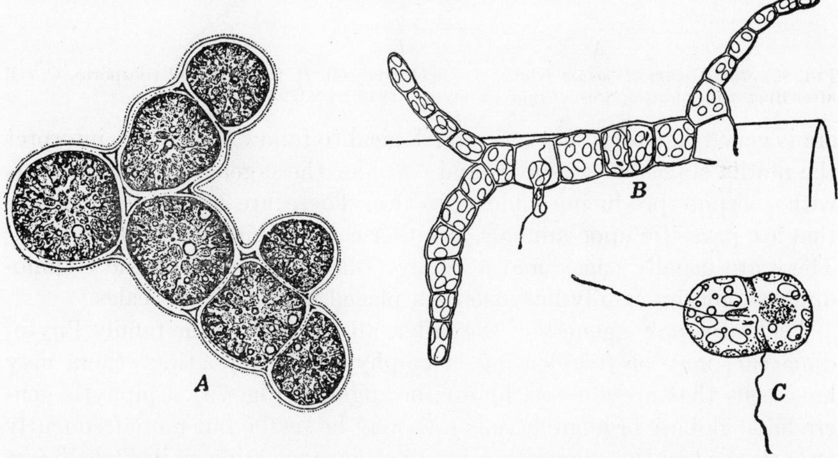

FIG. 88. Dinotrichales. *A*, filament of *Dinothrix paradoxa* Pascher. *B–C*, filament and zoospore of *Dinoclonium conradi* Pascher. (*From Pascher*, 1927.)

transverse cell division. The protoplast of a cell divides into two daughter protoplasts which may have a gymnodinoid transverse furrow and eyespot when first formed, but these features disappear after each protoplast becomes invested with a wall of its own.[2]

[1] Killian, 1924; Thompson, 1949. [2] Pascher, 1927.

Reproduction of Dinotrichales is due to a formation of *Gymnodinium*-like zoospores that are liberated through a pore in the lateral wall of a cell (Fig. 88*B*). The entire protoplast may develop into a single zoospore; or it may divide to form two daughter protoplasts, each of which becomes a zoospore.

ORDER 7. DINOCOCCALES

The Dinococcales are immobile unicellular Dinophyceae with homogeneous cell walls and without transverse grooves or flagella. The cells do not divide vegetatively and new cells are formed only by a production of zoospores or aplanospores (autospores).

There are 8 genera with some 20 species, most of which are found in fresh waters. Certain of these genera which are free-floating have been considered[1] cyst-like in nature and have been placed in the Gymnodiniales because of their motile stages. Since the motile phase in these gen-

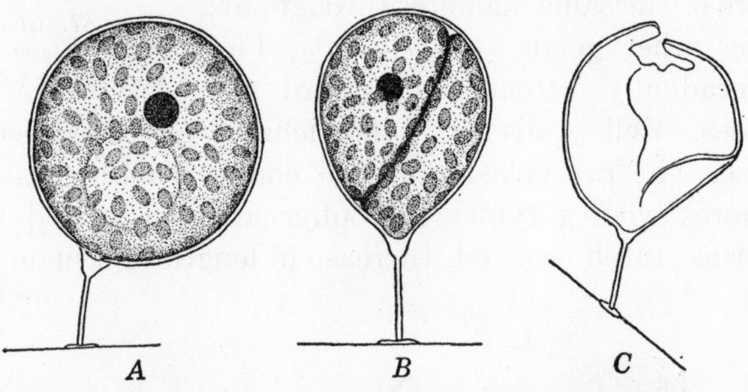

FIG. 89. *Stylodinium globosum* Klebs. *A*, vegetative cell. *B*, formation of zoospores. *C*, cell after liberation of zoospores. (*From Thompson*, 1949.) (× 725.)

era is very transitory, it seems more logical to follow those[2] who interpret the motile stages as zoospores and consider these genera as homologous with zoospore-producing Chlorococcales. There are also several genera that are parasitic upon animals, as either ectoparasites or endoparasites.[3] These are usually considered a family (Blastodiniaceae) of the Gymnodiniales but this family has also been placed in the Dinococcales.[4]

The autotrophic genera of the order, all referred to the family Phytodiniaceae, may be free-floating or epiphytic.[5] Free-floating genera may have cells that are globose, lunate, or angular (Fig. 79). Epiphytic genera have globose or angular cells that may be sessile but more frequently are attached to the substratum by a conspicuous stipe as in *Stylodinium* (Fig. 89). All Phytodiniaceae are uninucleate and with homogeneous cell walls. The protoplasts contain numerous brown chromatophores, granules of starch, and frequently a large reddish globule of oil.

[1] Klebs, 1912; Kofoid and Swezy, 1921; Lindemann, 1928.
[2] Fritsch, 1935; Graham, 1951; Pascher, 1927. [3] Chatton, 1920.
[4] Smith, 1950. [5] Geitler, 1928; Klebs, 1912; Pascher, 1927; Thompson, 1949.

Reproduction is generally by a division of the cell contents into two, four, or eight gymnodinoid zoospores. One species has been found[1] producing zooids of two different sizes and there is a possibility that the smaller of the two is gametic in nature. Zoospores (Fig. 89*B–C*) are usually liberated through a rent in the parent-cell wall. They swarm for a comparatively short time, become immobile, assume the same shape as the vegetative cell, and secrete a homogeneous wall. Daughter protoplasts within a parent-cell wall may assume the shape characteristic of the species and secrete a wall before they are liberated from the old parent-cell wall. Such aplanospores are autospores and comparable to those formed by certain of the Chlorococcales.

Bibliography

Chatton, E. **1920.** *Arch. d. Zool. Expér. et Gén.* **59:** 1–475. 18 pl. 159 figs. [Parasitic Dinococcales.]

Diwald, K. **1937.** *Flora* **132:** 174–192. 8 figs. [*Glenodinium.*]

Entz, G. **1921.** *Arch. Protistenk.* **43:** 415–430. 2 pl. 10 figs. [Mitosis.]

Fritsch, F. E. **1935.** The structure and reproduction of the algae. Vol. 1. Cambridge. 791 pp. 245 figs.

Geitler, L. **1926.** *Arch. Protistenk.* **53:** 343–346. 1 fig. [Chromatophores.]

1928. *Ibid.* **61:** 1–8. 4 figs. [Dinococcales.]

Graham, H. W. **1951.** Pyrrophyta. In G. M. Smith (editor), Manual of phycology. Waltham, Mass. Pp. 105–118. 3 figs.

Hall, R. P. **1925.** *Univ. Calif. Publ. Zool.* **28:** 29–64. 5 pl. 5 figs. [Mitosis.]

1925A. *Ibid.* **28:** 281–324. 5 pl. 7 figs. [Mitosis.]

Hofeneder, H. **1930.** *Arch. Protistenk.* **71:** 1–32. 2 pl. 9 figs. [Nutrition.]

Höll, K. **1928.** *Pflanzenforschung* **11:** 1–105. 10 figs. [Ecology.]

Killian, C. **1924.** *Arch. Protistenk.* **50:** 50–66. 2 pl. 2 figs. [*Gloeodinium.*]

Klebs, G. **1884.** *Bot. Zeitg.* **42:** 721–733, 737–745. 1 pl. [*Exuviaella.*]

1912. *Verh. Naturh.-Med. Ver. Heidelberg* N.F. **11:** 369–451. 1 pl. 15 figs. [Dinococcales.]

Kofoid, C. A. **1907.** *Zool. Anzeiger* **32:** 177–183. 8 fig. [Peridiniales.]

1909. *Arch. Protistenk.* **16:** 25–47. 1 pl. [Peridiniales.]

1926. *Univ. Calif. Publ. Zool.* **28:** 203–216. 1 pl. [Dinoflagellates.]

Kofoid, C. A., and T. Skogsberg. **1928.** *Mem. Mus. Comp. Zool. Harvard Coll.* **51:** 1–766. 31 pl. 103 figs. [Dinophysidales.]

Kofoid, C. A., and Olive Swezy. **1921.** *Mem. Univ. Calif.* **5:** 1–538. 12 pl. 48 figs. [Gymnodiniales.]

Köhler-Wieder, R. **1937.** *Oesterr. Bot. Zeitschr.* **86:** 198–221. 6 figs. [Mitosis.]

Lauterborn, R. **1895.** *Zeitschr. Wiss. Zool.* **59:** 167–190. 2 pl. [Mitosis.]

Lindemann, E. **1928.** Peridineae. In A. Engler and K. Prantl, Die natürlichen Pflanzenfamilien. 2d ed. Bd. 2. Pp. 1–104. 92 figs.

Mangin, L. **1907.** *Compt. Rend. Acad. Sci. Paris* **144:** 1055–1057. [Cell wall.]

1911. *Internat. Rev. gesamt. Hydrobiol. Hydrograph.* **4:** 44–54. 2 pl. [Cell wall.]

Pascher, A. **1911.** *Ber. Deutsch. Bot. Ges.* **29:** 193–203. [Cryptophyceae.]

1914. *Ibid.* **32:** 136–160. [Flagellates and algae.]

1915. *Arch. Protistenk.* **36:** 118–136. 1 pl. 4 figs. [*Dinamoebidium.*]

1927. *Ibid.* **58:** 1–54. 38 figs. [Dinophyceae.]

[1] Pascher, 1928.

1928. *Ibid.* **63:** 241–254. 7 figs. [Dinococcales.]
1931. *Beih. Bot. Centralbl.* **48:** 317–332. [Classification.]
Pringsheim, E. G. **1944.** *New Phytol.* **43:** 143–150. [Classification.]
Schiller, J. **1931–1937.** Dinoflagellatae. In L. Rabenhorst, Kryptogamen-Flora von Deutschlands, Österreich und der Schweiz. Leipzig. Bd. 10. 1 Teil. 617 pp. 631 figs. 2 Teil. 590 pp. 610 figs.
Schilling, A. J. **1891.** *Flora* **74:** 220–299. 3 pl. [Dinoflagellates.]
Schütt, F. **1890.** *Ber. Deutsch. Bot. Ges.* **8:** 9–32. 2 pl. [Pigments.]
1896. Peridiniales. In A. Engler and K. Prantl, Die natürlichen Pflanzenfamilien. Teil 1. Abt. 1^{b}. Pp. 1–30. 43 figs.
Smith, G. M. **1950.** The fresh-water algae of the United States. New York. 2d ed. 719 pp. 559 figs.
Tai, Li-Sun, and T. Skogsberg. **1934.** *Arch. Protistenk.* **82:** 380–482. 2 pl. 14 figs. [Dinophysidales.]
Thompson, R. H. **1947.** State of Maryland, Board of Nat. Resources. Publ. 67. 28 pp. 4 pl. [Dinoflagellates.]
1949. *Amer. Jour. Bot.* **36:** 301–308. 24 figs. [Dinococcales.]
Vlk, W. **1938.** *Arch. Protistenk.* **90:** 448–488. 1 pl. 12 figs. [Flagella.]
West, G. S. **1909.** *New Phytol.* **8:** 181–196. 7 figs. [Peridiniales.]
1916. Algae. Vol. 1. Cambridge. 475 pp. 271 figs.
Woloszyńska, J. **1917.** *Bull. Acad. Sci. Cracovie* Ser. *B.* **1917:** 114–122. 3 pl. [Dinoflagellates.]
1925. *Acta. Soc. Bot. Poloniae* **3:** 1–16. 7 figs. [Peridiniales.]
Zederbauer, E. **1904.** *Ber. Deutsch. Bot. Ges.* **22:** 1–8. 1 pl. [Sexual reproduction.]

CHAPTER 5

CHRYSOPHYTA

The Chrysophyta have their pigments localized in chromatophores that are yellowish green to golden brown because of a predominance of carotenes and xanthophylls. The food reserves include both **leucosin,** a carbohydrate of unknown chemical composition, and oils. There is never a formation of starch. The cell wall is generally composed of two overlapping halves and is frequently impregnated with silica. The cells may be flagellated or nonflagellated, and solitary or united in colonies of definite or indefinite shape.

Asexual reproduction of immobile genera may be by means of flagellated or nonflagellated spores. There is a widespread, although not universal, formation of a unique type of nonflagellated spore, the **statospore.**

Sexual reproduction is usually isogamous and by a union of flagellated or nonflagellated gametes, but it may also be anisogamous or oögamous. Autogamy also occurs within the Chrysophyta.

There are approximately 300 genera and 6,000 species. About three-fourths of the species are fresh-water, and one-fourth are marine.

Pascher[1] was the first to suggest a relationship between Xanthophyceae, Chrysophyceae, and Bacillariophyceae and to propose that these be united in a common group which he called the Chrysophyta. Previous to this the Xanthophyceae were thought to be related to the Chlorophyceae, the Chrysophyceae were grouped among the Flagellatae, and the Bacillariophyceae were considered a series distantly related to the Phaeophyta. Among the reasons given by Pascher[2] for considering Xanthophyceae, Chrysophyceae, and Bacillariophyceae related to one another are similarities in pigmentation, similarities in nature of food reserves, cell walls with two overlapping halves in vegetative cells or in spores, and formation of a distinctive type of spore, the statospore. Except for similarity of pigments, all these features have proved valid. In the case of the pigments, a fuller knowledge has shown that there are certain differences in pigmentation of the three classes (see Table I, page 4).

[1] Pascher, 1914. [2] Pascher, 1914, 1924.

Phycologists are generally agreed that there is a relationship between Xanthophyceae and Chrysophyceae. They are less certain about relationships of Bacillariophyceae to them, and all who place the Bacillariophyceae among the Chrysophyta think that their relationship to Xanthophyceae and Chrysophyceae is not so close as that between Xanthophyceae and Chrysophyta.

CLASS 1. XANTHOPHYCEAE (HETEROKONTAE)

The Xanthophyceae have yellowish-green chromatophores which contain chlorophyll *a*, chlorophyll *e*, beta-carotene, and but one xanthophyll. Food reserves generally occur as leucosin, but there may be an accumulation of oil. There is never a formation of starch. Vegetative cells of certain genera have a wall differentiated into two overlapping halves of equal or unequal size. The plant body may be unicellular or multicellular. Motile vegetative and reproductive cells are biflagellate, with the two flagella borne at the anterior end and differing in length and structure.

Asexual reproduction is generally by means of zoospores or aplanospores. Certain genera are known to have an endogenous production of statospores.

Sexual reproduction is known for but few genera. In most cases it is by an isogamous union of zoogametes, but in one genus it is oögamous.

There are about 75 genera and 375 species.

Occurrence. With a few exceptions the Xanthophyceae are fresh-water organisms. Fresh-water species are usually aquatic, but some of them are aerial. Certain aerial species grow on tree trunks, on damp walls, or intermingled with mosses and liverworts; other aerial species are terrestrial and grow intermingled with other algae of the soil or in dense stands on drying mud. Most aquatic species grow in soft waters only. The nonfilamentous aquatic species usually grow sparingly intermingled with other algae, but filamentous species may grow in almost pure stands.

Cell Structure. Cell walls of Xanthophyceae are composed chiefly of pectic compounds, either pectose or pectic acid. They may be somewhat impregnated with silica. Slight traces of cellulose have been found in walls of *Tribonema*,[1] and it has been held that the wall of *Botrydium*[2] consists almost wholly of cellulose. Many genera have cells that are enclosed by walls with two overlapping halves that fit together as do the two halves of a bacteriologist's Petri dish. In unicellular genera the two parts may be of equal size or markedly unequal in length. The two-parted nature of a wall cannot usually be made out unless the cells have been treated with concentrated potassium hydroxide or with a strong (30 to 40 per cent) chromic acid solution. Detailed study[3] of the wall of

[1] Tiffany, 1924. [2] Miller, 1927; Pascher, 1937–1939. [3] Bohlin, 1897.

one unicellular genus (*Ophiocytium*) has shown that the longer half consists of successive cup-shaped layers fitted one inside the other; the smaller half of the cell wall, the cover, is homogeneous in structure. In filamentous genera, as *Tribonema*, the wall of a filament is composed of a linear file of pieces that are **H**-shaped in optical section (Fig. 90). They alternately overlap one another so that each protoplast is enclosed by halves of two successive **H**-pieces. Each segment (**H**-piece) of a wall consists of two cup-shaped cylinders with a common base that constitutes

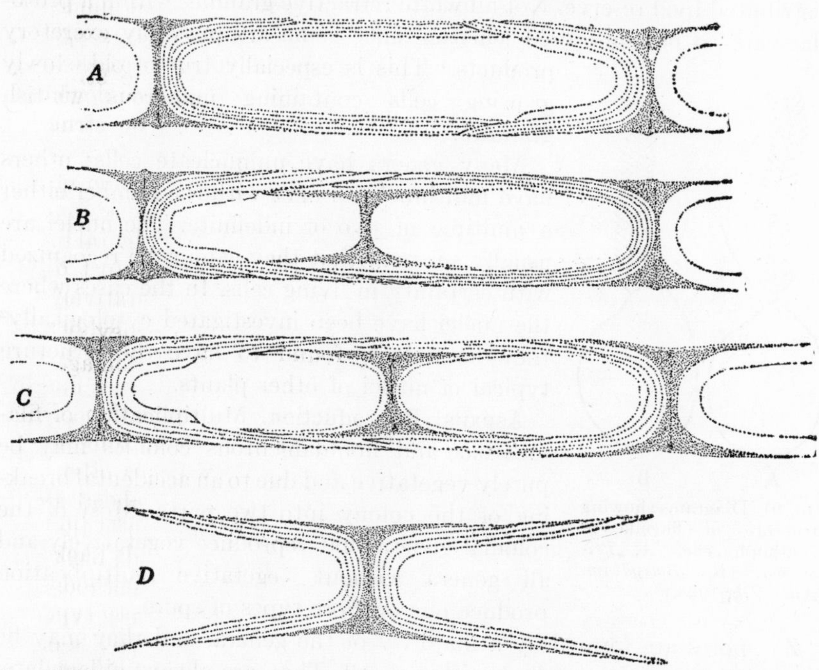

FIG. 90. Wall structure of *Tribonema bombycinum* (Ag.) Derbes and Sol. after treatment with potassium hydroxide. *A*, two **H**-pieces articulated to enclose a single protoplast. *B–C*, recently divided cells showing the intercalation of a new **H**-piece. *D*, **H**-piece. (× 900.)

a transverse wall of the filament. Each **H**-piece has a homogeneous **H**-shaped middle piece, the cross bar of the **H** constituting the median portion of the cell's cross wall, and the uprights of the **H** constituting the outermost layer of the lateral wall.[1] There are also additional layers of wall material lining the inner faces of the middle piece, and they lie so that each successively formed layer projects beyond the free margin of the previously formed one. The middle piece is the first-formed portion of a new wall segment, and the additional layers are successively deposited against it as a cell grows in length.

[1] Bohlin, 1897; Tiffany, 1924.

According to the genus, the protoplast of a cell contains one, two, a few, or innumerable chromatophores. These are parietal in position and almost always disk-shaped. Chromatophores of most species are without pyrenoids; but those of certain species, as *Botrydium*, may have evident ones. Pyrenoids, when present, are of the "naked" type and are not intimately concerned with the accumulation of reserve foods.

Oil is the chief food reserve accumulated in protoplasts of Xanthophyceae, but leucosin, an insoluble white substance, is also a rather widely distributed food reserve. Not all white refractive granules within a protoplast are to be considered leucosin since some are probably excretory products.[1] This is especially true of old, slowly growing cells containing numerous whitish granules.

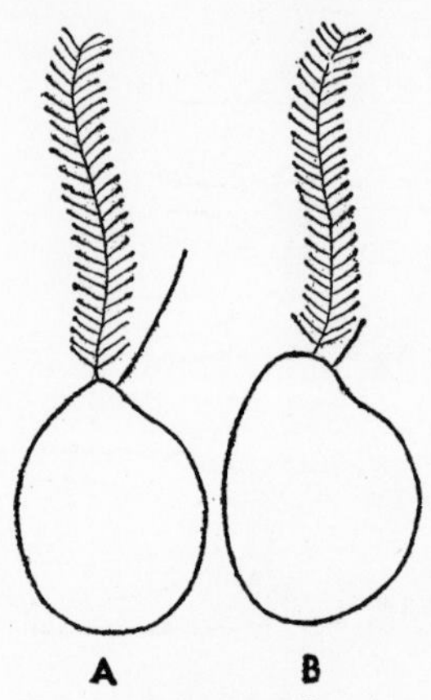

Fig. 91. Diagrams showing structure of flagella of Xanthophyceae. *A*, *Tribonema*. *B*, *Botrydium*. (*After Vlk*, 1938.)

Many genera have uninucleate cells; others have multinucleate ones with the number either a multiple of two or indefinite. The nuclei are usually so small that they cannot be recognized with certainty in living cells. In the cases where the nuclei have been investigated cytologically[2] they have been found to have the structure typical of nuclei of other plants.

Asexual Reproduction. Multiplication of filamentous and nonfilamentous colonies may be purely vegetative and due to an accidental breaking of the colony into two parts. Most of the colonial genera that reproduce vegetatively and all genera without vegetative multiplication produce one or more types of spore.

Zoospores are formed by a majority of the genera, and they may be formed singly or in numbers within a cell. They are always biflagellate, with the two flagella anterior in insertion and markedly different in length (Fig. 98*B*, page 175). The longer flagellum, which is often four to six times longer than the shorter one, extends straight ahead and is the propulsive organ of a zoospore. The shorter one, sometimes called the "trailing flagellum," is borne near the longer one and extends backward from the point of insertion. Staining of flagella by special methods[3] has shown that the two differ in structure. The longer is of the tinsel type and beset with a double row of mastigonemes ("cilia"); the shorter is of the whiplash type and is without mastigonemes (Fig. 91). Zoospores of Xanthophyceae are always naked and are usually pyriform They generally have one or more contractile vacuoles and one to a few chromatophores, but rarely an eyespot.

[1] Pascher, 1925. [2] Carter, 1919; Gross, 1937. [3] Vlk, 1931, 1938.

Instead of producing zoospores, the entire protoplast may produce a single aplanospore or divide into a number of parts, each of which becomes an aplanospore (Fig. 98*C–D*, page 175). An aplanospore liberated from the parent cell may grow directly into a new plant (Fig. 100*C–E*, page 178); or it may give rise to zoospores which, in turn, give rise to new plants.[1] Autospores are also formed by certain of the Heterococcales, and more than one of them is always formed within a cell. They develop the characteristic shape and wall structure of the parent cell before being liberated from the old parent-cell wall (Fig. 92*C*).

Vegetative cells may change directly into spore-like resting stages with much thicker walls and more abundant food reserves than vegetative

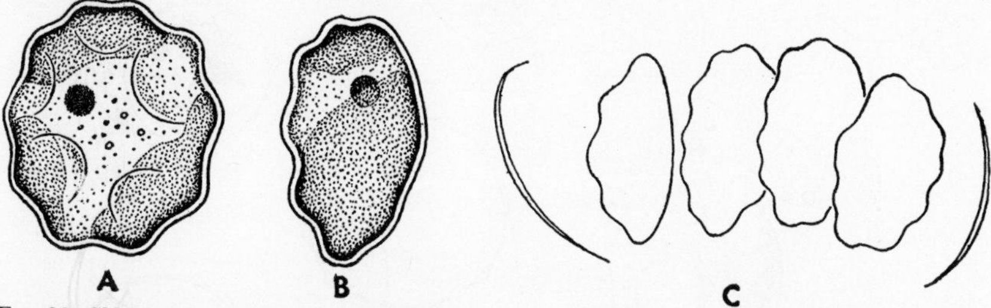

Fig. 92. *Chlorogibba trochisciaeformis* Geitler. *A*, top view. *B*, side view. *C*, liberation of autospores. (*Drawn by R. H. Thompson.*) (× 3,230.)

cells. Such spore-like cells are akinetes. Akinetes are most frequently encountered among filamentous Xanthophyceae, but they have also been reported for nonfilamentous genera. In filamentous genera, only an occasional cell, several consecutive cells, or all cells of a filament may develop into akinetes.

A few flagellated and rhizopodial Xanthophyceae are known[2] to form endoplasmic (endogenous) spores within their protoplasts. Such spores are frequently called cysts but they have also been called statospores because they seem to be homologous with the statospores of diatoms. In the formation of a statospore there is an internal differentiation of a spherical mass of protoplasm that is separated from the peripheral portion of the original protoplast by plasma membranes only (Fig. 93). The newly formed statospore then secretes a wall with two overlapping halves of equal or unequal size. A germinating statospore has its protoplast dividing to form two or four daughter protoplasts. The daughter protoplasts may be liberated as naked amoeboid bodies or liberated as biflagellate zoospores.[3]

Sexual Reproduction. Sexual reproduction by a fusion of zoogametes is definitely established for only two genera. In *Tribonema* one gamete of

[1] Pascher, 1932, 1937–1939. [2] Pascher, 1932*A*, 1937–1939.
[3] Pascher, 1932*A*.

a uniting pair is immobile and the other motile;[1] in *Botrydium* (Fig. 94) both of a fusing pair are motile and gametic union may be isogamous or anisogamous.[2] Sexual reproduction in the well-known genus *Vaucheria* is oögamous.

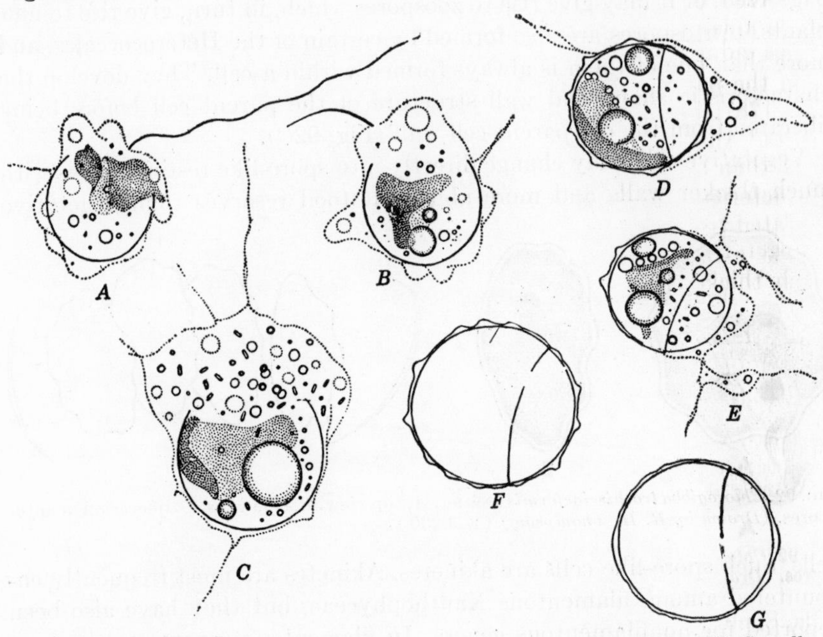

Fig. 93. *Chloromeson agile* Pascher. *A–E*, stages in formation of statospores. *F–G*, walls of mature statospores. (*From Pascher*, 1932*A*.)

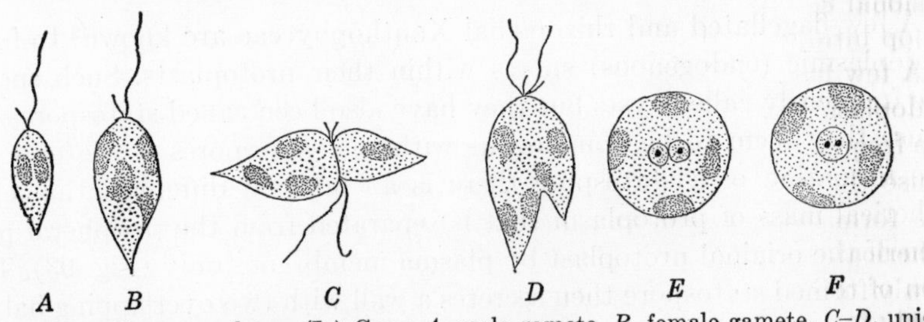

Fig. 94. *Botrydium granulatum* (L.) Grev. *A*, male gamete. *B*, female gamete. *C–D*, union of gametes. *E–F*, zygotes before and after union of gamete nuclei. (*After Moewus*, 1940.) (× 1,000.)

Classification. When first recognized[3] as a distinct class (called the Heterokontae) the motile genera were placed in one order and all other genera in another. Shortly afterward it was pointed out[4] that evolutionary lines evident among the Chlorophyceae are also evident among

[1] Scherffel, 1901. [2] Moewus, 1940. [3] Luther, 1899. [4] Pascher, 1913.

Xanthophyceae, and that Xanthophyceae could be segregated into orders homologous with those of Chlorophyceae. When classified in such a manner the Heterochloridales are comparable to the Volvocales, the Heterocapsales to the Tetrasporales, the Heterotrichales* to the Ulotrichales, the Heterococcales to the Chlorococcales, and the Heterosiphonales* to the Siphonales. The Rhizochloridales are an order without counterpart among the Chlorophyceae.

ORDER 1. HETEROCHLORIDALES

The Heterochloridales include all Xanthophyceae with flagellated vegetative cells. All genera are unicellular and without cell walls. A cell contains one, two, or more discoid to bacilliform chromatophores; and one or more contractile vacuoles. Reproduction is by cell division. One genus is known to form statospores.

The order includes about 9 genera and 15 species. Four of the genera are marine; the others are fresh-water. All are very rare organisms.

Cells of all genera show a marked tendency to change from a flagellated to an amoeboid state, and many of them, when in an amoeboid state, supplement their autotrophic nutrition by engulfing solid food. Cell division may take place while the cells are actively motile or after they have passed into temporary palmelloid or amoeboid stages.

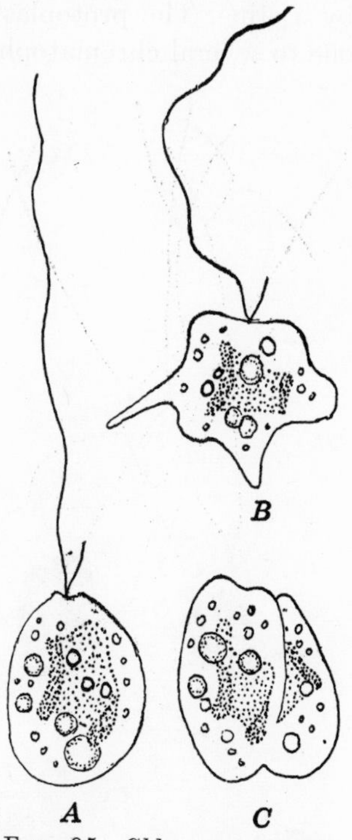

FIG. 95. *Chloromeson agile* Pascher. *A–B*, motile cells. *C*, dividing cell. (*After Pascher*, 1932*A*.)

Chloromeson, with the single species *C. agile* Pascher, grows in brackish water. Its cells are usually ovoid and somewhat compressed when motile but they may be distinctly amoeboid (Fig. 95*B*). A cell contains numerous droplets of oil and a single laminate chromatophore that lies in the central portion of the cell.[1] One flagellum is about six times the length of the other. Reproduction is by longitudinal division and takes place while cells are motile (Fig. 95*C*). Amoeboid cells, with or without flagella, may also have an endogenous formation of statospores[2] (see page 170).

* The ordinal names Heterotrichales and Heterosiphonales proposed by Pascher (1913) are not in accord with Article 27 of the International Code of Botanical Nomenclature which states that "The name of an order is taken from that of its type family." Despite their illegality, these names are universally used by phycologists.

[1] Pascher, 1930. [2] Pascher, 1932*A*.

ORDER 2. RHIZOCHLORIDALES

The Rhizochloridales have amoeboid protoplasts with pseudopodia. The protoplasts may be solitary or joined to one another by cytoplasmic bridges. Solitary protoplasts may be naked or partially surrounded by an envelope (**lorica**) that may be sessile and attached to the substratum by a stipe. The protoplasts are uninucleate or multinucleate and have one to several chromatophores.

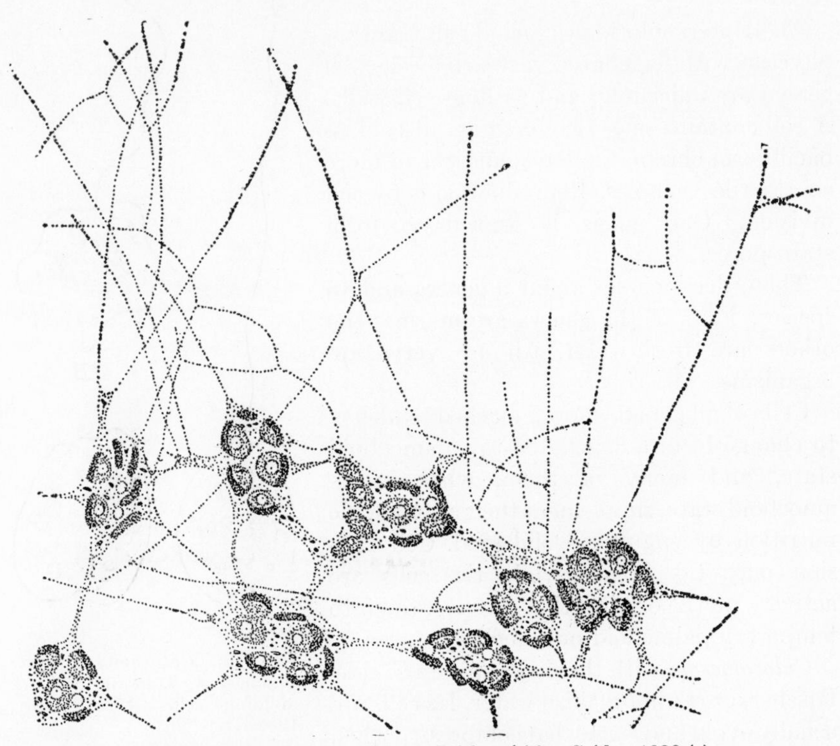

FIG. 96. *Chlorarachnion reptans* Geitler. (*After Geitler*, 1930*A*.)

Reproduction is by vegetative division or by a division of the protoplast into zoospores. The entire protoplast may round up, secrete a wall, and become aplanospore-like; or it may have an endoplasmic formation of statospores.

The order contains about 7 genera and 10 species, most of which are fresh-water.

The Rhizochloridales are Xanthophyceae in which the vegetative cells are permanently amoeboid instead of temporarily so as in the Heterochloridales. The amoeboid protoplasts may separate from one another immediately after division, or they may remain united by cytoplasmic strands until they have become plasmodial masses with as many as 150 cells.[1] Protoplasts of most Rhizochloridales are uninucleate, but those of at least one genus[2] are multinucleate. In some genera the only known method of reproduction is a vegetative division into two daughter protoplasts.[3] In the only known multinucleate genus the protoplast may divide to form several zoospores.[3] This may take place while the protoplast is in a vegetative condition or after it has rounded up and secreted a wall. Endoplasmic statospores are also known for this genus, and they have been shown[4] to form zoospores when they germinate.

Chlorarachnion, a marine genus with the single species *C. reptans* Geitler (Fig. 96), is the largest of all Rhizochloridales. It is a naked plasmodium one cell in thickness, with as many as 150 cells joined to one another by long cytoplasmic bridges.[5] The multicellular body may creep slowly in a plasmodial fashion across the bottom of a culture dish, or it may be free-floating. The individual cells have a single centrally located nucleus and a half-dozen or more disk-shaped chromatophores. Most of the chromatophores in a cell contain a conspicuous pyrenoid. Chromatophores are never present in the cytoplasmic strands connecting cells one to another. The protoplast also contains minute granules, presumably particles of reserve food. Nutrition of a plasmodium is partly autotrophic and partly holozoic by a mass ingestion of diatoms or other unicellular algae.

Multiplication is exclusively by cell division, and division may take place in either peripheral or interior cells of a plasmodium.

ORDER 3. HETEROCAPSALES

The Heterocapsales include those palmelloid Xanthophyceae whose immobile vegetative cells have the ability to return directly to a motile condition, or whose zoospores have the ability to divide directly into new zoospores. Immobile vegetative cells are surrounded by a gelatinous envelope that unites them in amorphous or dendroid colonies containing an indefinite number of cells. Cells of Heterocapsales have characteristically yellowish-green chromatophores and, so far as known, only fats and leucosin as reserve foods.

Reproduction, aside from vegetative cell division, is by means of naked zoospores. Thick-walled akinetes may also be formed.

The order contains about eight genera and nine species, all fresh-water.

Gloeochloris, a genus with two species, has spherical to subspherical colonies that may be 20 mm. or more in diameter. The colonies are a

[1] Geitler, 1930. [2] Pascher, 1930*A*. [3] Geitler, 1930*A*; Pascher, 1932.
[4] Pascher, 1932*A*. [5] Geitler, 1930*A*.

very pale yellowish green, and they may be free-floating or attached to submerged aquatics (Fig. 97*A*). The cells are ellipsoidal and lie irregularly distributed within the homogeneous gelatinous colonial matrix (Fig. 97*B*). Each cell contains two to six disk-shaped chromatophores, a single nucleus, and two to four leucosin granules.

Reproduction is by a direct metamorphosis of vegetative cells into elongate naked zoospores with two flagella of unequal length at the anterior end.[1] There may also be a formation of thick-walled akinete-like spores with a wall composed of two overlapping halves.

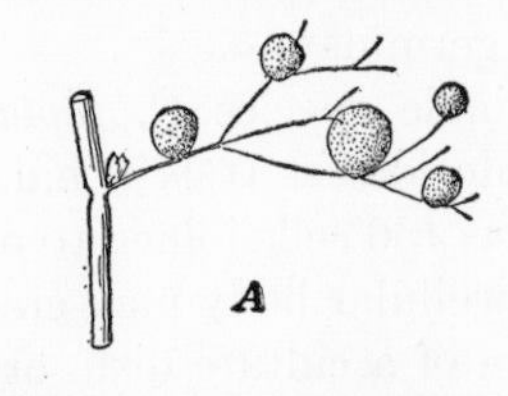

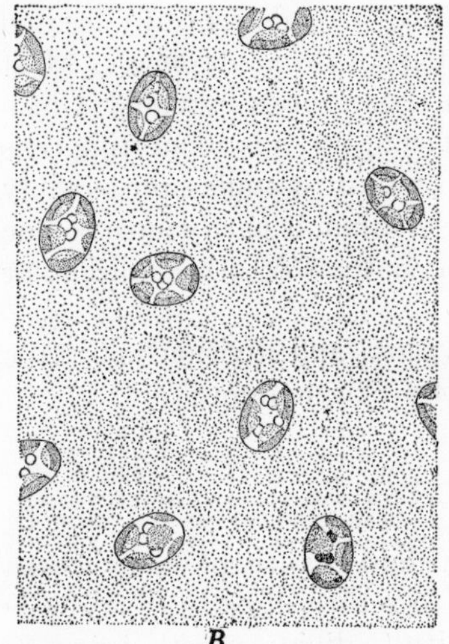

FIG. 97. *Gloeochloris smithiana* Pascher. *A*, colonies epiphytic upon *Ranunculus aquatilis* L. *B*, portion of a colony. (*A*, × ½; *B*, × 600.)

ORDER 4. HETEROTRICHALES

The Heterotrichales include all the Xanthophyceae with the cells united end to end in simple or branched filaments. Asexual reproduction may be by means of zoospores, aplanospores, or akinetes. One genus is known to reproduce sexually by a union of zoogametes.

There are about 8 genera and 35 species, all fresh-water.

Tribonema, with about 10 species, is a widely distributed fresh-water alga that frequently grows in abundance in temporary pools during early spring. Its cells are cylindrical or barrel-shaped, two to five times longer than broad, and joined end to end in unbranched filaments of indefinite length (Fig. 98*A*). The manner in which the **H**-pieces of the wall are articulated, and their structure, have already been discussed (page 167). The protoplast of a cell is uninucleate and, according to the species, contains few or many discoid chromatophores. Pyrenoids are lacking and photosynthetic reserves are stored as oils or granules of leucosin, never as starch. Old protoplasts often have numerous refractive granules within the cytoplasm, the majority of which are probably waste products.

Asexual reproduction may be purely vegetative and result from an accidental breaking of filaments, or from a disarticulation of certain **H**-pieces at the time of spore formation.

[1] Pascher, 1932.

Reproduction by means of aplanospores appears to be of much more frequent occurrence than reproduction by means of zoospores. Aplanospores[1] may be formed singly within a cell or more than one may be formed (Fig. 98*C–D*). The aplanospores are liberated by a pulling apart of **H**-pieces of the old parent-cell wall. Aplanospores generally have a wall consisting of two overlapping halves. Germination of an aplanospore is direct and begins with a separation of the two halves of the wall due to an elongation of the protoplast; then the elongating protoplast becomes cylindrical in shape and secretes a wall distinct from the old aplanospore wall.[2] *Tribonema* may also form akinetes. They are usually formed in several successive cells of a filament.

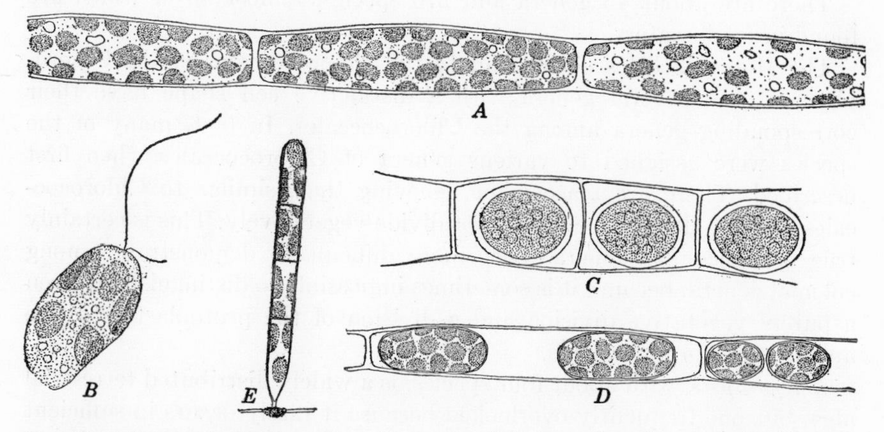

FIG. 98. *Tribonema bombycinum* (Ag.) Derbes and Sol. *A*, portion of a vegetative filament. *B*, zoospore. *C–D*, aplanospores. *E*, germling. (*A*, *D–E*, × 600; *B*, × 975; *C*, × 650.)

Zoospores (Fig. 98*B*) are generally formed singly within a cell. They are naked, are pyriform, contain two to several chromatophores, and have two flagella of unequal length at the anterior end.[3] A zoospore swarms for a short time and then comes to rest (possibly with the flagellated end downward) and secretes a wall which is attached to the substratum by a brownish discoid holdfast. One-celled germlings look very much like certain sessile unicellular Heterococcales, but this resemblance ceases after they have divided transversely and begun to grow into filaments (Fig. 98*E*). Sooner or later a developing filament, or the distal portion of it, breaks away and continues growth as a free-floating alga.

Sexual reproduction is isogamous and by the fusion of zoogametes.[4] One of a pair of gametes comes to rest and withdraws its flagella just before the other swims up to and unites with it.

[1] Lagerheim, 1889; Poulton, 1925; Wille, 1881. [2] Lagerheim, 1889.
[3] Luther, 1899; Pascher, 1925; Poulton, 1925; West, 1904. [4] Scherffel, 1901.

ORDER 5. HETEROCOCCALES

The Heterococcales include the nonfilamentous Xanthophyceae in which the immobile vegetative cells are surrounded by a wall and are not capable of returning directly to a motile condition. Vegetative cells are uninucleate or multinucleate. They have typical xanthophycean chromatophores and food reserves, and many of them have walls with two overlapping halves. Some genera are unicellular; others are multicellular and have the cells embedded within a common gelatinous matrix.

Reproduction may be by means of zoospores or aplanospores (autospores).

There are about 45 genera and 270 species, almost all of which are found in fresh waters.

The Heterococcales correspond to the Chlorococcales of the Chlorophyceae, and several genera with a distinctive cell shape have their corresponding genera among the Chlorococcales. In fact, many of the species were assigned to various genera of Chlorococcales when first described. There are reasons for believing that, similar to Chlorococcales, cells of Heterococcales do not divide vegetatively. This is certainly true of unicellular genera. It is more difficult to demonstrate among colonial genera, because it is sometimes impossible to distinguish between a purely vegetative division and a division of the protoplast into two aplanospores or autospores.

Botrydiopsis, with about four species, is a widely distributed terrestrial alga, but one frequently overlooked because it rarely occurs in sufficient quantity to form a conspicuous coating on the soil. The cells are always solitary. They are usually spherical, but they may be asymmetrical or biscuit-shaped. The wall of a cell is relatively thin and composed of two overlapping halves[1] that are sometimes slightly silicified.[2] A very young cell contains one or two discoid chromatophores; as the cell grows in size the chromatophores increase in number, and an adult cell may contain more than a hundred of them (Fig. 99*A–E*). Pyrenoids have been observed in stained cells of one species.[3] The food reserves are stored as minute droplets of oil.[4]

Zoospore formation may take place at any stage in the growth of a cell. When produced by young cells, only four or eight zoospores are formed; when produced by adult cells, they are formed in large numbers. The zoospores are broadly ovoid to pyriform, naked, and with two flagella of unequal length at the anterior end.[5] They contain one or two chromatophores, and possibly have an eyespot (Fig. 99*F*).

[1] Pascher, 1915. [2] Pascher, 1925. [3] Korshikoff, 1930.
[4] Borzi, 1895; Pascher, 1937–1939; Poulton, 1925.
[5] Chodat, 1913; Luther, 1899; Poulton, 1925; Smith, 1933; Vlk, 1931, 1938.

Frequently, and possibly because of environmental conditions, the cells form aplanospores instead of zoospores. Aplanospores usually enlarge directly into vegetative cells but sometimes they develop a very thick wall and have a greater content of food reserves.[1] Such hypnospores appear to enter into a period of rest before their contents divide to form zoospores or aplanospores.

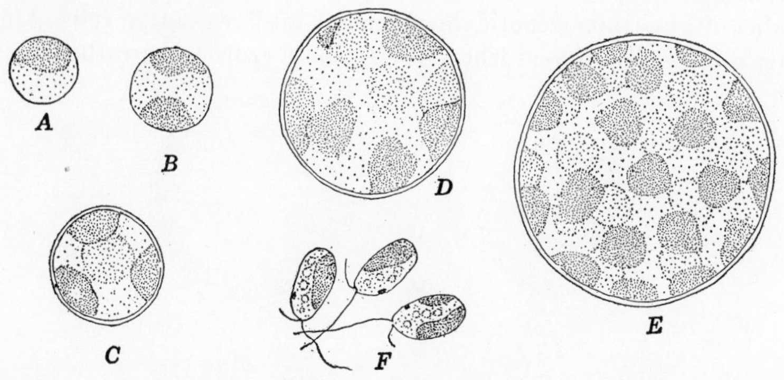

FIG. 99. *Botrydiopsis arhiza* Borzi. *A–E*, vegetative cells. *F*, zoospores. (× 900.)

ORDER 6. HETEROSIPHONALES

The Heterosiphonales include all the multinucleate siphonaceous unicellular Xanthophyceae. There are three or four genera, the two best-known being *Botrydium* and *Vaucheria*.

Botrydium has about six species, all of them terrestrial and growing either on drying muddy banks of streams and pools, or on bare damp soil. If conditions are favorable, the alga may form an extensive green coating on the soil.

The unicellular plant body of *Botrydium* consists of a vesicular aerial portion, which contains the chromatophores, and a colorless rhizoidal portion which penetrates the soil (Fig. 100*A–B*). The aerial portion may be 1 to 2 mm. in diameter. In most cases it is globose, but it may be a forked cylinder. The shape of the aerial portion is considerably influenced by environmental conditions and it tends to be cylindrical instead of globose if the plant grows in shade.[2] The vesicular portion has a relatively tough wall and internal to this is a thin layer of cytoplasm containing many nuclei and chromatophores. The chromatophores are discoid and often connected to one another by dense strands of cytoplasm. Pyrenoid-like bodies are often present in chromatophores of young plants, but there is never any starch in the protoplast and photosynthetic reserves accumulate as oils or as leucosin. The rhizoidal portion, which may be profusely or sparingly branched, is without chromatophores but con-

[1] Borzi, 1895; Poulton, 1925. [2] Kolkwitz, 1926.

tains many nuclei scattered throughout the vacuolate or nonvacuolate cytoplasm.

Cells of *Botrydium* do not divide vegetatively, and the only method by which new plants are formed is through a production of either aplanospores or biflagellate swarmers. The swarmers are usually called zoospores. However, they have been shown[1] to be gametic in nature but capable of a parthenogenetic development into vegetative cells. Aplanospores are usually formed when *Botrydium* is growing on rather dry soil.

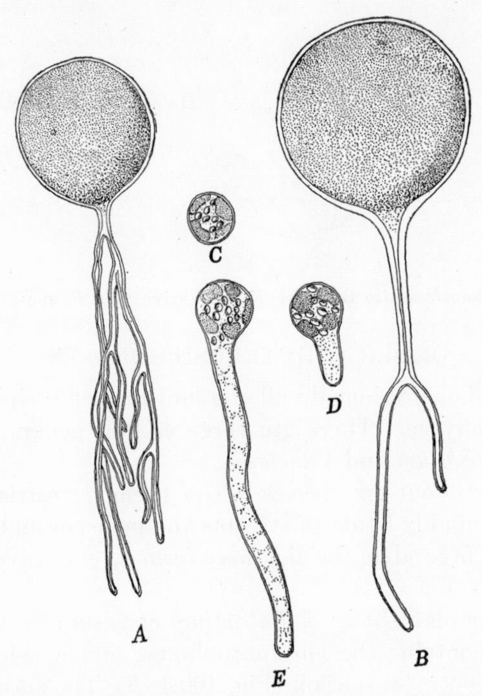

Fig. 100. *A*, *Botrydium granulatum* (L.) Grev. *B*, *B. wallrothii* Kütz. *C–E*, germinating aplanospores of *B. granulatum*. (*A–B*, × 25; *C–E*, × 310.)

In some cases the contents of the vesicular portion become divided into innumerable uninucleate protoplasts each of which rounds up and secretes a wall. In other cases, as in *B. wallrothii* Kütz., there is a cleavage of the cell contents into multinucleate protoplasts which become rounded and secrete a wall. Irrespective of whether uni- or multinucleate, an aplanospore develops directly into a new plant (Fig. 100*C–E*).

Aplanospores may become thick-walled spores (hypnospores). In some cases the hypnospores are formed in the aerial portion of a cell and are either uni- or multinucleate. In other cases practically all the protoplast of the aerial portion migrates into the rhizoids and there becomes di-

[1] Moewus, 1940.

vided into a number of multinucleate, serially arranged portions, each of which becomes a hypnospore.[1] In one species[2] a single hypnospore is formed at the tip of each branch in the rhizoidal system. Uninucleate hypnospores develop directly into new plants. Multinucleate ones have their protoplasts dividing to form a number of biflagellate swarmers or a number of aplanospores.

Formation of gametes usually takes place during rainy weather. The contents of the vesicular portion of a cell become divided into uninucleate protoplasts, each of which becomes a gamete. The gametes are pyriform, with one to four chromatophores, with or without an eyespot, and with the typical xanthophycean flagellation.[3] Liberation of gametes is generally by a gelatinization of the apical portion of the wall of the vesicle. *Botrydium* may be homothallic or heterothallic and gametic union may be isogamous or anisogamous.[3] A uniting pair of gametes become apposed at their anterior ends and then unite laterally to form a globose zygote (Fig. 94, page 170). Fusion of the two gamete nuclei is eventually followed by a division of the zygote into four or eight biflagellate zoospores that escape from the zygote wall. Genetic analysis of the products of germinating zygotes of a heterothallic species shows that division of the zygote nucleus is meiotic.[3]

For a long time certain phycologists questioned the practice of placing *Vaucheria* in the Siphonales of the Chlorophyceae, but it was not until 1945 that it was formally placed among the Xanthophyceae.[4] It was placed in this class because of the color of the chromatophores and the lack of starch. Since then, additional evidence has accumulated to show that *Vaucheria* belongs to the Xanthophyceae. The pigments in the chromatophores are those of typical Xanthophyceae, and there are neither of the two xanthophylls found only in Siphonales.[5] Of the two flagella borne by an antherozoid one is of the tinsel type and the other of the whiplash type.[6]

Vaucheria is a genus with about 40 species; about half a dozen marine, the remainder fresh-water and terrestrial or aquatic. Terrestrial species grow upon damp soil and in plowed fields where they may form extensive felty green mats. The thallus is a sparingly branched tubular cell that frequently attains a length of several centimeters. When terrestrial, the thallus is often attached to the soil by means of rhizoid-like branches with relatively few chromatophores. A cell increases in length by elongation of the terminal portion. The cell wall is relatively thin. Within the wall is a single central vacuole that runs without interruption from end to end. The layer of cytoplasm between wall and vacuole contains many chromatophores toward its outer face and numerous minute nuclei to-

[1] Miller, 1927; Rostafiński and Woronin, 1877. [2] Iyengar, 1925.
[3] Moewus, 1940. [4] Chadefaud, 1945. [5] Strain, 1948. [6] Koch, 1951.

ward its inner face. The chromatophores are small, circular to elliptical in outline, and without pyrenoids. There are also minute droplets of oil in the cytoplasm.

Asexual reproduction may take place in a variety of ways. The commonest method is by means of large multiflagellate zoospores. All the aquatic species form zoospores, and terrestrial species may form them

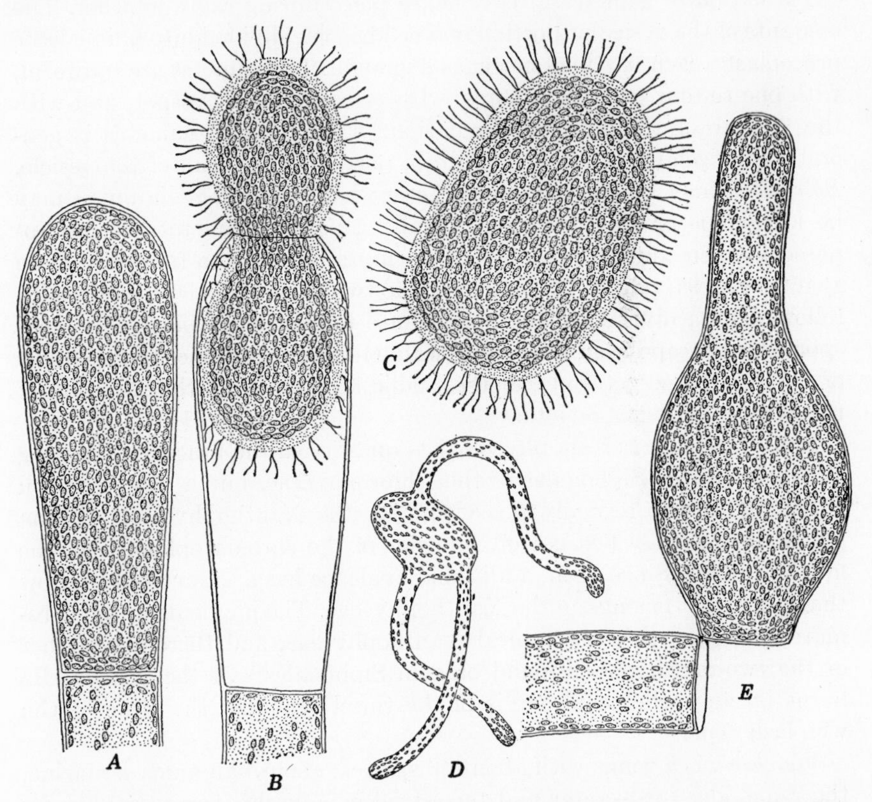

Fig. 101. *Vaucheria* sp. *A*, zoosporangium. *B*, liberation of zoospore. *C*, zoospore. *D*, germination of zoospore. *E*, germination of a sporangium that has become an akinete. (*A–C*, diagrammatic.) (*A–C*, × 430; *D*, × 60; *E*, × 325.)

when flooded. Zoospore formation may be induced in aquatic species by transferring them from light to darkness or from running to quiet water.[1] Zoospores are formed singly within club-shaped sporangia. Sporangial development begins with a club-shaped swelling of the distal end of a branch. There are many nuclei and chromatophores in this inflated portion. There is next a transverse division of the protoplast, a short distance back from the branch apex, and a development of a transverse wall between the two newly formed plasma membranes (Fig. 101*A*). Nuclei

[1] Klebs, 1896.

and chloroplasts within a sporangium reverse their position so that the nuclei lie just within the plasma membrane. Following this, the protoplast contracts slightly and develops a pair of flagella external to each nucleus[1] or external to nuclei in the anterior half of a sporangium.[2] After the zoospore is fully developed, the distal portion of the sporangial wall softens to form a pore smaller in diameter than the zoospore. Liberation of zoospores usually takes place shortly after daybreak. A zoospore[3] squeezes its way through the narrow pore and then swims freely in all directions (Fig. 101*B–C*). It moves slowly through the water for 15 to 30 minutes; then it comes to rest, withdraws its flagella, and secretes a wall. Germination takes place immediately by a sending forth of from one to three tubular outgrowths that may elongate indefinitely (Fig. 100*D*). The multiflagellate zoospore of *Vaucheria* is generally interpreted as a compound zoospore formed within a sporangium in which there has been a permanent obliteration of cleavage of the sporangial protoplast into uninucleate biflagellate spores.

Terrestrial species frequently have the entire contents of a sporangium developing into a thin-walled aplanospore or a thin-walled akinete, instead of into a zoospore. Production of these nonflagellated spores is largely dependent upon environmental conditions since there is a regular formation of zoospores when the species grows submerged. The aplanospores are liberated by an irregular rupture of the sporangial wall; the akinetes may become detached from a thallus, or they may germinate while attached to it (Fig. 101*E*). The entire protoplast of a cell may also divide into a large number of small aplanospores[4] (microaplanospores). Terrestrial species may also have a transverse segmentation of the entire protoplast into short segments and the secretion of a thick wall about each segment. Formation of these thick-walled aplanospores (hypnospores) is generally ascribed[5] to a drying out of the substratum, but in California[6] they are formed during the winter rainy season only when temperatures are near the freezing point. The hypnospores may germinate directly into a new filament, or their contents may divide into a number of thin-walled "cysts." The protoplast of a germinating cyst escapes through a pore in the wall and moves about in an amoeboid fashion. When amoeboid movement ceases, the protoplast assumes a spherical shape, secretes a wall, and develops directly into a filament.[5]

All species reproduce sexually. Sexual reproduction is of frequent occurrence among thalli growing on damp soil or in quiet water but is rarely found among plants growing in flowing water. All the fresh-water species are homothallic; two or three of the marine species are heterothallic. Homothallic species bear their antheridia and oögonia adjacent

[1] Strasburger, 1880. [2] Götz, 1897. [3] Birckner, 1912; Götz, 1897; Klebs, 1896.
[4] Smith, 1944. [5] de Puymaly, 1922; Stahl, 1897. [6] Smith, 1950.

to one another, either on a common lateral branch or on adjoining branches.

Antheridia are formed at the ends of short lateral branches and their development begins slightly before that of the oögonia. Most of the common fresh-water species have a hook-shaped antheridium opening by a terminal pore, but there are certain fresh-water species in which there is more than one pore and in which the antheridium is not hook-shaped. The distal end of a branch producing an antheridium is more or less densely filled with cytoplasm containing many nuclei and a few chloroplasts (Fig. 102*A*). There is a transverse cleavage separating this portion of the protoplast from that in the remainder of the branch and a formation of a transverse wall between the two newly formed plasma membranes (Fig. 102*C*). The protoplast of an antheridium becomes divided into a number of uninucleate fragments each of which is metamorphosed into a biflagellate antherozoid. The insertion of the flagella is usually described[1] as lateral, but they have been found[2] to be terminal in insertion and of equal length and unlike in structure. Antheridial development begins in the afternoon, and the formation of antherozoids is completed before daybreak the next morning.[3]

In species with the sex organs borne adjacent to one another, as *V. sessilis* (Vauch.) DC., oögonial development begins with an accumulation of a colorless multinucleate mass of cytoplasm in the main thread and near the base of an antheridial branch.[1] This is the "wanderplasm," and it moves into the young oögonium produced by a lateral bulging of the main thread (Fig. 102*A–B*). Many nuclei and chloroplasts migrate into the oögonial bulge as it increases in size. The oögonial bulge eventually becomes an oögonium separated from the main filament by a transverse wall. The oögonium contains a single uninucleate egg. Descriptions of oögonial development are at variance. It has been held[4] that the uninucleate condition of the egg is due to a degeneration of all except one nucleus of a developing oögonium, but there seems to be more evidence supporting those[5] who hold that all but one, or all but a very few, of the nuclei migrate out from an oögonium before formation of the cross wall. In any case, it is quite clear[6] that the cross wall is not formed until very late in oögonial development (Fig. 102*C*).

Antherozoids enter an oögonium through an apical pore produced by gelatinization of the oögonial wall. Antherozoids are liberated shortly before daybreak,[7] and fertilization follows immediately afterward. Several antherozoids may enter an oögonium, but only one of them pene-

[1] Couch, 1932; Oltmanns, 1895. [2] Koch, 1951. [3] Couch, 1932.

[4] Davis, 1904; Mundie, 1929; Williams, 1926.

[5] Couch, 1932; Gross, 1937; Heidinger, 1908; Oltmanns, 1895.

[6] Couch, 1932; Mundie, 1929. [7] Couch, 1932; Mundie, 1929; Oltmanns. 1895.

trates the egg. The small male nucleus migrates to the egg nucleus, which is considerably larger, but does not immediately fuse with it. The male nucleus increases in size until its volume approximates that of the egg nucleus; the two then fuse.[1] The fusing nuclei usually lie a short distance

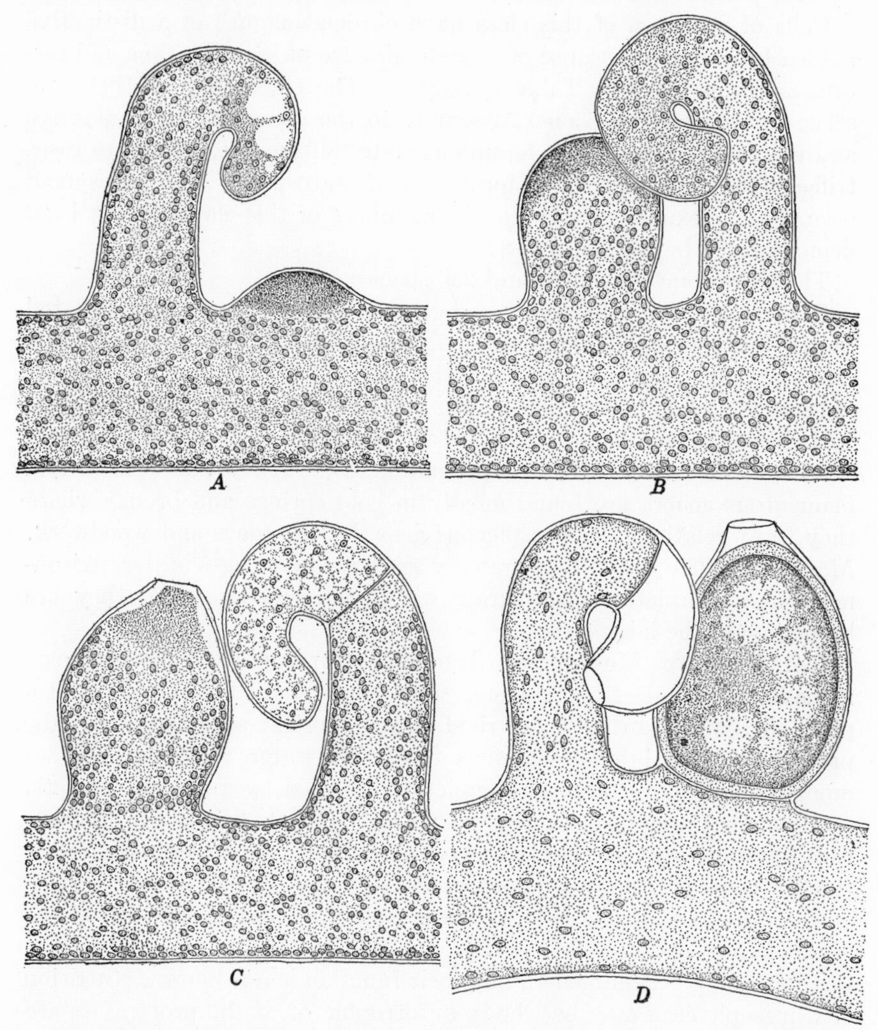

Fig. 102. Development of sex organs of *Vaucheria sessilis* (Vauch.) DC. (× 430.)

from the pore in the oögonial wall; the zygote nucleus formed by their fusion migrates to the center of the zygote.[2] The zygote secretes a thick wall, with three to seven layers, and its protoplast becomes densely filled with oil (Fig. 102*D*). The zygote generally enters upon a resting period

[1] Mundie, 1929; Williams, 1926. [2] Davis, 1904; Mundie, 1929; Williams, 1926.

of several months before it germinates directly into a new filament.[1] The rather inconclusive data indicate[2] that division of the zygote nucleus is meiotic.

CLASS 2. CHRYSOPHYCEAE

Cells of members of this class have chromatophores of a distinctive golden brown color because of a predominance of beta-carotene and certain xanthophylls (see Table I, page 4). The chief photosynthetic reserves are leucosin and oils. According to the genus, motile vegetative and reproductive cells may be uniflagellate, biflagellate, or in rare cases triflagellate. An endogenous formation of statospores is of widespread occurrence. Sexual reproduction in members of this class has not been demonstrated beyond all doubt.

There are some 70 genera and 250 species.

Occurrence. The Chrysophyceae contain a great wealth of flagellated forms, both unicellular and colonial, and relatively few nonflagellated forms. A very large proportion of the species are fresh-water and most of them are found only in soft waters and at seasons when the waters are cool. Many of the motile fresh-water species occur in the plankton of lakes and here they are often present in abundance. The coccoid and filamentous genera are found mostly in cold springs and brooks where they form gelatinous or crustaceous growths on stones and woodwork. Many of the Chrysophyceae are very sensitive to changes in the environment and completely disintegrate within a few hours after they are brought into the laboratory.

Cell Structure. Most of the flagellated Chrysophyceae, the **chrysomonads,** have naked protoplasts. Some chrysomonads have the protoplast surrounded by an open rigid sheath (**lorica**) separated from the protoplast by an intervening space filled with water. Still other chrysomonads have the protoplast completely enclosed by a sheath of pectic material that may contain siliceous scales. Cells of coccoid and filamentous Chrysophyta have cell walls that rarely have an evident differentiation into two overlapping halves.

A majority of all genera have protoplasts that contain but one or two golden brown chromatophores. Pyrenoid-like bodies are present in chromatophores of certain genera but their function is not known. Nutrition of Chrysophyceae may be wholly autotrophic or, if the protoplasts are naked, partly autotrophic and partly heterotrophic. There are a few saprophytic forms without chromatophores. All members of the class whose cells have been studied cytologically are uninucleate and it is rather probable that this holds for the entire class.

[1] Mundie, 1929; Pringsheim, 1855; Walz, 1866.
[2] Gross, 1937; Hanatschek, 1932; Williams, 1926.

Many of the motile forms have contractile vacuoles at the base of their flagella, and these vacuoles persist even after the flagellated phase has passed over into a temporary amoeboid phase. Uniflagellate genera have a flagellum of the tinsel type, with a row of mastigonemes ("cilia") on opposite sides of the flagellum.[1] Biflagellate genera have one flagellum of the tinsel type and one of the whiplash type.[2]

Asexual Reproduction. Asexual reproduction of motile unicellular genera is by cell division that is always longitudinal and into two daughter cells that immediately separate from each other. Multiplication of colonial motile genera may be by a colony fragmenting into two or more parts, or by a single cell breaking away from the colony and developing into a new

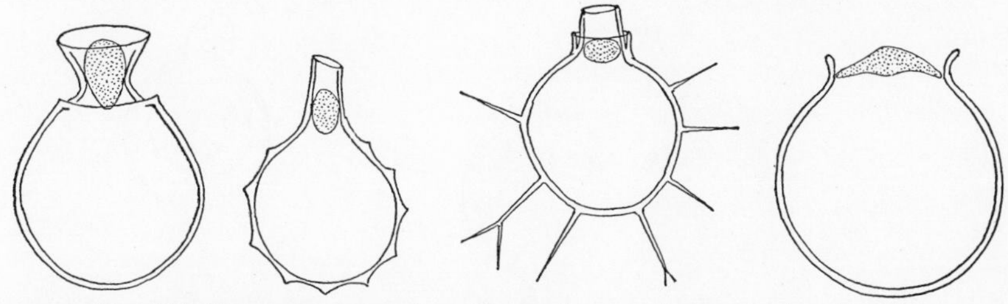

FIG. 103. Statospores of various Chrysophyceae. (*After Pascher*, 1932*A*.)

colony. Coccoid and filamentous nonmotile colonies may reproduce by vegetative fragmentation.

All the nonmotile genera may produce zoospores. These are usually formed singly within a cell but in certain genera the protoplast divides to form several zoospores. Zoospores of Chrysophyceae are naked and have one or two chromatophores. Some are uniflagellate; others are biflagellate and with the flagella of equal or unequal length. Aplanospores have not been recorded for Chrysophyceae.

Statospores, the unique type of spore found in Chrysophyta, are known for many genera of the Chrysophyceae. They are usually spherical, although sometimes ellipsoidal. The spore wall is silicified, composed of two overlapping halves, and has a pore closed by a conspicuous gelatinous plug that may or may not be silicified. Statospores of many species have smooth walls; those of other species have walls ornamented with punctae, spines, or flange-like extensions (Fig. 103). As is the case with zygotes of Desmidiaceae, no one particular sculpturing is characteristic for a particular genus, and there may be marked differences in ornamentation from species to species in a genus.

Most investigations of statospore formation have been upon chrysomonads,[3] but certain nonmotile genera are also known[4] to have an en-

[1] Vlk, 1938. [2] Petersen, 1929; Vlk, 1938.

[3] Cienkowski, 1870; Conrad, 1927, 1928; Doflein, 1923; Scherffel, 1911.

[4] Geitler, 1927.

doplasmic formation of them. A motile cell about to form a statospore comes to rest, retracts its flagella, and assumes a spherical shape. There is then an internal differentiation of a spherical protoplast that is separated only by plasma membranes from the peripheral portion of the original protoplast (Fig. 104*A–E*). Following this, there is a secretion of a wall between the two newly formed plasma membranes, except for a small circular area that becomes the pore. In certain genera the cytoplasm external to the statospore wall migrates inward through the pore and fuses with the cytoplasm within the wall, after which there is a formation of a plug that closes the pore.[1] In other genera there is a gradual disintegration of cytoplasm external to the wall as the statospore

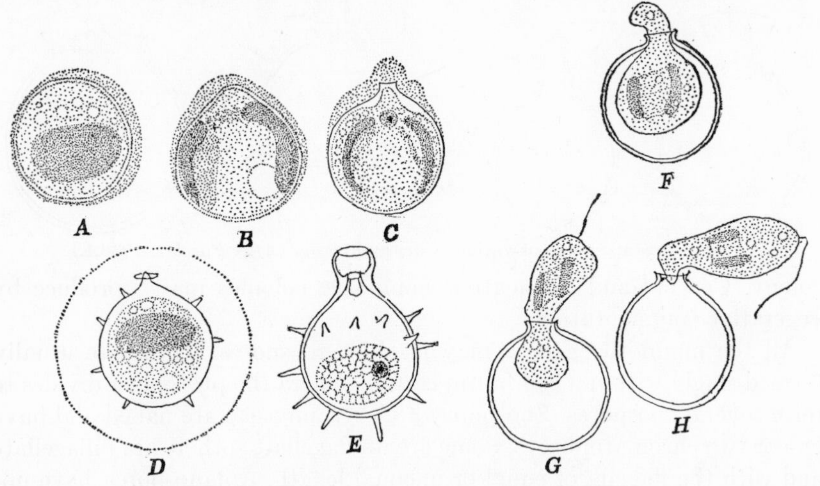

FIG. 104. *A–E*, statospore formation in *Ochromonas crenata* Klebs. *F–H*, germination of statospore of *Chromulina freiburgensis* Dofl. (*After Doflein*, 1923.)

matures. Statospores of most genera are uninucleate, but those of one genus have been shown[2] to be binucleate.

When a statospore germinates, there is a dissolution of the plug or a separation of it from the spore wall (Fig. 104*F–H*). Most genera have an amoeboid migration of the protoplast from the enclosing wall and a formation of flagella during or after the migration,[1] but in certain genera[3] the protoplast within a wall divides to form two or four zoospores before the contents are liberated.

Classification. Pascher's separation of the chrysophycean algae into orders homologous with the orders into which the Chlorophyceae are divided has met with general approval ever since it was proposed.[4] It is a matter of opinion whether one should follow those who place motile,

[1] Doflein, 1923. [2] Geitler, 1935*A*.
[3] Conrad, 1926; Hofeneder, 1913. [4] Pascher, 1914.

plasmodial, and tetrasporaceous Chrysophyceae in separate orders[1] or place them as suborders of a single order.[2]

ORDER 1. CHRYSOMONADALES

The Chrysomonadales include the genera in which the cells are motile during vegetative phases. According to the genus the cells may be uni-, bi-, or triflagellate and solitary or united in colonies of definite shape. The cells may be naked or with an envelope (lorica) that is open at the distal end. There are either one or two chromatophores within a cell. Many of the genera are known to produce statospores.

There are about 35 genera and 175 species, almost all of which are fresh-water.

Chromulina (Fig. 105), a genus with about 20 species, is representative of the unicellular genera. Its cells are uniflagellate; and spherical, ellip-

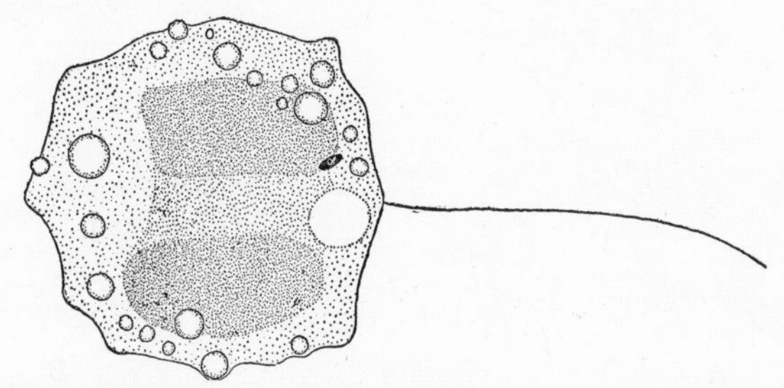

FIG. 105. *Chromulina globosa* Pascher. (*After Lackey*, 1939.)

soidal, ovoid, or fusiform. There may be one, two, or even more vacuoles at the base of the flagellum.[3] A protoplast may contain either one or two laminate chromatophores and if two are present they lie on opposite sides of the cell. In very rare cases, as in *C. dubia* Dofl., there is a single pyrenoid within each chromatophore. The position of the nucleus is extremely variable from species to species; and it may be in the anterior, median, or posterior portion of a cell. Some species have an eyespot near the point of insertion of the flagellum. Leucosin is usually formed in greater abundance than are fats, and it may accumulate in a single large granule or in numerous small granules.

Reproduction is by longitudinal division and may take place without a cell coming to rest and retracting its flagellum.[4] Rhizopodial stages are only occasionally seen in this organism[4] and palmella stages have been reported for but one species.[5] Statospores are known for several species. They are smooth-walled and some or all of the cytoplasm external to the statospore wall migrates inside the wall before the plug is formed.

[1] Prescott, 1951; Smith, 1950. [2] Fritsch, 1935. [3] Doflein, 1923.
[4] Doflein, 1923; Scherffel, 1911. [5] Pascher, 1910.

Synura, with some five species, is representative of the colonial genera. It is found in both fresh and brackish waters and sometimes is present in abundance in fresh-water pools and lakes. The cells are obpyriform and radiately arranged in spherical to oblong-ovoid colonies without a gelatinous colonial envelope (Fig. 106). Each cell is surrounded by a thin sheath of pectic material whose posterior end is prolonged into a hyaline stalk.[1] The distal end of each sheath is covered with spirally arranged siliceous plates each bearing a very short blunt spine.[2] The protoplast of a cell contains two curved chromatophores so placed that their concave faces are opposite. A protoplast contains a single centrally located nucleus and two or three contractile vacuoles near its base. Leucosin is the chief food reserve and it accumulates in a single large granule toward the

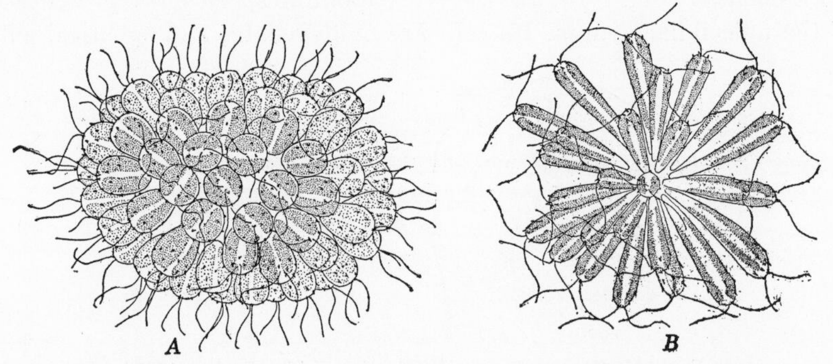

FIG. 106. *A*, *Synura uvella* Ehr. *B*, *S. adamsii* G. M. Smith. (× 400.)

base of a cell. There is no eyespot. The two flagella at the anterior end of a cell are of equal length, one being of the tinsel type, the other of the whiplash type.[3]

Cell division is always longitudinal. Ordinarily it only increases the number of cells in a colony. Reproduction of colonies generally takes place by the cells grouping themselves radially about two centers, and the two parts then separating from each other. Reproduction may also be due to amoeboid escape of a protoplast from its scale-covered sheath.[4] The liberated protoplast may remain amoeboid or it may become a biflagellate zoospore that swarms for a time and then develops into a palmella stage or into a new motile colony. *Synura* may also form endoplasmic statospores.[5]

ORDER 2. RHIZOCHRYSIDALES

The Rhizochrysidales include those Chrysophyceae in which the amoeboid phase is dominant in vegetative cells and not temporary. Unicellular

[1] Conrad, 1926. [2] Korshikov, 1929; Petersen, 1918.
[3] Petersen, 1918. [4] Pascher, 1912. [5] Conrad, 1926.

genera may be naked or partially surrounded by a lorica; colonial genera may be naked or with each cell enclosed by a lorica. Reproduction may be solely by cell division, or by both cell division and a formation of zoospores. Certain genera are known to form statospores.

There are about 12 genera and 20 species.

Chrysamoeba, with the single species *C. radians* Klebs (Fig. 107), is a rare fresh-water unicellular genus without a lorica. In very rare cases a few cells may be temporarily united in colonies. For the greater part of the life cycle the cell is in an amoeboid state with acutely pointed pseudopodia radiating in all directions. The protoplast may contain either one[1] or two[2] golden brown chromatophores that have or lack pyrenoids. Each cell contains a single large nucleus and, at times, a large granule of leucosin. Nutrition is in part photosynthetic and in part by a mass ingestion of foods. The change from an amoeboid to a flagellated stage is accomplished by a retraction of the pseudopodia, a change to an ovoid shape, and the protrusion of a single long flagellum whose length is somewhat greater than that of a cell. During the motile phase, there is a contractile vacuole in the anterior end of a cell. The motile phase seems to last for a short time only,[3] after which the organism becomes more nearly spherical and develops denticulations that grow into pseudopodia. The flagellum may persist for some time after the cell has become amoeboid.

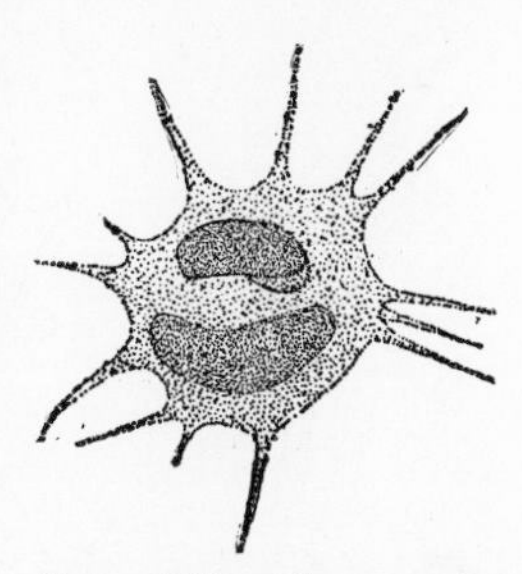

FIG. 107. *Chrysamoeba radians* Klebs. (× 1,000.)

Thus far, cell division has been observed only when the organism is in an amoeboid condition. There is a mitotic division of the nucleus into two daughter nuclei and a constriction of the chromatophore into two parts.[4] Division of these organelles is followed by a pulling apart of the cell into halves, each with a chromatophore and a nucleus.

Statospores of *Chrysamoeba* are endoplasmic in origin.[4] Their walls are smooth and have a conspicuous collar and plug.

ORDER 3. CHRYSOCAPSALES

The Chrysocapsales have immobile vegetative cells united in palmelloid colonies by a common gelatinous matrix. Cell division may take place anywhere in a colony or may be restricted to one end of it. Cells of most, if not all, genera may be metamorphosed directly into a flagellated condition. Certain genera are known to form statospores.

The order includes about 10 genera and 14 species, all fresh-water.

[1] Doflein, 1922; Penard, 1921. [2] Klebs, 1892.
[3] Penard, 1921. [4] Doflein, 1922.

Hydrurus, with the single species *H. foetidus* (Vill.) Kirchn., grows attached to rocks and stones in swiftly flowing cold-water streams. When conditions are favorable, the alga often covers the entire bottom of the stream. The plant body is greenish brown, of a tough gelatinous consistency, and 5 to 40 cm. in length (Fig. 108*A*). The basal portion is unbranched; the distal portion is divided into many branchlets arranged in dense tufts. Young plants and apices of branchlets of older plants have the cells uniseriately arranged within the gelatinous envelope.[1] Other portions of older plants are more than one cell in diameter (Fig. 108*B*). Here the majority of cells are ovoid, but they may be angular because of mutual compression. Each cell contains a single golden brown chromatophore with a conspicuous pyrenoid.[2] The chromatophore usually lies on the side of the cell toward the thallus apex. The colorless portion of the protoplast contains granules of reserve food and five or six vacuoles.[3] The single nucleus lies next to the chromatophore. Division of the terminal cell of a branchlet is transverse; that of other cells may be vertical or transverse. Cell division may continue indefinitely, and an adult plant is composed of hundreds of thousands of cells.

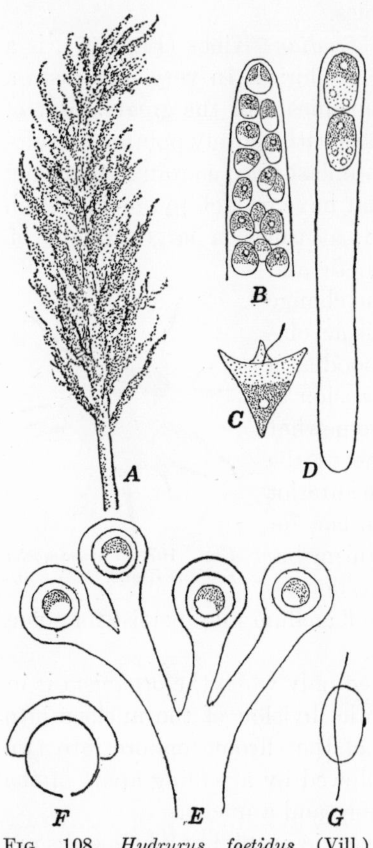

FIG. 108. *Hydrurus foetidus* (Vill.) Kirchn. *A*, portion of a thallus. *B*, apex of a thallus. *C*, zoospore. *D*, germling. *E*, statospores before liberation from thallus. *F–G*, front and side view of a statospore. (*B–G*, *after Klebs*, 1892.)

It is very doubtful whether accidentally severed portions of a colony continue growth as independent plants for any length of time. Reproduction by means of zoospores is of frequent occurrence and usually takes place during the early morning hours. Zoospores are formed by a direct metamorphosis of recently divided cells near the tips of branchlets. They are tetrahedral in shape. One face bears a single long flagellum, and in the corner opposite this face there is a single large chromatophore (Fig. 108*C*). There are several contractile vacuoles in the cytoplasm next to

[1] Klebs, 1892; Rostafiński, 1882. [2] Klebs, 1892; Lagerheim, 1888.
[3] Klebs, 1892.

the anterior face, but an eyespot is lacking.[1] When it stops swarming, a zoospore comes to rest with its anterior face downward, retracts its flagellum, assumes a spherical shape, and secretes a cylindrical gelatinous envelope. The first divisions of this germling are transverse (Fig. 108*D*).

Silicified statospores, with a fairly conspicuous plug and a wing-like ridge partially encircling the wall, are developed within cells borne in special gelatinous stalks protruding from the branchlets (Fig. 108*E–G*). The stimulus causing a formation of statospores seems to be a rise in temperature of the water.[2]

ORDER 4. CHRYSOTRICHALES

The Chrysotrichales are to be distinguished from other Chrysophyceae by their branching filamentous thalli. The branches may be free from one another or compacted into a pseudoparenchymatous mass. Cell structure, organization of the zoospores, and especially the typical chrysophycean statospores show that these algae belong to the Chrysophyceae.

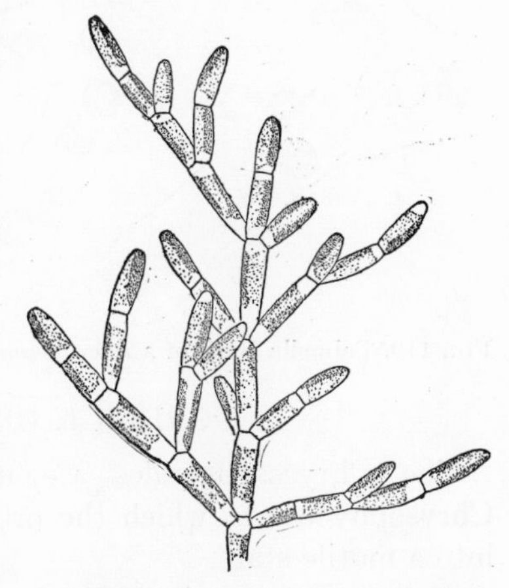

FIG. 109. *Phaeothamnion confervicola* Lagerh. (× 485.)

There are five genera and seven species. One genus is found in brackish water, the others in fresh water.

Phaeothamnion, with three species, is a rare fresh-water alga that grows epiphytically upon other algae. Its thallus is composed of cylindrical to subovoid cells joined end to end in branched filaments with a conspicuous central axis and suberect lateral branchlets (Fig. 109). The basal cell of a thallus is hemispherical and attached to the substratum. The basal cell is usually without chromatophores; all other cells contain one, two, or several golden brown chromatophores and store reserve foods mainly in the form of leucosin granules.[3] Palmelloid stages are of frequent occurrence. Palmelloid stages (Fig. 110) are usually branched gelatinous tubes in which the cells are spherical and uniseriate in arrangement,[4] but the cells may be irregular in shape and irregularly distributed.[5]

Reproduction is by the formation of one, two, four, or eight zoospores within a cell. They are liberated through a pore in the side of the parent-cell wall. The earlier descriptions[6] of structure of the zoospores are con-

[1] Klebs, 1892; Lagerheim, 1888. [2] Klebs, 1892.
[3] Lagerheim, 1884; Pascher, 1925. [4] Borzi, 1892; Pascher, 1925.
[5] Pascher, 1925. [6] Borzi, 1892; Lagerheim, 1884.

tradictory. Later study of them[1] seems to show that they are biflagellate and have the two flagella quite different in length. Zoospores may also be formed while the alga is in a palmelloid condition.

Typical silicified statospores are also formed by *Phaeothamnion.*[2] Their development has not been studied in *Phaeothamnion* but those of another genus of the order have been shown[3] to be endoplasmic.

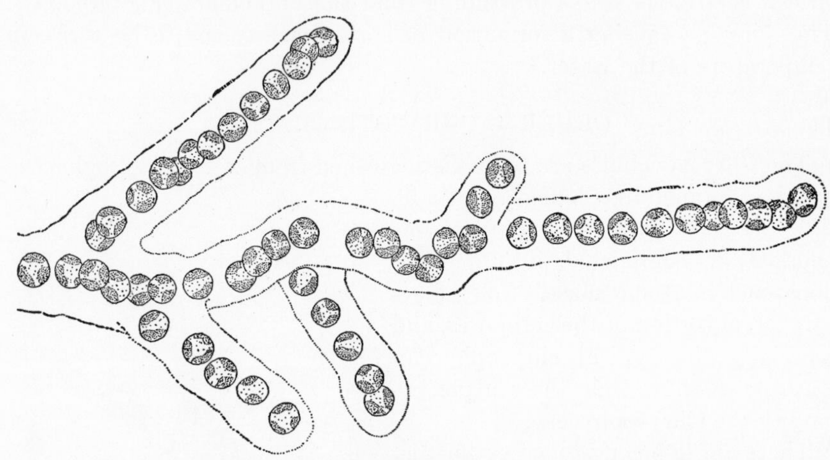

Fig. 110. Palmella stage of a *Phaeothamnion* species. [*P. borzianum* Pascher (?).] (× 650.)

ORDER 5. CHRYSOSPHAERALES

The Chrysosphaerales are unicellular or nonfilamentous colonial Chrysophyceae in which the protoplast is not metamorphosed directly into a motile state.

There are about six genera and seven species.

The Chrysosphaerales correspond to the Chlorococcales of the Chlorophyceae and to the Heterococcales of Xanthophyceae. Cells of certain Chrysosphaerales appear to be unable to divide vegetatively, but it is uncertain that, as in Chlorococcales, this is a universal character. None of the genera has been thoroughly investigated, and it is not improbable that certain genera now referred to the Chrysosphaerales will eventually be placed in the Chrysocapsales.

Epichrysis, with two species, has solitary or gregarious cells that grow epiphytically upon other fresh-water algae.[4] The cells are subspherical and somewhat flattened on the side toward the substratum (Fig. 111). The protoplast contains a single large golden brown chromatophore that lies toward the free side of the cell. The cytoplasm contains numerous small droplets of oil and small granules of leucosin.[5]

[1] Pascher, 1925. [2] Borzi, 1892; Pascher, 1925. [3] Geitler, 1927.
[4] Geitler, 1928; Meyer, K. I., 1930; Pascher, 1925. [5] Pascher, 1925.

Multiplication may be due to a vertical bipartition of the protoplast and a secretion of a wall about each of the daughter protoplasts (autospores?) while they still lie within the parent-cell wall.[1] There may also be a formation[2] of uniflagellate zoospores. Zoospores that have ceased swarming may come to rest upon a firm substratum and develop into typical vegetative cells, or they may be free-floating and develop into small palmelloid colonies. Cells of palmelloid colonies may produce either zoospores or statospores.[1]

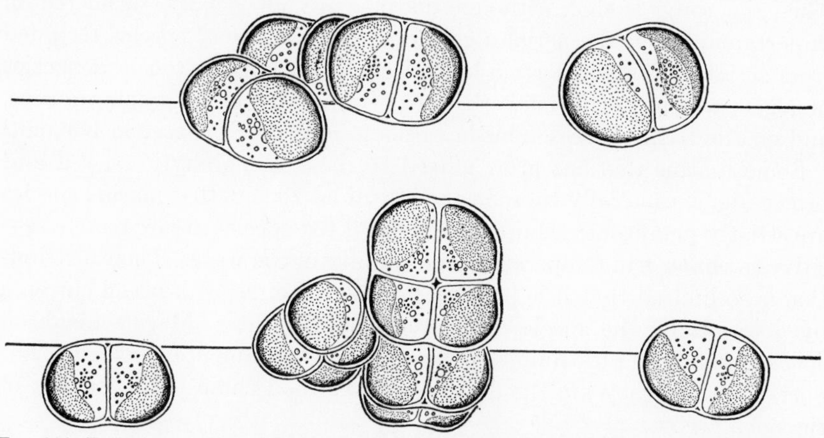

FIG. 111. *Epichrysis paludosa* (Korshikov) Pascher. (*Drawn by R. H. Thompson.*) (× 1,650.)

CLASS 3. BACILLARIOPHYCEAE

The Bacillariophyceae (diatoms) include a large number of unicellular and colonial algae with cells differing sharply from those of other algae. The primary distinguishing feature is that the cell wall is highly silicified and composed of two overlapping halves that fit together as do the two parts of a Petri dish. The nature of the cell wall cannot be determined by microscopical examination, but diatoms are easily recognized by the bilaterally or radially symmetrical markings on the wall when a cell is viewed from above. Within a cell are one to many, variously shaped yellowish to brownish chromatophores which contain chlorophyll *a*, chlorophyll *c*, beta-carotene, a unique carotene, and several xanthophylls most of which are found only in diatoms (see Table I, page 4).

Reproduction is usually by a cell dividing into two daughter cells of slightly different size. Now and then there is a formation of special rejuvenescent cells (**auxospores**) larger in size than the cells producing them. Auxospores are zygotic in nature and formed either by a union of gametes or by autogamy.

[1] Pascher, 1925. [2] Meyer, K. I., 1930; Pascher, 1925.

There are about 170 genera and 5,500 species of diatoms, the majority living but some known only in a fossil condition.

Occurrence. Certain genera of living diatoms are found only in fresh waters, others only in salt waters. Such genera as grow in both fresh and salt waters usually have some species that are strictly marine and other species strictly fresh-water. Most fresh-water species are aquatics, and they may be sessile in habit or free-floating. Many aquatic fresh-water diatoms develop in greatest abundance during spring or autumn months when the water is cool. Although diatoms are not usually considered an important part of the aerial algal flora, the number of species recorded from aerial habitats in certain localities may outnumber the other species of algae growing on brickwork, rocky walls, dry cliffs, among mosses, and on the bark of trees. This has been found to be the case in Iceland.[1]

Some marine diatoms grow affixed to rocks or epiphytic on red and brown algae, especially those in the intertidal zone. Other marine species are strictly planktonic. Many marine plankton species are extremely sensitive to changes in temperature and salinity of the water. Their distribution is so limited that it is possible to follow the paths of ocean currents by determining the species of diatoms in the water. Marine plankton species, together with dinoflagellates, are of fundamental biological importance since they are the first link in the food chain of all animals of the open ocean.

Fossil Diatoms. Since the siliceous portion of a cell wall remains unaltered after death and decay of a cell, great numbers of old cell walls accumulate at the bottom of any body of water in which diatoms live. Where conditions are exceptionally favorable and long continued, such accumulations may reach a considerable thickness. Deposits of fossil diatoms, known as **diatomaceous earth,** are found in various parts of the world.

Many different species are found in diatomaceous earth. Most of the fossil species are not older than the Cretaceous, and there is no satisfactory evidence that diatoms existed during the Palaeozoic.[2] Some genera are known only in the fossil condition, and certain others have more fossil than living species.

Some diatomaceous earths originated in fresh waters, others in the ocean. Fresh-water deposits consisting largely of plankton species were laid down in the beds of former lakes; those with nonplankton species predominating were not formed in lakes. Deposits of marine species are found inland and above sea level as a result of geological changes. The thickest deposits of diatomaceous earth thus far discovered are in the Santa Maria oil fields, California. Oil wells drilled in this region show, after correction for dip, that there is a subterranean deposit about 3,000 feet in thickness.

[1] Petersen, 1928. [2] Pia, 1927.

The largest known deposits at the surface of the earth are those at Lompoc, California, where the beds are miles in extent and over 700 feet in thickness. The Lompoc deposits, like most others of marine origin, are composed almost exclusively of littoral species. Beds of fresh-water diatomaceous earth are rarely more than a few feet in thickness.

Diatomaceous earth is assuming an increasing importance as a commercial product, and the average annual production in this country for the years 1949 to 1951 was 270,000 tons.[1] The enormous quantity produced annually is more readily visualized when one realizes that a

FIG. 112. Diatomaceous earth quarry at Lompoc, California. (*Photograph courtesy of Johns-Manville Products Corporation.*)

single ton has a volume of 50 to 260 cubic feet. Most marine deposits of diatomaceous earth are worked as open quarries (Fig. 112). Diatomaceous earth is also obtained from lakes in Florida by dredging with a suction pump and carrying the material through sluiceways to settling tanks.

The commercial uses of diatomaceous earth are varied, and research is continually revealing new applications for this material. The oldest commercial use is that of a very mild abrasive in silver polishes and tooth pastes. Utilization for this purpose is so generally known that many people think that it is the major use of diatomaceous earth. At one time diatomaceous earth was the absorbent used for liquid nitroglycerin to

[1] Chandler and Marks, 1954.

make an explosive (dynamite) that could be transported with comparative safety. The inert medium used in present-day manufacture of dynamite is wood meal.

About three-fifths of the present-day production of diatomaceous earth is used in the filtration of liquids, especially those of sugar refineries. When a small amount of powdered diatomaceous earth is added to a sugar solution and the mixture is forced through a filter press, the layer of diatomaceous earth deposited on the cloth screens out suspended materials in the liquid. About one-fourth of the total annual production is used as an inert mineral filler in a wide variety of products including paints and plastics. In the case of paints it is used as an inert extender. The addition of diatomaceous earth to paints used for painting traffic lanes increases their night visibility. Another major use is in the insulation of boilers, blast furnaces, and other places where a high temperature is maintained. If the temperature is over 1000°F., diatomaceous earth is a more effective heat insulator than magnesia or asbestos, since it is much more resistant to shrinkage and does not fail at red heat.

The Cell Wall. Diatomologists have centered their attention on the structure of the wall, and their taxonomic treatment of the group is based upon wall structure and ornamentation. This intensive specialization is largely responsible for the special terminology used to designate the various parts of a wall. Both the wall alone and the wall with its contained protoplast are called a **frustule.** The wall consists of two overlapping halves that fit together as do the two halves of a bacteriologist's Petri dish. The outer of the two halves is an **epitheca** and the inner a **hypotheca.** The silicified portion of either consists of a more or less flattened **valve** whose flange-like margin is attached to a **connecting band** or **cingulum.** The connecting band is usually firmly united to the valve, but in "cleaned" diatoms (those in which all organic material has been removed by oxidizing agents) and in diatomaceous earth one frequently sees connecting bands that have become separated from valves. A connecting band is an open instead of a closed hoop, and one with a gap between the approximated ends. Some diatoms have additional connecting bands (**intercalary bands**) interpolated between epitheca and hypotheca; and there may be one, two, or more of them. When a frustule lies so that the valve side is uppermost it is said to be in **valve view**; when the connecting band is uppermost it is in **girdle view.** According to the genus a water mount will show practically all individuals in valve view, practically all in girdle view, or indiscriminately in valve and girdle view.

Both the epitheca and hypotheca of a diatom consist of an organic matrix that is composed in large part of pectin.[1] The wall gives no reaction for cellulose or callose. The watery gelatinous envelope surrounding

[1] Liebisch, 1928; Mangin, 1908.

many planktonic species is probably pectic acid.[1] The valve and connecting-band portions of the wall are silicified, and some think[2] that this silicification is not a simple impregnation with silica but a chemical combination of silicon with the organic material in the wall. Others[3] hold that there is no organic material in the silicified portion of the wall. Silicification may be demonstrated by destroying the organic matter, either by incineration, or by treatment with such oxidizing agents as chromic acid or potassium chlorate. The amount of silicification is quite

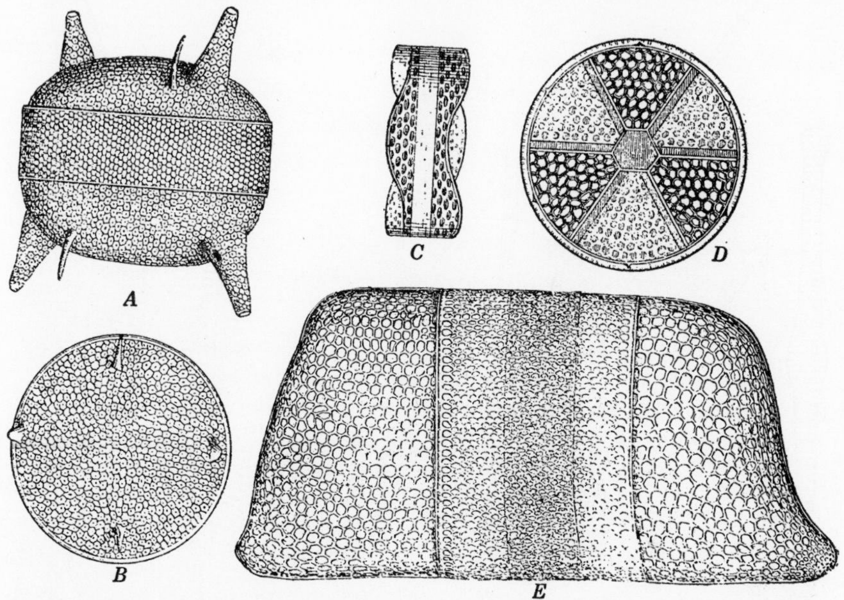

Fig. 113. Centric diatoms. *A–B*, girdle and valve views of *Biddulphia smithii* (Rab.) V.H. *C–D*, girdle and valve views of *Actinoptychus undulatus* Ralfs. *E*, girdle view of *Isthmia enervis* Ehr. (*From Schütt*, 1896.)

variable. It is usually scanty in plankton species and heavy in nonplanktonic ones. The extent to which a wall is silicified is dependent in part upon the amount of siliceous materials available in the water, and it has been shown[4] that aluminium silicate is the compound most used in silicification. An abundance of silicates favors multiplication of diatoms[5] and a direct correlation has been found[6] between increase in number of diatoms and a decrease in amount of silica in the water. Cultural studies have shown[7] that certain diatoms can multiply in an absence of silicon and have cells without siliceous walls.

[1] Schröder, 1902. [2] Mangin, 1908. [3] Liebisch, 1928.
[4] Coupin, 1922. [5] Pearsall, 1923. [6] Meloche, *et al.*, 1938.
[7] Bachrach and Lefèvre, 1929; Wiedling, 1941.

The siliceous material deposited in a valve is not laid down as a smooth sheet. Instead, the sheet is areolate or striate and has the areolae or striae in patterns characteristic for the genus and species. Ornamentation of a valve is according to one of two general patterns. In the **centric** diatoms (Centrales) it is radially symmetrical about a central point (Fig. 113); in the **pennate** diatoms (Pennales) it is bilaterally symmetrical or asymmetrical with respect to an axial strip (Fig. 114). Some species,

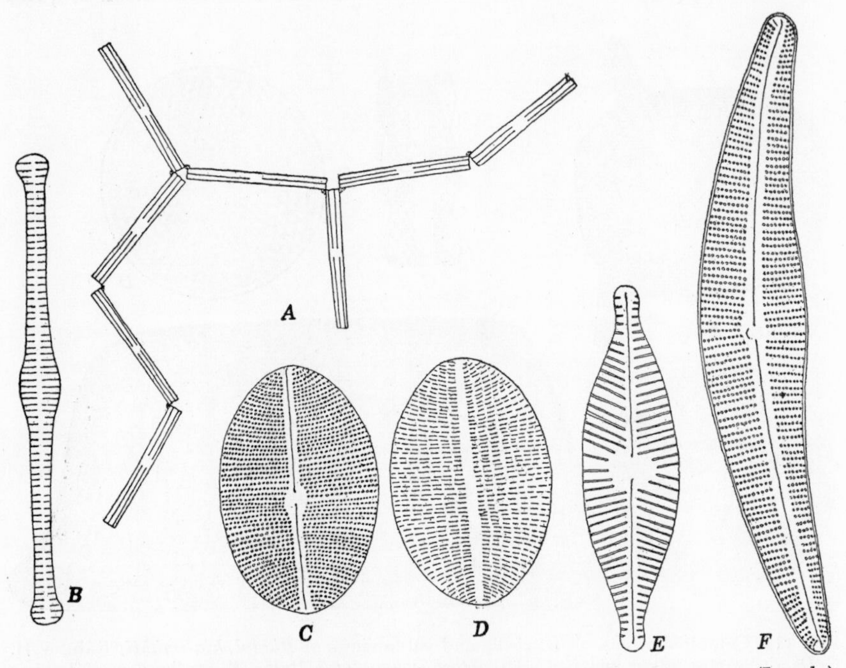

FIG. 114. Pennate diatoms. *A–B*, girdle and valve views of *Tabellaria fenestrata* (Lyngb.) Kütz. *C–D*, the two dissimilar valves of a cell of *Cocconeis pediculus* Ehr. *E*, *Navicula rhyncocephala* Kütz. *F*, *Cymbella lanceolata* (Ehr.) Brun. (*A*, × 400; *B*, × 1,000; *C–E*, × 1,300; *F*, × 650.)

especially those of marine Centrales, have very coarse markings; certain Pennales have punctae or striae so fine that they are revealed only by the best microscopes.

The coarse markings of many marine centric diatoms are due to thinner places (areolae) in the siliceous deposit. The areolae are generally bounded by ridges that lie on the inner or the outer face of the valve (Fig. 115*A–B*). Areolae may have minute vertical canals (pores) running through them or incomplete canals (poroids), which do not entirely perforate the wall.[1] Pores vary in size from 0.1 to 0.6μ.

[1] Müller, 1898, 1899, 1900, 1901.

The ornamentation of pennate diatoms is due to thin places, not perforations, in the wall. A few Pennales have valves with one or more true perforations (Fig. 115*C–D*) that are either median or polar.[1] The thin places (**punctae**) lie in rows bilaterally disposed with respect to a longitudinal strip (the **axial field**) running the length of a valve. In many cases the rows of punctae are so minute and so close together that they appear to be striae (Fig. 114*A*). The axial field usually coincides with the longitudinal axis of a valve but may be asymmetrical with respect to it. An axial field may be homogeneous in structure or it may be perforated by a longitudinal slot, the **raphe.** An axial field without a longitudinal slot is a **pseudoraphe.** Axial fields of the two valves of a

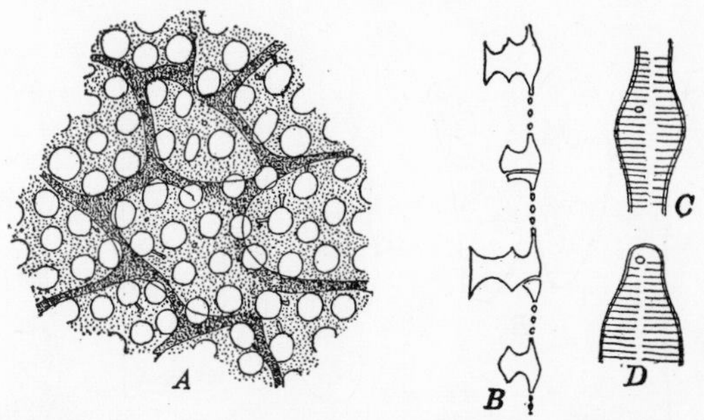

FIG. 115. *A–B*, surface view and cross section of a portion of the wall of *Isthmia nervosa* Kütz. *C*, median mucilage pore of *Fragilaria virescens* Ralfs. *D*, terminal mucilage pore of *Tabellaria fenestrata* Kütz. (*A–B, after Müller*, 1898; *C–D, after Müller*, 1899.)

frustule are usually alike, but there are certain genera in which one valve has a raphe and the other a pseudoraphe (Fig. 114*C–D*).

A raphe is usually interrupted midway between its ends by a thickening of the wall (the **central nodule**), and there are often similar swellings (**polar nodules**) at either end of it. The raphe is not a simple cleft in the wall. Instead, it is an extremely complicated structure (see page 202).

Structure of the Protoplast. Immediately within the cell wall is a fairly thick layer of cytoplasm in which the chromatophore or chromatophores are embedded. Internal to the cytoplasmic layer is a conspicuous central vacuole. Pennate diatoms often have the central portion of the vacuole interrupted by a broad band of cytoplasm in which lies a spherical or ovoid nucleus. The chromatophores vary in shape and number from species to species. The structure of chromatophores is quite constant for some genera and variable for others. For this reason systems of classification based largely upon the chromatophores are unsatisfactory. Protoplasts of Centrales usually contain many discoid or irregularly shaped chromatophores. Those of Pennales usually contain two chromatophores

[1] Gemeinhardt, 1926; Müller, 1899.

or a single irregularly lobed and perforated one (Fig. 116). If two chromatophores are present, they are laminate and extend longitudinally along opposite sides of the protoplast.[1] Chromatophores may contain one to several pyrenoids or may lack them entirely. Pyrenoids are usually ovoid, biconvex, or planoconvex in shape. Sometimes they lie in a bulge at the inner face of, or entirely separated from, the chromatophore.[2] Pyrenoids of diatoms are of the naked type (that is, devoid of a starch sheath) and their exact role in the metabolism of a cell is uncertain. Possibly they function as elaioplasts and are concerned in the formation of oils.

Typically the chromatophores are of a rich golden brown color, but a few species have chromatophores that are a vivid green or even a

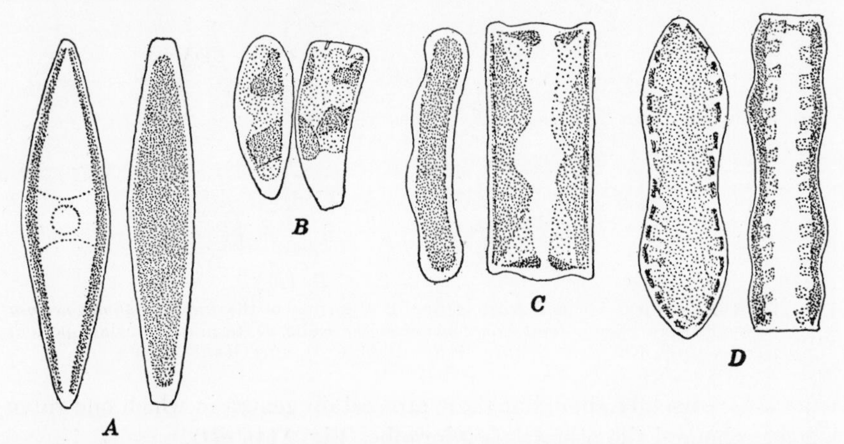

FIG. 116. Valve and girdle views of chromatophores of various diatoms. *A*, *Navicula radiosa* Kütz. *B*, *Rhoicosphenia curvata* (Kütz.) Grun. *C*, *Eunotia diodon* Ehr. *D*, *Cymatopleura solea* f. *interrupta*. (*After Ott*, 1900.)

bright blue.[3] Colorless diatoms in which there are no chromatophores and whose nutrition is saprophytic have been recorded.[4] The golden brown color of chromatophores is due to the presence of several xanthophylls, among which fucoxanthin is present in greatest abundance (see Table I, page 4).

Fats are the chief food reserves formed by photosynthetic activity of the chromatophores. These accumulate as droplets, often of considerable size, and either in the cytoplasm or in the chromatophores. That fats are a food reserve is shown by their gradual disappearance when cells are kept continuously in a dark room. Photosynthetic reserves may also accumulate as leucosin, and study of the leucosin in diatoms indicates that it is a carbohydrate.[5]

[1] Heinzerling, 1908; Ott, 1900. [2] Mereschkowsky, 1903.
[3] Molisch, 1903. [4] Benecke, 1900; Richter, 1909. [5] von Stosch, 1951*B*.

Diatom cells are uninucleate and the nucleus is spherical to biconvex. In centric diatoms it lies embedded in the cytoplasm next to the cell wall; in most pennate species it lies in a cytoplasmic bridge across the middle of the protoplast. Numerous cytological investigations have shown that the nucleus has a definite nuclear membrane, one or more nucleoli, and a chromatic network in the intervening space between the two. Nuclear division is mitotic, generally with the formation of a considerable number of chromosomes.

Locomotion of Diatoms. Many of the free-living, and some of the colonial, pennate diatoms have the ability to move spontaneously. All pennate diatoms with this ability have a raphe. Movement of a diatom is generally by a series of jerks and always in the longitudinal axis. After a cell has moved forward for a short distance it pauses for a short time and then, with the same jerky motion, moves backward along nearly the same route. Sometimes the movement is smooth instead of jerky, but there is always a forward and backward progression. None of the centric diatoms moves independently.

Numerous theories have been advanced to account for the motility of diatoms, but Müller's theory of cytoplasmic streaming is now almost universally accepted as explaining the locomotion of Bacillariophyceae. The intimate connection between movement and the presence of a raphe was brought out when it was shown[1] that motility is restricted to those pennate species that have a true raphe. A true raphe is not a simple cleft. Instead, it is an extremely complicated structure, and that of *Pinnularia* (Fig. 117) may be cited as fairly typical. In *Pinnularia* the raphe is interrupted midway between its ends by a thickening of the wall (**central nodule**) and there are similar thickenings (**polar nodules**) at either end of the raphe. As seen in valve view the raphe is a sigmoid cleft that runs from one polar nodule to the central nodule and thence to the other polar nodule (Fig. 117*B*). This cleft, as seen in vertical section midway between polar and central nodules (Fig. 117*C*), is not a vertical slot but is a >-shaped one.[2] The upper portion of the > is called the **outer fissure** and the lower portion is called the **inner fissure.** Near the vicinity of both polar nodules the outer fissure bends in a semicircle and terminates in a linear expansion called the **polar cleft** (Fig. 117*F*). In the same region the inner fissure bends in the opposite direction to the outer fissure and terminates in a **funnel cleft** that opens on the inner face of the cell wall. On either side of the central nodule the outer and inner fissures are connected by **vertical canals**[2] (Fig. 117*A*). In the region of the central nodule the inner fissures of posterior and anterior portions of the wall are connected with each other by a **horizontal canal.** True raphes of other pen-

[1] Müller, 1889. [2] Müller, 1889, 1896.

nate diatoms are essentially the same as in *Pinnularia*, but these differ from one another in minor details.[1]

According to Muller's theory locomotion of diatoms is due to a streaming of cytoplasm along the free face of the outer fissure. Beginning at the polar cleft the stream moves along the free face of the outer fissure to the central nodule and then moves vertically inward through a vertical canal. Coincident with this there is an upward flow of cytoplasm through the

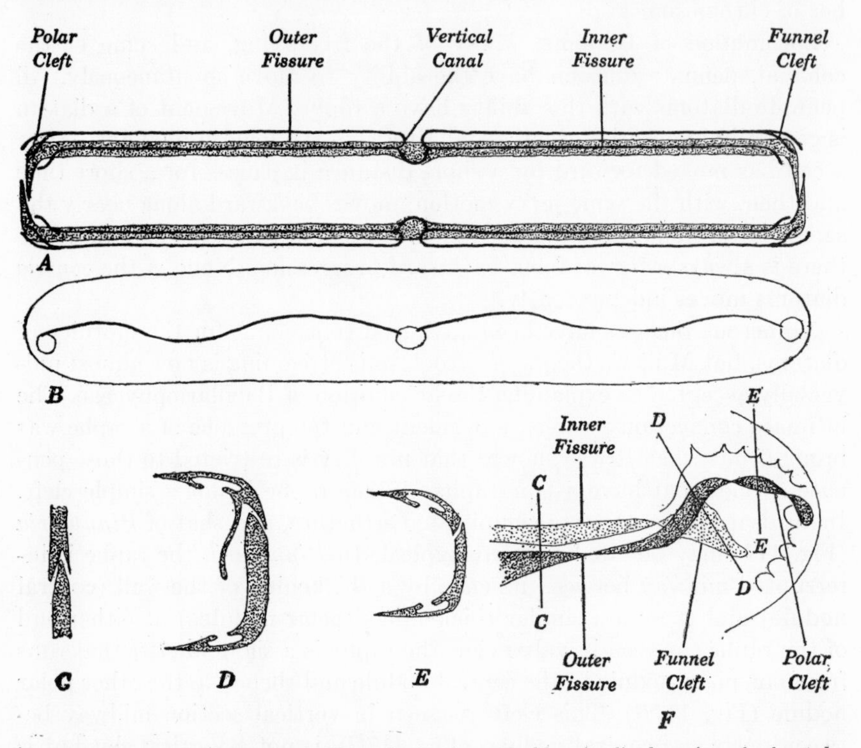

FIG. 117. Structure of the raphe of *Pinnularia*. *A*, vertical longitudinal section of a frustule. *B*, surface view of a valve. *C*, vertical section of a valve wall cut in the plane *CC* of Fig. *F*. *D*, a similar section cut at *DD*. *E*, a similar section cut at *EE*. *F*, terminal portion of a valve showing the inner and outer fissures in surface view. (*A–B*, *modified from Müller*, 1889; *C–F*, *after Müller*, 1896.)

other vertical canal at the central nodule, and this stream flows along the free face of the outer fissure to the polar cleft at the other end of the cell wall. In the inner fissures on both sides of the central nodule there is a compensatory stream of cytoplasm that travels in the opposite direction to the stream in the outer fissures.

Propulsion of a frustule is in a direction opposite to cytoplasmic streaming in the outer fissure (Fig. 118). Movement is thought to be due to

[1] Müller, 1889, 1896, 1909; Hustedt, 1926, 1926*A*, 1928, 1928*A*, 1929, 1929*A*.

water currents set up by the flowing cytoplasm and to cyclonic currents established in the region of the polar nodules. This concept is based upon observation of the behavior of the suspended particles when cells are mounted in dilute India ink. Girdle views of cells mounted in such suspensions show that there is a linear flow of particles from one polar nodule to the central nodule, a whirlpool of particles in the region of the central nodule, and a linear flow of particles from the central nodule to the other polar nodule.

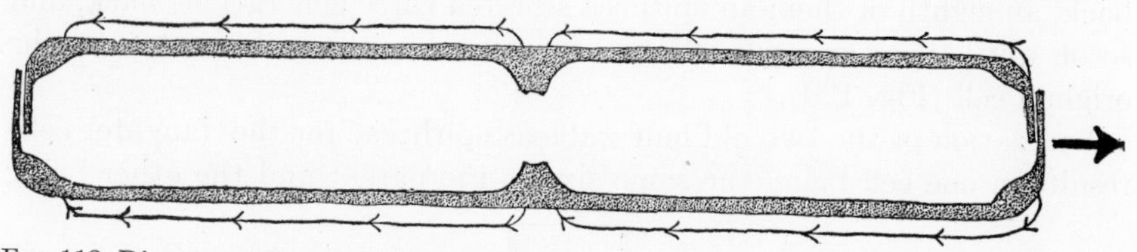

FIG. 118. Diagram of the streaming of cytoplasm on the outer face of a *Pinnularia* frustule. The heavy arrow indicates the direction of movement of the frustule. (*Modified from Müller*, 1893.)

Cell Division. When a diatom divides there is generally a formation of two daughter cells of slightly different size. The first indication of division is an expansion of the protoplast that causes a slight separation of overlapping epitheca and hypotheca. This is followed by a mitotic division of the nucleus in a plane perpendicular to the valves (Fig. 119*A*). Nuclear division of pennate diatoms is generally accompanied by a division of the chromatophores. If a cell has a single chromatophore, its division is always longitudinal; if there are two chromatophores, their

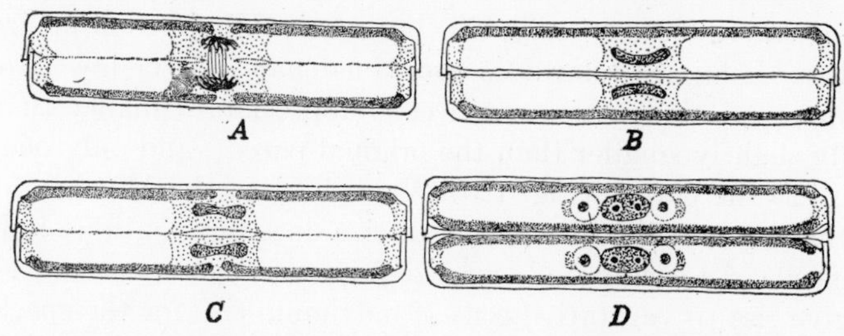

FIG. 119. Four stages in the cell division of *Navicula oblonga* Kütz. (*After Lauterborn*, 1896.)

division may be longitudinal or transverse.[1] Species with numerous chromatophores do not have a bipartition of them until after the daughter cells have been formed. Pyrenoids, at least in chromatophores with conspicuous ones, increase in number by division and not by formation *de novo*.[2] Duplication of cell organs is followed by a longitudinal bipartition of the protoplast in a plane parallel to the valves (Fig. 119*A–B*). One of the daughter protoplasts lies within the epitheca of the parent-

[1] Ott, 1900. [2] Heinzerling, 1908.

cell wall and the other within the hypotheca (Fig. 119*D*). Each daughter protoplast soon secretes a new half wall next its girdle and free face. The newly formed half wall is always the hypotheca of a daughter frustule, and the old half wall received from the parent cell, irrespective of whether it was formerly an epitheca or a hypotheca, is always the epitheca. It follows, therefore, that in a population descended from a single cell, half of the cells have an epitheca that was secreted in the previous cell generation, a quarter of them an epitheca that was secreted two cell generations back, an eighth of them an epitheca secreted three generations back, and so on until there are two cells, each with an epitheca derived from the original cell (Fig. 120).

Utilization of the two old half walls as epithecae for the daughter cells results in one cell being the same size as the parent and the other being

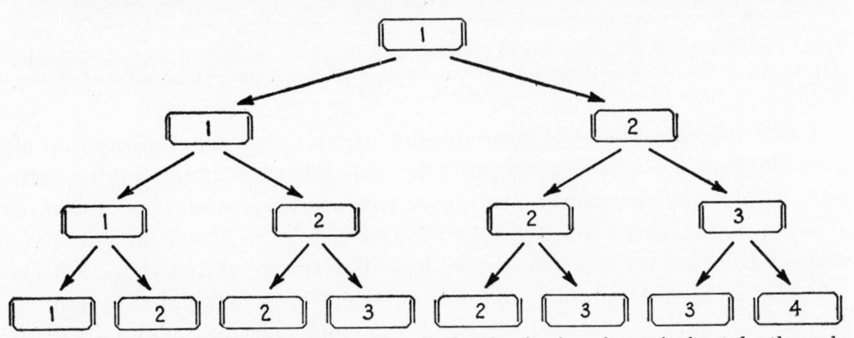

Fig. 120. Diagram showing the progressive diminution in size of certain frustules through successive cell generations of a diatom.

slightly smaller. Theoretically, this progressive diminution in size of certain cells (sometimes known as the Macdonald-Pfitzer law[1]) would result in a population with certain cells appreciably smaller than, other cells only slightly smaller than the original parent, and only one cell the same size as the parent (Fig. 120). A corollary of the Macdonald-Pfitzer law is that progressive diminution in size does not continue indefinitely because cells of a certain reduced size form **auxospores** (see next section) which give rise to vegetative cells of maximum size for the species.

The validity of the Macdonald-Pfitzer law has been tested in clones developed from a single cell. Many species have been found[2] to have this progressive diminution in size. However, other species have been found[3] where there is no appreciable diminution in size. The length of time involved in a progression from maximal to minimal size depends primarily upon the rate of cell division. Undoubtedly this varies greatly from

[1] Macdonald, 1869; Pfitzer, 1871, 1882.

[2] Geitler, 1932; Locker, 1950; Meinhold, 1911; Wiedling, 1948.

[3] Allen and Nelson, 1910; Gemeinhardt, 1927; Locker, 1950; Richter, 1909; Wiedling, 1948.

species to species, but even under the most favorable conditions it is probable that it takes a long time. Some indication of the time involved under natural conditions has been obtained from a study of successive deposits of diatom shells laid down in lakes of Switzerland. Here it has been estimated[1] that, for certain plankton species, the time interval is from 2 to 5 years.

Auxospores. Sooner or later, progressive diminution in size of diatoms is compensated for by a production of auxospores (Fig. 121). Auxospores of most Pennales are zygotic in nature and result from gametic union or from autogamy, but in certain cases they are formed parthenogenetically. For a long time auxospores of Centrales were thought to be formed asexually, but it is very probable that they are also zygotic in nature. For-

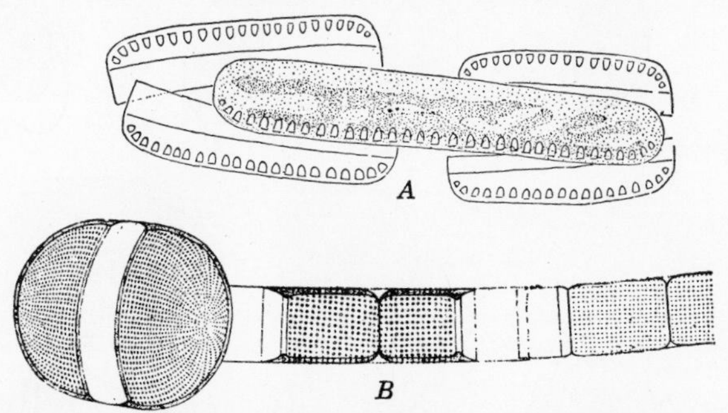

FIG. 121. *A*, auxospore of *Surirella saxonica* Auersw., a pennate diatom. *B*, auxospore of *Melosira islandica* Müller, a centric diatom. (*A*, *after Karsten*, 1900; *B*, *from Müller*, 1906.)

mation of an auxospore involves a liberation of a protoplast from the enclosing walls, a considerable enlargement of the naked liberated protoplast, and then a secretion of a two-parted silicified wall around the protoplast. This wall may be smooth or ornamented and in the latter case the ornamentation is not identical with that of vegetative cells of the species. The enlarged auxospore divides to form two vegetative cells whose size is near the maximum for the species. Since division of the auxospore nucleus is mitotic, the first generation of vegetative cells and all subsequent generations of vegetative cells are diploid.

Auxospores of Pennales. Auxospores of pennate diatoms may be formed in any one of the following five ways: (1) by two cells conjugating to form a single auxospore; (2) by two cells conjugating to form two auxospores; (3) by two cells becoming enveloped in a common envelope, but each giving rise to an auxospore without conjugation; (4) by a solitary cell giving rise to one auxospore; and (5) by a solitary cell giving rise to two auxospores. The first two of the foregoing methods are ob-

[1] Nipkow, 1928.

viously sexual; superficially the last three methods appear to be asexual, but cytological study has shown that they may be sexual.

Cells producing cells by the first method (conjugation in pairs to form a single auxospore) may be sister cells or may be two that are not derived from a common parent. In either case, the two are enclosed by a common gelatinous envelope. They generally lie side by side within the envelope but in certain cases[1] they lie end to end. Several species have been investigated cytologically and found to have a meiotic division of nuclei of conjugating cells. *Surirella saxonica* Auersw., the first diatom

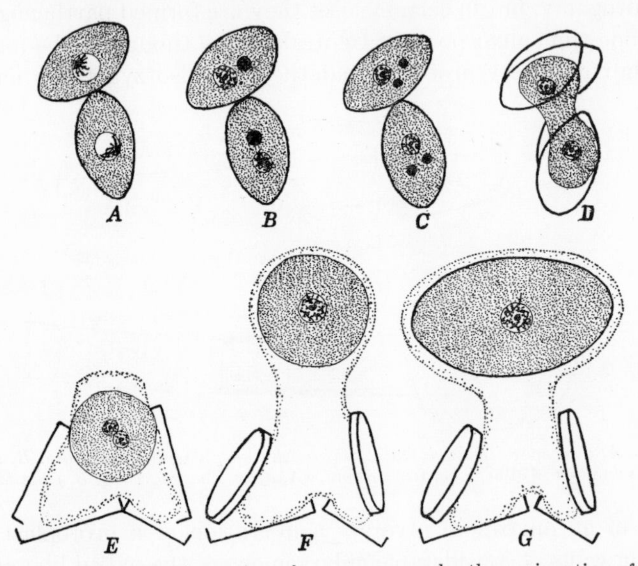

FIG. 122. Diagram showing the formation of one auxospore by the conjugation of two cells of the pennate diatom *Cocconeis placentula* var. *klinoraphis* Geitler. *A–C*, meiosis and degeneration of all but one nucleus in each frustule. *D*, gametic union. *E*, young zygote. *F–G*, enlargement of the zygote to form an auxospore. (*Diagram based upon Geitler*, 1927*A*.)

in which meiosis was demonstrated,[2] has an enlargement of one and a degeneration of three of the nuclei resulting from meiosis. After this the protoplasts escape from the walls and unite to form a zygote in which the two haploid nuclei soon unite to form a single diploid nucleus. The zygote then elongates to form an auxospore whose long axis lies parallel to the long axes of the empty frustules of the conjugating cells. Conjugating cells of *Cocconeis pediculus* Ehr. and *C. placentula* var. *klinoraphis* Geitler have an immediate degeneration of one daughter nucleus after the first meiotic division.[3] The persisting nucleus then divides and one of its daughter nuclei degenerates (Fig. 122*A–C*). The two protoplasts, each containing a haploid nucleus, then unite to form a binucleate zygote

[1] Karsten, 1900. [2] Karsten, 1912. [3] Geitler, 1927*A*.

which later becomes uninucleate by a fusion of the two nuclei. The zygote then enlarges and becomes an auxospore.

Cells producing auxospores according to the second method (by conjugating to form two auxospores) have both protoplasts dividing to form two gametes (Fig. 123). Certain genera have been shown[1] to have the nuclei dividing meiotically and two of the four nuclei degenerating before cytokinesis into two gametes. Cells of other species have been shown to form four nuclei, two of which degenerate after cytokinesis. Presum-

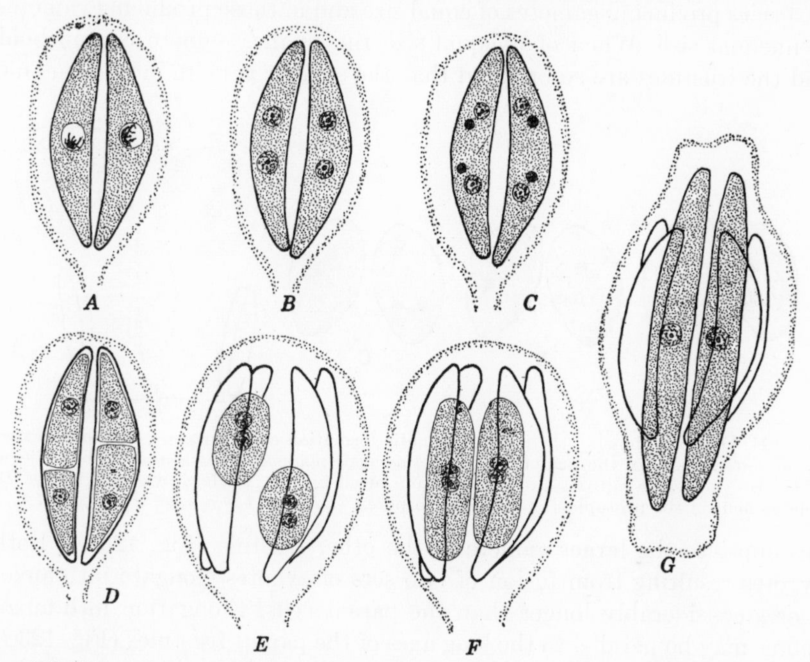

FIG. 123. Diagram showing the formation of two auxospores by two conjugating cells of the pennate diatom *Cymbella lanceolata* (Ehr.) Brun. *A–C*, meiosis and the degeneration of two nuclei in each frustule. *D*, after division of each protoplast into two gametes of unequal size. *E*, young zygotes. *F–G*, elongation of the zygotes to form auxospores. (*Diagram based upon Geitler*, 1927*B*.)

ably these nuclear divisions are also meiotic, but this has not been definitely established. The plane of division to form two gametes may be at right angles to long axes of the paired cells[2] or it may be parallel to the long axes.[3] The two gametes formed by a cell may be of equal or unequal size. Gametes of unequal size may result from unequal division (Fig. 123*D*) of the parent protoplast;[4] or division may be into two gametes of

[1] Cholnoky, 1927, 1928, 1929, 1933; Geitler, 1927*C*, 1928*A*; K. Meyer, 1929; Subrahmanyan, 1948.

[2] Karsten, 1896, 1897; Klebahn, 1896.

[3] Geitler, 1927*B*, 1928*A*. [4] Geitler, 1927*B*.

equal size and one of them enlarging.[1] The two gametes formed by a cell usually unite with those of the other cell instead of with each other. In most cases both gametes of a uniting pair are amoeboid and their union takes place midway between the parent frustules. Less frequently, one gamete of a uniting pair is amoeboid and the other immobile. When this occurs, the two gametes produced by one cell may be amoeboid, and the two produced by the other cell are immobile;[2] or each cell may form one amoeboid and one immobile gamete. The latter condition obtains both in species producing gametes of equal size and in those producing gametes of unequal size. When of unequal size the smaller gamete is amoeboid and the frustules are so oriented that the smaller gamete in one frustule

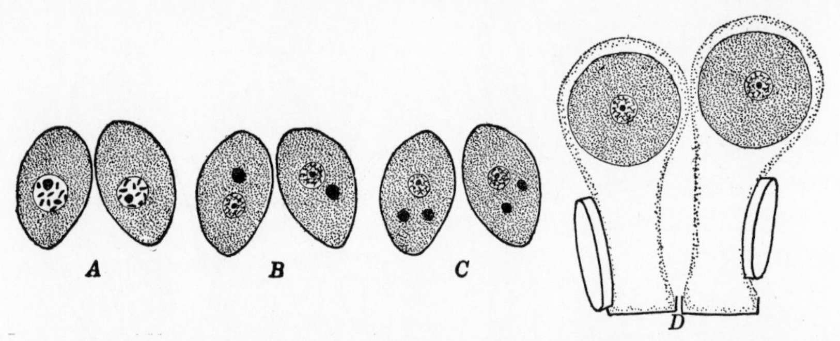

Fig. 124. Diagram showing the parthenogenetic formation of an auxospore in each of two "conjugated" cells of the pennate diatom, *Cocconeis placentula* var. *lineata* (Ehr.) Cleve. *A–C*, two successive mitoses and degeneration of all but one nucleus in each frustule. *D*, enlargement of the protoplasts to form auxospores. (*Diagram based upon Geitler*, 1927*A*.)

lies opposite the larger gamete in the other frustule (Fig. 123*D*). Both zygotes resulting from fusion of two sets of zygotes elongate into auxospores considerably longer than the parent cells. Elongation into auxospores may be parallel to the long axes of the parent frustules (Fig. 123*G*) or at right angles to them.

Production of auxospores according to the third method (a pair of cells forming two auxospores without conjugation) is of rare occurrence. In the one case where this has been studied cytologically[3] this is to be interpreted as a parthenogenetic development of a diploid gamete into an auxospore. The nucleus in both cells goes into a synapsis-like contraction which gives rise to single chromosomes instead of pairs of chromosomes. There then follows the usual double division, with one nucleus degenerating after the first division and one disintegrating after the second division (Fig. 124). The result is a uninucleate cell in which the protoplast is a gamete with a diploid instead of a haploid number of chromosomes. This gamete with a diploid nucleus develops directly into an auxospore.

[1] Karsten, 1896. [2] Subrahmanyan, 1948. [3] Geitler, 1927*A*.

Production of auxospores according to the fourth method (a single cell forming a single auxospore) may take place in various ways. One diatom has been found[1] to have a meiotic division of nuclei in solitary cells, and this is followed by a partial degeneration of two of the four resultant nuclei. The protoplast then divides to form two gametes, each with a normal and a degenerate nucleus. These sister gametes unite to form a zygote which enlarges and becomes an auxospore. In another diatom where a single cell produces a single auxospore it has been found that meiosis is not followed by cytokinesis and that there is a fusion of sister haploid nuclei to form a diploid nucleus in the enlarging auxospore.[2] The evidence presented in support of the latter type of autogamic fusion of nuclei is none too convincing.

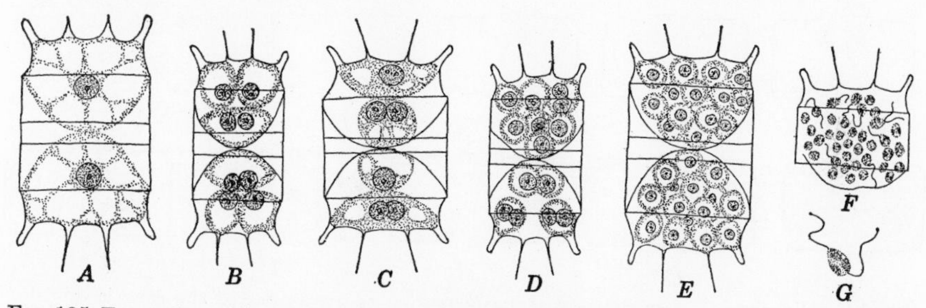

FIG. 125. Formation of "microspores" in *Biddulphia mobiliensis* Bailey. *A*, recently divided vegetative cell. *B–E*, stages in repeated bipartition of protoplasts. *F*, "microspores" before liberation. *G*, free-swimming "microspore." (*After Bergon*, 1907.) (*A–F*, × 200; *G*, × 1,000.)

Production of auxospores according to the fifth method (a single cell producing two auxospores) is of rare occurrence, and none of the reported cases[3] has been investigated cytologically.

Auxospores of Centrales. Auxospores are known for a wide variety of Centrales, and in all cases there is a production of a single auxospore by an old or by a recently divided cell (Fig. 121*B*). For a long time, auxospores of Centrales were thought to be of an asexual nature, but the discovery of nuclear division in connection with their formation casts doubt upon this interpretation.

The problem of auxospores of centric diatoms is also connected with the nature of the so-called **microspores** of Centrales. These have been recorded for numerous species, especially plankton ocean species. The number of "microspores" within a cell is a multiple of two and according to the species is 4, 8, 16, 32, 64, or 128. Earlier cytological study showed that a cell producing "microspores" might have a repeated simultaneous division of nuclei and a cytoplasmic cleavage following the last series of nuclear divisions,[4] or a cytoplasmic cleavage might follow each nuclear

[1] Geitler, 1939. [2] Geitler, 1928*B*, 1932.
[3] Karsten, 1897*A*. [4] Karsten, 1904; Schmidt, 1923.

division[1] until 8, 16, 32, or 64 uninucleate protoplasts have been formed (Fig. 125). More recent cytological study has shown[2] that meiosis occurs during the series of nuclear divisions accompanying the formation of "microspores." Motility has been demonstrated for a sufficient number of species to warrant the assumption that "microspores" of all species have flagella. Those of certain species have been described[3] as having one flagellum; those of other species are said[4] to be biflagellate.

For a long time "microspores" were generally thought to be zoosporic in nature but the suggestion was also made[5] that they are isogametes. An entirely different interpretation was proposed[6] when a living plankton

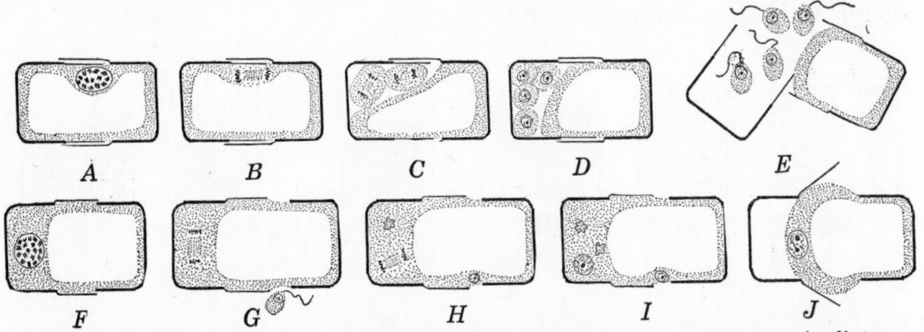

FIG. 126. Diagram of stages in oögamous formation of auxospore of the centric diatom, *Melosira varians* C.A.Ag. *A–E*, meiotic division of nucleus and formation of antherozoids in an antheridial cell. *F–J*, oögonial cell. *F–G*, first meiotic division and entrance of antherozoid during telophase. *H–I*, second meiotic division and before union of male and female nuclei. *J*, after union of male and female nuclei and at the beginning of enlargement of zygote to form an auxospore. (*Diagram based upon von Stosch*, 1951.)

haul from the middle of the Atlantic Ocean showed motile "microspores" of *Chaetoceros* swarming about cells with undivided contents. According to this interpretation the "microspores" are motile male gametes (antherozoids) which escape from a parent cell and swim to a female cell containing a single protoplast (the egg) that is not liberated from the cell. An oögamous union of gametes has been demonstrated for a number of other centric diatoms[7] and it has been found that the zygote develops into an auxospore. In a cell whose protoplast develops into an egg there is a meiotic division of the nucleus, and in the two genera where cytological details have been most studied an antherozoid enters the egg before meiosis is completed. In *Melosira* it enters after the nucleus has completed the first meiotic division;[8] in *Cyclotella* it enters during pro-

[1] Bergon, 1907; Hofker, 1928.
[2] Geitler, 1952; Hofker, 1928; Schmidt, 1931, 1933; von Stosch, 1951.
[3] Bergon, 1907; Schiller, 1919. [4] Pavillard, 1914; Schmidt, 1923.
[5] Schmidt, 1923. [6] Went in Geitler, 1932, pp. 11–12.
[7] Geitler, 1952; von Stosch, 1950, 1951, 1951*A*. [8] von Stosch, 1951.

phase of the first division.[1] However, nuclear fusion does not take place in either until after meiosis has been completed (Fig. 126*H–I*).

Auxospores of centric diatoms may also be formed by autogamy. In *Cyclotella meneghiniana* Kütz. a cell producing an auxospore has a meiotic division of the nucleus.[2] Two of the nuclei formed as a result of meiosis unite and the other two degenerate (Fig. 127). The protoplast with the fusion nucleus then enlarges to form an auxospore.

Statospores. Thick-walled spores (variously called statospores, endospores, or cysts) may be formed within frustules of centric diatoms (Fig. 128). They are most frequently encountered in marine plankton species but have also been found in three fresh-water plankton species. In their

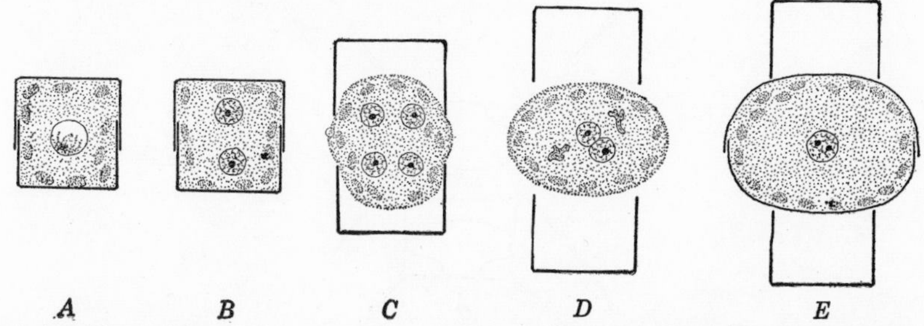

FIG. 127. Diagram showing the autogamous formation of an auxospore in the centric diatom *Cyclotella meneghiniana* Kütz. *A–C*, meiotic division to form four haploid nuclei. *D*, degeneration of two nuclei and the beginning of fusion of the other two nuclei. *E*, nuclear fusion completed and the protoplast enlarging to form an auxospore. (*Diagram based upon Iyengar and Subrahmanyan*, 1943.)

formation, the protoplast retracts from the frustule wall and then secretes a new wall composed of two overlapping halves. A statospore wall differs from a vegetative parent cell with respect both to ornamentation and to the spines it bears.[3] The details of statospore formation are unknown but it is probable that they are formed in the same endoplasmic manner as are homologous spores of Chrysophyceae and Xanthophyceae.

Classification. Practically all treatises on diatoms written within the past half century follow the classification of Schütt,[4] which is based entirely on the structure of the cell wall. This system has the great advantage of being equally applicable to living diatoms and to those known only in a fossil condition. Schütt placed all diatoms in a single family and established subfamilies, tribes, subtribes, and other family categories to show the affinities between closely related genera and those more distantly related. Later workers have raised Schütt's two subfamilies to the rank of orders and have given his categories in each of the two subfamilies

[1] Geitler, 1952. [2] Iyengar and Subrahmanyan, 1942.
[3] Boyer, 1914; Mangin, 1912; Schütt, 1896. [4] Schütt, 1896.

a correspondingly greater rank. Schütt differentiated between his two subfamilies on the basis of ornamentation of the valves; one having a radially symmetrical ornamentation, the other having a bilaterally symmetrical ornamentation with respect to the long axis of the valve. This distinction appears to be artificial, but it is quite natural and correlated with several other characters. Centric diatoms (Centrales) usually have many chromatophores, are always immobile, produce statospores, and have an oögamous formation of auxospores. Pennate diatoms (Pennales) usually have but one or two chromatophores, often are capable of spon-

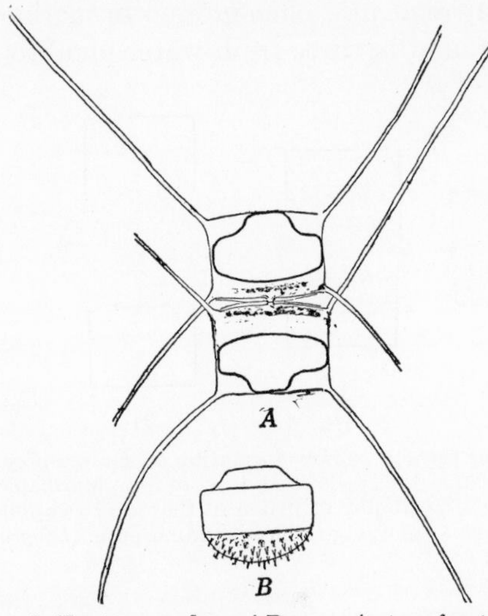

Fig. 128. Statospores of *Chaetoceros elmorei* Boyer. *A*, two frustules, each containing an immature statospore. *B*, a mature statospore. (*After Boyer*, 1914.)

taneous movement, and form auxospores by an isogamous or anisogamous conjugation of aplanogametes.

Bibliography

Allen, E. J., and E. W. Nelson. **1910.** *Jour. Marine Biol. Assoc. United Kingdom.* N.S. **8:** 421–474. [Size variation, diatoms.]

Bachrach, Eudoxie, and M. Lefèvre. **1929.** *Jour. Physiol. et Pathol. Gén.* **27:** 241–249. 2 pl. 9 figs. [Silicification, diatoms.]

Benecke, W. **1900.** *Jahrb. Wiss. Bot.* **35:** 535–572. 1 pl. [Colorless diatoms.]

Bergon, P. **1907.** *Bull. Soc. Bot. France* **54:** 327–358. 4 pl. [Microspores, diatoms.]

Birckner, V. **1912.** *Flora* **104:** 167–171. 3 figs. [Zoospores, *Vaucheria.*]

Bohlin, K. **1897** *Bih. Kgl. Svensk. Vetensk.-Ak. Handl.* **23,** Afd. 3, Nr. 3: 1–56. 2 pl. [Cell wall, Xanthophyceae.]

Borzi, A. **1892.** *Atti Congresso Bot. Internat.* **1892:** 1–19. 2 pl. (Ref. Just's *Bot. Jahresb.* **20**[1]**:** 51. 1894.) [*Phaeothamnion.*]

1895. Studi algologici. Fasc. 2. Palermo. Pp. 121–378. 22 pl.

Boyer, C. S. **1914.** *Proc. Acad. Nat. Sci. Phila.* **66:** 219–221. 1 pl. [Statospores, diatoms.]

Carter, Nellie **1919.** *New Phytol.* **18:** 177–186. 3 figs. [Xanthophyceae.]

Chadefaud, M. **1945.** *Bull. Soc. Bot. France* **92:** 47–50. [*Vaucheria.*]
Chandler, H. P., and A. L. Marks. **1954.** Abrasive materials. In U. S. Bureau of Mines, Minerals Yearbook for 1951. Pp. 111–127.
Chodat, R. **1913.** *Matér. pour la Flore Crypt. Suisse* **4²:** 1–266. 9 pl. 201 figs. [Xanthophyceae.]
Cholnoky, B. von. **1927.** *Arch. Protistenk.* **60:** 8–33. 1 pl. [Auxospores, Pennales.]
1928. *Ibid.* **63:** 23–57. 4 pl. [Auxospores, Pennales.]
1929. *Ibid.* **68:** 417–502. 3 pl. 2 figs. [Auxospores, Pennales.]
1933. *Ibid.* **80:** 321–348. 41 figs. [Auxospores, Pennales.]
Cienkowski, L. **1870.** *Arch. Mikrosk. Anat.* **6:** 421–438. 2 pl. [Statospores, Chrysophyceae.]
Conrad, W. **1926.** *Arch. Protistenk.* **56:** 167–231. 3 pl. 28 figs. [Chrysomonadales.]
1927. *Ibid.* **59:** 423–505. 4 pl. 41 figs. [Chrysomonadales.]
1928. *Ibid.* **60:** 415–439. 13 figs. [Chrysomonadales.]
1933. *Mém. Mus. Roy. Hist. Nat. Belgique* **56:** 1–82. 70 figs. [Chrysomonadales.]
Couch, J. N. **1932.** *Bot. Gaz.* **94:** 272–296. 35 figs. [Gametogenesis, *Vaucheria.*]
Coupin, H. **1922.** *Compt. Rend. Acad. Sci. Paris* **175:** 1226–1229. [Silicification, diatoms.]
Davis, B. M. **1904.** *Bot. Gaz.* **38:** 81–98. 2 pl. [Gametogenesis, *Vaucheria.*]
Doflein, F. **1922.** *Arch. Protistenk.* **44:** 206–212. 1 pl. [*Chrysamoeba.*]
1923. *Ibid.* **46:** 267–327. 7 pl. 5 figs. [Chrysomonadales.]
Fritsch, F. E. **1935.** The structure and reproduction of the algae. Vol. 1. Cambridge. 791 pp. 243 figs.
Geitler, L. **1927.** *Arch. Protistenk.* **58:** 272–280. 4 figs. [Chrysotrichales.]
1927A. *Ibid.* **59:** 506–549. 3 pl. 29 figs. [Auxospores, Pennales.]
1927B. *Ibid.* **58:** 465–507. 2 pl. 14 figs. [Auxospores, Pennales.]
1927C. *Mikrokosmos* **21:** 79–82. 2 figs. [Auxospores, Pennales.]
1928. *Arch. Protistenk.* **63:** 67–83. 1 pl. 2 figs. [*Epichrysis.*]
1928A. *Ibid.* **61:** 419–442. 13 figs. [Auxospores, Pennales.]
1928B. *Oesterr. Bot. Zeitschr.* **77:** 81–91. 3 figs. [Auxospores, Pennales.]
1930. *Arch. Protistenk.* **69:** 615–636. 1 pl. 15 figs. [*Chlorarachnion.*]
1932. *Ibid.* **78:** 1–226. 125 figs. [Size variation, diatoms.]
1935. *Bot. Rev.* **1:** 149–161. [Auxospores, diatoms.]
1935A. *Oesterr. Bot. Zeitschr.* **84:** 282–286. 2 figs. [*Dinobryon.*]
1939. *Planta* **30:** 551–566. 6 figs. [Auxospores, Pennales.]
1952. *Oesterr. Bot. Zeitschr.* **99:** 506–520. 5 figs. [Auxospores, Centrales.]
Gemeinhardt, K. **1926.** *Ber. Deutsch. Bot. Ges.* **44:** 517–525. 1 pl. [Cell wall, diatoms.]
1927. *Ibid.* **45:** 570–576. 1 pl. [Size variation, diatoms.]
Götz, H. **1897.** *Flora* **83:** 88–134. 55 figs. [*Vaucheria.*]
Gross, Catherine. **1937.** *Bull. Torrey Bot. Club* **64:** 1–15. 31 figs. [*Vaucheria.*]
Hanatschek, Herta. **1932.** *Arch. Protistenk.* **78:** 497–513. 2 figs. [Meiosis in *Vaucheria.*]
Heidinger, W. **1908.** *Ber. Deutsch. Bot. Ges.* **26:** 313–363. 1 pl. 18 figs. [Gametogenesis, *Vaucheria.*]
Heinzerling, O. **1908.** *Bibliotheca Bot.* **15,** Heft 69: 1–88. 3 pl. [Chromatophores, diatoms.]
Hofeneder, H. **1913.** *Arch. Protistenk.* **29:** 293–307. 1 pl. 3 figs. [Chrysomonadales.]
Hofker, J. **1928.** *Ann. de Protistol.* **1:** 167–194. 21 figs. [Microspores, diatoms.]
Hustedt, F. **1926.** *Ber. Deutsch. Bot. Ges.* **44:** 142–150. 1 pl. [Raphe, diatoms.]
1926A. *Ibid.* **44:** 394–400. 1 pl. [Raphe, diatoms.]
1928. *Ibid.* **46:** 148–157. 1 pl. [Raphe, diatoms.]
1928A. *Ibid.* **46:** 157–162. 1 pl. [Raphe, diatoms.]
1929. *Ibid.* **47:** 101–104. 1 pl. [Raphe, diatoms.]

1929A. *Ibid.* **47:** 104–110. 1 pl. [Raphe, diatoms.]
Iyengar, M. O. P. **1925.** *Jour. Indian Bot. Soc.* **4:** 193–201. 5 pl. [*Botrydium.*]
Iyengar, M. O. P., and R. Subrahmanyan. **1942.** *Ibid.* **21:** 231–237. 1 pl. 14 figs. [Auxospores, Centrales.]
Karsten, G. **1896.** *Flora* **82:** 286–296. 1 pl. [Auxospores, Pennales.]
1897. *Ibid.* **83:** 33–53. 2 pl. [Auxospores, Pennales.]
1897A. *Ibid.* **83:** 203–222. 1 pl. [Auxospores, Pennales.]
1900. *Ibid.* **87:** 253–283. 3 pl. [Auxospores, Pennales.]
1904. *Ber. Deutsch. Bot. Ges.* **22:** 544–554. 1 pl. [Microspores, diatoms.]
1912. *Zeitschr. Bot.* **4:** 417–426. 1 pl. [Auxospores, Pennales.]
Klebahn, H. **1896.** *Jahrb. Wiss. Bot.* **29:** 595–654. 1 pl. [Auxospores, Pennales.]
Klebs, G. **1892.** *Zeitschr. Wiss. Zool.* **55:** 353–445. 2 pl. [Chrysophyceae.]
1896. Die Bedingungen der Fortpflanzung bei einigen Algen und Pilzen. Jena. 543 pp. 3 pl. 15 figs.
Koch, W. J. **1951.** *Jour. Elisha Mitchell Sci. Soc.* **67:** 123–131. [Flagella of *Vaucheria.*]
Kolkwitz, R. **1926.** *Ber. Deutsch. Bot. Ges.* **44:** 533–540. 1 pl. 2 figs. [*Botrydium.*]
Korshikov, A. A. **1929.** *Arch. Protistenk.* **67:** 253–290. 4 pl. 1 fig. [Chrysomonadales.]
1930. *Beih. Bot. Centralbl.* **46:** 470–478. 2 figs. [Pyrenoids, Xanthophyceae.]
Lackey, J. B. **1939.** *Lloydia* **2:** 128–143. 38 figs. [*Chromulina.*]
Lagerheim, G. **1884.** *Bih. Kgl. Svensk. Vetensk.-Ak. Handl.* **9,** No. 19: 1–14. 1 pl. [*Phaeothamnion.*]
1888. *Ber. Deutsch. Bot. Ges.* **6:** 73–85. 3 figs. [*Hydrurus.*]
1889. *Flora* **72:** 179–210. 2 pl. [*Tribonema.*]
Lauterborn, R. **1896.** Untersuchungen über Bau, Kernteilung und Bewegung der Diatomeen. Leipzig. 165 pp. 1 fig. 10 pl.
Liebisch, W. **1928.** *Zeitschr. Bot.* **20:** 225–271. 2 pl. 22 figs. [Cell wall, diatoms.]
1929. *Ibid.* **22:** 1–65. 1 pl. 14 figs. [Cell wall, diatoms.]
Locker, F. **1950.** *Oesterr. Bot. Zeitschr.* **97:** 322–332. 1 fig. [Size variation, diatoms.]
Luther, A. **1899.** *Bih. Kgl. Svensk. Vetensk.-Ak. Handl.* **24,** Afd. 3, No. 13: 1–22. 1 pl. [Xanthophyceae.]
Macdonald, J. D. **1869.** *Ann. and Mag. Nat. Hist.* 4 ser. **3:** 1–8. [Size variation, diatoms.]
Mangin, L. **1908.** *Ann. Sci. Nat. Bot.* 9 ser. **8:** 177–219. 14 figs. [Cell wall, diatoms.]
1912. *Rev. Scientifique* **50**[2]: 481–487. 7 figs. [Statospores, diatoms.]
Meinhold, T. **1911.** *Beitr. Biol. Pflanzen* **10:** 353–378. 1 pl. [Size variation, diatoms.]
Meloche, V., G. Leader, L. Safranski, and C. Juday. **1938.** *Trans. Wis. Acad.* **31:** 363–376. [Diatoms and silica.]
Mereschkowsky, C. **1903.** *Flora* **92:** 77–83. 4 figs. [Pyrenoids, diatoms.]
Meyer, K. **1929.** *Arch. Protistenk.* **66:** 421–435. 2 pl. [Auxospores, Pennales.]
Meyer, K. I. **1930.** *Ibid.* **72:** 158–175. 11 figs. [*Epichrysis.*]
Miller, V. **1927.** *Ber. Deutsch. Bot. Ges.* **45:** 151–161. 1 pl. [*Botrydium.*]
Moewus, F. **1940.** *Biol. Zentralbl.* **60:** 484–498. 2 figs. [*Botrydium.*]
Molisch, H. **1903.** *Ber. Deutsch. Bot. Ges.* **21:** 23–26. 1 pl. [Chromatophores, diatoms.]
Müller, O. **1889.** *Ber. Deutsch. Bot. Ges.* **7:** 169–180. 1 pl. [Locomotion, diatoms.]
1893. *Ibid.* **11:** 571–576. 1 fig. [Locomotion, diatoms.]
1896. *Ibid.* **14:** 111–128. 1 pl. [Locomotion, diatoms.]
1897. *Ibid.* **15:** 70–86. [Locomotion, diatoms.]
1898. *Ibid.* **16:** 386–402. 2 pl. [Cell wall, diatoms.]
1899. *Ibid.* **17:** 423–452. 2 pl. [Cell wall, diatoms.]
1900. *Ibid.* **18:** 480–497. 1 fig. [Cell wall, diatoms.]
1901. *Ibid.* **19:** 195–210. 1 pl. 3 figs. [Cell wall, diatoms.]
1906. *Jahrb. Wiss. Bot.* **43:** 49–88. 2 pl. 3 figs. [Auxospores, Centrales.]
1909. *Ber. Deutsch. Bot. Ges.* **27:** 27–43. 1 pl. 1 fig. [Locomotion, diatoms.]

Mundie, J. R. **1929.** *Bot. Gaz.* **87**: 397–410. 2 pl. [*Vaucheria.*]
Nipkow, H. F. **1928.** *Zeitschr. Hydrol.* **4**: 71–120. [Auxospores, diatoms.]
Oltmanns, F. **1895.** *Flora* **80**: 388–420. 5 pl. [Gametogenesis, *Vaucheria.*]
Ott, Emma. **1900.** *Sitzungsber. Akad. Wiss. Wien* (Math.-Nat. Kl.) **109**[1]: 796–801. 6 pl. [Chromatophores, diatoms.]
Pascher, A. **1910.** *Ber. Deutsch. Bot. Ges.* **28**: 339–350. 1 pl. [*Chromulina.*]
1912. *Arch. Protistenk.* **25**: 153–200. 1 pl. 7 figs. [Chrysomonadales.]
1913. *Hedwigia* **53**: 6–22. 8 figs. [Classification, Xanthophyceae.]
1914. *Ber. Deutsch. Bot. Ges.* **32**: 136–160. [Homologies of Chrysophyta.]
1915. *Ibid.* **33**: 488–492. [*Botrydiopsis.*]
1915A. *Arch. Protistenk.* **36**: 81–117. 3 pl. 14 figs. [Rhizochrysidales.]
1916. *Ibid.* **37**: 15–30. 1 pl. 6 figs. [Rhizochrysidales.]
1916A. *Ibid.* **37**: 31–64. 1 pl. 20 figs. [Rhizochrysidales.]
1917. *Ibid.* **38**: 1–88. 65 figs. [Rhizochrysidales.]
1921. *Ber. Deutsch. Bot. Ges.* **39**: 236–248. 6 figs. [Homologies of Chrysophyta.]
1924. *Arch. Protistenk.* **48**: 196–203. 4 figs. [Homologies of Chrysophyta.]
1925. Heterokontae. In A. Pascher, Die Süsswasserflora Deutschlands, Österreichs und der Schweiz. Heft 11. Pp. 1–118. 96 figs.
1930. *Arch. Protistenk.* **69**: 401–451. 1 pl. 45 figs. [Xanthophyceae.]
1930A. *Ibid.* **72**: 311–358. 2 pl. 27 figs. [Rhizochloridales.]
1931. *Beih. Bot. Centralbl.* **48**: 317–332. [Classification of algae.]
1931A. *Arch. Protistenk.* **73**: 60–72. 1 pl. 9 figs. [Chrysotrichales.]
1931B. *Ibid.* **73**: 73–103. 18 figs. [Chrysocapsales.]
1931C. *Beih. Bot. Centralbl.* **47**: 325–345. 2 pl. 12 figs. [Chrysocapsales.]
1932. *Arch. Protistenk.* **77**: 305–359. 37 figs. [Xanthophyceae.]
1932A. *Beih. Bot. Centralbl.* **49**: 293–308. 13 figs. [Endoplasmic spores.]
1937–1939. Heterokonten. In L. Rabenhorst, Kryptogamen-Flora Deutschland, Österreich und der Schweiz. Bd. 11. 1092 pp. 912 figs.
Pavillard, J. **1914.** *Bull. Soc. Bot. France* **61**: 164–172. 2 figs. [Microspores, diatoms.]
Pearsall, W. H. **1923.** *Jour. Ecol.* **11**: 165–183. 10 figs. [Silicification, diatoms.]
Penard, E. **1921.** *Proc. Acad. Nat. Sci. Phila.* **73**: 105–168. 4 pl. [*Chrysamoeba.*]
Pergallo, H. **1906.** *Soc. Sci. d'Archachon Stat. Biol. Trav. des Laboratories* **8**: 127–144. (Ref. Just's *Bot. Jahresber.* **34**[2]: 622, 1908). [Microspores, diatoms.]
Petersen, J. B. **1918.** *Vidensk. Medd. fra Dansk. naturhist. Foren.* **69**: 345–357. 1 pl. [Chrysomonadales.]
1928. The aërial algae of Iceland. In The Botany of Iceland **2**: 328–447. 36 figs.
1929. *Bot. Tidsskr.* **40**: 373–389. 1 pl. [Flagella of Chrysophyceae.]
Pfitzer, E. **1871.** Untersuchungen über Bau und Entwicklung der Bacillariaceen. In Hanstein, Botanische Abhandlungen aus dem Gebiet der Morphologie und Physiologie. Bd. 1. Heft 2. Pp. 1–189. 6 pl.
1882. Die Bacillariaceen (Diatomaceen), In A. Schenk, Handbuch der Botanik. Bd. 2. Pp. 403–445. 16 figs.
Pia, J. **1927.** Thallophyta. In M. Hirmer, Handbuch der Paläobotanik. Bd. 1. Pp. 31–136. 116 figs.
Poulton, Ethel M. **1925.** Etude sur les Hétérokontes. Geneva. 96 pp. 13 figs.
1930. *New Phytol.* **29**: 1–26. 4 figs. [Xanthophyceae.]
Prescott, G. W. **1951.** Algae of the western Great Lakes area. Bloomfield Hills, Mich. 946 pp. 136 pl.
Pringsheim, N. **1855.** *Monatsber. Akad. Wiss. Berlin* **1855**: 133–165. 1 pl. [Zygote, *Vaucheria.*]
Puymaly, A. de. **1922.** *Compt. Rend. Acad. Sci. Paris* **174**: 824–827. [Hypnospores, *Vaucheria.*]

Richter, O. **1909.** *Denkschr. kais. Akad. Wiss. Wien* (Math.-Nat. Kl.) **84**: 660–772. 4 pl. 6 figs. [Colorless diatoms.]
Rostafiński, J. **1882.** *Ann. Sci. Nat. Bot.* 6 ser. **14**: 5–25. 1 pl. [*Hydrurus.*]
Rostafiński, J., and M. Woronin. **1877.** *Bot. Zeitg.* **35**: 649–671. 5 pl. [*Botrydium.*]
Scherffel, A. **1901.** *Ibid.* **59**: 143–158. 1 pl. [*Tribonema.*]
1911. *Arch. Protistenk.* **22**: 299–344. 1 pl. [Chrysomonadales.]
Schiller, J. **1909.** *Ber. Deutsch. Bot. Ges.* **27**: 351–361. 1 pl. [Microspores, diatoms.]
Schmidt, P. **1923.** *Internat. Rev. gesamt. Hydrobiol. Hydrograph.* **11**: 114–147. 5 pl. [Microspores, diatoms.]
1929. *Ibid.* **21**: 289–334. 4 pl. [Microspores, diatoms.]
1931. *Ibid.* **25**: 68–101. 3 pl. [Microspores, diatoms.]
1933. *Flora* **128**: 235–268. 2 pl. [Microspores, diatoms.]
Schröder, B. **1920.** *Verhandl. Naturh.-Med. Ver. Heidelberg* N.F. **7**: 139–196. 2 pl. [Cell wall, diatoms.]
Schütt, F. **1896.** Bacillariales. In A. Engler and K. Prantl, Die natürlichen Pflanzenfamilien. Teii 1, Abt. 1^b. Pp. 31–150. 239 figs.
Smith, G. M. **1933.** The fresh-water algae of the United States. New York. 716 pp. 449 figs.
1944. *Farlowia* **1**: 387–389. 2 figs. [Microaplanospores, *Vaucheria.*]
1950. The fresh-water algae of the United States. 2d ed. New York. 719 pp. 559 figs.
Stahl, E. **1879.** *Bot. Zeitg.* **37**: 129–137. 1 pl. [Hypnospores, *Vaucheria.*]
Stosch, H. A. von. **1950.** *Nature* **165**: 531. [Auxospores, Centrales.]
1951. *Arch. Microbiol.* **16**: 101–135. 2 pl. 22 figs. [Auxospores, Centrales.]
1951A. *Naturwissensch.* **38**: 191–192. [Auxospores, Centrales.]
1951B. *Ibid.* **38**: 192–193. [Leucosin.]
Strain, H. H. **1948.** *Carnegie Inst. Washington Yearbook* **47**: 97–100. [Pigments of *Vaucheria.*]
Strasburger, E. **1880.** Zellbildung und Zelltheilung. 3d ed. Jena. 392 pp. 14 pl.
Subrahmanyan, R. **1948.** *Jour. Indian Bot. Soc. Iyengar Commemoration Vol.* Pp. 289–303. 44 figs.
Tiffany, L. H. **1924.** *Ohio Jour. Sci.* **24**: 65–98. 1 pl. [Cell wall, *Tribonema.*]
Vlk, W. **1931.** *Beih. Bot. Centralbl.* **48**: 214–220. 15 figs. [Flagella, Xanthophyceae.]
1938. *Arch. Protistenk.* **90**: 448–488. 1 pl. 12 figs. [Flagella, Chrysophyta.]
Walz, J. **1866.** *Jahrb. Wiss. Bot.* **5**: 127–160. 3 pl. [*Vaucheria.*]
West, G. S. **1904.** A treatise on the British fresh-water algae. Cambridge. 372 pp. 166 figs.
Wielding, S. **1941.** *Bot. Notiser* **1941**: 33–36. 2 figs. [Silicification, diatoms.]
1948. *Ibid.* **1948**: 322–354. [Size variation, diatoms.]
Wille, N. **1881.** *Öfvers. Kgl. Svensk. Vetensk.-Ak. Förh.* **38**, No. 8: 1–26. 2 pl. (Ref. Just's *Bot. Jahresber.* 9^1: 360–362, 1884.) [*Tribonema.*]
Williams, May M. **1926.** *Proc. Linn. Soc. New South Wales* **51**: 283–295. 16 figs. [Gametogenesis, *Vaucheria.*]

Rostafiński, J. **1882.** *Ann. Sci. Nat. Bot.* 6 ser. **14**: 5–25. 1 pl. [*Hydrurus.*]

Rostafiński, J., and M. Woronin. **1877.** *Bot. Zeitg.* **35**: 649–671. 5 pl. [*Botrydium.*]

Scherffel, A. **1901.** *Ibid.* **59**: 143–158. 1 pl. [*Tribonema.*]

1911. *Arch. Protistenk.* **22**: 299–344. 1 pl. [Chrysomonadales.]

Schiller, J. **1909.** *Ber. Deutsch. Bot. Ges.* **27**: 351–361. 1 pl. [Microspores, diatoms.]

Schmidt, P. **1923.** *Internat. Rev. gesamt. Hydrobiol. Hydrograph.* **11**: 114–147. 5 pl. [Microspores, diatoms.]

1929. *Ibid.* **21**: 289–334. 4 pl. [Microspores, diatoms.]

1931. *Ibid.* **25**: 68–101. 3 pl. [Microspores, diatoms.]

1933. *Flora* **128**: 235–268. 2 pl. [Microspores, diatoms.]

Schröder, B. **1920.** *Verhandl. Naturh.-Med. Ver. Heidelberg* N.F. **7**: 139–196. 2 pl. [Cell wall, diatoms.]

Schütt, F. **1896.** Bacillariales. In A. Engler and K. Prantl, Die natürlichen Pflanzenfamilien. Teii 1, Abt. 1^b. Pp. 31–150. 239 figs.

Smith, G. M. **1933.** The fresh-water algae of the United States. New York. 716 pp. 449 figs.

1944. *Farlowia* **1**: 387–389. 2 figs. [Microaplanospores, *Vaucheria.*]

1950. The fresh-water algae of the United States. 2d ed. New York. 719 pp. 559 figs.

Stahl, E. **1879.** *Bot. Zeitg.* **37**: 129–137. 1 pl. [Hypnospores, *Vaucheria.*]

Stosch, H. A. von. **1950.** *Nature* **165**: 531. [Auxospores, Centrales.]

1951. *Arch. Microbiol.* **16**: 101–135. 2 pl. 22 figs. [Auxospores, Centrales.]

1951A. *Naturwissensch.* **38**: 191–192. [Auxospores, Centrales.]

1951B. *Ibid.* **38**: 192–193. [Leucosin.]

Strain, H. H. **1948.** *Carnegie Inst. Washington Yearbook* **47**: 97–100. [Pigments of *Vaucheria.*]

Strasburger, E. **1880.** Zellbildung und Zelltheilung. 3d ed. Jena. 392 pp. 14 pl.

Subrahmanyan, R. **1948.** *Jour. Indian Bot. Soc. Iyengar Commemoration Vol.* Pp. 289–303. 44 figs.

Tiffany, L. H. **1924.** *Ohio Jour. Sci.* **24**: 65–98. 1 pl. [Cell wall, *Tribonema.*]

Vlk, W. **1931.** *Beih. Bot. Centralbl.* **48**: 214–220. 15 figs. [Flagella, Xanthophyceae.]

1938. *Arch. Protistenk.* **90**: 448–488. 1 pl. 12 figs. [Flagella, Chrysophyta.]

Walz, J. **1866.** *Jahrb. Wiss. Bot.* **5**: 127–160. 3 pl. [*Vaucheria.*]

West, G. S. **1904.** A treatise on the British fresh-water algae. Cambridge. 372 pp. 166 figs.

Wielding, S. **1941.** *Bot. Notiser* **1941**: 33–36. 2 figs. [Silicification, diatoms.]

1948. *Ibid.* **1948**: 322–354. [Size variation, diatoms.]

Wille, N. **1881.** *Öfvers. Kgl. Svensk. Vetensk.-Ak. Förh.* **38**, No. 8: 1–26. 2 pl. (Ref. Just's *Bot. Jahresber.* $\mathbf{9}^1$: 360–362, 1884.) [*Tribonema.*]

Williams, May M. **1926.** *Proc. Linn. Soc. New South Wales* **51**: 283–295. 16 figs. [Gametogenesis, *Vaucheria.*]

CHAPTER 6

PHAEOPHYTA

Cells of Phaeophyta, the brown algae, have yellowish-brown chromatophores because xanthophylls are present in greater abundance than other pigments. There are six xanthophylls, three of which are found only in brown algae (see Table I, page 4). Carbohydrate food reserves are stored in a soluble state, the two principal reserves being laminarin and mannitol.

Thalli of Phaeophyta are always multicellular and usually of macroscopic size and distinctive shape. Motile reproductive cells, irrespective of whether zoosporic or gametic, are pyriform, with two laterally inserted flagella, one of which is of the tinsel type. Asexual reproduction is by zoospores or by aplanospores without walls. Most genera reproduce sexually, and sexual reproduction may be isogamous, anisogamous, or oögamous. In the life cycle of most genera there is an alternation of free-living sporophytic and gametophytic generations and the alternation may be isomorphic or heteromorphic.

There are about 195 genera and 1,000 species of brown algae.

Distribution. There are three rare fresh-water Phaeophyta. All others are marine. Generally speaking, the marine Phaeophyta are algae of cold waters. They are the predominating element in the littoral flora of Arctic and Antarctic seas, and they constitute a progressively less conspicuous element in the flora as one goes toward the tropics. However, certain of the brown algae, notably the Dictyotales and *Sargassum*, are distinctly warm-water plants.

Many of the marine species grow attached to rocks or to some other inanimate substratum. Other species grow in association with other algae, as either epiphytes or endophytes. In many cases, as *Myrionema strangulans* Grev. (page 246), brown algae grow only upon a single host species.

There is a distinct vertical zonation of marine brown algae at any given station. Many species grow only in the intertidal region and even here there is a definite vertical distribution. The rockweeds (Fucaceae) are usually restricted to the upper littoral belt and the kelps (Laminariales) to the lowermost portion of it. Other littoral genera, as *Sphacelaria* (page 233) and *Leathesia* (page 246), tend to be restricted to the midlittoral zone. There are also species which grow only in the sublittoral region. The most notable of these are certain of the giant kelps found along the Pacific Coast of this country. These algae grow on rocky reefs 10 to 20 meters below the surface of the ocean. The kelps are anchored to the reef by a holdfast from which arises a long slender axis whose upper portion is expanded into a number of blades that float on the surface of the water. Other sublittoral Phaeophyta, as certain species of *Sargassum* (page 264) and of *Desmarestia* (page 146), never extend to the surface of the water. Sublittoral brown algae of northern seas are rarely found below the 25-meter level, but in warmer waters, as those off the coast of Florida[1] and in the Mediterranean,[2] they may grow at greater depths. The greatest depth at which brown algae have been found is 110 meters.[2]

Economic Uses. At one time the ash obtained by burning kelps and rockweeds cast ashore by gales was an important source of potassium and iodine. The discovery of mineral deposits containing these elements has, however, made their recovery from algae unprofitable.

The colloidal gel **algin** obtained from kelps is used in a wide variety of industries. Algin comprises about 10 per cent of the wet weight of kelps. It[3] is wholly or in large part the calcium salt of alginic acid, a polyuric acid with the empirical formula $(C_6H_8O_6)_n$. A certain amount of algin is extracted from kelps (*Alaria* and *Laminaria*) growing along the coasts of Europe. Until very recently the cost of producing algin in Europe was high because the kelps had to be harvested by hand. The development of a mechanical device capable of collecting kelps directly from the rocks on which they grow has greatly reduced the cost of collecting kelps in European waters. On the Pacific Coast of the United States algin is obtained exclusively from *Macrocystis*, a kelp that grows in offshore stands and with the upper portion floating on the surface of the water. Here, mechanical harvesting is a much simpler matter. *Macrocystis* is harvested by means of barges (Fig. 129) equipped with scythe-like blades attached about 3 feet below the surface of the water. The five-man crew of a barge can harvest 300 tons of kelp in a day.

One of the uses of algin is in the making of ice cream, and practically all commercial producers of ice cream add algin before freezing their product. This prevents the water in the ice cream from forming coarse ice crystals and thus results in a smoother product. The water-retaining properties of algin are utilized in a variety of ways in the baking industry, including the addition of algin to frostings to prevent undue drying. The colloidal nature of algin makes it useful as a suspending and emulsifying agent. In the rubber industry it is used as a creaming and stabilizing

[1] Taylor, 1928. [2] Funk, 1927. [3] Kylin, 1915; Miwa, 1932; Tseng, 1945.

agent in the processing of natural and synthetic rubber latex. When added to paint, alginates help keep the pigments in suspension and make a product which can be brushed on a surface without showing brush marks. Alginates are also used as suspending agents in a wide variety of pharmaceutical products.

Kombu, a product made from various kelps, especially *Laminaria* and *Alaria*, is widely used as a food in Japan. It is boiled with fish, meat, or in soups, and is eaten by itself as a cooked vegetable. In the years preceding World War II over a quarter of a million tons of kelps were harvested

Fig. 129. A barge harvesting *Macrocystis* along the coast of California. (*Photograph courtesy of Kelco Company, San Diego, California.*)

annually for manufacture into kombu.[1] The kelps are gathered by fishermen and spread out to dry. The rough-dried plants are then sent to manufacturers for conversion into kombu.[2] Upon arriving at a factory, the dried algae are boiled in fresh water for a few minutes and then allowed to dry until the surface is no longer wet. The blades are then spread out one by one in flat wooden presses and the whole mass is compressed as tightly as possible. The compressed mass is then reduced to shreds by hand planes, the cutting being done along the edges of the parallel algal blades. Kombu is also prepared by soaking the algae in vinegar and then shredding them one by one.

Cell Structure. Cells of the Phaeophyta have a distinct wall and one differentiated into an inner firm portion and an outer gelatinous portion.

[1] Chapman, 1950. [2] H. M. Smith, 1905.

The major constituent of the firm portion is cellulose, held[1] to be chemically identical with that of vascular plants. The gelatinous portion of cell walls consists of algin, and in nonfilamentous thalli it may fill all intercellular spaces.

Protoplasts of vegetative cells generally have a central vacuole and a single nucleus. The nuclei resemble those of vascular plants in that there is a nuclear membrane, a nucleolus, and a chromatic network. Nuclear division is mitotic and in a considerable number of genera there are centrospheres or centrosomes at the polar foci of the mitotic figure. Genera in which these polar bodies have been found include those of Sphacelariales,[2] Cutleriales,[3] Dictyotales,[4] Punctariales,[5] Laminariales,[6] and Fucales.[7]

Vegetative cells of brown algae generally contain more than one chromatophore. Some species have disciform chromatophores; others have flattened elongate chromatophores with a very irregular outline. The chromatophores lack pyrenoids, but they (or the cytoplasm) may contain one or more irregularly shaped whitish **fucosan granules.** At one time the fucosan granules were thought to be an insoluble food reserve stored in the cell. Today,[8] they are interpreted as by-products of metabolic processes within the cell.

Reserve Foods. Carbohydrate formation in brown algae is comparable to that in sugar-storing vascular plants rather than to that in starch-storing ones. All reserve carbohydrates of Phaeophyta are stored in a dissolved state; but it is uncertain whether they accumulate in the vacuoles, in the cytoplasm, or throughout the protoplast. Cells of brown algae contain small amounts of simple reducing sugars, probably dextrose.[9] The chief carbohydrate reserve is **laminarin,** a compound found only in Phaeophyta. There may also be an accumulation of mannitol. When laminarin is extracted from brown algae it is a white tasteless soluble powder. It consists of a number of linked glucose units but it is uncertain[10] whether there are 16 or 20 glucose units. Laminarin may accumulate in sufficient quantity to constitute 7 to 35 per cent of the dry weight of a plant.[11] The gradual increase in the amount of laminarin throughout the growing season and the diminution in the amount of it at the time of reproduction or when new parts are being regenerated show that it serves as a reserve food.[11] Mannitol, the other reserve carbo-

[1] Percival and Ross, 1948. [2] Higgins, 1931; Swingle, 1897.
[3] Yamanouchi, 1912, 1913.
[4] Carter, 1927; Haupt, 1932; Mottier, 1900; Williams, 1904, 1904*A*.
[5] Mathias, 1935. [6] McKay, 1933.
[7] Farmer and Williams, 1898; Strasburger, 1897; Walker, 1931; Yamanouchi, 1909.
[8] Chadefaud, 1936; Kylin, 1938. [9] Kylin, 1944.
[10] Barry, 1938; Connell *et al.*, 1950. [11] Kylin, 1915.

hydrate, is a hexahydric alcohol. The amount in a plant is at a minimum in the winter and reaches its maximum in the summer. The amount in a plant is also correlated with the depth at which a thallus grows, and is greater in more deeply submerged ones than in those growing near the surface of the water.[1]

Vegetative Structure. All Phaeophyta but the Fucales may have an alternation of free-living gametophytic and sporophytic generations.

There is great variation in size of the adult thallus from genus to genus. At one extreme stand the minute gametophytes or sporophytes with only a few cells; at the other extreme are the sporophytes of the Pacific Coast giant kelps that attain a height of 25 to 30 meters. There is no particular correlation between longevity and size of the plant body. Thus, among the sporophytes of kelps, that of *Nereocystis* is an annual which grows to a height of 15 to 20 meters, whereas that of *Pterygophora* lives for 15 years or more and never becomes more than 3 meters tall.

The mature sporophyte or gametophyte may either be amorphous or of definite form. In the latter case it is generally differentiated into a holdfast and an erect portion. The erect portion may be simple or branched; solid or hollow; and tubular, spherical, or compressed. The greatest complexity of form is found among the kelps where there is an external differentiation comparable to that of a vascular plant. There is a root-like holdfast from which arises a simple or branched stem-like stipe that bears one to many leaf-like blades.

The growing apex of many Phaeophyta is a branched uniseriate filament in which cell division is intercalary. Growth by means of such an apical filament is said to be **trichothallic.** In some trichothallic genera mature portions of a thallus have a filamentous organization similar tc that of the growing apex. This is clearly evident in genera where the branches lie free from one another, as in *Ectocarpus* (page 230), and it is less clearly evident in genera, such as *Leathesia* (page 246), where the branches lie apposed to one another. In still other genera, as *Desmarestia* (page 251), the trichothallic nature of mature portions of a thallus is completely obliterated by a cortication of the filaments.

Terminal growth of other Phaeophyta is initiated by a single apical cell (*Dictyota*, page 242), or a transverse row of apical cells. According to the species, the apical cell cuts off derivatives at the posterior face only, or at both the posterior and the lateral faces.

Growth of the kelps is unique in that it is not apical, but is due to the activity of a meristematic region at the juncture of stipe and blade, or at the base of the stipe.

Mature regions of most thalli have more or less differentiation between the external and the internal portions. Superficial cells are always smaller

[1] Black, 1948.

and more densely filled with chromatophores than are the internal ones. The transition from small superficial to large internal cells may be gradual (*Leathesia*, page 246), or the superficial cells may be differentiated into an epidermis-like layer (*Desmarestia*, page 251). Thalli of Fucales and Laminariales are internally differentiated into two distinct tissues: the central **medulla,** composed of elongate colorless cells, and the encircling **cortex** of more or less isodiametric cells in which those toward the exterior contain chromatophores. The greatest internal differentiation of tissues is found in certain Pacific Ocean kelps where there are sieve tubes in the medulla.

Asexual Reproduction. Several of the Phaeophyta reproduce vegetatively by a fragmentation of the thallus. This may take place at either the juvenile or the adult stage. An attached thallus may split vertically into two or more portions which remain attached to the substratum. In such cases a single individual may be replaced by a cluster of individuals. Vegetative multiplication may also be effected by detachment of fragments that float away and develop into new plants. The best example of multiplication by means of detached fragments is seen in the *Sargassa* which are so abundant in the Gulf Stream and the Sargasso Sea. The most prolific of these is *Sargassum natans* (L.) Meyen, a species known only in the free-floating condition and one which has never been found with fructifications.[1] Vegetative multiplication may also be due, as in *Sphacelaria* (page 233), to the formation and abscission of special reproductive branches (**propagula**).

All Phaeophyta but the Fucales produce either naked zoospores or naked aplanospores. Zoospores are biflagellate, with the two flagella of unequal length and laterally inserted—the longer flagellum projecting forward and the shorter projecting backward. Study of flagella by special staining techniques[2] and by means of the electron microscope[3] shows that the anterior flagellum is of the tinsel type (see page 142) and with a double row of mastigonemes ("cilia"). The posterior flagellum has been found to be of the whiplash type.[2]

Flagellated reproductive cells may be formed within one-celled or within many-celled reproductive organs. The widespread usage of the name that Thuret[4] gave the many-celled organ (**plurilocular sporangium**) is misleading since it is indiscriminately applied both to many-celled sporangia and to many-celled gametangia. The one-celled zooid-producing reproductive organ that Thuret called a **unilocular sporangium** is sporangial in nature. Its development begins with an enlargement of a uninucleate cell and a division and redivision of the nucleus into 4, 8, 16, 32, 64, or 128 daughter nuclei; and then a cleavage into uninucleate proto-

[1] Collins, 1917. [2] Longest, 1946.
[3] Manton and Clark, 1951. [4] Thuret, 1855.

plasts that do not become separated from one another by walls. Finally there is a metamorphosis of each protoplast into a biflagellate zoospore or into a nonflagellated aplanospore, and a liberation of the spores by rupture of the sporangial wall. In all species that have been investigated cytologically[1] a thallus producing unilocular sporangia is diploid and division of the primary nucleus is meiotic. Hence, one is justified in assuming that any thallus producing unilocular sporangia is diploid and not haploid. There are several reports[2] of a fusion in pairs of zoospores from unilocular sporangia. One of the most convincing cases is that of *Desmarestia* where all stages in fusion and succeeding stages in germination of the zygote have been figured.[3] However, it has also been argued[4] that all reported cases of fusion of zoospores from unilocular sporangia are due to a misinterpretation of observations, and that these zoospores never function as gametes.

The nature of the so-called plurilocular sporangium was a matter of dispute until the introduction of the culture method of studying life histories. This has shown that some "plurilocular sporangia" are gametangia and others are sporangia. When a plurilocular sporangium is a sporangium, it is always borne on a diploid thallus, and the zoospores produced by it germinate to form new diploid plants. These have been called **neutral spores**[5] because they germinate to form the same instead of the alternate generation. The sporangium producing them should be called a **neutral sporangium** rather than a plurilocular sporangium. A neutral sporangium develops from a single cell which divides and redivides to form an elongate multicellular structure composed of many small cubical cells (Fig. 131*I–J*, page 230). Neutral sporangia of most Phaeophyta are many cells in height and several cells broad; but in some genera, as *Leathesia* (Fig. 143, page 247), they are only a few cells in height and one cell broad. The protoplast of each cell in a neutral sporangium is eventually metamorphosed into a neutral zoospore with two laterally inserted flagella. Neutral zoospores are liberated by a rupture of the surrounding cell walls. A few of the brown algae are heterosporous and with two morphologically different neutral sporangia, one producing small spores, the other large ones.[6]

Sexual Reproduction. The earlier confusion concerning the nature of "plurilocular sporangia" was due to the fact that many of the Phaeo-

[1] Abe, 1940, 1940*A*; Clint, 1927; Dammann, 1930; Haupt, 1932; Higgins, 1931; Knight, 1923, 1929; Kylin, 1918; McKay, 1933; Mathias, 1935, 1935*A*; Papenfuss, 1935; Parke, 1933; Schussnig and Kothbauer, 1934; Williams, 1904*A*; Yamanouchi, 1912, 1913.

[2] Abe, 1935, 1935*A*, 1938; Clint, 1927; Hygen, 1934; Knight, 1929; Schussnig and Kothbauer, 1934.

[3] Abe, 1938. [4] Kylin, 1937. [5] Svedelius, 1928.

[6] Sauvageau, 1896; Svedelius, 1928.

phyta produce gametangia whose development and mature structure are identical with those of their neutral sporangia. We now know that when produced upon a haploid thallus the plurilocular organ is a gametangium and when produced upon a diploid thallus it is a sporangium. For many genera with an alternation of vegetatively identical sporophyte and gametophyte it is impossible to determine microscopically whether the plurilocular organs borne by a particular individual brought into the laboratory are gametangia or neutral sporangia. The nature of the organ can be determined only by knowing the type of spore that the thallus developed from, or by following the behavior of swarmers liberated from the organ, or by knowing the number of chromosomes in vegetative cells. For those genera in which the diploid plants never form neutral sporangia, all multicellular organs are obviously gametangia.

Union of gametes from multicellular (plurilocular) gametangia may be **isogamous** and by a union of two motile gametes of equal size; or it may be **anisogamous** and with the two motile gametes unequal in size. Sexual reproduction in most of the Ectocarpales, Sphacelariales, Punctariales, and Dictyosiphonales is isogamous. The gametophytes may be homo- or heterothallic. Both isogametes may be actively motile at the time of gametic union, or one of them (the female) may be motionless at the time when the other (the male) swims to and unites with it. Gametic union is immediately followed by a development of the zygote into a sporophyte. There is usually a disintegration of gametes that have failed to conjugate, but sometimes[1] they develop parthenogenetically into new gametophytes.

Relatively few of the brown algae are anisogamous.[2] Gametangia of anisogamous species are multicellular and the two morphologically different. Male gametangia are distinguishable from female ones because of their much smaller cells (Fig. 137, page 238). Male gametes usually have but one chromatophore, and the female gametes usually contain several. At the time of gametic union the male gametes are actively motile, and the female immobile or moving sluggishly. In the Cutleriales[3] fusion of the two nuclei takes place within a few hours after gametic union and the zygote begins to develop into a sporophyte within a day. Unfertilized female gametes of Cutleriales regularly develop parthenogenetically into new gametophytes.[3]

Sexual reproduction may also be **oögamous** and by union of a small flagellated male gamete (**antherozoid**) with a large nonflagellated female gamete (the **egg**). All known gametophytes of Desmarestiales, Laminariales, and Dictyotales are oögamous and heterothallic. The male sex

[1] Hygen, 1934; Papenfuss, 1935.

[2] Karsakoff, 1892; Kuckuck, 1912A; Sauvageau, 1896A; Yamanouchi, 1912, 1913.

[3] Yamanouchi, 1912, 1913.

organs (**antheridia**) are multicellular in Dictyotales, and unicellular in Desmarestiales and Laminariales. These two types of antheridium are homologous with gametangia producing iso- or anisogametes in having the entire protoplast within an antheridial cell metamorphosing into a single biflagellate antherozoid. The female sex organs (**oögonia**) are always one-celled and with a single large nonflagellated egg. Eggs of Dictyotales are discharged from the oögonia, and fertilization takes place while they are floating in the water. Those of Desmarestiales and Laminariales are extruded from, but remain attached to, the apices of the oögonia. Parthenogenesis is quite common in the Dictyotales. It has also been found in *Laminaria*[1] and here the parthenogenetically developed germling has the structure of a sporophyte.

All thalli of Fucales are diploid and with one-celled reproductive organs in which the primary nucleus divides meiotically. Thus, as first pointed out by Kylin,[2] these organs are homologous with unilocular sporangia rather than with gametangia. From this standpoint the thalli of Fucales can be considered heterosporous sporophytes, with microsporangia producing small flagellated microspores, and macrosporangia producing large nonflagellated macrospores. Spores liberated from sporangia of Fucales function as gametes. This gametic union is oögamous; the microspores functioning as antherozoids, and the macrospores functioning as eggs. The terms oögonium, egg, antheridium, and antherozoid were used in connection with reproductive structures of Fucales before the nature of oögamy of Fucales was realized, and these terms will be used on pages to follow even if they are incorrect from the strict morphological standpoint.

According to the genus, the oögonia of Fucales produce one, two, four, or eight eggs. The antheridia generally produce 64 antherozoids. Antherozoids of Fucales differ from other swarmers of Phaeophyta in that the posterior flagellum is longer than the anterior one. Similar to Dictyotales, the eggs are free-floating when gametic union takes place. Under normal conditions unfertilized eggs disintegrate a few hours after liberation, but they have been induced[3] to germinate parthenogenetically by chemical stimulation.

Alternation of Generations. For a long time an alternation of generations was thought to be quite exceptional among Phaeophyta. Today, the results obtained by cultivation of a wide range of Phaeophyta justify the generalization that all brown algae but the Fucales typically have an alternation of generations.

Gametophyte and sporophyte may be alike in vegetative structure, or the two may be markedly different. If any plant brought into the laboratory bears unilocular sporangia, one may be certain that it is a

[1] Schreiber, 1930. [2] Kylin, 1917. [3] Overton, 1913.

sporophyte. The same cannot be said for any brown alga bearing only "plurilocular sporangia" since these may be gametangia borne upon a gametophyte or sporangia borne upon a sporophyte. Thus one cannot be certain whether there is an isomorphic or heteromorphic alternation of generations until a genus has been studied in cultures started from zoospores and zygotes.

Some Phaeophyta, including Laminariales and Dictyotales, have an obligatory alternation of gametophyte and sporophyte. Many other Phaeophyta have the regular alternation of gametophyte and sporophyte complicated by a reduplication of either generation. Reduplication of the sporophyte is by means of neutral spores. Production of neutral sporangia is generally accompanied by a reduction in number of unilocular sporangia, and frequently there is a complete suppression of unilocular sporangia. Reduplication by means of neutral spores may be seasonal, as in *Ectocarpus siliculosus* (Dillw.) Lyngb. (page 232), or it may continue throughout the year. The life cycle in these genera producing only neutral spores is merely a succession of sporophytic generations.[1]

Neutral spores may also give rise to filamentous dwarf stages (**plethysmothalli**[2]) resembling gametophytes developed from haploid zoospores. Sometimes a lateral branch of a plethysmothallus develops into a typical adult thallus. Such a plethysmothallus has been called a protonema, but it is thought[3] that such a distinction should be abandoned. A plethysmothallus frequently bears neutral sporangia and sometimes forms unilocular sporangia. Plethysmothalli of most, if not of all, brown algae are developed during the winter and when they produce neutral sporangia there may be a succession of plethysmothallic plants.

Reduplication of the gametophytic generation is by a parthenogenetic germination of gametes. Reduplication of this generation is of much less frequent occurrence than is that of the sporophyte.

The Fucales have a life cycle in which there is an alternation of a many-celled diploid generation with a one-celled haploid phase. Many phycologists accept the interpretation[4] of nuclear divisions subsequent to meiosis in antheridia and oögonia as being the equivalent of a gametophyte with a few cells. According to such an interpretation the life cycle of Phaeophyta with free-living multicellular gametophytes does not begin with the zoospore from a unilocular sporangium, but begins immediately after meiosis is completed in the sporangium.

Origin and Evolution of Phaeophyta. The fundamental metabolic features of brown algae are so distinctive that they do not appear to be related to, or derived from, other algae. It is very probable that the Phaeophyta are a series of considerable antiquity, but undoubted

[1] Kylin, 1933. [2] Sauvageau, 1932.

[3] Fritsch, 1945; Papenfuss, 1951. [4] Strasburger, 1906.

fossil members of the division have not been found earlier than the Triassic.[1]

The universal presence of motile reproductive cells among Phaeophyta indicates that they arose from a unicellular flagellated ancestor. Certain of the present-day fresh-water flagellated organisms with brown chromatophores were at one time thought to be analogous to ancestors of the brown algae, but all of them are now placed in another algal series—the Chrysophyta. All the present-day Phaeophyta are multicellular, and there are no known connecting links with the hypothetical unicellular flagellated ancestors. One explanation for this absence of primitive brown algae is that they were evolved in the ocean at a time when it was much less saline than at present, and that there was a dying off of the more

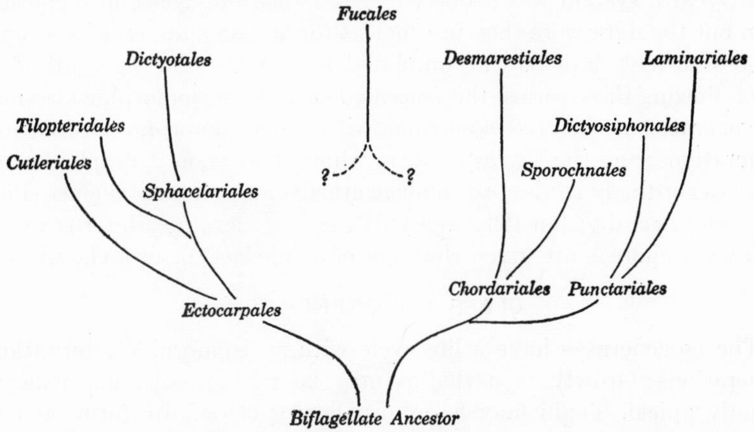

FIG. 130. Diagram showing the suggested interrelationships among the Phaeophyta.

primitive forms as the salinity of the ocean increased. However, this plausible suggestion fails to explain why there was not a migration of them from the fresh-water ocean to inland fresh waters of the early land masses.

There is good reason for believing that two divergent series were established early in evolution of the Phaeophyta (Fig. 130); one with an isomorphic alternation of generations, the other with a heteromorphic alternation. In both series there was a progressive evolution from isogamy to oögamy and in both of them the thallus structure became increasingly complex.

The origin of the Cyclosporeae, a series without a free-living haploid generation, is obscure. According to one view,[2] they are a series independent of those Phaeophyta with alternating sporophytic and gametophytic free-living generations. According to another view[3] the Cyclosporeae arose by a gradual decrease in the gametophyte to a one-celled plant. The one-

[1] Pia, 1927. [2] Kylin, 1933, 1940. [3] Kniep, 1928; Svedelius, 1921, 1928.

celled female gametophytes which may be formed by certain Laminariales are cited in support of this view. A third theory on the origin of the Cyclosporeae holds[1] that they arose by a complete dropping of a multicellular gametophyte and not by its gradual reduction. This took place by zoospores from unilocular sporangia functioning as gametes instead of developing into gametophytes. Evidence in support of this is seen in the reported cases where zoospores from unilocular sporangia occasionally function as gametes (see page 223). There is nothing to indicate whether the putative ancestor has an isomorphic or a heteromorphic alternation of generations.

Classification. Before 1922 all systems for the classification of brown algae were based upon vegetative structure and method of reproduction. That year a system was proposed[2] which took life cycles into consideration but the data were then insufficient for an adequate classification. By 1933 sufficient data had accumulated to warrant the segregation[3] into the following three series: the *Isogeneratae* with an isomorphic alternation of generations; the *Heterogeneratae* with a heteromorphic alternation of generations; and the *Cyclosporeae* in which there is only a diploid generation. Accordingly as the brown algae are given the rank of a class (Phaeophyceae) or a division (Phaeophyta) the Isogeneratae, Heterogeneratae, and Cyclosporeae are given the rank of a subclass[4] or of a class.[5]

CLASS 1. ISOGENERATAE

The Isogeneratae have a life cycle with an isomorphic alternation of generations. Growth of a thallus may be trichothallic, intercalary, or strictly apical. Thalli may be amorphous or of definite form, and with or without an internal differentiation of tissues. The sporophytic generation may produce zoospores, aplanospores, or neutral spores. Sexual reproduction of the gametophyte may be isogamous, anisogamous, or oögamous.

The class is divided into five orders differing from one another in vegetative structure, mode of growth, and structure of reproductive organs.

ORDER 1. ECTOCARPALES

The Ectocarpales have an isomorphic alternation of generations and have a branched filamentous thallus in which cell division is not localized. Branches of a thallus may stand free from one another or may be laterally adherent to form a pseudoparenchymatous tissue. Reproductive organs may be borne singly or in a uniseriate row. Those of the sporophyte produce either zoospores or neutral spores, and those of the gametophyte produce either isogamous or anisogamous gametes.

[1] G. M. Smith, 1938. [2] Taylor, 1922. [3] Kylin, 1933.
[4] Kylin, 1933; Levring, 1937. [5] Papenfuss, 1951; G. M. Smith, 1938.

Systems of classification based wholly upon vegetative structure and method of reproduction refer a hundred or more genera to the order. When, as here, the order is restricted to trichothallic filamentous forms with a known or suspected isomorphic alternation of generations there are about 50 genera. These have been grouped into two families.[1]

The type genus, *Ectocarpus*, is world wide in distribution and contains many species. The genus is a common one along the Atlantic Coast of this country, and certain species grow in abundance upon Fucaceae of the upper littoral zone. It is a scarcer genus along the Pacific Coast, where most of the species grow upon Laminariales.

The thallus is sparingly to profusely branched, with the cells joined end to end in a single series (Fig. 131*A*). It is differentiated into a prostrate attached portion and an erect portion. The prostrate portion is irregularly and more or less profusely branched; the erect portion is a branched tuft in which the ultimate branchlets are generally attenuated to an acute point. In some species the older portions of major branches are ensheathed (corticated) by a layer of descending rhizoidal branches. Cells of *Ectocarpus* are uninucleate and either with a few band-shaped chromatophores of irregular outline or with many small disk-shaped chromatophores.

Reproduction is by means of biflagellate zooids produced within unilocular reproductive organs or within plurilocular ones. These are usually borne terminally and singly on lateral branchlets, but in rare cases they are borne seriately.

Development of a unilocular sporangium begins with an enlargement of the terminal cell of a short lateral branchlet. The young sporangium becomes ellipsoidal and enlarges to several times its original size, with a considerable increase in the number of chromatophores. The single nucleus within a young sporangium divides, its daughter nuclei divide, and simultaneous division of their daughter nuclei continues until there are 32 or 64 nuclei. Division of the original nucleus is reductional and that of the daughter nuclei is equational. When nuclear division ceases, there is a cleavage into uninucleate protoplasts, each with a single chromatophore. Each protoplast is then metamorphosed into a pyriform zoospore, in which the longer of the two laterally inserted flagella is directed forward and the shorter is directed backward. The zoospores are extruded en masse through a small opening at the distal end of the sporangial wall. Individual zoospores of the extruded mass remain quiescent for from 30 to 60 seconds: then they become motile and swim freely in all directions. After zoospores have been discharged from a sporangium, there may be a proliferation of a new sporangium within the old sporangial wall.

[1] Papenfuss, 1951.

Plurilocular reproductive organs, whether gametangia or neutral sporangia, also develop from the terminal cell of a lateral branchlet. Repeated transverse division of this cell produces a vertical row of 6 to 12 cells (Fig. 131*D–F*). Beginning with median members of the row, there is then a vertical division of all cells (Fig. 131*G–H*). Repeated vertical

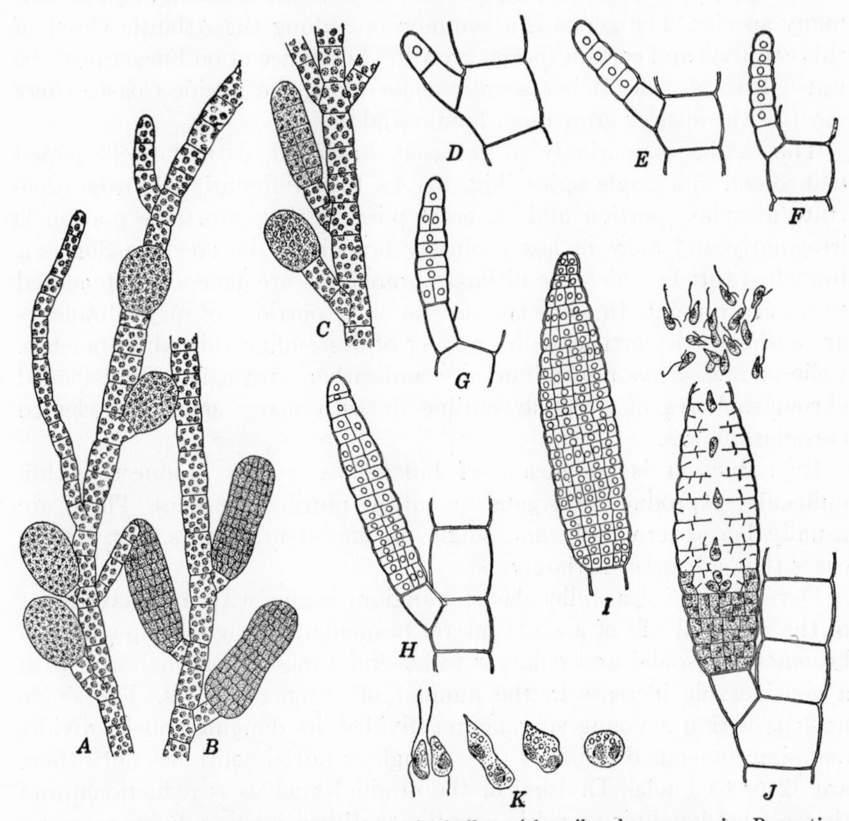

FIG. 131. *Ectocarpus cylindricus* Saunders. *A*, thallus with unilocular sporangia. *B*, portion of thallus with neutral sporangia. *C*, portion of a thallus bearing both unilocular and neutral sporangia. *D–J*, *E. acutus* Setchell and Gardner. *D–I*, stages in development of neutral sporangia. *J*, liberation of neutral spores. *K*, *E. siliculosus* (Dillw.) Lyngb. (*K*, *after Kuckuck*, 1912*A*) (*A–C*, × 120; *D–J*, × 650; *K*, × 600.)

and transverse division continues until there are several hundred small cubical cells arranged in 20 to 40 transverse tiers (Fig. 131*I*). The protoplast of each cell is then metamorphosed into a single biflagellate zooid. Liberation of the zooids is gradual and is through a terminal or a lateral pore. Zooids just beneath the pore escape in an irregular mass; those more remote from it move out in a single file and in an orderly procession (Fig. 131*J*).

Reproduction has been most thoroughly investigated in *E. siliculosus* (Dillw.) Lyngb. The nature of zooids from plurilocular organs of this species was long a matter of dispute among European phycologists, since those studying plants from Mediterranean waters repeatedly found gametic union and those studying plants from North European waters never found it. These discrepancies have been reconciled within the past decades by studies following development from zooid to mature fruiting plant in controlled culture and by studies on the nuclear cycle. All cytological investigations of the species[1] show that diploid plants with unilocular and plurilocular sporangia have a reduction division in the

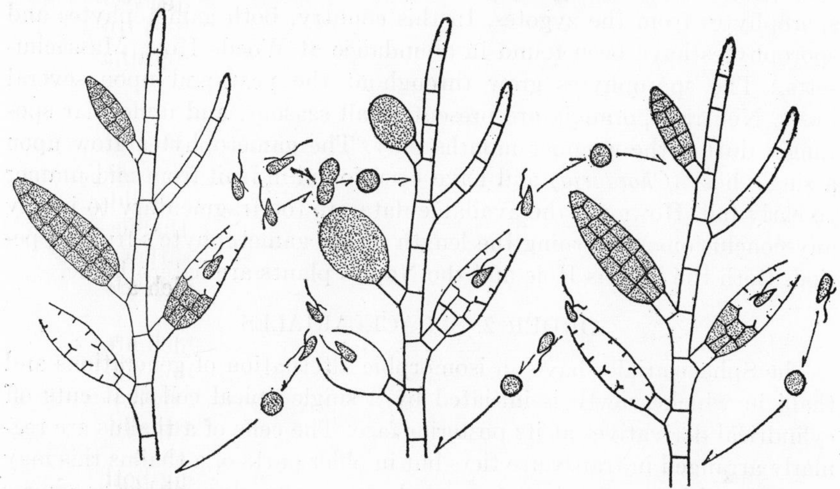

FIG. 132. Diagram showing variations in the life cycle of *Ectocarpus*. Cells containing diploid nuclei are outlined with a heavy line.

former and none in the latter. Diploid zooids from neutral (plurilocular) sporangia germinate to form sporophytes which bear either unilocular or neutral sporangia.[2] Zoospores from unilocular sporangia develop into gametophytes whose gametes may either unite in pairs or develop parthenogenetically into new gametophytes.[3] Germination of a zygote produces a new sporophyte. A gametic pairing of zoospores from unilocular sporangia has also been recorded,[4] but nothing is known concerning further development of this fusion product. Thus, in addition to a regular alternation of generations, *E. siliculosus* may have a reduplication of either generation (Fig. 132). Reduplication of the sporophyte is by means of neutral spores and possibly by a gametic union

[1] Knight, 1929; Papenfuss, 1935; Schussnig and Kothbauer, 1934.
[2] Knight, 1929; Kylin, 1933; Papenfuss, 1935. [3] Papenfuss, 1935.
[4] Knight, 1929; Schussnig and Kothbauer, 1934.

of zoospores; that of the gametophyte is by a parthenogenetic germination of gametes.

Environmental conditions, possibly temperature or duration and intensity of illumination, have a direct effect on the life cycle of *E. siliculosus.* Plants growing in Swedish[1] and British[2] waters are exclusively sporophytic, and there does not seem to be a development of the alternate gametophyte even when unilocular sporangia produce haploid zoospores in abundance. In Mediterranean waters near Naples the plants have been reported[2] as exclusively gametophytic, but sporophytes have been found[3] in this region. There seems to be a regular formation of zygotes from gametes of the Naples plants but only an occasional development of sporophytes from the zygotes. In this country, both gametophytes and sporophytes have been found in abundance at Woods Hole, Massachusetts.[4] The sporophytes grow throughout the year and upon several hosts. Neutral sporangia are present at all seasons, and unilocular sporangia during the summer months only. The gametophytes grow upon a single host (*Chordaria*) and have been found in fruit from midsummer to early fall. However, the available data are too fragmentary to justify any conclusions concerning the length of the gametophyte's fruiting period. Both the Woods Hole and the Naples plants are heterothallic.

ORDER 2. SPHACELARIALES

The Sphacelariales have an isomorphic alternation of generations and thalli in which growth is initiated by a single apical cell that cuts off cylindrical derivatives at its posterior face. The cells of a thallus are regularly arranged in transverse tiers but in older parts of a thallus this may be obscured by cortication. A sporophyte may produce either zoospores or neutral spores. Union of gametes formed by a gametophyte may be isogamous, anisogamous, or oögamous.

The order includes some 15 genera and 175 species, which are grouped into either three or four families. The order is a natural one whose members are easily distinguishable from other Phaeophyta by their polysiphonous vegetative organization in which the cells are vertically elongate and regularly arranged in transverse tiers.

The type genus, *Sphacelaria,* is a rather rare alga along both the Atlantic and Pacific coasts of this country. It grows attached to rocks, or to other algae, by means of a small more or less disk-shaped holdfast. One or more freely branched cylindrical shoots arise from the holdfast. Each branch terminates in a conspicuous, uninucleate, cylindrical, apical cell (Fig. 133*A*). Division of the apical cell is transverse. Derivatives two to four cells posterior to the apical cell divide and redivide in a vertical

[1] Kylin, 1933. [2] Knight, 1929.
[3] Schussnig and Kothbauer, 1934. [4] Papenfuss, 1935.

plane to form a transverse tier of 4 to 20 vertically elongate cells. Branching of a shoot is due to enlargement of a cell in the polysiphonous portion and to its functioning as an apical cell. Some species have multicellular hairs in which the cells are arranged in a uniseriate row (Fig. 133*B*).

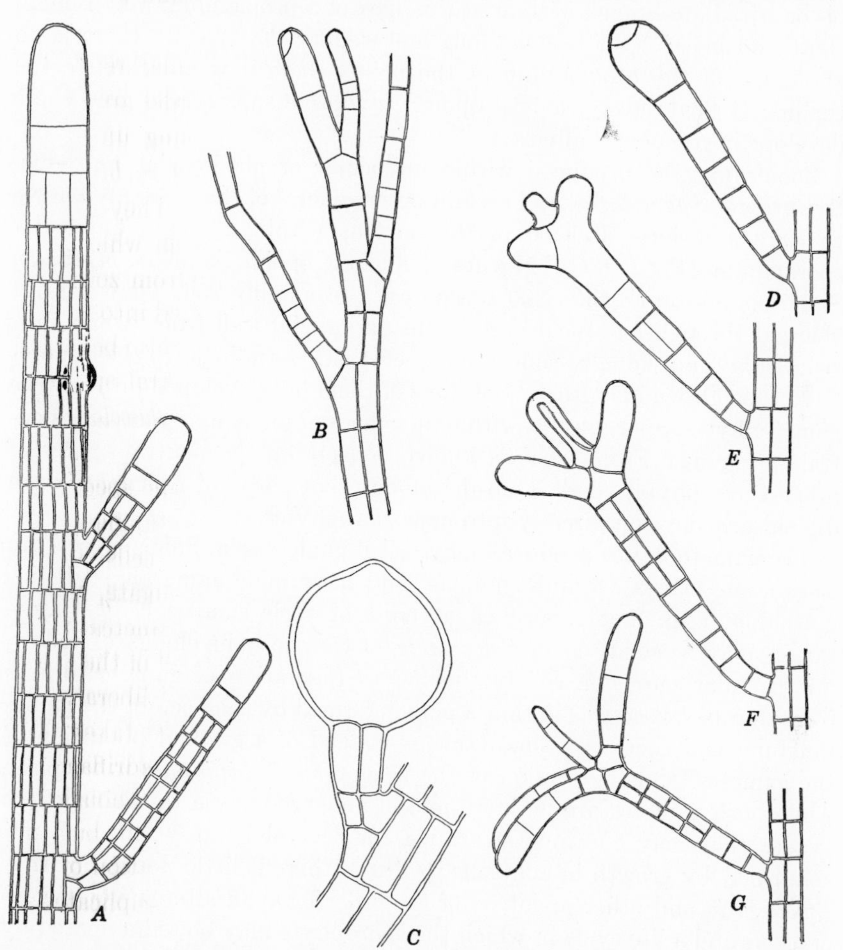

FIG. 133. *A*, apex of thallus of *Sphacelaria californica* Saunders. *B–G*, *S. radicans* (Dillw.) Harv. *B*, hairs. *C*, unilocular sporangium. *D–G*, stages in development of propagula. (*A*, *D–G*, × 160; *B*, × 215; *C*, × 325.)

Initials developing into hairs are formed by an asymmetrical division of the apical cell.[1] Vegetative cells of *Sphacelaria* contain a single large nucleus and many small disciform chromatophores.

Many species of *Sphacelaria* reproduce vegetatively by means of **propagula,** and at certain seasons of the year they may be the only means of

[1] Sauvageau, 1900–1904.

multiplication. Development of a propagulum (Fig. 133*D–G*) begins in the same manner as that of a lateral branch, but, after it has become a few cells long there is a vertical division of the apical cell into two or three daughter cells. Each daughter cell is the initial of a branch. The bi- or triradiate branch system at the apex of a propagulum may remain short and massive, or become long and slender. Eventually there is an abscission of the propagulum at the point where it is attached to the thallus. It floats away, lodges upon a favorable substratum, and there develops into a new thallus.

Zooids may be produced within unilocular or plurilocular reproductive organs. *Sphacelaria*[1] and certain other genera[2] of the order are known to have a meiotic division of the nucleus within a young unilocular sporangium (Fig. 133*C*). Mature unilocular sporangia of *S. bipinnata* Sauv. contain more than 200 zoospores,[3] presumably 256. They are discharged through an apical pore in the sporangial wall from which they swim away individually soon after liberation. Germlings from zoospores have been grown in culture,[4] but none of them has developed into mature gametophytes. Sporophytes with unilocular sporangia may also bear neutral sporangia.[5] From what is known concerning the neutral spores of other Phaeophyta, there is no doubt but that those of *Sphacelaria* are diploid and develop directly into new sporophytes.

The gametophytes produce many-celled gametangia. Some species are isogamous; others are anisogamous[6] and have male gametangia distinguishable from female ones on account of their smaller cells. Gametangia may be solid,[3] as in *Ectocarpus*, or they may be elongate, hollow, multicellular sacs, one cell in thickness.[6] Liberation of gametes differs from that of *Ectocarpus* in that a pore is formed by each cell of the gametangium, and there is a simultaneous instead of a gradual liberation of the gametes.[3] Gametic union of the isogamous *S. bipinnata* takes place while both gametes are actively motile and produces a quadriflagellate zygote that may continue swarming for several hours.[3] Although not confirmed by growth in controlled culture, there is little doubt but that *Sphacelaria* and other members of the order have an alternation of generations and a life cycle in which the sporophyte may be reduplicated by neutral spores.

ORDER 3. TILOPTERIDALES

Thalli of Tilopteridales are freely branched and with a trichothallic mode of growth. Upper portions of them are *Ectocarpus*-like with the cells joined end to end in a single row (**monosiphonous**); lower portions

[1] Clint, 1927. [2] Higgins, 1931; Knight, 1929; Mathias, 1935*A*.
[3] Papenfuss, 1934. [4] Clint, 1927; Papenfuss, 1934.
[5] Papenfuss, 1934; Sauvageau, 1900–1904. [6] Sauvageau, 1900–1904.

are generally *Sphacelaria*-like with the cells in transverse tiers (**polysiphonous**). The available evidence, although incomplete, indicates that there is an alternation of similar generations. The sporophyte produces unilocular sporangia, each containing a single quadrinucleate aplanospore. The gametophyte seems to be oögamous.

The order includes about 5 genera and 10 species.

Haplospora, with the single species *H. globosa* Kjellm., is known from England and the Scandinavian Peninsula. It has a freely and alternately branched thallus[1] in which the upper portion is monosiphonous and the lower portion polysiphonous (Fig. 134). Cells of both the mono- and

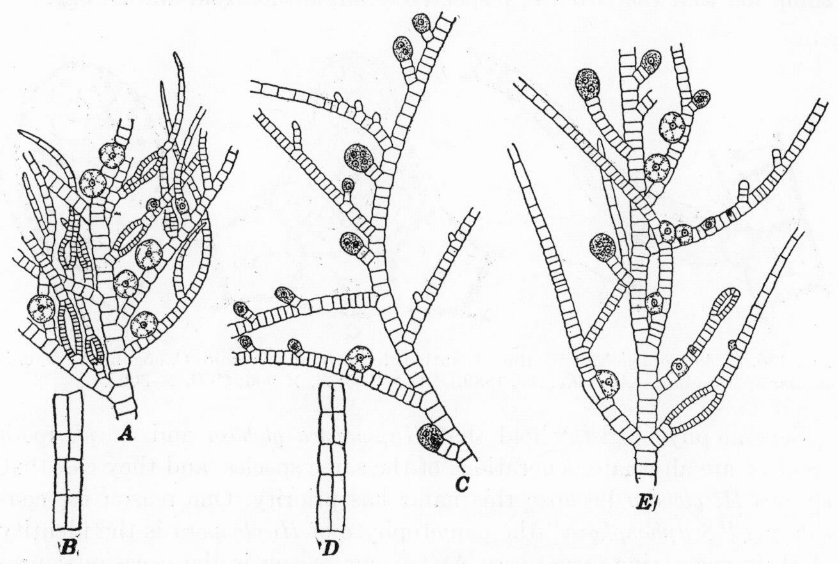

FIG. 134. *Haplospora globosa* Kjellm. *A–B*, upper and lower portions of a gametophyte. *C–D*, upper and lower portions of a sporophyte. *E*, upper portion of a sporophyte bearing both unilocular and neutral sporangia. (*After Brebner*, 1896.) (*A–C*, × 100; *D–E*, × 75.)

polysiphonous portions contain many small disciform chromatophores. The thallus is attached to the substratum by means of rhizoids.

Reproduction is by means of large quadrinucleate aplanospores (**monospores**) formed singly within globose sporangia borne terminally on short lateral branchlets. The demonstration[2] of a reductive division when the four nuclei are formed within a sporangium shows that the plant bearing sporangia is a sporophyte. Sporangia of *H. globosa* are homologous with unilocular sporangia of other Phaeophyta, but they are of a unique type in that there is not a cleavage of the quadrinucleate protoplast into uni-

[1] Brebner, 1896; Reinke, 1889. [2] Nienburg, 1923; Dammann, 1930.

nucleate spores (Fig. 135*D*). The monospore escapes through a large pore at the distal end of the sporangial wall.[1] A germinating spore sends forth a long germ tube, and then it divides into uninucleate cells.[2]

The alga known as *Scaphospora speciosa* Kjellm. (Fig. 134*A*) is vegetatively identical with *H. globosa.* It bears two kinds of reproductive organs: an intercalary unicellular organ producing a single large, uninucleate, nonflagellated, aplanospore-like body (Fig. 135*C*), and an intercalary multicellular organ in which each cell produces a single biflagellate zooid (Fig. 135*B*). Gametic union of the zooid and the nonflagellated body has not been demonstrated, but there is a strong presumption that the two are, respectively, an antherozoid and an egg.

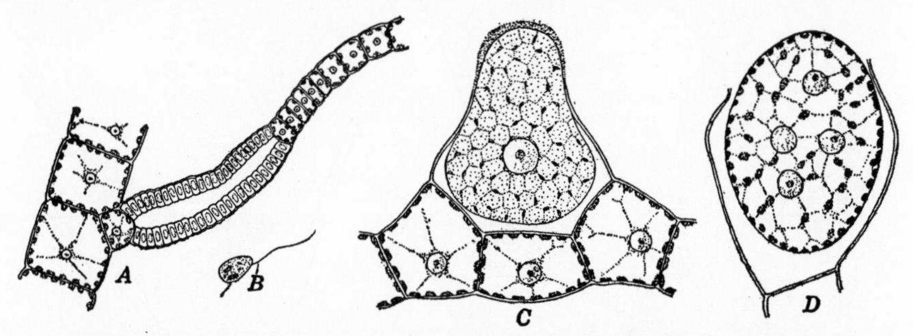

Fig. 135. *Haplospora globosa* Kjellm. *A*, antheridium. *B*, antherozoid. *C*, oögonium. *D*, unilocular sporangium. (*After Reinke*, 1889.) (*A*, × 150; *B*, × 600; *C–D*, × 300.)

Several phycologists[3] hold that *Haplospora globosa* and *Scaphospora speciosa* are alternate generations of the same species, and they call that species *H. globosa* because this name has priority. One reason for considering "*Scaphosphora*" the gametophyte of *Haplospora* is the identity of their vegetative structures. A stronger reason is the occasional production of the *Scaphospora* type of reproductive organs upon thalli of *Haplospora* (Fig. 134*E*). In addition to terminal unilocular sporangia with quadrinucleate protoplasts, the sporophyte of *Haplospora* may bear intercalary, one-celled, uninucleate organs[4] comparable to oögonia of *Scaphospora,* or it may bear both kinds of *Scaphospora* organs.[5] The *Scaphospora*-like organs upon sporophytes of *Haplospora* have been called "antheridia" and "oögonia,"[5] but it is much more probable that their nuclei are diploid and that their homologies lie with neutral sporangia of other Phaeophyta. According to their structure, neutral sporangia of *Haplospora* produce a single large neutral aplanospore or many small neutral zoospores.

[1] Reinke, 1889. [2] Neinburg, 1923.
[3] Brebner, 1896; Kylin, 1917, 1933; Oltmanns, 1922; Reinke, 1889.
[4] Brebner, 1896; Reinke, 1889. [5] Brebner, 1896.

ORDER 4. CUTLERIALES

The Cutleriales have a flattened, blade- or disk-like thallus in which growth is entirely or partially trichothallic. The sporophytes produce unilocular sporangia only. The gametophytes are heterothallic and markedly anisogamous.

There are but two genera. One (*Zanardinia*) has an alternation of identical generations; the other (*Cutleria*) has an alternation of somewhat different ones. However, the two genera seem closely related, because

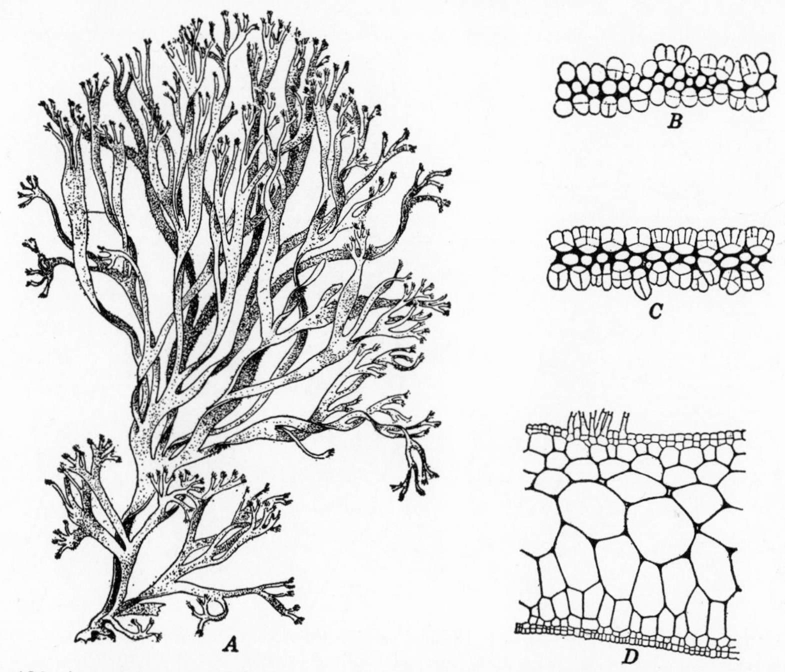

FIG. 136. *A*, gametophyte of *Cutleria multifida* Grev. *B–D*, successive transverse sections of apex of gametophyte of *C. adspersa* DeNot. (*A*, *after Thuret, in Oltmanns*, 1922; *B–D*, *from Sauvageau*, 1899.) (*A*, × ½; *B–C*, × 150; *D*, × 75.)

they have several distinctive features in common, including a unique method of trichothallic growth, a unilocular sporangia with a small number of large zoospores, and similar anisogamous sex organs.

Cutleria is found in the Mediterranean and along the coast of Europe where the water is warm. The sporophyte of one species is known from Florida and the West Indies. The gametophyte is an erect flattened blade with numerous irregular dichotomies (Fig. 136*A*). Growth takes place at the upper margin of a blade where there are many erect uniseriate hairs. Each hair has an intercalary growing region, and cells posterior to the growing region divide in a vertical plane. Multiseriate portions of the hairs abut on one another and lie compacted in a more or less homogeneous parenchymatous mass.[1] With maturation of these cells, there is a differentiation into an epidermis-like layer one or two cells in thickness, an underlying cortex-like layer of much larger isodiametric cells, and an axial group of vertically elongate cells (Fig. 136*B–D*).

Gametophytes of *Cutleria* are heterothallic and have the sex organs developing in small or large clusters upon both flattened surfaces of

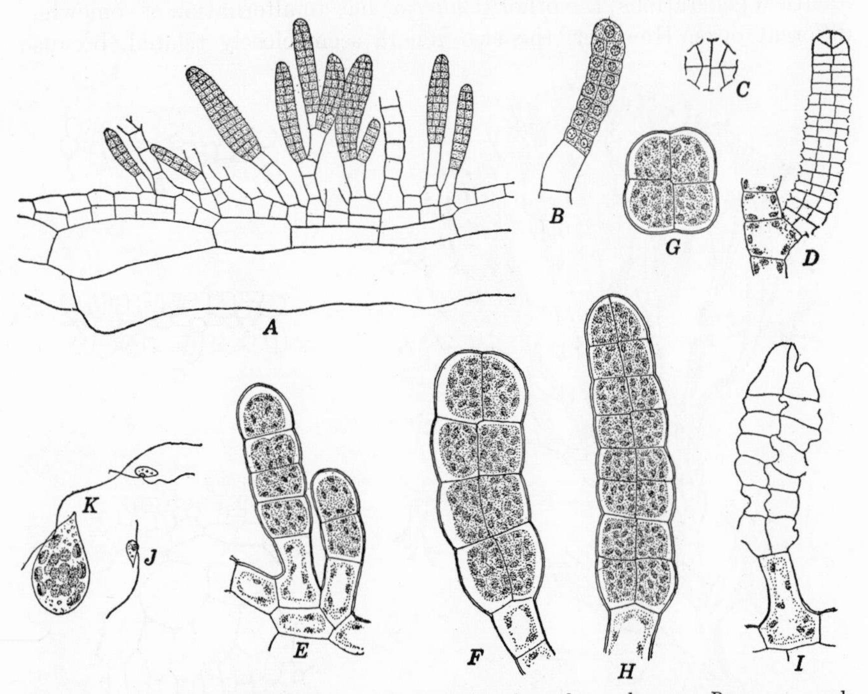

Fig. 137. *Cutleria multifida* Grev. *A*, vertical section through a male sorus. *B*, a young male gametangium. *C–D*, transverse and vertical sections of empty male gametangia. *E–H*, stages in development of female gametangia. *I*, an empty female gametangium. *J*, male gametes. *K*, female gamete. (*J–K*, *after Kuckuck*, 1929.) (*A*, × 325; *B–I*, × 650; *J–K*, × 500.)

the thallus. A superficial epidermal cell may develop directly into a male gametangium, or it may develop into a branched hair which bears several gametangia (Fig. 137*A*). A fertile cell first divides transversely into a **primary stalk cell** and an **antheridial initial.** The primary stalk cell may remain undivided, or it may divide transversely to form a vertical row or two or more stalk cells. Transverse division of the antheridial initial and of its daughter cells produces a row of four or five cells. Further division may be in a vertical or in a transverse plane. Divi-

[1] Sauvageau, 1899.

sion continues[1] until the fertile portion is 20 or more tiers in height and with each tier composed of eight cells (Fig. 137*B*). The protoplast of each cell is then metamorphosed into a biflagellate male gamete which escapes through a pore into the free face of the wall enclosing it (Fig. 137*C–D*).

The sequence of development in a female gametangium is similar, except for the production of a much smaller number of cells (Fig. 137*E–I*). Female gametangia are but four to seven tiers in height, with only four cells in each tier.[1] Each female gamete also escapes through a pore in the surrounding wall.

Free-swimming male gametes are pyriform and with a single reddish chromatophore at the point of flagellar insertion (Fig. 137*J*). Free-swimming female gametes (Fig. 137*K*) are also pyriform, but they contain a dozen or more chromatophores.[2] At the time of gametic union the male gametes are actively motile, and the female are sluggish or immobile. Fusion of the two gamete nuclei follows within a few hours, and the zygote begins to develop into a sporophyte within a day.[1] Unfertilized female gametes develop parthenogenetically into gametophytes.

The sporophyte of *Cutleria* was first described as a separate genus (*Aglaozonia*). Although germlings from zygotes of *Cutleria* and from zoospores of *Aglaozonia* have not been grown to maturity in culture, they have been grown to a sufficiently advanced stage to show[3] that the two are alternate generations of each other. At first, growth of a young sporophyte is trichothallic and vertically upward into a columnar structure (Fig. 138*C*). Upward growth ceases when the plant is about 10 days old, and all further growth is laterally outward from the base of the column. Repeated cell division at the base of the column produces a flat, disk-like tissue[4] which expands laterally as a result of division and redivision of the marginal cells (Fig. 138*D–E*). The sporophyte is homologous with a minute gametophyte subtended by an extraordinarily enlarged, fertile holdfast. The prostrate "holdfast" of the sporophyte, which constitutes almost all the thallus, is several cells in thickness and has the outermost cells differentiated into an epidermis-like layer. It is attached to the substratum by numerous multicellular rhizoids growing out from ventral epidermal cells.

The unilocular sporangia are arranged in a palisade-like manner in sori borne upon the dorsal surface of a thallus (Fig. 138*A*). Each sporangium is developed from a single epidermal cell. This fertile cell divides transversely into a primary stalk cell and a sporangial initial. The primary stalk cell may remain undivided, or it may divide to form

[1] Yamanouchi, 1912. [2] Kuckuck, 1929; Yamanouchi, 1912.
[3] Falkenberg, 1879; Church, 1898; Sauvageau, 1899; Yamanouchi, 1912.
[4] Sauvageau, 1899; Yamanouchi, 1912.

as many as six stalk cells; the sporangial initial develops directly into a sporangium. The single nucleus of the initial divides reductionally,[1] and simultaneous nuclear division continues until there are 8, 16, or 32 nuclei. There is then a cleavage into uninucleate protoplasts, each of which is metamorphosed into a large pyriform, biflagellate zoospore with several chromatophores (Fig. 138*B*). The zoospores escape through a large apical pore in the sporangial wall. After swarming 10 to 90 minutes, they be-

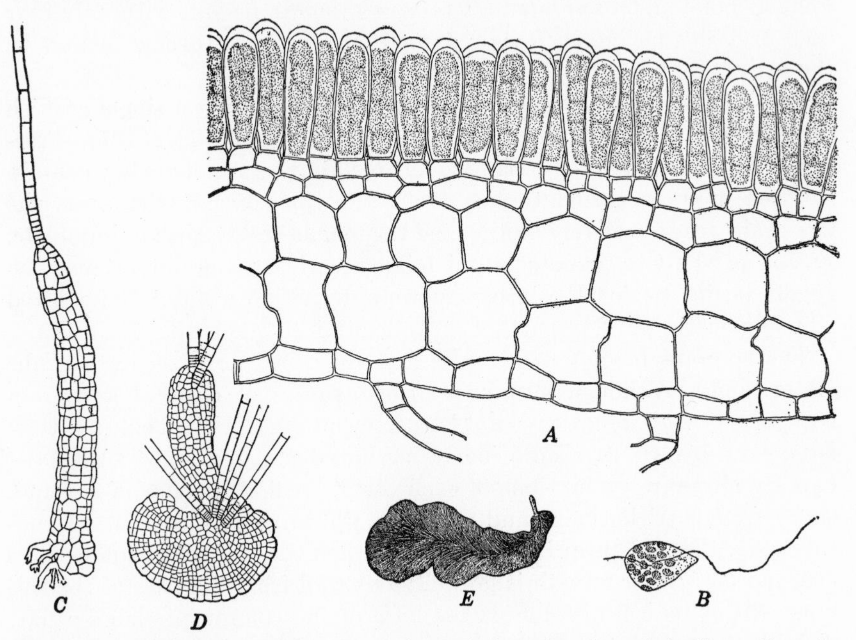

Fig. 138. *A–B*, *Cutleria multifida* Grev. *A*, vertical section through fertile portion of a sporophyte. *B*, zoospore. *C–E*, *C. adspersa* DeNot. *C–D*, young sporophytes. *E*, old sporophyte. (*B*, *after Kuckuck*, 1899; *C–E*, *from Sauvageau*, 1899.) (*A*, × 325; *B*, × 650; *C*, × 100, *D*, × 75; *E*, × 9.)

come quiescent, round up, and secrete a wall. This cell divides and redivides to form a typical young gametophyte.[1]

The longevity of the two generations has been followed at Plymouth, England,[2] and at Naples.[3] The sporophyte is perennial and fruits in winter or spring. The gametophyte is a spring annual which disappears during the summer.

ORDER 5. DICTYOTALES

The Dictyotales have an isomorphic alternation of generations in which the thalli are erect, flattened, parenchymatous, and with growth initiated by a single apical or a marginal row of apical cells at the apex of each

[1] Yamanouchi, 1912. [2] Church, 1898. [3] Funk, 1927.

branch. The sporophytes produce unilocular sporangia with four or eight large naked aplanospores. Gametophytes of most genera are oögamous but one genus is anisogamous.

There are some 20 genera and 100 species. The Dictyotales are found in temperate and tropical seas but occur in greatest abundance in the warmer waters of the tropics. On the Atlantic Coast of the United States, Dictyotales are found from Beaufort, North Carolina, southward; on the Pacific Coast they range southward from Santa Barbara, California.

At one time the Dictyotales were considered quite distinct from other Phaeophyta because the asexual generation produces nonflagellated spores. In *Dictyota* and most other genera there are four spores within a sporangium. Because of this, the spores are often called **tetraspores.** This name is misleading, both because it implies a relationship with the tetraspore-forming Rhodophyta and because it obscures the fact that sporangia of Dictyotales are in reality unilocular sporangia. The unilocular nature of the sporangia is more evident in *Zonaria* and *Pocockiella,* genera in which there is a formation of eight spores within a sporangium. The lack of flagella, although striking, is not a matter of deep significance. The homologies between antheridia of Dictyotales and typical gametangia of other Phaeophyta are obvious. So, also, are those between oögonia and typical gametangia, if the oögonium is interpreted as a gametangium that does not develop beyond the one-celled stage.

Dictyota, the type genus, has about 35 species. This genus is widely distributed in warm seas. On the coasts of the United States it is the member of the order that ranges farthest to the north. *Dictyota* has an erect, dichotomously branched, ribbon-like thallus in which all dichotomies may lie in the same plane. The thalli, which may attain a height of 30 or more centimeters in robust species, are attached to the substratum by a disk-shaped or irregularly shaped rhizome-like holdfast. Those of *D. dichotoma* (Huds.) Lamx. (Fig. 139*A*) are annuals.

Growth is restricted to the ends of branches, each of which has a single biconvex **apical cell** that cuts off derivatives at its posterior face (Fig. 139*B*). Each derivative divides asymmetrically and in a plane parallel to the thallus surface (Fig. 139*C*). The larger of the two daughter cells thus formed also divides asymmetrically and in the same plane. Since there are no further divisions parallel to the thallus surface, the thallus never becomes more than three cells in thickness. Cells of all three layers divide in a plane perpendicular to the thallus surface but as there are more divisions in the two superficial layers than there are in those of the central layer each cell of the central layer is adjoined by several superficial-layer cells. In mature portions of a thallus the small cells at the surface contain many chromatophores and those of the median layer contain but few chromatophores. In older parts of a thallus each cell in a group of superficial cells may give rise to an erect unbranched hair whose growth is due to cell division in the lowermost portion.

Dichotomous branching begins with a vertical instead of a transverse division of an apical cell at the apex of a branch. Each of the two daughter cells functions as an apical cell and begins to cut off derivatives at its posterior face (Fig. 139*D*). With continued growth the dichotomy thus initiated becomes more conspicuous as the two apical cells come to lie farther and farther apart. In some species the dichotomous branching is very regular because both dichotomies at the apex of a branch grow

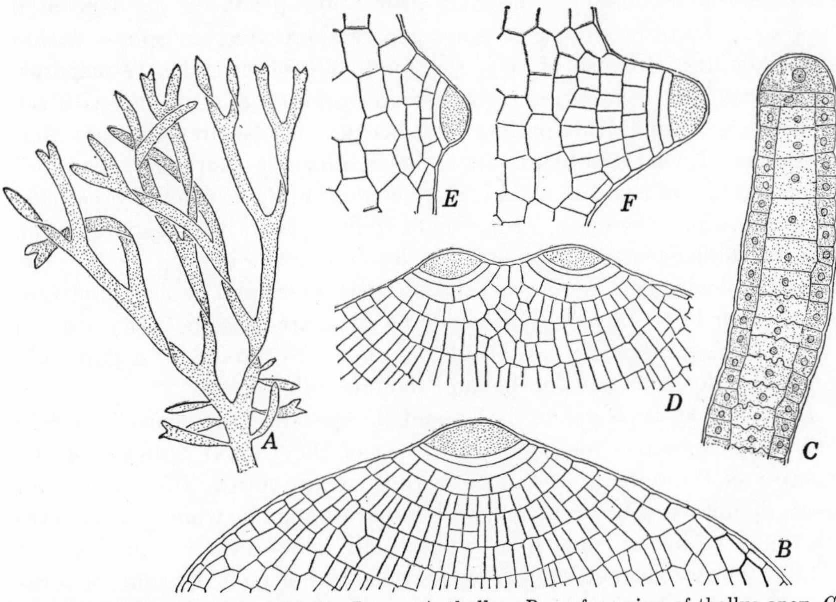

FIG. 139. *Dictyota dichotoma* (Huds.) Lamx. *A*, thallus. *B*, surface view of thallus apex. *C*, vertical section through thallus apex. *D*, thallus apex with beginning of a dichotomy. *E–F*, early stages in formation of lateral adventitious branches. (*A*, × 1/3; *B–F*, × 200.)

at an equal rate; in other species it is less regular because of unequal growth of dichotomies. Cells along the margin of a dichotomy may begin to function as apical cells and division of them results in a formation of adventitious branches (Fig. 139*A*, *E–F*).

Dictyota has a distinct periodicity in formation of sex organs and liberation of gametes. This is definitely correlated with the lunar month and its fortnightly sequence of spring and neap tides. In Europe the fruiting is fortnightly. Along the coast of England, sex organs begin to develop during one series of spring tides and to liberate their gametes during the next series of spring tides.[1] The reverse condition obtains at Naples where formation of sex organs begins during neap tides and gamete liberation is

[1] Williams, 1905.

during the next succeeding series of neap tides.[1] Studies on periodicity made along the American coast at North Carolina show that liberation of gametes takes place but once during each lunar month.[2] It is always during the spring tides of the full moon, regardless of whether these are the greater or the lesser set of spring tides of the lunar month. Although periodicity in *Dictyota* is obviously correlated with the tidal cycle, the manner in which this environmental factor operates is obscure. It becomes even more obscure when one takes into consideration the demonstration[3] that thalli maintain their fortnightly fertility when removed from the ocean and cultured in the laboratory.

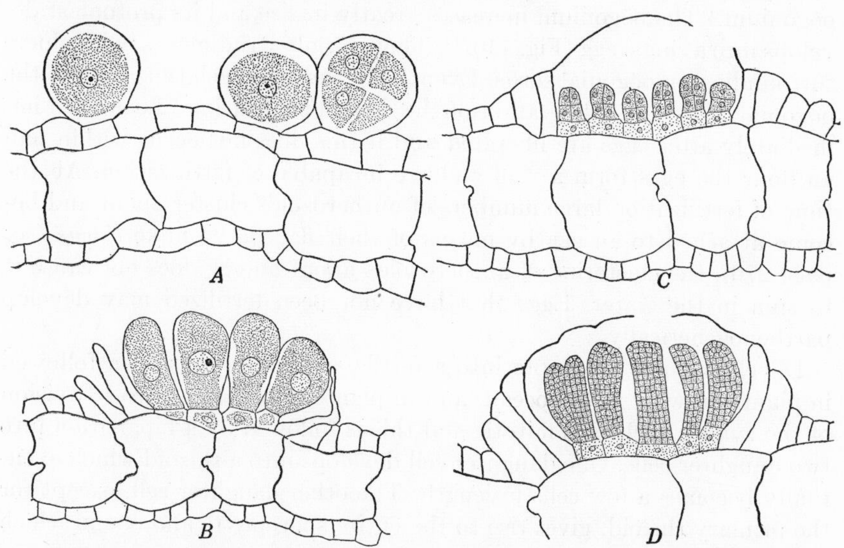

FIG. 140. *Dictyota dichotoma* (Huds.) Lamx. *A*, cross section through a portion of a sporangial sorus with immature and mature sporangia. *B*, cross section through an oögonial sorus. *C–D*, cross sections through very young and nearly mature antheridial sori. (× 165.)

The gametophytes are heterothallic and with the sex organs borne in elliptical sori on both sides of a thallus. Fertile male and female plants may be distinguished from each other by the deeper color of oögonial sori.

Each antheridium in a male sorus is developed from a superficial thallus cell. This cell divides transversely into a stalk cell, which does not divide again, and an antheridial initial. The antheridial initial divides vertically into two cells, both of which divide vertically to form a quadrat of four cells.[4] By vertical and transverse division these cells ultimately give rise to a cellular column that is 20 to 24 cells in height and with 16 cells in each tier (Fig. 140*C–D*). Upon the cessation of cell division

[1] Lewis, 1910. [2] Hoyt, 1907, 1927. [3] Williams, 1905. [4] Williams, 1904*A*.

there is a rounding up of the protoplasts and a gelatinization of the walls between them. There is then a metamorphosis of each protoplast into an antherozoid. Antherozoids have but one flagellum.[1] Development of antheridia is accompanied by an upward elongation of vegetative cells immediately adjacent to the sorus to form a cup-like **involucre** the same height as the antheridia (Fig. 140*D*).

Oögonia are developed from superficial thallus cells and there are 25 to 50 oögonia in an oögonial sorus. Superficial thallus cells developing into oögonia elongate vertically to three to four times their original height and then divide transversely into a stalk cell and a cell that becomes the oögonium.[1] The oögonium increases greatly in size and its protoplast develops into a single egg (Fig. 140*B*). There is only a rudimentary involucre surrounding an oögonial sorus. Eventually there is a gelatinization of the oögonial walls and a liberation of the eggs. Fertilization takes place immediately after eggs are liberated and if this does not occur within half an hour the eggs form a wall and are incapable of fertilization. At the time of fertilization large numbers of antherozoids cluster about and become attached to an egg by means of their flagella.[1] Unlike *Fucus* (see page 270), the clustering of antherozoids about an egg does not cause it to spin in the water. Eggs that have not been fertilized may develop parthenogenetically.

Development of a zygote into a fertile sporophyte has been followed in plants growing in the ocean[2] and in plants growing in vitro.[3] Division of the zygote nucleus is mitotic and this is followed by a bipartition into two daughter cells. One daughter cell develops into a rhizoid which eventually becomes a few cells in length. The other daughter cell, except for the primary rhizoid, gives rise to the entire sporophyte and one in which there is a very early establishment of an apical cell.

Sporangia produced by a sporophyte are borne on both sides of the thallus and are grouped in rather poorly defined sori that are not surrounded by involucres. In development of a sporangium, a superficial thallus cell elongates vertically to two to three times its original height and then divides transversely. The lower cell is a stalk cell which does not enlarge further. The upper cell enlarges to form a spherical sporangium whose diameter about equals the thickness of the thallus (Fig. 140*A*). Division of the single nucleus in a young sporangium is meiotic,[4] and this is followed by a division of the quadrinucleate protoplast into four large aplanospores that are liberated by an apical rupture of the sporangial wall. There is a genotypic determination of sex at the time of meiosis so that two of the four spores develop into male gametophytes and two into female gametophytes.[3]

[1] Williams, 1904*A*. [2] Hoyt, 1910. [3] Schreiber, 1935. [4] Williams, 1904.

CLASS 2. HETEROGENERATAE

The Heterogeneratae have a heteromorphic alternation of generations and one in which the sporophyte is always larger than the gametophyte. Sporophytes are usually of macroscopic size and definite shape; gametophytes are always filamentous and of microscopic size. In fact, knowledge concerning gametophytes of all members of the class has been obtained only by growing them in cultures started from zoospores liberated from unilocular sporangia. Sporophytes of Heterogeneratae may produce either zoospores or neutral spores. Reproduction of gametophytes may be isogamous, anisogamous, or oögamous.

According to vegetative structure of the sporophyte the Heterogeneratae are divided into two subclasses, the *Haplostichineae* and the *Polystichineae.*

SUBCLASS 1. HAPLOSTICHINEAE

Sporophytes of Haplostichineae are composed of filaments which may be free from one another, interwoven with one another, or so densely compacted or corticated that the thallus seems to be parenchymatous. In all cases growth is trichothallic. A sporophyte may produce either neutral or unilocular sporangia. The gametophytes are always microscopic filaments and isogamous, anisogamous, or oögamous.

The subclass is divided into three orders.[1]

ORDER 1. CHORDARIALES

The Chordariales include those Haplostichineae in which the branched filamentous sporophyte is not markedly compacted into a pseudoparenchymatous thallus. Thus far, all known gametophytes are isogamous.

About 50 genera are referred to the order. But little is known concerning the life cycle of most genera and it is not improbable that certain genera will eventually be shown to be members of the Ectocarpales. The genera have been grouped in eight families.[2]

Myrionema, a genus with several species, has a minute thallus which grows epiphytically upon various other algae. Opinion is divided as to whether it is a primitive small plant or a small reduced form of a more advanced type. *M. strangulans* Grev., the only species that has been studied in culture,[3] grows epiphytically upon *Ulva.* It is found along both coasts of this country.

The thallus appears to be a parenchymatous disk when it is viewed from above, but in reality it consists of radiately branched horizontal filaments laterally apposed to one another. Growth of the horizontal filaments is terminal or subterminal. Each cell inward from the growing

[1] Kylin, 1933. [2] Kylin, 1940; Papenfuss, 1951. [3] Kylin, 1934.

tip cuts off a daughter cell toward its free (upper) surface. Most of the daughter cells develop into erect unbranched filaments four to six cells tall or into erect unbranched hairs with many more cells (Fig. 141*A*). Other of the daughter cells develop into unilocular or into plurilocular reproductive organs. The first reproductive organs formed by the thallus are usually plurilocular. They are several cells in height, uniseriate,

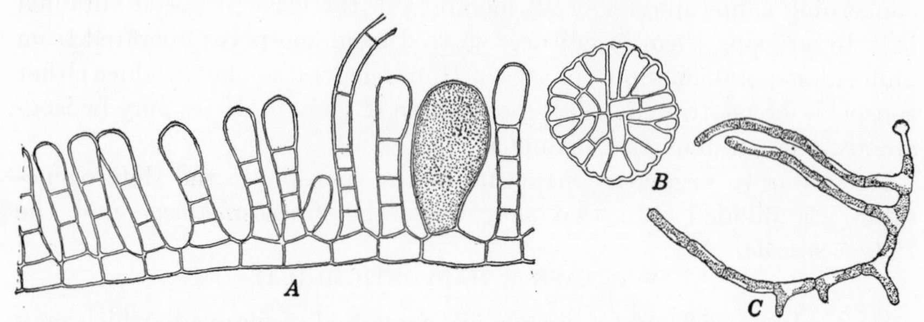

FIG. 141. *Myrionema strangulans* Grev. *A*, vertical section through a mature sporophyte. *B*, surface view of a young sporophyte. *C*, gametophyte. (*B–C*, *after Kylin*, 1934.) (*A*, × 650; *B*, × 400; *C*, × 375.)

and with each cell producing a typical zooid. The zooid grows into a thallus identical with that producing it (Fig. 141*B*) and one which bears either unilocular or plurilocular organs.[1] Thus *Myrionema* is a sporophytic generation in which there may be a reduplication of the sporophyte by neutral spores from multicellular neutral sporangia.

Old sporophytes usually bear unilocular sporangia only (Fig. 141*A*). Zoospores from these sporangia germinate to form branched filamentous thalli[1] in which the branches are free from one another as in *Ectocarpus*. It is thought that the filamentous plants (Fig. 141*C*) are gametophytes, but as yet none of them has been grown to a mature fruiting condition. The fact that neutral spores develop into typical *Myrionema* thalli makes it very improbable that the *Ectocarpus*-like plants developing from zoospores of unilocular sporangia are cultural monstrosities.

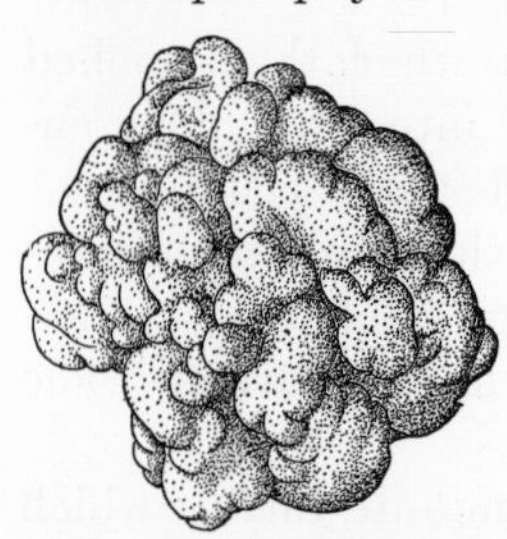

FIG. 142. Sporophyte of *Leathesia amplissima* Setchell and Gardner. (× ½.)

Leathesia is another of the Chordariales found along both coasts of this country. It is a common alga of the midlittoral zone. *L. difformis* (L.) Aresch is an annual which appears early in spring, reaches its maximum size in midsummer, and begins to degenerate early in the fall. Mature thalli are irregularly globose, with a much convoluted surface, generally hollow at the center, and up to 8 cm. in diameter (Fig. 142). Solid portions of a thallus have a gelatinous fleshy texture. The solid portion consists of a radiating mass of di- or trichotomously branched filaments,

[1] Kylin, 1934.

with more or less gelatinous material between the branches (Fig. 143*A*). The lowermost cells of the branches (those toward the thallus center) are irregularly cylindrical and colorless. Cells toward the tips of branches are progressively smaller. Most of the branches terminate in palisade-like branchlets four or five cells long, but here and there they terminate in a cluster of long multicellular hairs. Cells of the palisade-like branchlets are the only ones with chromatophores.

L. difformis may produce either unilocular or plurilocular reproductive organs, or both. This shows that it is a sporophyte. Fruiting generally

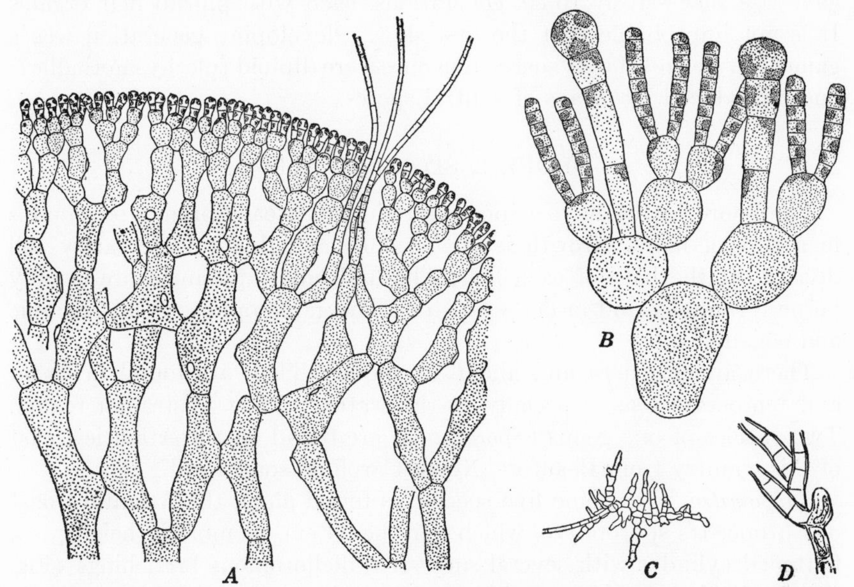

FIG. 143. *Leathesia difformis* (L.) Aresch. *A*, vertical section through the outer portion of a sporophyte. *B*, outer portion of a sporophyte bearing neutral sporangia. *C*, gametophyte. *D*, empty gametangia. (*C–D*, *after Dammann*, 1930.) (*A*, × 120; *B*, × 485; *C*, × 155; *D*, × 430.)

begins with a formation of unilocular sporangia. Sooner or later there is a formation of neutral sporangia, and these are frequently the only reproductive organs present on old thalli (Fig. 143*B*). The neutral spores are undoubtedly diploid, and it has been shown[1] that they develop into *Leathesia* plants which bear neutral sporangia. Neutral spores may also develop into small *Myrionema*-like plants which produce neutral sporangia.[2] These are considered plethysmothalli[3] rather than precociously fruiting thalli. One of the reasons for considering them distinct from juvenile stages of typical thalli is the presence of but one chromatophore in each cell, instead of several as in cells of adult plants.[4]

[1] Kylin, 1933. [2] Sauvageau, 1925.
[3] Sauvageau, 1928, 1932. [4] Sauvageau, 1932.

The gametophyte generation (Fig. 143*C–D*) is but imperfectly known. Cultures started from zoospores in midsummer contained minute branched thalli which remained small and did not fruit until the following June.[1]

At that time they produced plurilocular reproductive organs. The gametangial nature of these organs was not definitely established because liberation of zooids and their fusion were not observed. Within a month after fruiting, there was a development of a new crop of microscopic plants bearing plurilocular organs. Before the end of December, these gave rise successively to six generations, each with plurilocular organs. It is not improbable that the first slowly developing generation was a gametophyte and the six succeeding ones were diploid (plethysmothallic?) and reproduced by means of neutral spores.

ORDER 2. SPOROCHNALES

The Sporochnales have a sporophyte in which each branch terminates in a tuft of hairs. Growth is trichothallic and due to intercalary cell division at the base of each hair. The unilocular sporangia are usually borne terminally and in dense clusters. The gametophyte is microscopic and oögamous.

There are 6 genera and about 25 species. They are found in warm and temperate seas, especially in the waters of the Australian region. Two species of one genus (*Sporochnus*) are found on the Atlantic Coast of this country from Beaufort, North Carolina, southward.[2]

Carpomitra, with some five species, is found along the Atlantic Coast of Europe. Its sporophyte, which may be 30 cm. or more in height, is a flattened cylinder with several successive dichotomous branchings (Fig. 144*A*). Each branch has an evident midrib, and at each branch tip there is a conspicuous tuft of hairs. Growth of a branch apex is trichothallic, the meristematic region being situated in a group of cells at the base of the terminal tuft of hairs. The tissue formed posterior to the meristem is solidly parenchymatous. It is differentiated into a medullary region with vertically elongated cells and a cortical region with approximately isodiametric cells.

Sporophytes produce only unilocular sporangia. At the time of reproduction there is a development of a miter-like inflation, the **receptacle,** immediately below the tuft of hairs terminating a fertile branch (Fig. 144*B*). Many of the superficial receptacular cells develop into branched fertile hairs (paraphyses).[3] The sporangia develop from ter-

[1] Dammann, 1930. [2] Hoyt, 1920; Taylor, 1928.
[3] Johnson, 1891; Sauvageau, 1926.

minal cells of a paraphysis. They are ovoid and contain a relatively small number of zoospores (Fig. 144*C*).

Germinating zoospores[1] develop into uniseriate, sparingly branched, filamentous gametophyte (Fig. 144*D*). The antheridia are produced at the tips of short lateral branchlets. Their size and shape are much the same as in *Laminaria*. Antherozoids have never been observed, but the discovery of many empty antheridia upon the gametophyte indicates that there is a liberation of motile male gametes. The oögonia

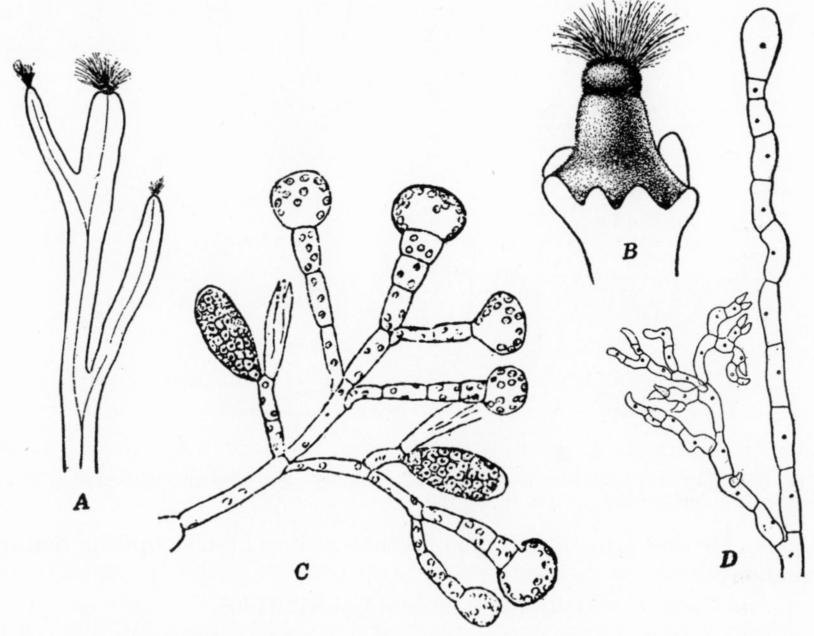

FIG. 144. *Carpomitra cabrerae* Kütz. *A*, upper portion of a sporophyte. *B*, apex of a sporophyte. *C*, fertile paraphysis from a sporophyte apex. *D*, gametophyte. (*From Sauvageau*, 1926.) (*A*, × 3½; *B*, × 15; *C*, × 480; *D*, × 330.)

are large, ovoid, and develop from terminal or intercalary cells of the main branches. The oögonial nature of the cells interpreted as oögonia is not established beyond all doubt because there is neither an extrusion of an egg nor a development of a pore in the oögonial wall. Instead, there is a direct division and redivision of the oögonial cell to form the new sporophyte. This parthenogenetic germination of the egg differs from other known cases of parthenogenesis in that the germinating egg does not become invested with a wall distinct from the oögonial wall.

[1] Sauvageau, 1926.

The young sporophyte develops into an erect, unbranched, uniseriate filament 20 or more cells tall (Fig. 145*A–B*). Following this there is a horizontal division of the sixth to eighth cell below the apex. The superior daughter cell divides vertically to form initials which develop into hairs; the inferior daughter cell divides vertically to form a meristem which begins to form tissues similar to those of an adult thallus (Fig.

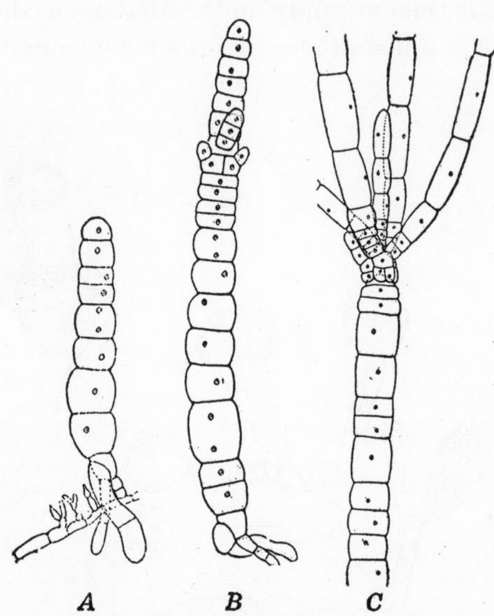

Fig. 145. *Carpomitra cabrerae* Kütz. Stages in development of young sporophytes. (*From Sauvageau*, 1926.) (*A–B*, × 180; *C*, × 120.)

145*C*). Further growth is similar to that at any branch tip of a mature sporophyte.

ORDER 3. DESMARESTIALES

Thalli of Desmarestiales have a single filament at each growing apex. Posterior to this there is a pseudoparenchymatous cortication of the filament to form a thallus of definite macroscopic form. The gametophyte is microscopic, oögamous, and has the discharged egg remaining attached to the oögonial apex.

The order contains but three genera.

Desmarestia has two centers of distribution, namely, north Atlantic and north Pacific waters as contrasted with Antarctic and adjoining regions. There are two or three species along the Atlantic Coast of this country and about eight along the Pacific Coast. Most of them grow below the low-tide mark. *Desmarestia* is one of the larger brown algae, and certain species, as *D. latissima* Setchell and Gardner, attain a length of more than 5 meters. Several of the species[1] differ from other

[1] Blinks, 1951.

brown algae in that they accumulate malic and sulfuric acids in abundance; the cell sap of certain species growing along the coast of California[1] has a pH of 1 to 3.

The thallus, the sporophyte, grows attached to rocks by means of a disk-like holdfast. Above this is an axis of variable length and one which may be sparingly or profusely branched. The branches of an axis may be subcylindrical or they may be flattened into conspicuous blades (Fig. 146). Blades of the largest species along the Pacific Coast (*D. latissima*) are sometimes more than 2.5 meters long and 20 cm. broad.

FIG. 146. Upper portion of sporophyte of *Desmarestia herbacea* (Turn.) Lamx. (Natural size.)

The growing apex of each branch terminates in an axial filament in which the cells are joined end to end in a single row. The axial filament bears many lateral, unbranched, uniseriate filaments, all in the same plane and either in opposite pairs (Fig. 147*A*) or alternate with one another. Growth of axial and lateral filaments is due to an intercalary meristematic region. The lowermost cells of lateral filaments, three or four back from the growing zone of the central axis, send out multicellular rhizoidal outgrowths that become closely applied to the axial filament. Repeated cell division in this ensheathing layer eventually produces a corticating tissue several cells in thickness and one in which the super-

[1] Blinks, 1951.

ficial cells may continue division indefinitely (Fig. 147*B*). There is generally a disappearance of lateral filaments along the corticated portion of an axial filament, but now and then one of them continues growth as an axial filament by sending out lateral filaments and becoming corticated. Many of the plants that one collects lack axial filaments at their branch

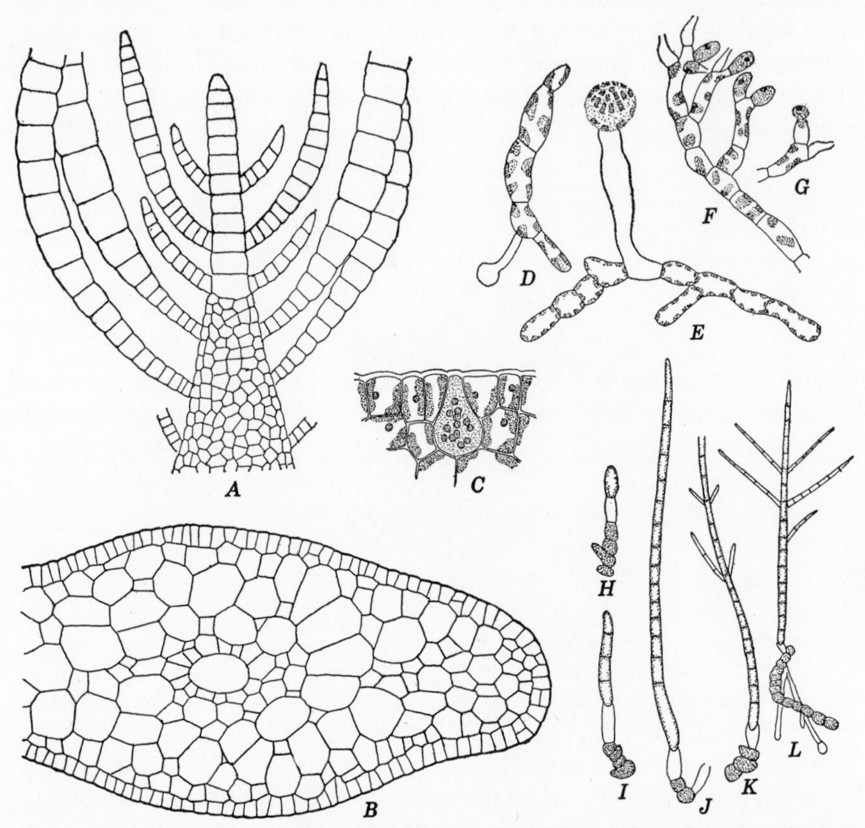

Fig. 147. *A–C*, sporophyte of *Desmarestia herbacea* (Turn.) Lamx. *A*, surface view of growing apex. *B*, transverse section of corticated portion. *C*, unilocular sporangium. *D–L*, *D. aculeata* (L.) Lamx. *D–E*, female gametophytes. *F*, male gametophyte. *G*, liberation of antherozoid. *H–L*, early stages in development of sporophytes. (*D–L*, *after Schreiber*, 1932.) (*A*, × 215; *B*, × 160; *C*, × 650.)

apices. This may have been due to an abscission or to an accidental breaking off of the filament. In either case there is no further apical growth of the blade.

Unilocular sporangia are the only reproductive organs formed by a sporophyte. They are usually formed in corticated portions of a thallus but may be developed from cells of an axial filament or its appendages.[1]

[1] Johnson, 1891, Kuckuck, 1894.

When formed in corticated portions of a thallus they usually develop from superficial cells (Fig. 147*C*), but at times[1] they also develop from deeper-lying cells. A vegetative cell developing into a sporangium has a meiotic division of its nucleus,[1] and nuclear division continues until there are 32, 64, or 128 nuclei. The protoplast then divides to form typical zoospores.

The zoospores swarm for an hour or more and then lose their flagella, come to rest, and secrete a wall. This cell sends forth a germ tube and most of the protoplasm migrates into its somewhat swollen tip.[2] The tip becomes partitioned off by a transverse wall, and the cell thus formed develops into a microscopic, sparingly branched, filamentous gametophyte of 20 to 40 cells. *Desmarestia* is heterothallic with male gametophytes distinguishable from female ones because of their smaller cells. Male gametophytes are also composed of more cells and are more freely branched than are female gametophytes. Antheridia are developed in clusters at the tips of lateral branches (Fig. 147*F–G*). Each antheridium is one-celled, and its protoplast is metamorphosed into a single antherozoid. A female gametophyte may begin to form oögonia at the three- or four-celled stage of development, or it may not begin to form them until it is many-celled (Fig. 147*D–E*). In either case, oögonia are developed by a vertical enlargement of an intercalary cell. An oögonium contains a single large egg which is extruded through, but remains attached to, the apex of the oögonial wall.[1]

The egg remains attached to the oögonial apex during fertilization. The zygote, still attached to the oögonial apex, divides transversely and repeated division in the same plane produces an erect filament of 15 or more cells (Fig. 147*H–J*). Lateral branches then grow outward from the upper portion of the filament, and rhizoidal branches grow downward from the lowermost cells (Fig. 147*K–L*). The gametophyte disappears shortly after the young sporophyte develops rhizoids. The branched upper part of the juvenile sporophyte continues trichothallic growth and soon becomes corticated in exactly the same manner as the growing apex of an adult plant.

Gametophytes of *Desmarestia* and of the Laminariales have several unique features in common. These include clusters of unicellular antheridia, vertically elongate intercalary oögonia, attachment of the extruded egg to the oögonial apex, and early development of the sporophyte upon the oögonial apex. Because of this the Desmarestiales and Laminariales have been thought to be rather closely related to each other,[3] but this seems improbable in view of the marked differences in structure and mode of growth of sporophytes in the two orders.

[1] Abe, 1938. [2] Abe, 1938; Schreiber, 1932. [3] Schreiber, 1932.

SUBCLASS 2. POLYSTICHINEAE

Sporophytes of Polystichineae have parenchymatous thalli in which growth is by division of intercalary cells. A sporophyte may produce either zoospores or neutral spores. The gametophytes are microscopic, filamentous; and either isogamous, anisogamous, or oögamous.

The subclass has been divided[1] into three orders (Punctariales, Dictyosiphonales, Laminariales) but it has been held[2] that the first two should be combined in a single order.

ORDER 1. PUNCTARIALES

Sporophytes of Punctariales are of medium size, parenchymatous, and grow by means of intercalary cell divisions which are not localized in a definite meristem. Reproductive organs of a sporophyte may or may not be localized in definite sori, and they may produce either zoospores or neutral spores. Gametophytes are microscopic filaments that may be isogamous or anisogamous.

There are about 30 genera, but there is no general agreement as to how these should be grouped in families.

Soranthera is the first member of the order in which an alternation of generations was demonstrated.[3] It is found only in the Pacific Ocean and there is but one species, *S. ulvoidea* Post. and Rupr. *Soranthera* is an epiphyte restricted to *Rhodomela* and *Odonthalia* but is a common alga along the entire Pacific Coast of this country. Mature sporophytes are subspherical, hollow, and up to 7 cm. in diameter (Fig. 148*A*). The cellular portion consists of a superficial epidermis-like layer of small cells and an underlying layer four to five cells in thickness which is composed of much larger cells. Chromatophores are restricted to the superficial layer.

Unilocular sporangia, the only reproductive organs produced by the sporophyte, are borne in sori about 1 mm. in diameter. The sori are irregularly distributed over the entire surface of a thallus. Soral development begins with a periclinal division of each "epidermal" cell in a future fertile area. Repeated division of each outer daughter cell produces an unbranched erect filament (**paraphysis**) 10 to 20 cells long. Cells toward the free end of paraphyses are rounded and contain chromatophores (Fig. 148*B*). Certain of the inner daughter cells formed by division of "epidermal" cells cut off a cell which develops into a unilocular sporangium. Mature sporangia discharge their zoospores in a mass through a small pore at the sporangial apex when the thallus is reflooded by the incoming tide. The zoospores remain motionless for a few seconds after discharge and then swim freely in all directions.

[1] Kylin, 1933; Taylor, 1936. [2] Papenfuss, 1947. [3] Angst, 1926.

Development of a mature fruiting gametophyte from a zoospore may be completed within three weeks.[1] The gametophyte is an irregularly branched *Ectocarpus*-like filament of 50 or more cells (Fig. 148*C*). The gametangia are borne at the tips of one- or two-celled lateral branchlets. They are 15 to 20 tiers in height and with several cells in each of the median tiers. Gametic union is anisogamous[1] and with a small active

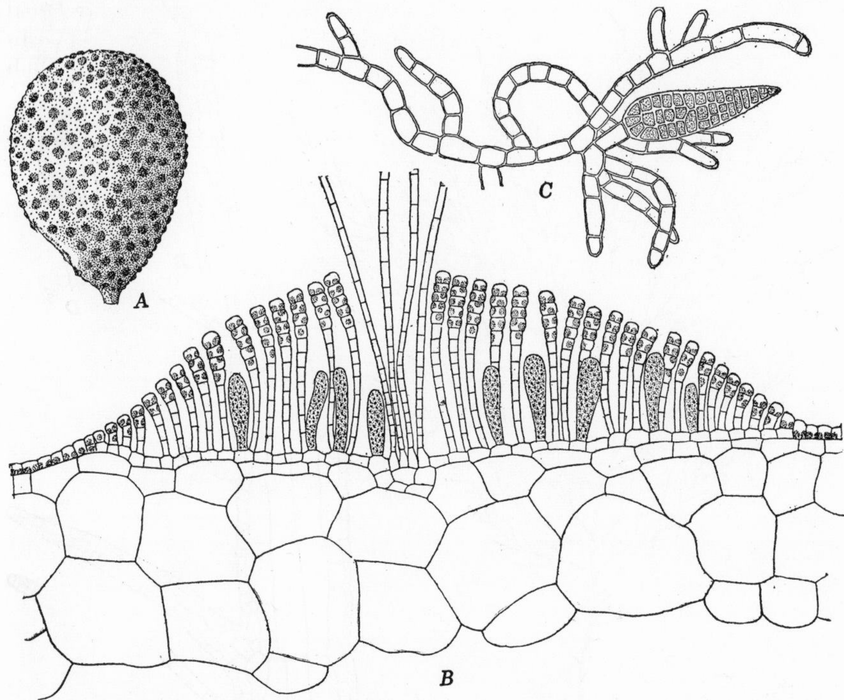

Fig. 148. *Soranthera ulvoidea* Post. and Rupr. *A*, sporophyte. *B*, vertical section through a sorus. *C*, gametophyte. (*C*, *after Angst*, 1926.) (*A*, natural size; *B*, × 160; *C*, × 280.)

male gamete uniting with a larger, more sluggish one. Development of the zygote into a sporophyte has not been studied experimentally.

ORDER 2. DICTYOSIPHONALES

The Dictyosiphonales have profusely branched cylindrical thalli in which growth is initiated by a single apical cell. Mature portions of a thallus are internally differentiated into two or into three regions. The sporophytes usually produce unilocular sporangia only. The gametophytes are microscopic and isogamous.

There is but one family, the *Dictyosiphonaceae*, with some 4 genera and 15 species.

[1] Angst, 1926.

Dictyosiphon is found in cold waters along both coasts of this country. *D. foeniculaceus* (Huds.) Grev., the commonest species, is a summer annual which grows in the midlittoral zone. Its thread-like cylindrical thallus is freely branched and with the ultimate branchlets tapering to an acute point (Fig. 149*A*). Each branch tip has a single apical cell which

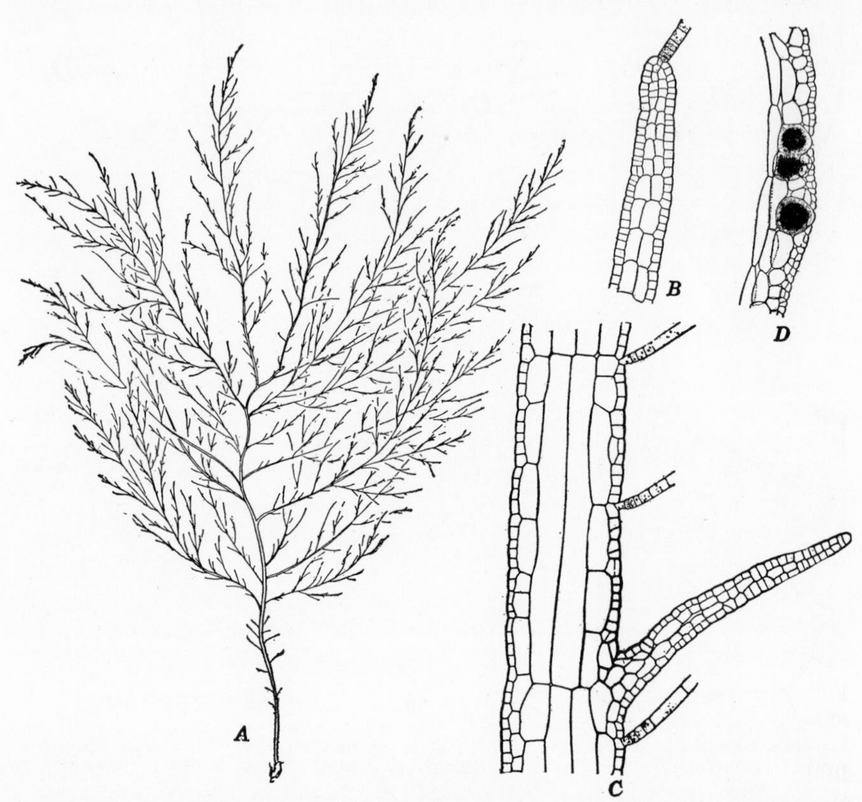

FIG. 149. *A–C. Dictyosiphon foeniculaceus* (Huds.) Kütz. *A*, sporophyte. *B*, branch apex of a sporophyte. *C*, vertical section through mature region of a sporophyte. *D*, unilocular sporangia of *D. macounii* Farl. (*B–D, from Kuckuck*, 1929.) (*A*, × ½; *B–C*, × 150; *D*, × 100.)

persists as long as growth continues, after which[1] it may be replaced by a hair (Fig. 149*B*).

Mature portions of a thallus may be solid or hollow (Fig. 149*C*). Solid portions have a central core of vertically elongated colorless cells surrounded by an ensheathing layer of small isodiametric cells containing chromatophores. Certain of the superficial cells develop into long unbranched multicellular hairs.

[1] Kuckuck in Oltmanns, 1922.

The unilocular sporangia lie embedded just beneath the thallus surface and are much larger than adjoining vegetative cells (Fig. 149*D*). They are formed by enlargement of isodiametric cells next to the axial core of elongated cells. Division of the primary nucleus of a unilocular sporangium has been shown[1] to be meiotic.

Zoospores from unilocular sporangia germinate immediately to form branched filamentous *Ectocarpus*-like gametophytes.[2] The gametangia are uniseriate, 2 to 12 cells in height, and with each cell producing a single motile gamete. Germination of the zygote follows immediately after an isogamous union of gametes. Gametes that have failed to conjugate round up, secrete a wall, and germinate parthenogenetically. A germinating zygote develops into a protonema-like filament. Later on, certain cells of the filament develop into an upright columnar structure resembling the growing apex of an adult sporophyte.[2]

ORDER 3. LAMINARIALES

Most members of the Laminariales (the kelps) have a sporophyte externally differentiated into holdfast, stipe, and blade or blades. Growth is due to an intercalary meristematic region, and it usually lies between stipe and blade. Mature regions anterior and posterior to the meristem have more or less internal differentiation of tissues. The sporophytes produce unilocular sporangia only, which lie in extensive sori borne upon the blade. Several genera have the sori restricted to special blades (**sporophylls**). The gametophytes are microscopic, filamentous, and oögamous.

The order includes about 30 genera and 100 species. They are inhabitants of the colder waters of the ocean. Kelps do not occur in tropical regions or in temperate regions except where the water is cool. In polar regions they are found as close to the pole as where there is a bottom free from permanent or nearly permanent ice. Most of the kelps grow below the low-tide line. There are four genera of Laminariales along the Atlantic Coast of this country. Eighteen genera are found along the Pacific Coast, and 14 of them are known only from the Pacific Ocean.

Gametophytes of Laminariales are practically identical from genus to genus. The sporophytes are extremely diverse from genus to genus. Many of the Pacific Coast kelps are notable for both their size and their external complexity of form. The most striking of these are the "giant kelps" which grow in water 10 to 30 meters in depth. The commonest giant kelp of the West Coast, *Macrocystis pyrifera* (L.) C.A.Ag. (Fig. 150*A*), has a repeatedly branched stipe, 30 to 50 meters long, in which there is a continuous formation of new blades at the apex of each branch of the stipe. Mature blades are borne at regular intervals along a branch,

[1] Abe, 1940. [2] Sauvageau, 1917.

and each of them has an elongate gas bladder at its base. *Nereocystis luetkeana* (Mert.) Post. and Rupr. (Fig. 150*B*), another common Pacific Coast giant kelp, is an annual. It has an unbranched stipe 20 to 25 meters long and one that terminates in a single large gas bladder. Above the bladder are numerous short dichotomously forked branches, each terminating in a single blade 3 to 4.5 meters long. The "sea palm," *Postelsia palmaeformis* Rupr. (Fig. 151), is the most striking of the smaller Pacific Coast kelps. It grows in the intertidal zone, but only on rocky headlands

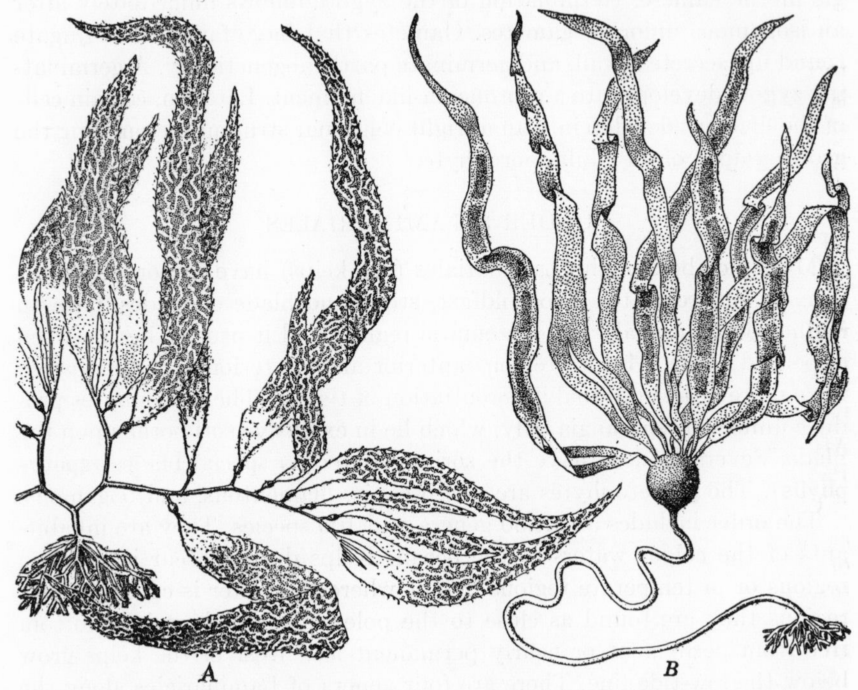

Fig. 150. *A*, *Macrocystis pyrifera* (L.) C.Ag. *B*, *Nereocystis luetkeana* (Mert.) Post. and Rupr. (*A*, × 1/12; *B*, × 1/20.)

exposed to the full pounding of the surf. It has a stout flexible stipe, about half a meter long, with numerous short dichotomies at the distal end, each terminating in a single narrow blade.

Laminaria, the genus after which the order is named, is found along both coasts of this country. Most of the species are perennial, but at least one of them (*L. ephemera* Setchell) is an annual. The sporophyte is differentiated into three distinct parts: holdfast, stipe, and blade (Fig. 152*A*). The holdfast may be a solid disk but it is usually a system of forked root-like branches (**hapetra**). The stipe is always unbranched and either cylindrical or somewhat flattened. The single blade terminating a stipe may be entire or vertically incised into a number of segments.

Growth of the sporophyte is due to an intercalary meristem at the juncture of stipe and blade. Meristematic activity results in a continuous increase in length of the stipe. On the other hand, the length of a mature blade remains approximately constant because increase in length at the base about equals abrasion at the apex.[1] Blades of most species persist for but one year. They stop growing late in the summer and begin to disintegrate after the plant has discharged its zoospores in the autumn. As the blade begins to disintegrate, there is an elongation of the axial portion of the meristem below it.[1] This causes a transverse rupture of the cortical portion of the meristem. The exposed axial portion becomes flattened as it increases in length, and, as growth continues, it becomes distinctly blade-like (Fig. 152*B–C*). The old blade may persist for a time upon the apex of the new intercalated blade, but eventually there is an abrasion of the old blade.

FIG. 151. *Postelsia palmaeformis* Rupr. (× ¼.)

The stipe is differentiated into a central axis (**medulla**), cortex, and epidermis, each containing distinctive elements. However, the transition from one region to another is gradual, not abrupt. The medulla of young stipes and the meristematic medulla of older ones consist of vertical, parallel, unbranched filaments ("hyphae") which lie close to one another. In slightly more mature medullae the vertical filaments lie a short distance from one another (Fig. 153*A–E*). Certain cells of a filament divide diagonally to cut off initial cells of **connecting filaments** and the apposed initials elongate laterally until they meet each other.[2] Many of these connected cells develop into connecting filaments by repeated transverse division. The many-celled connecting filaments tend to run horizontally across the medulla, but many of them run diagonally because of unequal elongation of the vertical filaments to which they are attached. Elongation of the vertical filaments is accompanied by cell division, so that they remain composed of relatively short cells. In other filaments there is but little cell division and the cells become long. These filaments have been called **trumpet hyphae**[3] because their cells are much broader and inflated at the ends (Fig. 153*F*). There is some evidence that trumpet hyphae are vertical conducting elements comparable to the sieve tubes

[1] Setchell, 1905. [2] Killian, 1911. [3] Oliver, 1887.

of vascular plants.[1] The trumpet hyphae of certain other kelps, notably *Nereocystis* and *Macrocystis*, are sieve tubes with conspicuous sieve plates resembling the sieve plates of many angiosperms. Measurements of the rates of growth and of photosynthesis in different parts of a *Macrocystis* sporophyte show that the rate of growth at the apex can be accounted for

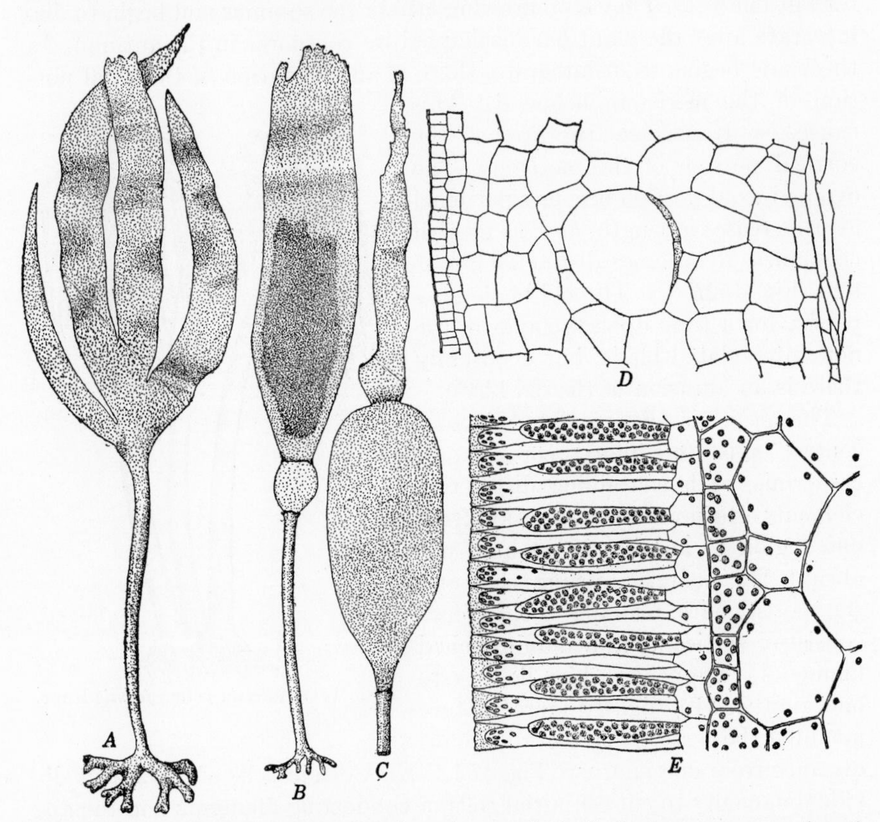

FIG. 152. *A–C*, *Laminaria andersonii* Farlow. *A*, sporophyte. *B–C*, stages in regeneration of new blades. *D–E*, *L. farlowii* Setchell. *D*, transverse section of portion of a blade containing a mucilage canal. *E*, transverse section through a portion of a sorus. (*A*, × ¼; *B–C*, × ½; *D*, × 215; *E*, × 485.)

only by a massive upward translocation of organic matter through the stipe,[2] and if this is the case it is very probable that translocation is through the sieve tubes.

The cortex is formed by division and redivision of superficial cells of a young stipe. It is composed of more or less radially arranged, vertically elongated cells. There is a continuous increase in diameter at the periphery of the cortex as long as the plant remains alive. Cells formed

[1] Oliver, 1887; Sykes, 1908. [2] Sargent and Lantrip, 1952.

at the end of a growing season are smaller than those formed early in the season. Because of this, the cortex contains one or more concentric rings resembling the annual rings in the secondary wood of a dicotyledonous stem. Cortices of many species contain **mucilage ducts,** either just beneath the epidermis or just outside the medulla. They are an anastomosing system of canals filled with mucilage. The mucilage is produced by groups of secretory cells at the inner face of a duct.[1]

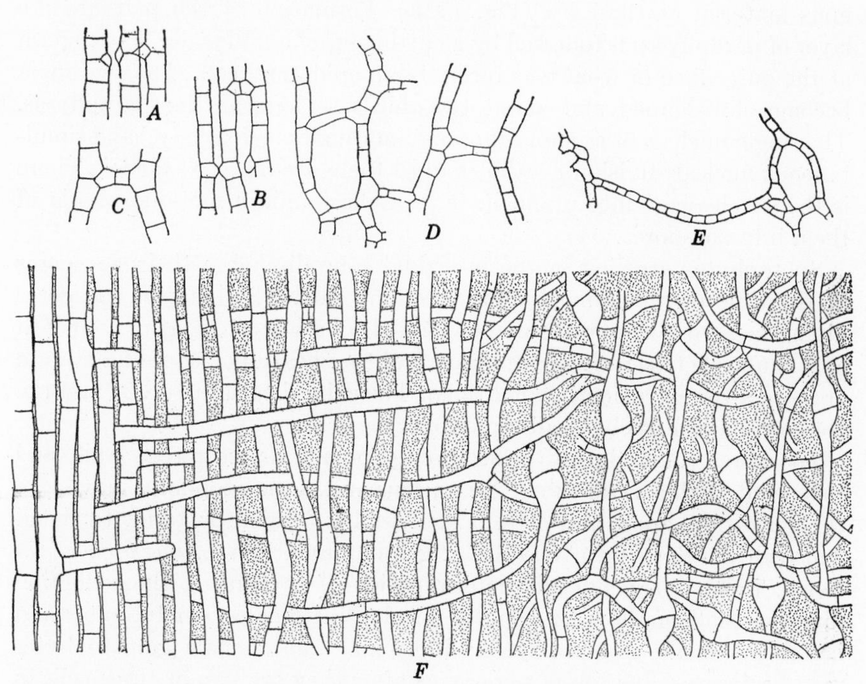

FIG. 153. *A–E*, vertical sections through the embryonic region showing early stages in development of medullary tissue in stipe of *Laminaria digitata* (Turn.) Lamx. *F*, diagrammatic longitudinal section through medulla of stipe of *L. andersonii* Farlow. Outer region at the left, inner at the right. (*A–E, after Killian*, 1911.) (*F*, × 215.)

The epidermis is one or two cells in thickness and composed of small cubical cells containing many chromatophores.

The internal structure of a blade resembles that of a stipe. At the center is a flattened medulla with vertical and connecting filaments. External to the medulla is a cortex composed of isodiametric cells that are progressively smaller toward the epidermis (Fig. 152*D*). Several species have mucilage ducts in their cortices. The epidermis is usually but one cell in thickness. Both it and the outermost cortical cells contain numerous chromatophores.

[1] Guignard, 1892.

Unilocular sporangia, which are the only reproductive organs produced by the sporophyte, are generally formed at a specific season, either summer or autumn. They are borne in extensive sori nearly covering both surfaces of a blade (Fig. 152*B*). Each epidermal cell of a young soral area sends forth a finger-like outgrowth at its outer face. A transverse wall is formed at the base of the outgrowth, and the cell thus cut off elongates to form an erect unicellular paraphysis with a conspicuous cap of gelatinous material at the apex (Fig. 152*E*). Formation of the palisade-like layer of paraphyses is followed by a cutting off of a unilocular sporangium at the outer face of what was formerly an epidermal cell. The sporangia become club-shaped and about two-thirds as long as the paraphyses. The single nucleus of a young sporangium divides meiotically,[1] and simultaneous nuclear division continues until there are 32 or 64 nuclei. There is then a cleavage into uninucleate protoplasts and a metamorphosis of them into zoospores.

Sporophytes growing in the intertidal zone discharge their zoospores at the time of reflooding by the incoming tide. The mass of zoospores discharged from a sporangium is enclosed by a watery gelatinous sheath as it exudes between the paraphyses, and the sheath persists for a minute or more after extrusion beyond them. Then the sheath dissolves, and the zoospores swim freely in all directions.

Zoospores round up, after swarming for a time, secrete a wall, and soon send forth a germ tube. The nucleus and chromatophores move into the germ-tube apex, and a transverse wall is formed posterior to them. This cell develops into the cellular gametophyte.[2] In *L. saccharina* (L.) Lamx. there is a genotypic determination of sex during the reduction division. Half of the 32 zoospores develop into male gametophytes and half into female gametophytes.[3] Both male and female gametophytes may begin a production of sex organs after they are two or three cells in length, but the male gametophytes usually become many-celled before they fruit. Fruiting is directly dependent upon temperature, and it has been shown[1] that gametophytes remain vegetative if the temperature of the culture is above 15°C. Sterile gametophytes may be distinguished from each other because cells of female gametophytes are twice the diameter of those of male plants. Many-celled male gametophytes produce antheridia in abundance and at the tips of one- or two-celled lateral branches (Fig. 154*A*). Each antheridium is one-celled, and its protoplast is metamorphosed into a single antherozoid with two lateral flagella. Oögonia of female gametophytes are developed from both intercalary and terminal cells. In either case, the oögonium elongates vertically, and

[1] Abe, 1939.
[2] Kanda, 1936, 1938; Kylin, 1916; Myers, 1925; Sauvageau, 1918; Schreiber, 1930.
[3] Schreiber, 1930.

its protoplast develops into a single egg. The egg is extruded through, but remains attached to, a pore at the apex of the oögonial wall.

An antherozoid swims to and fuses with the egg attached to the oögonial apex. Union of gametes is followed by a union of their nuclei.[1] Soon after this, the zygote begins to develop into a sporophyte. By successive transverse divisions it develops into a vertical row of 6 to 10

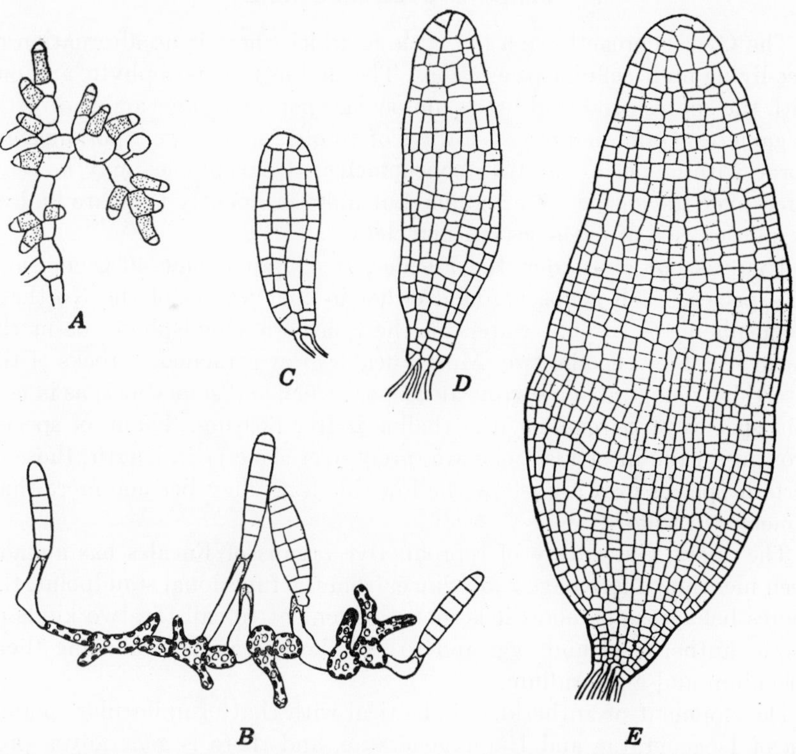

FIG. 154. *Laminaria flexicaulis* Le Jol. *A*, male gametophyte. *B*, female gametophyte with young sporophytes. *C–E*, somewhat later stages in development of sporophyte. (*From Sauvageau*, 1918.) (*A*, × 480; *B–E*, × 180.)

cells. Median cells of the row then divide vertically, and this is soon followed by a vertical division of all cells but the lowermost.[2] The lowermost cell elongates to form a rhizoid in much the same manner as a root hair grows out from an epidermal cell of a root of a vascular plant.[3] Continued division in two planes produces an expanded blade-like sheet, one cell in thickness but with several hundred cells (Fig. 154*B–E*). Additional rhizoids are developed from the lowermost cells of the blade, and

[1] Williams, 1921.
[2] Kanda, 1936, 1938; Kylin, 1916; Myers, 1925; Sauvageau, 1918.
[3] Sauvageau, 1918.

the gametophyte disappears after three or four rhizoids have been produced. Eventually cells in the lowermost portion of the blade divide in a third plane, producing a meristematic region comparable to that of an adult sporophyte. The upper face of this meristem contributes to the blade; the lower face gives off derivatives that mature into a stipe.

CLASS 3. CYCLOSPOREAE

The Cyclosporeae have a life cycle in which there is no alternation of free-living multicellular generations. The thallus is a sporophyte, and one with the spores produced by its unilocular sporangia functioning directly as gametes. Gametic union is always of an oögamous type. Sporangia are borne within special cavities (**conceptacles**). Conceptacles may be scattered over the surface of a thallus, but more frequently they are limited to inflated tips of branches (**receptacles**).

There is but one order, the Fucales. It contains some 40 genera and 350 species. Each genus is found either in cold waters of the Northern Hemisphere, or in cold waters of the Southern Hemisphere, or in the warm seas between the two. Most Fucales grow attached to rocks of the intertidal zone, but some grow at deeper levels; and sometimes, as in certain species of *Sargassum*, the thallus is free-floating. Thalli of species growing in the intertidal zone are rarely over a meter in length; those of certain species growing below the low-tide level may become more than 5 meters in length.

The sporangial nature of reproductive organs of Fucales has already been mentioned (see page 225). Since, from the functional standpoint, the spores behave as gametes it is more convenient to call the two kinds of spores antherozoid and egg, and to call the sporangia producing them oögonium and antheridium.

Development of antheridia is identical with that of unilocular sporangia of Isogeneratae and Heterogeneratae, and there is generally a production of 64 antherozoids. These differ from zoospores and zoogametes of other Phaeophyta in that the posterior flagellum is the longer of the two.[1]

Developing oögonia have a meiotic division of the primary nucleus and a mitotic division of the resultant four nuclei to form eight nuclei. There are no further nuclear divisions and subsequent development is according to one of the following types: (1) the *Fucus* type (Fig. 155*A*) in which there is a cleavage into eight uninucleate eggs; (2) the *Ascophyllum* type (Fig. 155*B*) in which four uninucleate eggs are formed and four supernumerary nuclei are extruded between them; (3) the *Pelvetia* type (Fig. 155*C*) with two eggs and six supernumerary nuclei between them; (4) the

[1] Kylin, 1916*A*, 1920.

Hesperophycus type (Fig. 155*D*) with one large uninucleate egg and a small seven-nucleate egg; (5) the *Cystoseira* type (Fig. 155*E*) in which extrusion of seven nuclei results in a single uninucleate egg; and (6) the *Sargassum* type (Fig. 155*F*) in which degeneration of all but one nucleus results in a single uninucleate egg. The *Fucus* type appears to be the most primitive and the other types a modification of it.

Fucus is a cold-water alga of the Northern Hemisphere. It grows in profusion in the intertidal zone wherever the ocean shore is rocky along the coasts of Europe, Asia, and North America. On both shores of the

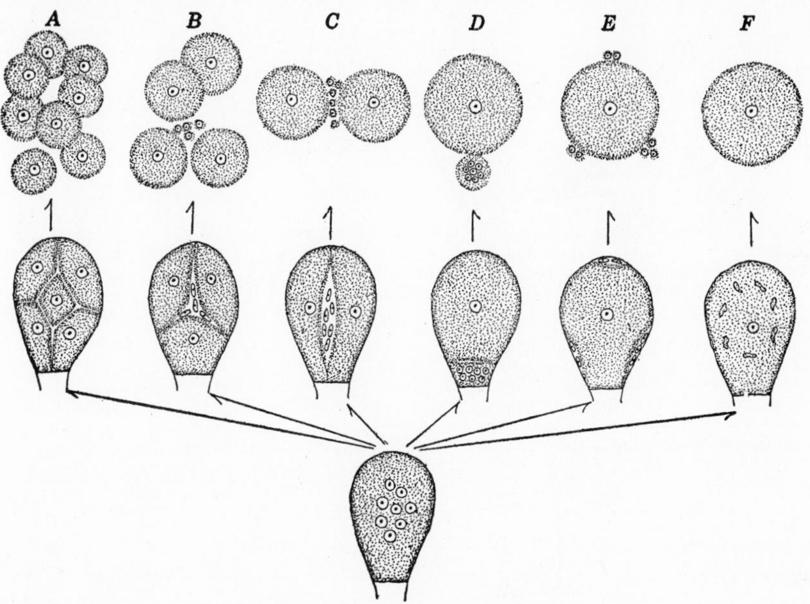

FIG. 155. Diagrams showing the development of the various types of oögonia found among the Fucales. *A*, *Fucus* type. *B*, *Ascophyllum* type. *C*, *Pelvetia* type. *D*, *Hesperophycus* type. *E*, *Cystoseira* type. *F*, *Sargassum* type.

Atlantic Ocean it also grows in salt marshes where the salinity is less than that of the ocean. Here it grows either free-floating or partially embedded in mud.

A thallus (Fig. 156*A*) growing upon a rock has a discoid holdfast from which arises a dichotomously branched shoot. Dichotomies of a shoot are flattened ribbons with a more or less evident midrib, but the lowermost dichotomies may have all portions except the midrib worn away and so appear stem-like. Certain species, as *F. vesiculosus* L., have hollow, bladder-like, air-filled expansions here and there along the dichotomies. These help buoy up the thallus when it is submerged.

Growth of a thallus is at the tip of each ultimate dichotomy and is initiated by a single apical cell. An apical cell has the form of a truncate four-sided pyramid, and cuts off segments laterally and basally (Fig. 156*B*). The first division of a lateral segment is periclinal. Outer daughter cells of lateral segments divide and redivide to form the parenchymatous cortical tissue of mature regions. Inner daughter cells of lateral segments, together with derivatives from the basal face of the apical cell, divide and redivide to form the medulla of mature regions. This medulla is composed of cylindrical cells joined end to end in parallel longitudinal

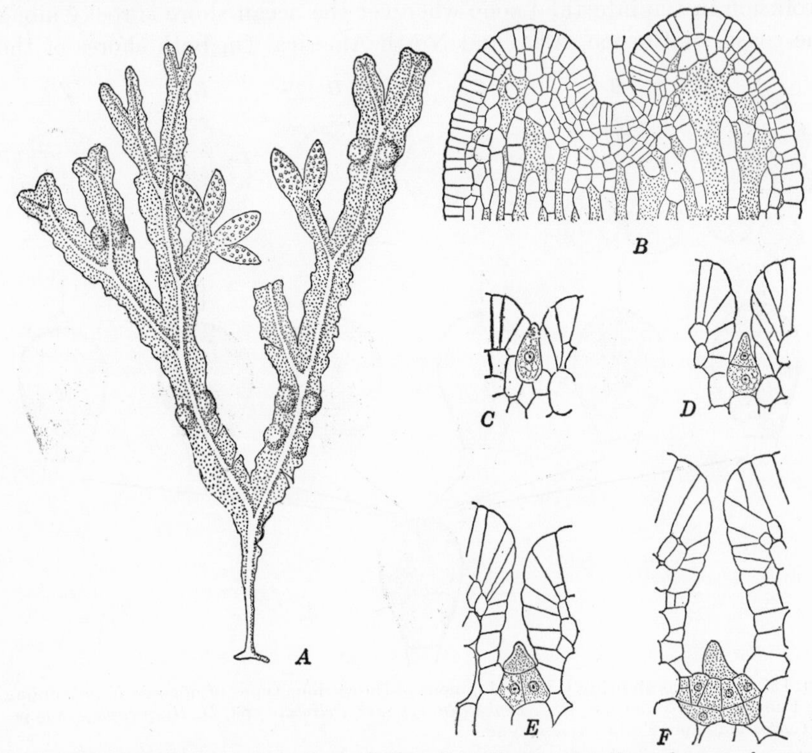

Fig. 156. *A–B*, *Fucus vesiculosus* L. *A*, thallus. *B*, vertical section through apex of a young thallus. *C–F*, early stages in development of conceptacle of *F. serratus* L. (*B*, *after Oltmanns*, 1889; *C–F*, *after Nienburg*, 1913.)

filaments laterally separated from one another by gelatinous algin. Occasionally an apical cell divides vertically into two daughter cells of equal size, each of which becomes an apical cell. Growth initiated by the pair of apical cells produces a new dichotomy of the branch bearing them.

Some species of *Fucus* are dioecious (Fig. 157*A*); others are monoecious and either with but one kind of sex organ in a conceptacle or with the conceptacle containing both kinds. The time of fruiting is not the same from species to species, nor in the same species is it always the same at different localities. In England,[1] the period during which receptacles dis-

[1] Knight and Parke, 1950.

charge gametes lasts about six months for *F. vesiculosus* and eight months for *F. serratus* L. On the coasts of Devon and the Isle of Man, thalli of *F. vesiculosus* discharge gametes at the same time of the year, but those of *F. serratus* do not. Fruiting may also be throughout the entire year, as is the case with *F. furcatus* C.A.Ag. growing along the coast of central California.

Each conceptacle of a receptacle is developed from a single superficial cell which lies close to the apical cell of the receptacle. At first, the initial cell of a conceptacle lies level with the adjoining surface cell, but as adjoining cells divide and redivide the conceptacle initial comes to lie below the thallus surface (Fig. 156*C*). The initial divides transversely. The outer daughter cell, the **tongue cell,** does not divide again and eventually disappears.[1] The inner daughter cell, the **basal cell,** divides and redivides to form a layer, the **fertile sheet,** two or three cells in thickness (Fig. 156*D–F*). The fertile sheet is the layer lining the flask-shaped open cavity (the conceptacle) resulting from continued enlargement and division of cells lateral to the conceptacular initial. A mature conceptacle (Fig. 157*A*) is globose and with a relatively small opening, the **ostiole.** Superficial cells of the fertile layer may produce filaments of cells (**paraphyses**) or they may produce sex organs. Filaments (**periphyses**) developed in the upper portion of a conceptacle are unbranched, do not bear sex organs, and project through the ostiole and a very short distance beyond it.

Antheridia develop directly from cells of the fertile layer, or develop at the base of branched paraphyses growing out from them (Fig. 158*A*). Division of the primary nucleus of an antheridium is meiotic,[2] and after meiosis is completed there are mitotic divisions that continue until there are 64 nuclei. Nuclear division is followed by a cleavage of the antheridial contents into uninucleate protoplasts which metamorphose into biflagellate antherozoids. Antherozoids of *Fucus,* similar to those of other Fucales, have the posterior flagellum the longer of the two.[3] The wall of an antheridium is differentiated into an outer firm layer (the **exochite**) and an inner more gelatinous layer (the **endochite**).

Superficial cells of the fertile layer function as initial cells of oögonia. An oögonial initial divides transversely into a **stalk cell** and an **oögonium,** neither of which divides again (Fig. 157*B–C*). The oögonium increases greatly in size. Its nucleus divides meiotically and the four nuclei formed by meiosis divide once to form eight nuclei.[4] There is then a cleavage of the oögonial protoplast into eight uninucleate eggs (Fig. 157*C–F*). The wall of an oögonium consists of three concentric layers: **exochite, meso-**

[1] Nienburg, 1913. [2] Yamanouchi, 1909. [3] Kylin, 1920.
[4] Farmer and Williams, 1898; Strasburger, 1897; Yamanouchi, 1909.

chite, and **endochite.**[1] In the region where stalk cell and oögonium adjoin, the so-called **basal pit,** the wall is thin and not differentiated into layers.

Liberation of antherozoids and eggs generally takes place when *Fucus* is reflooded by the incoming tide. Imbibition of water by the oögonial mesochite and endochite causes them to swell, burst the exochite, and

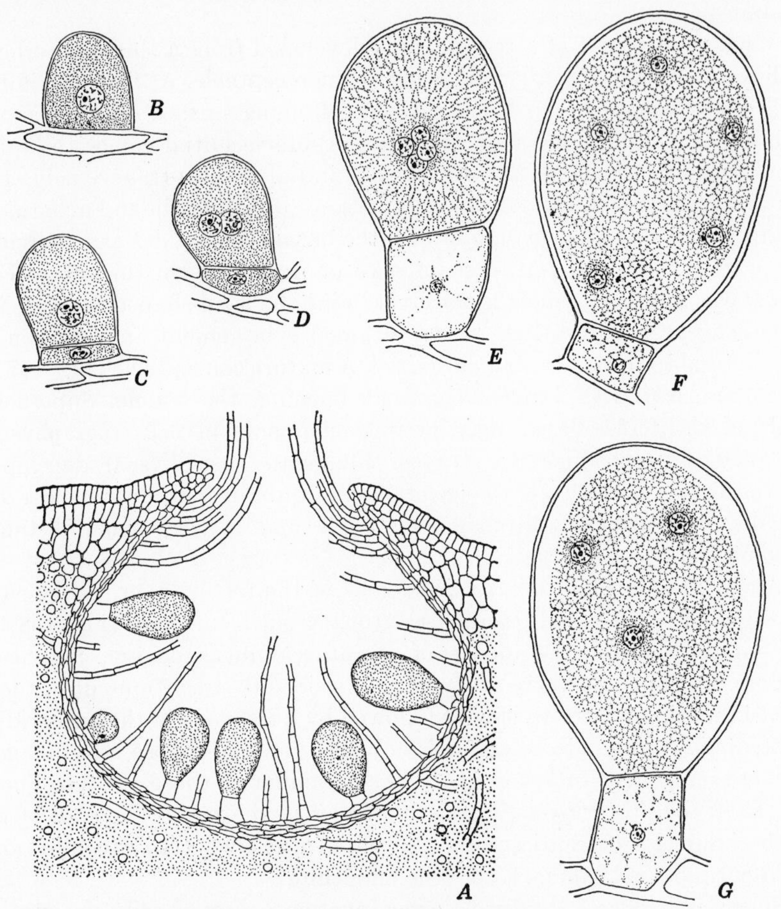

FIG. 157. *Fucus vesiculosus* L. *A*, section through oögonial conceptacle. *B–G*, stages in development of oögonium. (*A*, × 90; *B–G*, × 400.)

slip out of it (Fig. 158*D*). The eight eggs, still surrounded by the two inner wall layers, are then passively pushed between the paraphyses until they reach the vicinity of the ostiole, and then are pushed out through between the periphyses. This passive extrusion of eggs and the surrounding wall layers seems to be due to a swelling of gelatinous material within the conceptacle. After being extruded from a conceptacle, the endochite

[1] Farmer and Williams, 1898.

imbibes more water and its swelling causes the mesochite to rupture apically, invaginate, and expose the endochite.[1] As the exposed endochite continues to imbibe water and become softer the mutually compressed eggs become rounded, separate from one another, and eventually float away from one another through the watery endochite (Fig. 158*E–G*). Reflooding of a thallus also causes a rupture of the exochite of an antheridium and an extrusion of the contained mass of antherozoids through the ostiole. The mass of antherozoids is still surrounded by the endochite

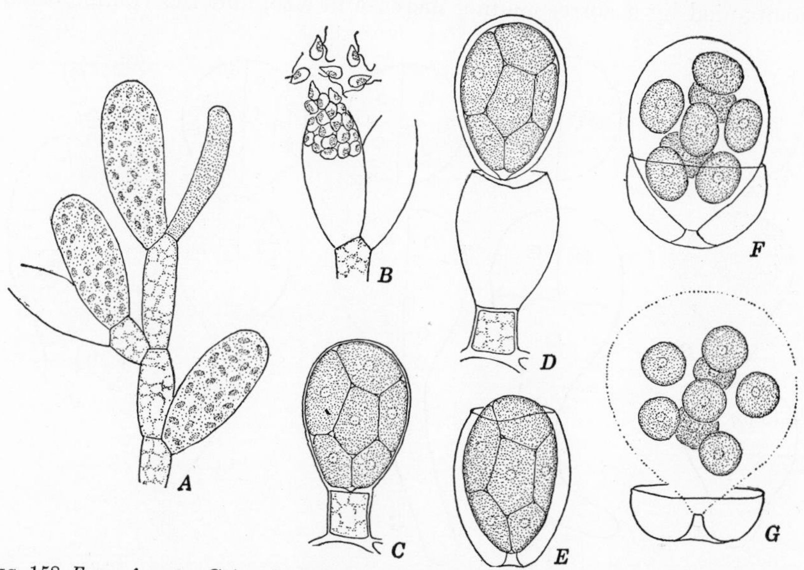

FIG. 158. *Fucus furcatus* C.Ag. *A*, antheridial paraphysis. *B*, antheridium liberating antherozoids. *C*, oögonium before liberation of eggs. *D*, liberation of eggs surrounded by mesochite and endochite. *E*, beginning of evagination of mesochite. *F–G*, swelling of exposed endochite and rounding up of eggs. (*A–B*, × 800; *C–G*, × 110.)

when first extruded, but this soon gelatinizes and the antherozoids swim freely in all directions (Fig. 158*B*).

Gametic union is seen to best advantage in dioecious species. Here, as first shown by Thuret,[1] the antherozoids cluster in such numbers about each egg as to cause it to rotate in the water (Fig. 159*A*). Usually but one antherozoid enters an egg but a few cases of polyspermy have been observed.[2] Within less than an hour after fertilization the zygote forms a gelatinous wall that firmly affixes it to any substratum upon which it has lodged.[3] In less than a day the zygote shows a definite polarity, as is evidenced by the sending out of a rhizoidal protuberance (Fig. 159*B*). External factors affecting the polarity include: gradients in light (both

[1] Thuret, 1854. [2] Farmer and Williams, 1898; Yamanouchi, 1909.
[3] Whitaker, 1931.

visible[1] and ultraviolet[2]), temperature,[3] hydrogen-ion concentration,[4] and proximity of other zygotes.[5] The establishment of polarity, as evidenced by protrusion of a rhizoidal initial, is thought to be due to the effect of some growth regulator. Presumably this is auxin, a substance which has been shown to be present in eggs of *Fucus*.[6]

Early stages in development of an embryo are at a rapid rate. In *F. furcatus* there are 4 to 12 cells in an embryo two days old, and approximately 50 cells in one four days old. Increase in number of cells is not accompanied by a corresponding increase in size, and the volume of an

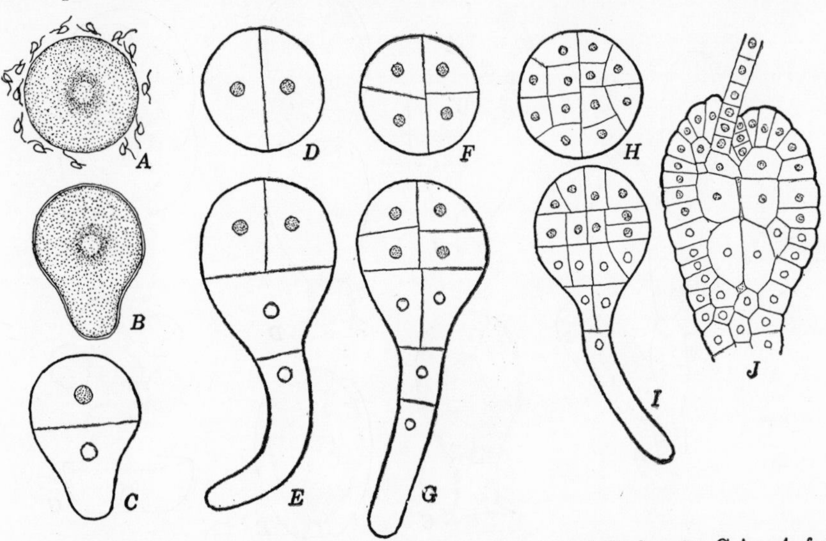

Fig. 159. Early stages in development of thallus of *Fucus*. *A–I*, *F. furcatus* C.Ag. *A*, fertilization of egg. *B*, zygote after formation of rhizoidal protuberance. *C*, vertical section of day-old embryo. *D-G*, vertical and transverse sections of two-day-old embryos. *H–I*, vertical and transverse sections of four-day-old embryos. *J*, vertical section of embryo of *F. vesiculosus* L. after formation of first apical hair. (*J*, *after Nienburg*, 1931.) (*A–I*, × 225.)

embryo with some 50 cells is not much greater than that of a two-celled embryo (Fig. 159*C–I*). The early development of an embryo is at the expense of reserve foods contributed by the egg; later development is at a much slower rate because growth is dependent upon photosynthesis by the growing embryo.

Division of a zygote into a two-celled embryo is in a plane at right angles to the rhizoidal initial (Fig. 159*C*). The upper cell of a two-celled embryo divides vertically and the lower (that with the rhizoidal protuberance) divides transversely,[7] to form a four-celled embryo three cells in height (Fig. 159*E*). The two cells in the upper tier of the four-celled

[1] Whitaker, 1936. [2] Whitaker, 1942. [3] Lowrance, 1937. [4] Whitaker, 1937.
[5] Whitaker, 1931. [6] du Buy and Olson, 1937.
[7] Nienburg, 1931; Oltmanns, 1889.

embryo divide vertically and each cell in the resultant quadrat divides transversely. Immediately succeeding divisions are periclinal. The peripheral cells thus formed are the primordium of the cortical tissue, and central cells are the primordium of the medulla of later embryonic stages (Fig. 159*H–I*). The median cell of the four-celled embryo divides vertically and then following vertical and transverse divisions differentiate primordia of cortical and medullary tissues in the lower portion of older embryos. The lowermost cell of a four-celled embryo develops into a primary rhizoid that may be several cells in length and two cells broad in the upper portion. Secondary rhizoids are usually formed from upper cells of the primary rhizoid.

As growth continues a superficial cell at the apex of an embryo gives rise to an unbranched multicellular hair (Fig. 159*J*) and later adjoining superficial cells also produce hairs.[1] The terminal tuft of hairs lies in a small depression resulting from enlargement of adjoining portions of the embryo. Eventually there is a disappearance of all but the basal cell of the first-formed hair. This cell then begins to function as an apical cell[1] and all further growth is initiated by this apical cell or by others derived from it. Different from apical cells of older portions of a thallus, the first-formed apical cell has only three lateral cutting faces.

Bibliography

Abe, K. **1935**. *Sci. Rept. Tohoku Imp. Univ. Biol.* **9**: 329–337. 1 pl. 6 figs. [Life histories various genera.]

1935A. *Ibid.* **10**: 287–290. 2 figs. [Punctariales.]

1938. *Ibid.* **12**: 475–482. 1 pl. 6 figs. [*Desmarestia.*]

1940. *Ibid.* **14**: 317–320. 1 pl. 2 figs. [*Dictyosiphon*]

1940A. *Ibid.* **14**: 321–327. 2 pl. [Meiosis, *Laminaria.*]

Angst, Laura. **1926**. *Publ. Puget Sound Biol. Sta.* **5**: 159–163. 1 pl. [*Soranthera.*]

Barry, V. C. **1938**. *Sci. Proc. Roy. Dublin Soc.* **21**: 615–622. [Laminarin.]

Black, W. A. P. **1948**. *Jour. Soc. Chem. Eng.* **67**: 165–176. [Mannitol in Phaeophyta.]

Blinks, L. R. **1951**. Physiology and biochemistry of algae. In G. M. Smith (editor), Manual of phycology. Waltham, Mass. Pp. 263–291.

Brebner, G. **1896**. *Proc. Bristol Nat. Soc.* **8**: 176–187. 1 pl. [*Haplospora.*]

du Buy, H. G., and R. A. Olson. **1937**. *Amer. Jour. Bot.* **24**: 609–611. [Auxin in *Fucus.*]

Carter, P. W. **1927**. *Ann. Bot.* **41**: 139–159. 2 pl. 4 figs. [Dictyotales.]

Chadefaud, M. **1936**. *Rev. Algologique* **8**: 1–286. 38 pl. 31 figs. [Fucosan.]

Chapman, V. J. **1950**. Seaweeds and their uses. London. 287 pp. 20 pl. 52 figs.

Church, A. H. **1898**. *Ann. Bot.* **12**: 75–109. 3 pl. [*Cutleria.*]

Clint, Hilda B. **1927**. *Univ. Liverpool Publ. Hartley Bot. Lab.* **3**: 5–25. 5 figs. [*Sphacelaria.*]

Collins, F. S. **1917**. *Rhodora* **19**: 77–84. [*Sargassum.*]

Connell, J. J., E. L. Hurst, and E. G. V. Percival. **1950**. *Jour. Chem. Soc. (London)* **1950**: 3493–3500. [Laminarin.]

Dammann, Hildegard. **1930**. *Wiss. Meeresuntersuch. Abt. Helgoland.* N.F. **18**, Abhandl. **4**: 1–36. 1 pl. 22 figs. [Development of various Phaeophyta.]

[1] Nienburg, 1931; Oltmanns, 1889.

Falkenberg, P. **1879.** *Mitteil. Zool. Sta. Naples* **1:** 420–447. 1 pl. [*Cutleria.*]

Farmer, J. B., and J. L. Williams. **1898.** *Phil. Trans. Roy. Soc. London B.* **190:** 623–645. 6 pl. [Fucales.]

Fritsch, F. E. **1945.** The structure and reproduction of the algae. Vol. 2. Cambridge. 939 pp. 336 figs.

Funk, G. **1927.** *Pubbl. Stazione Zool. Napoli* **7** (supplemento): 1–507. 20 pl. 50 figs. [Algae of Gulf of Naples.]

Gardner, N. L. **1910.** *Univ. Calif. Publ. Bot.* **4:** 121–136. 2 pl. [Oögonia of Fucales.]

Guignard, L. **1892.** *Ann. Sci. Nat. Bot.* 7 ser. **15:** 1–46. 20 figs. [Mucilage ducus of *Laminaria.*]

Haupt. A. W. **1932.** *Amer. Jour. Bot.* **19:** 239–254. 4 pl. 4 figs. [Dictyotales.]

Higgins, E. Marion. **1931.** *Ann. Bot.* **45:** 345–353. 1 pl. [Sphacelariales.]

Hoyt, W. D. **1907.** *Bot. Gaz.* **43:** 383–392. 2 figs. [Periodic fruiting, *Dictyota.*]

1910. *Ibid.* **49:** 55–57. [*Dictyota.*]

1920. *Bull. U.S. Bureau of Fisheries* **36:** 371–556. 36 pl. 47 figs. [Marine algae of Beauford, N.C.]

1927. *Amer. Jour. Bot.* **14:** 592–619. [Periodic fruiting, *Dictyota.*]

Hygen, G. **1934.** *Nyt. Mag. Naturvidenskab.* **74:** 187–268. 16 pl. 11 figs. [Chordariales.]

Johnson, T. **1891.** *Ann. Bot.* **5:** 135–144. 1 pl. [Reproduction of various algae.]

Kanda, T. **1936.** *Sci. Papers Inst. Algol. Research Hokkaido Imp. Univ.* **1:** 221–260. 3 pl. 27 figs. [Gametophyte of *Laminaria.*]

1938. *Ibid.* **2:** 87–111. 2 pl. 24 figs. [Gametophyte of *Laminaria.*]

Karsakoff, N. **1892.** *Jour. de Bot.* **6:** 433–444. 1 pl. 1 fig. [Punctariales.]

Killian, K. **1911.** *Zeitschr. Bot.* **3:** 433–494. 32 figs. [*Laminaria.*]

Kniep, H. **1928.** Die Sexualität der niederen Pflanzen. Jena. 544 pp. 221 figs.

Knight, Margery. **1923.** *Trans. Roy. Soc. Edinburgh* **53:** 343–360. 6 pl. [Ectocarpales.]

1929. *Ibid.* **56:** 307–332. 6 pl. 3 figs. [*Ectocarpus.*]

Knight, Margery, and Mary Parke. **1950.** *Jour. Marine Biol. Assn.* **29:** 439–514. 33 figs. [Biology of *Fucus.*]

Kuckuck, P. **1894.** *Wiss. Meeresuntersuch.* N.F. **1**[1]: 225–263. 29 figs. [Algae of Helgoland.]

1899. *Wiss. Meeresuntersuch. Abt. Helgoland.* N.F. **3:** 95–116. 2 pl. 15 figs. [*Cutleria.*]

1912. *Ibid.* **5:** 117–152. 3 pl. 18 figs. [Ectocarpales.]

1912A. *Ibid.* **5:** 153–186. 2 pl. 4 figs. [*Ectocarpus.*]

1929. *Ibid.* **17,** Abhandl. 4: 1–93, 155 figs. [Morphology of various Phaeophyta.]

Kylin, H. **1912.** *Ark. Bot.* **11,** No. 5: 1–26. 1 pl. [Fucosan.]

1912A. *Hoppe-Seyler's Zeitschr. Physiol. Chem.* **82:** 221–230. [Pigments.]

1915. *Ibid.* **94:** 337–425. [Biochemistry.]

1916. *Svensk Bot. Tidsskr.* **10:** 551–561. 5 figs. [Gametophyte of *Laminaria.*]

1916A. *Ber. Deutsch. Bot. Ges.* **34:** 194–201. 1 pl. [Antherozoids of Fucales.]

1917. *Ibid.* **35:** 298–310. [Tilopteridales.]

1918. *Svensk Bot. Tidsskr.* **12:** 1–60. 30 figs. [Development of various Phaeophyta.]

1920. *Ber. Deutsch. Bot. Ges.* **38:** 74–78. 2 figs. [Antherozoids of Fucales.]

1933. *Lunds. Univ. Ärsskr.* N.F. **29,** Nr. 7: 1–102. 2 pl. 35 figs. [Life histories of Phaeophyta.]

1934. *Ibid.* **30,** Nr. 9: 1-189. 10 figs. [*Myrionema.*]

1937. *Ibid.* **33,** Nr. 1: 1–34. 5 figs. [Morphology various Phaeophyta.]

1938. *Förh. Kgl. Fysiogr. Sällsk. Lund* **8,** Nr. 20: 1–10. [Fucosan.]

1940. *Lunds. Univ. Ärsskr.* N.F. **36,** Nr. 9: 1–68. 8 pl. 30 figs. [Chordariales.]

1940A. *Svensk Bot. Tidsskr.* **34:** 301–314. 1 fig. [Origin of Cyclosporeae.]

1944. *Förh. Kgl. Fysiogr. Sällsk. Lund* **14,** Nr. 18: 1–13. [Biochemistry.]

Levring, T. **1937.** *Lunds. Univ. Årsskr.* N.F. **33,** Nr. 8: 1–147. 4 pl. 19 figs. [Marine algae of Norway.]

Lewis, I. F. **1910.** *Bot. Gaz.* **50:** 59–64. 1 fig. [Periodic fruiting, *Dictyota.*]

Longest, Pauline M. **1946.** *Jour. Elisha Mitchell Sci. Soc.* **62:** 249–252. 3 figs. [Structure of flagella.]

Lowrance, E. W. **1937.** *Jour. Cellular and Comp. Physiol.* **10:** 321–337. 2 figs. [Polarity *Fucus* eggs.]

McKay, Hazel H. **1933.** *Univ. Calif. Publ. Bot.* **17:** 111–148. 7 pl. [Laminariales.]

Manton, Irene, and B. Clarke. **1951.** *Jour. Exper. Bot.* **2:** 242–246. 17 figs. [Structure of flagella.]

Mathias, W. T. **1935.** *Univ. Liverpool Publ. Hartley Bot. Lab.* **13:** 1–23. 52 figs. [Punctariales.]

1935A. *Ibid.* **13:** 24–28. 10 figs. [Sphacelariales.]

Miwa, T. **1932.** *Bot. Mag. Tokyo* **46:** 261–262. [Cell wall.]

Mottier, D. M. **1900.** *Ann. Bot.* **14:** 163–192. 1 pl. [*Dictyota.*]

Myers, Margret E. **1925.** *Univ. Calif. Publ. Bot.* **13:** 109–124. 3 pl. [Gametophyte of *Laminaria.*]

1928. *Ibid.* **14:** 225–246. 4 pl. [Gametophytes of Laminariales.]

Nienburg, W. **1913.** *Zeitschr. Bot.* **5:** 1–27. 9 figs. [Conceptacles of Fucales.]

1923. *Ber. Deutsch. Bot. Ges.* **41:** 211–217. 1 fig. [*Haplospora.*]

1931. *Wiss. Meeresuntersuch. Abt. Kiel.* N.F. **21:** 49–63. 14 figs. [Embryo of *Fucus.*]

Oliver, F. W. **1887.** *Ann. Bot.* **1:** 95–117. 2 pl. [*Laminaria.*]

Oltmanns, F. **1889.** *Bibliotheca Bot.* **3,** Heft 14: 1–94. 15 pl. [Embryology Fucales.]

1922. Morphologie und Biologie der Algen. 2 Aufl. Bd. 2. Jena. 439 pp. 325 figs.

Overton, J. B. **1913.** *Science,* N.S. **37:** 841–844. [Parthenogenesis in *Fucus.*]

Papenfuss, G. F. **1934.** *Bot. Notiser* **1934:** 437–444. 9 figs. [*Sphacelaria.*]

1935. *Bot. Gaz.* **96:** 421–446. 2 pl. 13 figs. [*Ectocarpus.*]

1947. *Bull. Torrey Bot. Club.* **74:** 398–402. [Dictyosiphonales.]

1951. Phaeophyta. In G. M. Smith (editor), Manual of phycology. Pp. 119–158. 9 figs.

Parke, Mary. **1933.** *Univ. Liverpool Publ. Hartley Bot. Lab.* **9:** 5–43. 11 pl. 20 figs. [Life histories of various genera.]

Percival, E. G. V., and A. G. Ross. **1948.** *Nature.* **162:** 895–896. [Cell wall.]

Pia, J. **1927.** Thallophyta. In M. Hirmer, Handbuch der Paläobotanik. Bd. **1.** Pp. 31–136. 129 figs.

Reinke, J. **1889.** *Bot. Zeitg.* **47:** 101–118, 125–139, 155–159. 2 pl. [*Haplospora.*]

Sargent, M. C., and L. W. Lantrip. **1952.** *Amer. Jour. Bot.* **39:** 99–107. 4 figs. [Translocation in Laminariales.]

Sauvageau, C. **1896.** *Jour. de Bot.* **10:** 98–107, 113–126. 7 figs. [*Ectocarpus.*]

1896A. *Ibid.* **10:** 357–367, 388–399. 1 fig. [Anisogamy in Ectocarpales.]

1899. *Ann. Sci. Nat. Bot.* 8 ser. **10:** 265–362. 1 pl. 25 figs. [*Cutleria.*]

1900–1904. *Jour. de Bot.* **14:** 213–234, 247–259, 304–322. **15:** 22–36, 50–62, 94–116, 137–149, 222–236, 368–380, 408–410. **16:** 325–349, 379–416. **17:** 45–56, 69–95, 332–353, 378–424. **18:** 88–104. 68 figs. [*Sphacelaria.*]

1915. *Compt. Rend. Acad. Sci. Paris* **161:** 796–799. 3 figs. [Gametophytes of Laminariales.]

1917. *Ibid.* **164:** 829–831. [*Dictyosiphon.*]

1918. *Mém. Acad. Sci. Paris* **56:** 1–240. 85 figs. [Gametophyte of *Laminaria.*]

1925. *Compt. Rend. Acad. Sci. Paris* **180:** 1632–1635. [*Leathesia.*]

1926. *Bull. Sta. Biol. Arcachon* **23:** 141–191. 17 figs. [*Carpomitra.*]

1928. *Recueil Trav. Bot. Néerland.* **25A:** 260–270. [Plethysmothalli.]

1932. *Bull. Sta. Biol. Arcachon* **29:** 1–16. [Plethysmothalli.]
1933. *Ibid.* **30:** 1–128. 29 figs. [Plethysmothalli.]
Schreiber, E. **1930.** *Planta* **12:** 331–353. 12 figs. [*Laminaria.*]
1932. *Zeitschr. Bot.* **25:** 561–582. 12 figs. [*Desmarestia.*]
1935. *Planta* **24:** 266–275. 4 figs. [*Dictyota.*]
Schussnig, B., and E. Kothbauer. **1934.** *Oesterr. Bot. Zeitschr.* **83:** 81–97. 4 figs. [*Ectocarpus.*]
Setchell, W. A. **1905:** *Univ. Calif. Publ. Bot.* **2:** 139–168. 3 pl. [*Laminaria.*]
Smith, G. M. **1938.** Cryptogamic botany. Vol. 1. New York. 545 pp. 299 figs.
Smith, H. M. **1905.** *Bull. U.S. Bureau of Fisheries* **24:** 135–165. 4 pl. 24 figs. [Economic uses.]
Strasburger, E. **1897.** *Jahrb. Wiss. Bot.* **30:** 351–374. 2 pl. [*Fucus.*]
1906. *Bot. Zeitg.* **64,** Abt. 2: 1–7. [Alternation of generations in *Fucus.*]
Svedelius, N. **1921.** *Ber. Deutsch. Bot. Ges.* **39:** 178–187. [Alternation of generations.]
1927. *Bot. Gaz.* **83:** 364–384. [Alternation of generations.]
1928. *Svensk Bot. Tidsskr.* **22:** 289–304. 4 figs. [*Ectocarpus.*]
Swingle, W. T. **1897.** *Jahrb. Wiss. Bot.* **30:** 297–350. 2 pl. [Sphacelariales.]
Sykes, M. G. **1908.** *Ann. Bot.* **22:** 291–325. 3 pl. [Anatomy of Laminariales.]
Taylor, W. R. **1922.** *Bot. Gaz.* **74:** 431–441. [Classification.]
1928. *Carnegie Inst. Wash. Publ.* **379:** 1–219. 37 pl. [Marine algae of Florida.]
1936. *Bot. Rev.* **2:** 554–563. [Classification.]
Thuret, G. **1854.** *Ann. Sci. Nat. Bot.* 4 ser. **2:** 197–214. 4 pl. [*Fucus.*]
1855. *Ibid.* **3:** 1–28. 3 pl. [*Fucus.*]
Tseng, C. K. **1945.** *Science* **101:** 597–602. [Algin.]
Walker, Ruth I. **1931.** *Cellule* **40:** 175–192. 3 pl. 1 fig. [Fucales.]
Wenderoth, Hilde. **1933.** *Flora* **127:** 185–189. 8 figs. [*Dictyota.*]
Whitaker, D. M. **1931.** *Biol. Bull.* **61:** 294–308. 4 figs. [Polarity, *Fucus* eggs.]
1936. *Ibid.* **70:** 100–108. 2 figs. [Polarity, *Fucus* eggs.]
1937. *Jour. Gen. Physiol.* **21:** 833–845. 3 figs. [Polarity, *Fucus* eggs.]
1942. *Biol. Bull.* **72:** 127–137. 1 fig. [Polarity, *Fucus* eggs.]
Williams, J. L. **1904.** *Ann. Bot.* **18:** 141–160. 2 pl. [*Dictyota.*]
1904A. *Ibid.* **18:** 183–204. 3 pl. [*Dictyota.*]
1905. *Ibid.* **19:** 531–560. 6 figs. [Periodic fruiting, *Dictyota.*]
1921. *Ibid.* **35:** 603–607. [Gametophyte of *Laminaria.*]
Woodward, F. N. **1951.** Institute of seaweed research. Director's annual report for 1950. Edinburgh. 35 pp. 5 figs.
Yamanouchi, S. **1909.** *Bot. Gaz.* **47:** 173–197. 4 pl. [*Fucus.*]
1912. *Ibid.* **54:** 441–502. 10 pl. 15 figs. [*Cutleria.*]
1913. *Ibid.* **56:** 1–35. 4 pl. 24 figs. [Cutleriales.]

CHAPTER 7

CYANOPHYTA

The Cyanophyta, the blue-green algae, differ from other algae in a number of respects. They are the only algae in which the pigments are not localized in definite chromatophores. The pigments are localized in the peripheral portion of the protoplast and include chlorophyll *a*, carotenes, and distinctive xanthophylls (see Table I, page 4). In addition, there is a blue pigment (*c*-phycocyanin) and a red pigment (*c*-phycoerythrin). Another unique feature of Cyanophyta is a primitive type of nucleus, the **central body,** which lacks a nucleolar membrane and nucleoli. Equally important, although negative in character, are the lack of flagellated reproductive cells and the total lack of gametic union.

There are about 150 genera and 1,500 species. These are all placed in a single class, the *Myxophyceae* (*Cyanophyceae*).

Occurrence. A large majority of the species in two of the three orders are fresh-water. The reverse condition obtains in the third order (Chamaesiphonales). Most marine species grow in the intertidal zone. Some of them are free-living; many more grow upon algae of other divisions or within their tissues.

Fresh-water Cyanophyta are found in a wide variety of habitats. Many of them are aquatics that grow in either permanent or temporary waters. Certain of those in permanent waters are found only in the plankton, and are usually abundant only during warm months of the year. At such times one or two of the species may develop to such an extent that the water is colored by them. Such "water blooms" may be of sporadic occurrence, or they may occur annually.

Other fresh-water species are subaerial and grow upon either damp cliffs, dripping rocky ledges, or damp soil. Growths of terrestrial Cyanophyta are not usually conspicuous; but in certain regions, especially those with a pronounced rainy season, they may develop to such an extent that they form an extensive coating on the soil. Terrestrial blue-green algae may also grow beneath the surface of the soil and at a depth of a meter or more.

Cyanophyta growing within, or in the outflow from, hot springs have long aroused the botanist's interest and have been studied in practically every country where there are hot springs. Records for the upper temperature limits at which blue-green algae can exist must be scrutinized with care because portions of a spring but a few centimeters apart may differ in temperature by as much as 10°C. The highest well-authenticated record at which they have been found[1] is 85°C. In hot springs whose waters are highly charged with soluble calcium and magnesium compounds, especially bicarbonates, blue-green algae cause a precipitation of the calcium and magnesium salts in the form of an insoluble carbonate. The amount of carbonates thus precipitated is so considerable that the material deposited (travertine) may attain a thickness of 2 to 4 mm. during the course of a week. The terraces of travertine thus formed are usually brilliantly colored by an overlying layer of algae.

Organization of the Thallus. A few Cyanophyta have an immediate separation of daughter cells after cell division and are therefore truly unicellular. In the great majority of species the daughter cells remain united after cell division, and this adhesion results in either a filamentous or a nonfilamentous colony.

Nonfilamentous colonies (Fig. 160) result from a persistence or a confluence of the gelatinous envelopes surrounding the individual cells. The confluence may be so complete that all traces of individual cell sheaths disappear, or it may be incomplete and with a more or less evident sheath about each cell. Broadly speaking, genera with evident sheaths about the individual cells show a strong tendency toward colonial dissociation and have smaller colonies than do genera in which the cell sheaths are fused to form a homogeneous gelatinous matrix. The shape of nonfilamentous colonies is dependent upon the planes in which the cells divide. If divisions are restricted to two planes, the result is a layer one cell in thickness and either a flat plate or a hollow sphere (Fig. 160*B*, *F*). When divisions are in three planes, the sequence may be so regular that there is a formation of a cubical colony (Fig. 160*D*), but the sequence in division is usually so irregular that there is no regular arrangement of cells within a colony (Fig. 160*E*).

Repeated division in a single plane produces a filamentous colony (Fig. 161). Cells of filamentous colonies may be held together solely by walls common to two abutting cells, but usually there is also a cylindrical sheath of gelatinous material enveloping the file of cells. A single row of cells in a filamentous colony is called a **trichome,** and the trichome with its enclosed sheath is called a **filament.** According to the genus, a filament contains a single trichome (Fig. 161*F*) or it contains several trichomes (Fig. 161*G*). A trichome may be of the same diameter throughout, or it may be markedly attenuated at one (Fig. 161*H*) or at both ends. Trichomes of most genera are unbranched, but there are a few genera in

[1] Copeland, 1936.

which they are branched (Fig. 161*C*). Some genera with more than one trichome in a filament have them so arranged that they appear to be branched. This "false branching" (Fig. 161*D*) is due to a growth of free ends of trichomes through the surrounding sheath.

The Cell Wall. The wall surrounding protoplasts of nonfilamentous genera is composed of two concentric portions: an inner thin firm layer

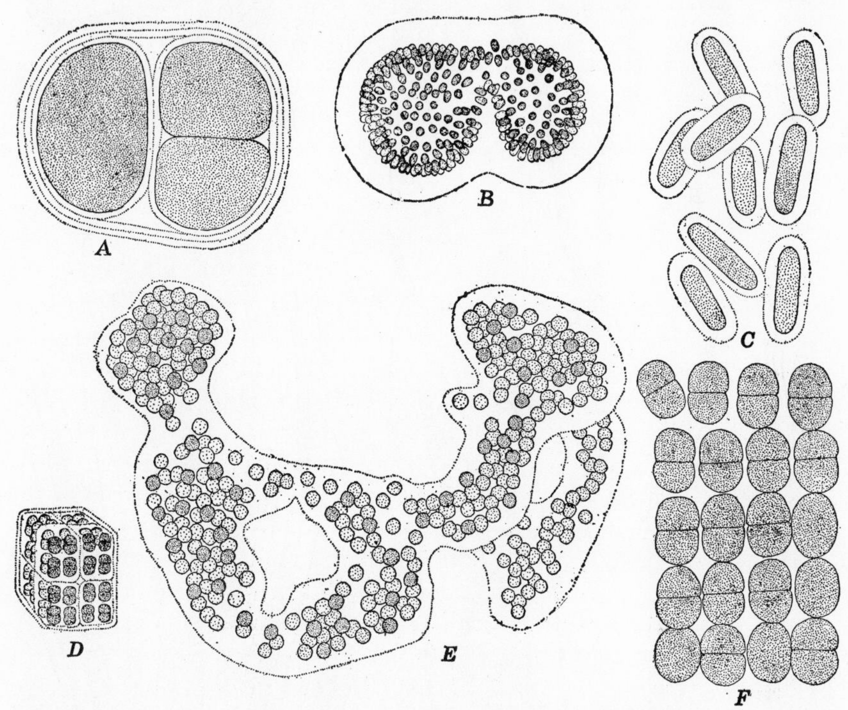

Fig. 160. Nonfilamentous Myxophyceae. *A*, *Chroococcus turgidus* Näg. *B*, *Coelosphaerium naegelianum* Unger. *C*, *Gloeothece linearis* Näg. *D*, *Eucapsis alpina* Clements and Shantz. *E*, *Polycystis aeruginosa* Kütz. *F*, *Merismopedia elegans* A.Br. (*D*, *after Clements and Shantz*, 1909) (*A*, × 825; *B*, *E*, × 400; *C*, *F*, × 1,000; *D*, × 250.)

immediately external to the plasma membrane, and an outer more gelatinous portion (the sheath) that is often of considerable thickness. Filamentous blue-green algae have the gelatinous sheath restricted to free faces of the cells. The sheath consists of pectic compounds: the inner firm portion contains a certain amount of cellulose.[1]

The sheath surrounding individual cells, or that surrounding individual trichomes, may or may not be distinctly stratified. In many plankton species the colorless unstratified sheath is of so watery a consistency that special techniques must be employed to make it evident. Instead of being colorless, a sheath may be yellow, brown, red, or violet. Yellow and brown

[1] Kylin, 1943.

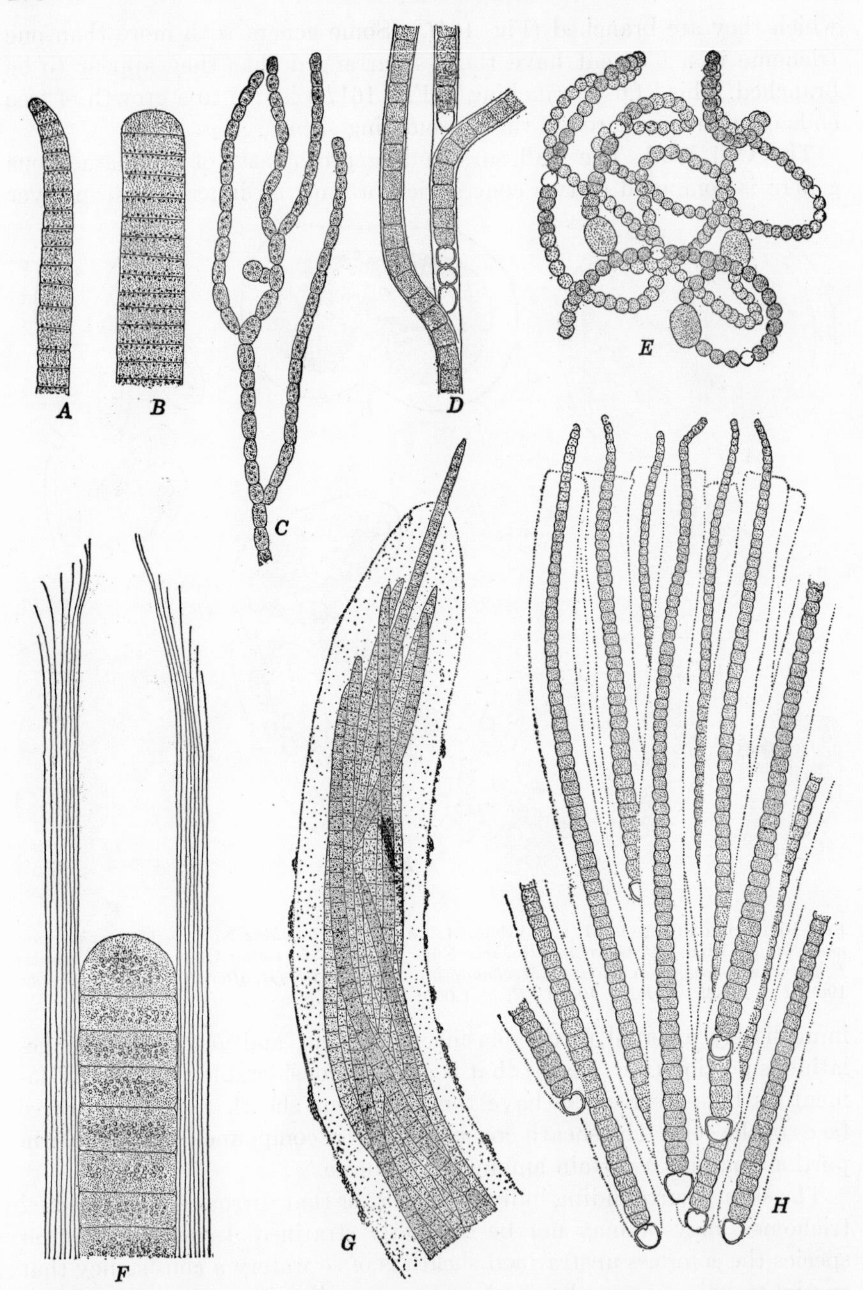

FIG. 161. Filamentous Myxophyceae. *A*, *Oscillatoria formosa* Bory. *B*, *O. limosa* C.Ag. *C* *Nostochopsis lobatus* Wood. *D*, *Tolypothrix tenuis* Kütz. *E*, *Anabaena circinalis* (Kütz.) Rab *F*, *Porphyrosiphon notarisii* (Menegh.) Kütz. *G*, *Microcoleus vaginatus* (Vauch.) Gom. *H*, *Rivularia dura* Roth. (*A–C*, × 650; *D*, × 375; *E*, × 400; *F*, × 600; *G*, × 300; *H*, × 485.

coloration of a sheath is due to a mixture of the pigments **fuscorhodin** and **fuscochlorin.**[1] Red and violet coloration is due to a pigment called **gloeocapsin.**

Structure of the Protoplast. From the earliest attempts[2] to determine the structure of cells of Cyanophyta there has been a recognition of the fact that the protoplast is differentiated into an outer colored portion (the **chromoplasm**) and an inner colorless portion (the **central body**). All investigations by means of cytological techniques find that all or a portion of the central body is differentially stainable in much the same fashion as is the chromatic material of true nuclei. The demonstration[3] of a

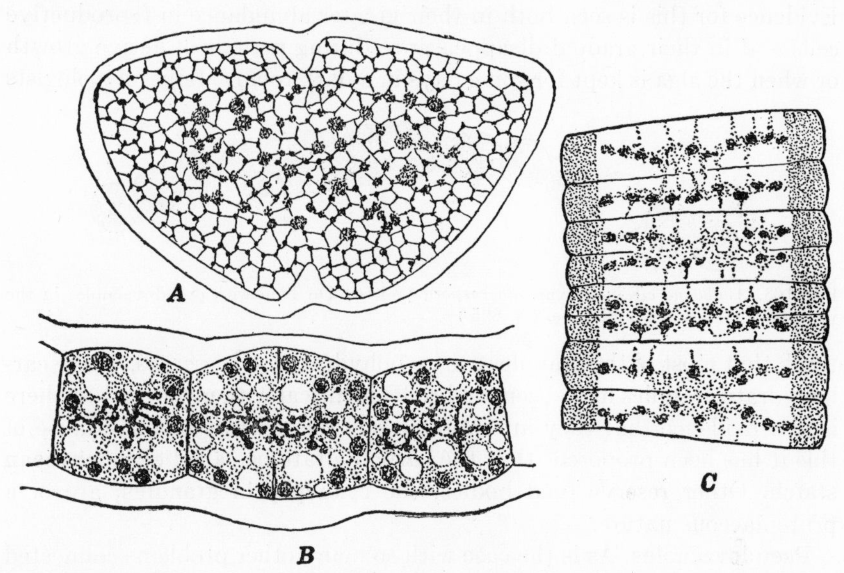

FIG. 162. Cell structure of various Myxophyceae. *A*, *Chroococcus turgidus* Näg. *B*, structure and division of cells of *Anabaena circinalis* (Kütz.) Rab. *C*, structure and division of cells of *Oscillatoria princeps* Vauch. (*A*, *after Acton*, 1914; *B*, *after Haupt*, 1923; *C*, *after Olive*, 1904.)

positive Feulgen reaction in the central body shows that it is to be considered nuclear in nature. However, the central body is a nucleus without nucleoli and without a definite nuclear membrane. Opinions vary concerning organization of the central body. There are those[4] who think that the nuclear material is regularly or irregularly localized at certain junctures of the protoplasmic reticulum. According to the species, the nuclear material may be very irregularly distributed throughout the central portion of a cell, or it may be organized into a definite reticulum (Fig. 162*A*). Others hold that the central body is entirely nuclear in nature. Advocates of this interpretation are not in accord as to the method by which it di-

[1] Kylin, 1943. [2] Schmitz, 1879, 1880. [3] Poljansky and Petruschewsky, 1929.
[4] Acton, 1914; Guilliermond, 1906, 1925.

vides. Some[1] think that in division of the central body there is a spindle apparatus resembling the spindle apparatus in other groups of plants. Others[2] hold that division of the central body is of an amitotic type and results only in a quantitative division of material in the central body.

The chromoplasm is usually of a finely alveolar structure. Embedded in it are a number of small spherical or irregularly shaped granules. In some species these bodies are irregularly distributed; in others, they are so regularly distributed as to be a character of taxonomic importance. It is clear that all these bodies are not of the same chemical composition and that some of them, probably the majority, are reserve food materials. Evidence for this is seen both in their greater abundance in reproductive cells and in their gradual disappearance during periods of active growth or when the alga is kept for some days in a dark room. Many phycologists

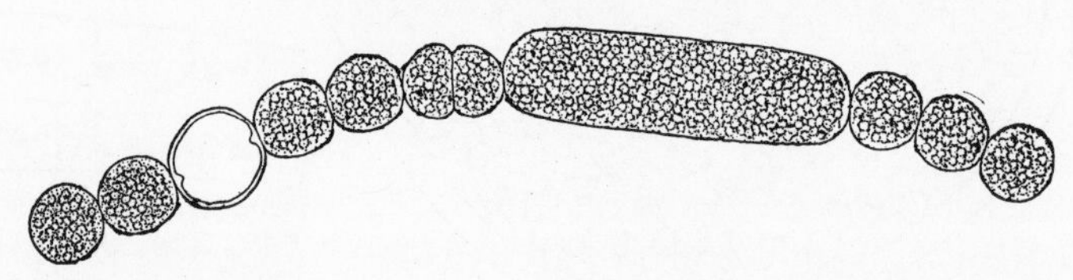

FIG. 163. *Anabaena circinalis* var. *macrospora* (Wittr.) De Toni with pseudovacuoles in the vegetative cells and the akinete. (× 825.)

think that most of the granules are carbohydrate food reserves. These carbohydrate granules have been held to be identical with glycogen but there is also evidence that they are more closely related to starch. Because of this it has been proposed[3] that the carbohydrate be called **cyanophycean starch.** Other reserve food bodies, the **cyanophycin granules,** are of a proteinaceous nature.

Pseudovacuoles. As is the case with so many other problems connected with the Cyanophyta, there is diversity of opinion concerning the so-called **pseudovacuoles** or **gas vacuoles.** These are frequently present in certain plankton species including those of *Coelosphaerium* (Fig. 160*B*), *Polycystis* (Fig. 160*E*), and *Anabaena* (Fig. 161*E*). At times all individuals of a particular species will contain pseudovacuoles; at other times only certain individuals will have them. In the latter case, the pseudovacuoles frequently appear a few hours after the alga is collected and stored in a tightly stoppered bottle.

Under low powers of the microscope the pseudovacuoles appear as black bodies, larger than other inclusions, and they are frequently present in such numbers that they obscure all other contents of the cell (Fig. 163). When examined under higher magnification they are reddish and

[1] Baumgärtel, 1920; Brown, 1911; Lee, 1927; Olive, 1904; Poljansky and Petruschewsky, 1929.

[2] Acton, 1914; Gardner, 1906; Guilliermond, 1906; Hegler, 1901. [3] Kylin, 1943.

this is probably a refraction phenomenon. Investigations seem to prove that a pressure or a partial vacuum will cause the pseudovacuoles to disappear and gas bubbles to collect at the surface of the cells.[1] This has been interpreted as showing that pseudovacuoles are gas-filled cavities, but it has also been held[2] that in reality a pseudovacuole is a cavity filled with a viscous substance. The formation of pseudovacuoles has been ascribed[3] to aerobic respiration induced by an oxygen deficiency at the bottom of a lake. When this continues for some time, the gas-filled cavities make the alga so buoyant that it rises to the surface of the water.

Pigments and Chromatic Adaptation. The chromoplasm of a cell may contain a green pigment (chlorophyll *a*), yellowish pigments (carotenes and xanthophylls), a blue pigment (*c*-phycocyanin), and a red pigment (*c*-phycoerythrin). Not all these pigments are always present, or present in equal amounts. Some Cyanophyta lack *c*-phycoerythrin; others lack or contain but traces of *c*-phycocyanin.[4] From the theoretical standpoint, variations in the proportions of red, blue, and yellow pigments would make possible any color in the chromoplasm. The occurrence of grass-green, blue-green, olive, yellow, orange, pink, red, violet, purple, brown, and blackish Cyanophyta shows how closely this theoretical possibility is found in nature. However, it should be noted that all such shades and colors of Cyanophyta are not due entirely to pigments in the chromoplasm but may be due partially to colors in the gelatinous envelopes of cells.

The causes for the development of the various pigments in different proportions are not known with certainty. The theory of **complementary chromatic adaptation** was first applied[5] to Cyanophyta to explain experiments with certain species of *Oscillatoria* which assumed different colors when cultivated in light of different colors. This theory, originally proposed[6] to explain variation in color of Rhodophyta, holds that color of the pigmented portions of a protoplast is directly complementary to the quality (color) of the light in which the plant is growing. Such complementary color changes among Cyanophyta, sometimes called the **Gaidukov phenomenon,** have been found to hold for certain species but not for others.[7] Thus, in one series of experiments[8] only 4 out of 18 species gave a definite Gaidukov response. The observed chromatic changes have been thought[9] to be due to variations in amount of each pigment formed by a cell and to be limited to species capable of producing both *c*-phycocyanin and *c*-phycoerythrin in considerable amounts. Most experiments with light and color changes of Cyanophyta have been with respect to

[1] Klebahn, 1922, 1925. [2] van Goor, 1925. [3] Canabaeus, 1929.
[4] Boresch, 1921. [5] Gaidukov, 1902, 1903. [6] Engelmann, 1883, 1884.
[7] Boresch, 1919, 1921*A*; Gaidukov, 1923; Harder, 1922; Sargent, 1934; Susski, 1929.
[8] Boresch, 1921*A*. [9] Boresch, 1921*A*; Kylin, 1912, 1937.

the quality of the light. That intensity of illumination must also be taken into consideration is shown by the bluish color of cultures when daylight illumination is intense and the reddish color when the intensity is reduced.[1] The best natural example of the Gaidukov phenomenon is the universal red color of Cyanophyta that grow at any considerable depth below the surface of a lake or any other deep body of water. A change in color may also be due to factors other than light, chief among which is a depletion of nitrogen in the substratum. Opponents[2] of the theory of complementary chromatic adaptation think that nutritional effects are the sole cause for the color changes found in cultures of Cyanophyta.

Fixation of Nitrogen. The early accounts[3] of a fixation of atmospheric nitrogen by blue-green algae were received with skepticism because both the purity of the cultures and the methods of determining nitrogen were questioned. Since 1928, study of a number of Cyanophyta in bacteria-free cultures shows[4] that they are able to grow in mineral nutrients lacking combined nitrogen and that after a time there is combined nitrogen in the medium. The most convincing evidence for the fixation of nitrogen has been obtained[5] by use of the isotope N^{15}. Blue-green algae capable of fixing atmospheric nitrogen do not do so when combined nitrogen is available, either as ammonium salts or as nitrates.[6] A survey of genera in which nitrogen fixation has been definitely established shows[7] that all are members of the same family, the Nostocaceae. Negative results have been obtained with *Phormidium foevolarum* Gom. (one of the Oscillatoriaceae) by an investigator[8] who obtained positive results with one of the Nostocaceae. An inability to fix nitrogen has also been found in two of the Chroococcales.[9] Thus it seems very probable that the ability to fix nitrogen is restricted to certain groups among the Cyanophyta.

Movements of Cyanophyta. Many filamentous blue-green algae, especially members of the family Oscillatoriaceae, have the ability to move spontaneously. The movement may be a forward and backward gliding of a trichome, a spiral progression and retrogression, or a slow waving of the terminal portion of a trichome. Movements of Nostocaceae are most noticable in hormogonia or in germlings composed of a few cells. These movements are chiefly a forward and backward locomotion. A waving of the terminal portion of a trichome, although reported for *Anabaena*,[10] is very rare for Nostocaceae. *Oscillatoria* generally show both a waving and an axial movement.

[1] Kylin, 1937. [2] Magnus and Schindler, 1912; Pringsheim, 1914; Schindler, 1913.

[3] Beijerinck, 1901; Frank, 1889; Molisch, 1925.

[4] Allison *et al.*, 1937; Bortels, 1940; Burris *et al.*, 1943; De, 1939; Drewes, 1928; Fogg, 1942; Winter, 1935.

[5] Burris *et al.*, 1943. [6] Fogg, 1942, 1947. [7] Fogg, 1947.

[8] De, 1939. [9] Williams in Gerloff *et al.*, 1952. [10] Castle, 1926.

Locomotion by means of secretion of gelatinous materials has been repeatedly observed in desmids. Some investigators[1] think that movement of Cyanophyta is also due to a secretion of gelatinous material. It is thought that this is secreted through minute pores in the cell walls and that rotating movements are due to arrangement of the pores in two crossing spiral series. The terminal cells of trichomes have been held to be of major importance in movement, but it has been shown[2] that killing of these cells does not inhibit the ability to move. There are those who do not subscribe to the theory of locomotion through secretion of slime. One alternative theory is that movement of trichomes is due to rhythmic waves of alternate expansions and contractions passing along the length of a trichome.[3]

Vegetative Reproduction. Cell division is the only regular method of reproduction in Chroococcales. Ordinarily two daughter cells remain united to each other within a common gelatinous envelope, and the continued repetition of cell division may result in a colony containing many cells. Colony reproduction is a matter of chance and depends upon accidental breaking of the colonial envelope. If the colonial envelope is soft and tends to dissolve, as in *Chroococcus* (Fig. 160*A*) or *Gloeothece* (Fig. 160*C*), the colony never grows to a large size before it becomes separated into two or more daughter colonies. In genera with a tough envelope, as in *Coelosphaerium* (Fig. 160*B*), the colony usually becomes many-celled before it breaks into smaller pieces.

Trichomes of filamentous species are, from the theoretical standpoint, capable of infinite growth in length; but under ordinary conditions the filament sooner or later breaks into two or more parts. Breaking may result from animals feeding on the filament, from death of certain cells in the row, or from a weaker adhesion between certain cells than between others. Instances of the last sort are confined largely to filamentous genera with heterocysts (see page 286), and the zone of weak adhesion is where a heterocyst and a vegetative cell abut on each other. Many filamentous genera regularly delimit short sections of trichomes, and these **hormogonia** (hormogones) are an important method of propagation among filamentous Cyanophyta. Hormogones (Fig. 164*A*) are delimited by a development of double concave disks of gelatinous material (**separation disks**) between two adjoining vegetative cells. The formation of hormogones and separation disks is seen to best advantage in large-celled species of filamentous genera with discoid or cylindrical cells. Here the hormogones may be but two or three cells in length, or they may be several cells long. Hormogones have an even greater capacity for locomotion than do vegetative trichomes, and, sooner or later after the hormogones

[1] Fechner, 1915; Harder, 1918; Prell, 1921; Schmid, 1918, 1921, 1923.

[2] Schmid, 1923. [3] Ullrich, 1926, 1929.

are formed, they move away from the filament in which they were produced and grow into new filaments. Hormogones usually develop directly into typical filaments, but occasionally[1] the juvenile filament produced by a germinating hormogone has but little resemblance to an adult one.

Hormogones developed at the tips of trichomes of certain genera have differently shaped cells and much thicker walls (Fig. 164*B–D*). These multicellular spore-like bodies are **hormospores.**[2] They germinate directly into new filaments.

Spore Formation. Zoospores and flagellated gametes have never been observed among the Cyanophyta, and there is no reason for expecting

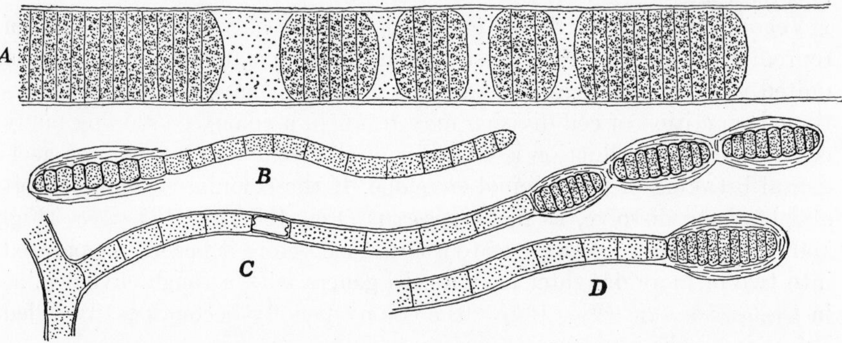

FIG. 164. *A*, hormogones of *Lyngbya birgei* G. M. Smith. *B–D*, hormospores of *Westiella lanosa* Frémy. (*B–D*, *after Frémy*, 1930.) (*A*, × 730; *B–D*, × 375.)

that they will be discovered in the future. However, many of the blue-green algae are known to produce nonmotile spores.

Most of the filamentous genera, except those belonging to the Oscillatoriaceae, regularly have certain cells of a trichome developing into nonmotile spores. Development of these spores begins with an enlargement of, and an accumulation of food reserves within, a cell. During the later stages of spore development, there is an appreciable thickening of the wall, and this is often accompanied by a differentiation of distinct exospore and endospore wall layers. This type of spore, which contains the entire protoplast and in which the original wall of the vegetative cell is the outermost portion of the spore wall, is called an **akinete.** Cells developing into akinetes usually lie isolated from one another along a trichome, but in certain genera several successive cells may develop into akinetes (Fig. 165). An akinete may be formed at a specific place in a trichome, or it may develop anywhere along a trichome. If it develops in a specific place, it is always next to a heterocyst, either one at the end of a trichome or one that is intercalary in position.

[1] Geitler, 1921. [2] Borzi, 1914; Frémy, 1930; Geitler, 1930–1932.

Resting spores of the akinete type, which are structures for tiding the alga over unfavorable periods, usually germinate into a vegetative filament as soon as favorable conditions return. One of the best examples of this is seen in the regular germination of akinetes of several terrestrial species immediately after a heavy rain and a thorough soaking of the soil. Akinetes may retain their viability for extremely long periods, and it has been shown[1] that there was a germination of them from samples of dried soil that had been stored for 70 years. However, akinetes are not absolutely necessary to tide Cyanophyta over long unfavorable periods since, in the experiments just cited, it was found that genera that do not form akinetes could withstand storage for 50 years.

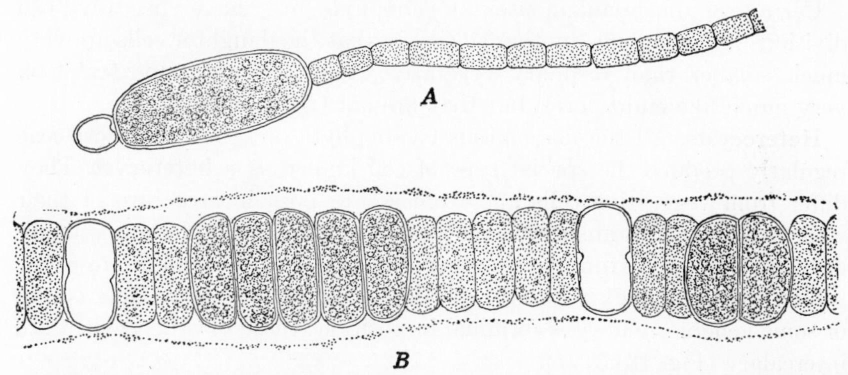

Fig. 165. Akinetes. *A*, *Cylindrospermum muscicola* Kütz. *B*, *Nodularia spumigena* Mertens. (× 900.)

A germinating akinete (Fig. 166) usually grows directly into a more or less typical filament, but there may be a formation of a juvenile structure with but little resemblance to the mature trichome.[2] In most cases germination begins with a transverse division of the protoplast, and there may be several additional transverse divisions before it grows through the end of the softened or ruptured spore wall.[3] Less frequently, germination begins with a gelatinization of the inner spore-wall layer and a bursting of the outer layer. The undivided protoplast may be extruded after these changes in the spore wall, or it may divide transversely before it is extruded. Germlings from akinetes of many species are frequently motile, and, up to the time they become several cells in length, they may glide backward and forward in and out of the old akinete wall.[4]

All genera of the Chamaesiphonales and a few genera of other orders[5] have the protoplasts of all or of certain cells dividing to form a number of small spores. These are usually called **endospores,** but they are similar

[1] Bristol, 1919, 1920. [2] Bristol, 1920.
[3] Bristol, 1920; Fritsch, 1904; Rose, 1934; Spratt, 1911.
[4] Harder, 1918. [5] Brand, 1903; Schmidle, 1901.

to the aplanospores of Chlorophyceae in that the spore wall is not fused with the wall of the parent cell. In most cases there is a repeated division of the entire protoplast to form a mass of endospores that completely fills the old parent-cell wall, the sporangial wall (Fig. 167*A*). These endospores are usually spherical, but they may be angular because of mutual compression. A distinction is sometimes made between endospore formation through bipartition of the entire protoplast and that in *Chamaesiphon* where the spores are successively cut off at the distal end of a protoplast (Fig. 167*B*). Spores produced in the latter manner have been called **exospores,**[1] but such a distinction is needless because the exospore is only a special type of endospore.

Certain of the nonfilamentous Cyanophyta may have successive cell divisions following one another so closely that the daughter cells are very much smaller than ordinary vegetative cells. These **nannocytes**[1] look very much like endospores, but they are not true spores.

Heterocysts. All the filamentous Cyanophyta but the Oscillatoriaceae regularly produce the special type of cell known as a **heterocyst.** They differ from vegetative cells and from spores both in structure of their walls and in their transparent contents. In most genera, heterocysts are developed isolated from one another in a trichome, but there are a few genera in which they regularly develop in adjoining pairs. Heterocysts of some genera are always terminal in position; those of other genera are intercalary (Fig. 161*E*, *H*).

Heterocysts arise by a metamorphosis of vegetative cells and usually only from recently divided ones. The metamorphosis may involve a change in shape, but in the majority of genera there is no appreciable change from the shape characteristic of a vegetative cell. The first step in heterocyst formation is a secretion of a new wall layer internal to that originally surrounding the cell. Depending upon the terminal or intercalary position of the heterocyst in a trichome, there is a pore at one or at both poles of the new wall layer. Cytoplasmic connections with adjoining vegetative cells are usually evident through the polar pores, but, as the heterocyst approaches maturity, the pores become filled with prominent button-like thickenings of wall material, the **polar nodules.** The protoplast within a heterocyst becomes more and more transparent after the polar nodules have been formed. Preparations stained with iron-alum-hematoxylin show that transparency of a mature heterocyst is not due to a disappearance of the protoplast but to a transformation of it into a homogeneous viscous substance.

The nature and function of the heterocyst are topics that have been debated at length. Formerly there were quite diverse opinions concerning the nature of the heterocyst, but present-day opinion is more or less

[1] Geitler, 1925, 1930–1932.

unanimous that it is spore-like in nature. The general agreement concerning its nature has come about through the accumulation of several well-authenticated exceptional cases[1] in which a heterocyst germinates to form a new filament (Fig. 168). The changes in nature and structure of the wall show that heterocysts are not analogous to akinetes. The nonakinete nature of the heterocyst is also shown by the formation and subsequent germination of endospores within a heterocyst.[2] These exceptional cases seem to show that heterocysts are reproductive structures, but structures which have become functionless as such, except in occasional instances.

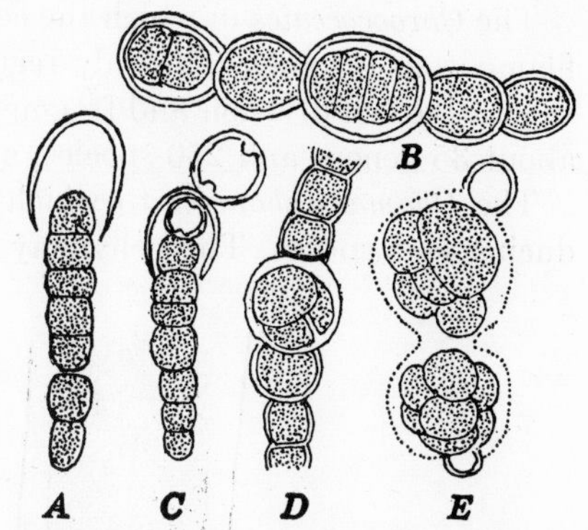

Fig. 166. Germination of akinetes. *A*, *Anabaena oscillarioides* Bory. *B–C*, *A. sphaerica* Born. and Flah. *D–E*, *Nostoc muscorum* Kütz. (*After Bristol*, 1920.) (× 825.)

Although ordinarily functionless as spores, or sporangia, the heterocysts have in many instances taken on certain secondary functions. Sometimes they have a definite relationship to the development of akinetes, and certain genera, as *Cylindrospermum* (Fig. 165*A*), always develop their akinetes next to a heterocyst. Heterocysts may also serve as a specific device for multiplication of trichomes; there are a number of species whose trichomes always fragment at the point where two heterocysts adjoin or at the juncture of a heterocyst and a vegetative cell. Genera with a true or a false branching may have a definite correlation between the position of heterocysts and the point of origin of true or false branches (Fig. 161*D*).

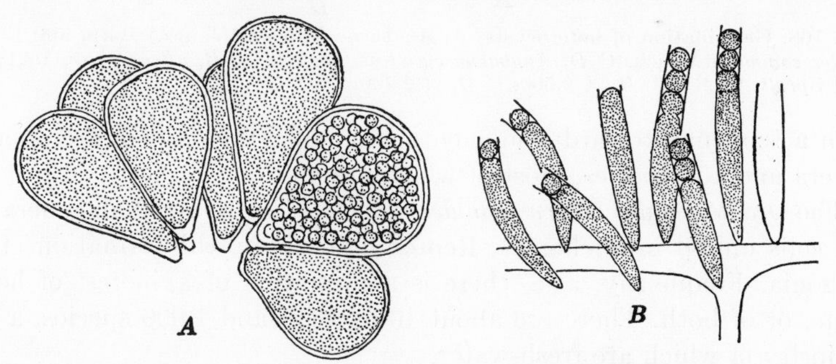

Fig. 167. Endospores. *A*, *Dermocarpa pacifica* Setchell and Gardner. *B*, *Chamaesiphon incrustans* Grun. (*A*, × 510; *B*, × 900.)

[1] Brand, 1901, 1903; Canabaeus, 1929; Desikachary, 1946; Geitler, 1921; Hollerbach, 1928.

[2] Spratt, 1911.

Classification. All Cyanophyta are placed in a single class, the *Myxophyceae*, and almost all phycologists divide them into three orders differing from one another in vegetative organization and in methods of reproduction. These three orders are:

The *Chroococcales* in which the cells are either solitary or united in nonfilamentous colonies. The only regular method of reproduction is that of vegetative cell division and fragmentation of colonies. The order includes about 35 genera and 250 species, almost all of which are fresh-water.

The *Chamaesiphonales* to which are referred all genera regularly producing endospores. The cells may be solitary, gregarious, or in colonies

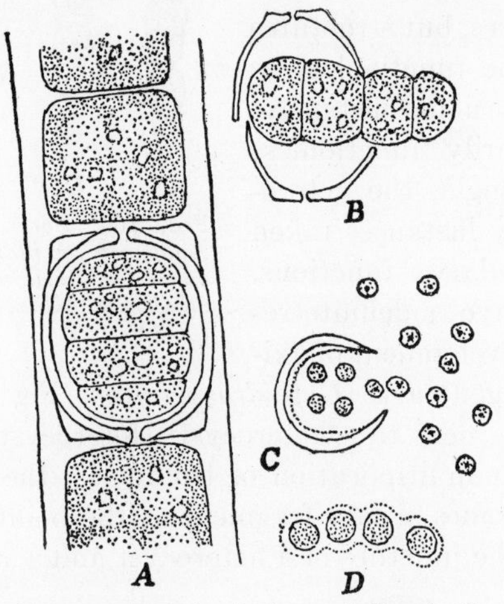

FIG. 168. Germination of heterocysts. *A*, *Anabaena hallensis* (Jancz.) Born. and Flah. *B*, *Nostoc commune* Vauch. *C–D*, *Anabaena cycadeae* Reinke. (*A–B*, *after Geitler*, 1921; *C–D*, *after Spratt*, 1911.) (*A–B*, × 2,500; *C–D*, × 2,200.)

with a tendency toward a filamentous organization. There are about 30 genera and 150 species, most of which are marine.

The *Oscillatoriales* (*Hormogonales*) to which are referred all genera with the cells united in trichomes. Reproduction is by the formation of hormogonia. Frequently, also, there is a formation of akinetes, of heterocysts, or of both. There are about 100 genera and 1,000 species, a large majority of which are fresh-water.

Bibliography

Acton, Elizabeth. **1914.** *Ann. Bot.* **28:** 434–454. 2 pl. [Cell structure.]

Allison, F. E., S. R. Hoover, and H. J. Morris. **1937.** *Bot. Gaz.* **98:** 433–463. 9 figs. [Nitrogen fixation.]

Baumgärtel, O. **1920.** *Arch. Protistenk.* **41:** 50–148. 1 pl. [Cell structure.]

Beijerinck, M. W. **1901.** *Centralbl. f. Bakt.* II, **7:** 561–582. [Nitrogen fixation.]

Boresch, K. **1919.** *Ber. Deutsch. Bot. Ges.* **37:** 25–39. [Chromatic adaptation.]

1921. *Biochem. Zeitschr.* **119:** 167–214. 34 figs. [Pigments.]

1921A. *Arch. Protistenk.* **44:** 1–70. 3 pl. 7 figs. [Chromatic adaptation.]

Bortels, H. **1940.** *Arch. Mikrobiol.* **11:** 155–186. [Nitrogen fixation.]
Borzi, A. **1914.** *Nuovo Gior. Bot. Ital.* **21:** 307–360. [Hormospores.]
Brand, F. **1901.** *Ber. Deutsch. Bot. Ges.* **19:** 152–159. 4 figs. [Pseudovacuoles, heterocysts.]
1903. *Beih. Bot. Centralbl.* **15:** 31–64. 1 pl. [Endospores, heterocysts.]
Bristol, B. Muriel. **1919.** *New Phytol.* **18:** 92–107. 2 figs. [Longevity.]
1920. *Ann. Bot.* **34:** 35–80. 1 pl. 12 figs. [Longevity.]
Brown, W. H. **1911.** *Bot. Gaz.* **51:** 390–391. [Cell division.]
Burris, R. H., F. J. Eppling, H. B. Wahlin, and P. W. Wilson. **1943.** *Jour. Biol. Chem.* **148:** 349–357. [Nitrogen fixation.]
Canabaeus, Lotte, **1929.** Über die Heterocysten und Gasvakuolen der Blaualgen und ihre Beziehungen zueinander. *Pflanzenforschung* **13:** 1–48. 16 figs.
Castle, E. S. **1926.** *Biol. Bull.* **51:** 69–72. 1 fig. [Motility.]
Clements, F. E., and H. L. Shantz. **1909.** *Minn. Bot. Studies* **4:** 133–135. 1 pl. [Chroococcales.]
Copeland, J. J. **1936.** *Ann. New York Acad. Sci.* **36:** 1–232. 73 figs. [Thermal algae.]
De, P. K. **1939.** *Proc. Roy. Soc. London B.* **127:** 121–139. [Nitrogen fixation.]
Desikachary, T. V. **1946.** *Jour. Indian Bot. Soc.* **25:** 11–17. 1 pl. 27 figs. [Heterocysts.]
Drewes, K. **1928.** *Zentralbl. f. Bakt.* II. **76:** 88–101. [Nitrogen fixation.]
Engelmann, T. W. **1883.** *Bot. Zeitg.* **41:** 1–13, 17–29. [Chromatic adaptation.]
1884. *Ibid.* **42:** 81–93, 97–105. [Chromatic adaptation.]
Fechner, R. **1915.** *Zeitschr. Bot.* **7:** 289–364. 1 pl. 10 figs. [Motility.]
Fogg, G. E. **1942.** *Jour. Exper. Biol.* **19:** 78–87. 2 figs. [Nitrogen fixation.]
1947. *Endeavour* **6:** 172–175. [Nitrogen fixation.]
Frank, B. **1889.** *Ber. Deutsch. Bot. Ges.* **7:** 34–42. [Nitrogen fixation.]
Frémy, P. **1930.** *Arch. Bot.* **3,** Mém. 2: 1–507. 362 figs. [African Cyanophyta.]
Fritsch, F. E. **1904.** *New Phytol.* **3:** 216–228. 1 pl. [Akinetes.]
Gaidukov, N. **1902.** *Abhandl. k. Akad. Wiss. Berlin* **1902:** Anhang. (Phys.-Math. Kl.) Abhandl. 5: 1–36. 4 pl. [Chromatic adaptation.]
1903. *Ber. Deutsch. Bot. Ges.* **21:** 484–492. 1 pl. [Chromatic adaptation.]
1923. *Ibid.* **41:** 356–361. [Chromatic adaptation.]
Gardner, N. L. **1906.** *Univ. Calif. Publ. Bot.* **2:** 237–296. 6 pl. [Cell structure.]
Geitler, L. **1921.** *Sitzungsber. Akad. Wiss. Wien* (Math.-Nat. Kl.) **130**[1]: 223–245. 1 pl. [Heterocysts.]
1925. Cyanophyceae. In A. Pascher, Die Süsswasserflora Deutschlands, Österreichs und der Schweiz. Heft 12. Pp. 1–450. 560 figs.
1930–1932. Cyanophyceae. In L. Rabenhorst, Kryptogamen-Flora von Deutschland, Österreich und der Schweiz. Bd. 14. 1196 pp. 780 figs.
Gerloff, G. C., G. C. Fitzgerald, and F. Skoog. **1952.** *Amer. Jour. Bot.* **39:** 26–32. [Mineral nutrition.]
Goor, A. C. J. van. **1925.** *Rev. Algologique.* **2:** 19–38. [Pseudovacuoles.]
Guilliermond, A. **1906.** *Rev. Gén. Bot.* **18:** 392–408, 447–465. 5 pl. 4 figs. [Cell structure.]
1925. *Compt. Rend. Soc. Biol.* **93:** 1504–1508. 22 figs. [Cell structure.]
Harder, R. **1918.** *Zeitschr. Bot.* **10:** 177–244. 8 figs. [Motility.]
1922. *Ber. Deutsch. Bot. Ges.* **40:** 26–32. [Chromatic adaptation.]
Haupt, A. W. **1923.** *Bot. Gaz.* **75:** 170–190. 1 pl. [Cell structure.]
Hegler, R. **1901.** *Jahrb. Wiss. Bot.* **36:** 229–354. 2 pl. 5 figs. [Cell structure.]
Hollerbach, M. M. **1928.** *Arch. Russ. Protistol.* **7:** 159–178. 2 pl. 1 fig. [Heterocysts.]
Klebahn, H. **1922.** *Jahrb. Wiss. Bot.* **61:** 535–589. 8 figs. [Pseudovacuoles.]
1925. *Ber. Deutsch. Bot. Ges.* **43:** 143–159. 2 figs. [Pseudovacuoles.]
Kylin, H. **1912.** *Hoppe-Seyler's Zeitschr. Physiol. Chem.* **76:** 396–425. [Chromatic adaptation.]
1937. *Förh. Kgl. Fysiograf. Sällsk. i Lund* **7,** Nr. 12: 1–28. [Chromatic adaptation.]
1943. *Ibid.* **13,** Nr. 7: 1–14. [Biochemistry.]

Lee, Sybil. **1927.** *Bot. Gaz.* **83:** 420–424. 1 pl. [Cell structure.]
Magnus, W., and B. Schindler. **1912.** *Ber. Deutsch. Bot. Ges.* **30:** 314–320. [Chromatic adaptation.]
Molisch, H. **1925.** *Sci. Repts. Tohoku Imp. Univ.* 4 ser. (Biol.) **1:** 168–188. 1 pl. [Nitrogen fixation.]
Olive, E. W. **1904.** *Beih. Bot. Centralbl.* **18:** 9–44. 2 pl. [Cell structure.]
Poljansky, G., and G. Petruschewsky. **1929.** *Arch. Protistenk.* **67:** 11–45. 1 pl. [Cell structure.]
Prell, H. **1921.** *Ibid.* **42:** 99–156. 11 figs. [Motility.]
Pringsheim, E. G. **1914.** *Beitr. Biol. Pflanzen* **12:** 49–108. 1 pl. [Chromatic adaptation.]
Rose, E. T. **1934.** *Univ. Iowa Studies in Nat. Hist.* **16:** 129–140. 2 pl. [Akinetes.]
Sargent, M. C. **1934.** *Proc. Nat. Acad. Sci. of U.S.* **20:** 251–254. [Chromatic adaptation.]
Schindler, B. **1913.** *Zeitschr. Bot.* **5:** 497–575. 5 figs. [Chromatic adaptation.]
Schmid, G. **1918.** *Flora* **111:** 327–379. 11 figs. [Motility.]
1921. *Jahrb. Wiss. Bot.* **60:** 572–627. 26 figs. [Motility.]
1923. *Ibid.* **62:** 328–419. 6 figs. [Motility.]
Schmidle, W. **1901.** *Ber. Deutsch. Bot. Ges.* **19:** 10–24. 1 pl. [Endospores.]
Schmitz, F. **1879.** *Sitzungsber. Niederrheinisch. Ges. Nat. u. Heilk. Bonn* **1879:** 345–376. [Cell structure.]
1880. *Ibid.* **1880:** 159–198. [Cell structure.]
Spratt, Ethel R. **1911.** *Ann. Bot.* **25:** 369–380. 1 pl. [Akinetes.]
Susski, E. P. **1929.** *Beitr. Biol. Pflanzen* **17:** 45–50. [Chromatic adaptation.]
Ullrich, H. **1926.** *Planta* **2:** 295–324. 8 figs. [Motility.]
1929. *Ibid.* **9:** 144–194. 15 figs. [Motility.]
Winter, G. **1935.** *Beitr. Biol. Pflanzen* **23:** 295–335. [Nitrogen fixation.]

CHAPTER 8

RHODOPHYTA

The Rhodophyta, the red algae, are primarily distinguished from other algae by their sexual reproduction, in which nonflagellated male gametes (**spermatia**) are passively transported to and lodge against the female sex organ, the **carpogonium.** Some Rhodophyta have the zygote dividing directly into spores (**carpospores**), but in most cases there is an indirect formation of carpospores from the zygote. Red algae also differ from all other algae except the Cyanophyta in their lack of flagellated reproductive cells. Plastids of Rhodophyta contain several pigments (see Table I, page 4), among which *r*-phycoerythrin is usually present in sufficient quantities to mask the other pigments and so give the plant a distinctive red color.

All the Rhodophyta are placed in a single class, the *Rhodophyceae*, that contains some 400 genera and 2,500 species.

Distribution. About 50 species, belonging to a dozen or more genera, are fresh-water plants. Most of them are rather closely restricted to well-aerated waters of rapids, falls, and mill dams in cold rapidly flowing streams.

An overwhelming majority of the red algae are marine. Under normal conditions all the marine species are sessile, and in most cases death soon ensues if a thallus becomes detached and free-floating. Marine species are found in all oceans, including the Arctic and Antarctic, but only a small minority of the species grow in polar seas. Geographical distribution of marine species is generally correlated with the surface temperature of the ocean. The gradual increase in temperature of surface waters as one passes from polar to tropical regions is correlated with a change in composition of the rhodophycean element in the flora. Most species of Rhodophyta are confined to geographical zones of amplitude of approximately 5°C. of the maximum summer water temperature,[1] but some extend over zones with an amplitude of 10°C., and a few are known with an amplitude of 20°C. According to an old survey,[1] 34 per cent of the marine species are found in extratropical waters of the Northern Hemi-

[1] Setchell, 1915.

sphere, 22 per cent are found in tropical waters, and 44 per cent in the imperfectly known extratropical waters of the Southern Hemisphere.

There is also a definite vertical distribution of Rhodophyta in the intertidal zone. On the Pacific Coast of the United States, where the two daily tides are not of the same amplitude, five distinct zones have been recognized.[1] The zones are delimited by maximum low and high waters of spring and neap tides, and the time interval for which adjacent zones are exposed may differ by several hours (Fig. 169*A–B*). Many of the species are restricted to a single zone (Fig. 169*C*) and the primary factor

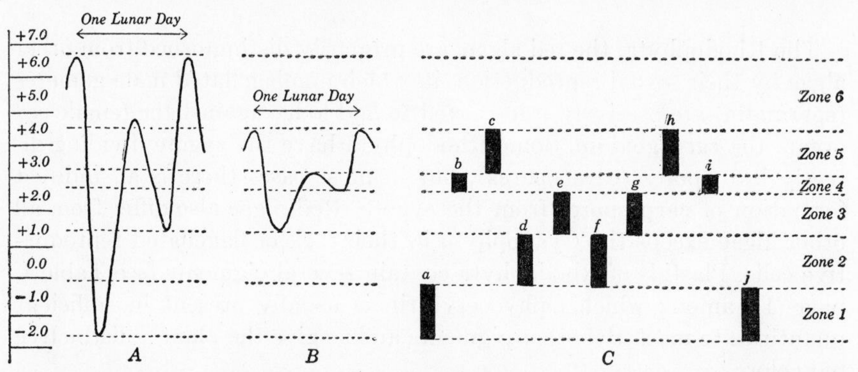

FIG. 169. Charts showing maximum and minimum range of daily tides at Monterey, California, and vertical distribution of certain Rhodophyta with respect to critical tide levels. The scale at the left is range in feet above and below the mean of the low point of the lower of the two daily tides. *A*, range of the greatest spring tide. *B*, range of the least neap tide. *C*, vertical distribution of the following species: (*a*) *Gigartina corymbifera* Harv., (*b*) *G. cristata* (Setch.) Setch. and Gardn., (*c*) *G. papillata* (C.Ag.) J. Ag., (*d*) *Halosaccion glandiforme* (Gmelin) Rupr., (*e*) *Iridophycus flaccidum* Setch. and Gardn., (*f*) *I. splendens* Setch. and Gardn., (*g*) *Microcladia borealis* Rupr., (*h*) *Porphyra lanceolata* (Hus) Smith and Hollenb., (*i*) *P. perforata* J. Ag., (*j*) *Rhodomela larix* (Turn.) J. Ag. (*Charts based upon Doty, 1946.*)

determining vertical distribution of a species is its ability to withstand exposure while the tide is out. A similar, though not so sharply marked, correlation between tidal levels has been found in England,[2] South Africa,[3] and New Zealand.[4]

Some Rhodophyta grow at levels never exposed by tides and here, as in the Mediterranean,[5] there may also be a vertical zonation of species. The maximum depth at which sublittoral algae will grow depends upon the amount of light penetrating the water and this is contingent both upon the latitude and upon the turbidity of the water. Algae in the North Atlantic rarely grow below the 30-meter level.[6] Here the algae found at

[1] Doty, 1946. [2] Coleman, 1933. [3] Isaac, 1937.
[4] Beveridge and Chapman, 1950. [5] Feldmann, 1938.
[6] Børgesen, 1905; Hoyt, 1920; Printz, 1926.

the lowest levels are almost exclusively Rhodophyta. In Florida[1] and in the Mediterranean,[2] where the water is clearer and the sun more directly overhead, algae have been found in abundance at the 75- to 90-meter level. At these deep-water stations there are Chlorophyta and Phaeophyta intermingled with the Rhodophyta. The greatest depth at which algae have been found is about 200 meters.[3] They have been reported from much greater depths, but these records are considered extremely dubious.

A majority of the marine Rhodophyta grow upon rocks or upon some other inanimate substratum. There are also many species which grow upon other algae (either Rhodophyta, Phaeophyta, or Chlorophyta) and most of them are restricted to a single host. The relationship may be one of epiphytism, internal space parasitism, or true parasitism. Parasitic Rhodophyta always grow upon other Rhodophyta and almost always a member of a closely related genus.

Economic Uses. *Porphyra* (page 299) is a highly esteemed foodstuff in the Orient, where it is used both as a condiment and in the making of soups. Most of the *Porphyra* consumed in the Orient comes from Japan and in 1938 the market value of the year's crop was about $4,000,000. Some of the crop is sold fresh, but most of it is sun-dried before reaching the consumer. The supply is obtained almost exclusively by cultivation on suitable tidelands, and the annual return from a good "*Porphyra* farm" may run as high as $150 per acre.

The tidelands are prepared for cultivation by implanting bundles of bamboo or brush in the muddy bottom of waters less than 3 to 5 meters deep. The bundles intercept and afford lodgement for spores of *Porphyra* floating in the water. The bundles are set out about the first of October and by the middle of November they are covered with germlings just visible to the naked eye. The thalli are harvested in January when they have attained full size.[4]

Agar, a colloid obtained from various red algae, is used in a variety of ways. One important use is that of a laxative. In the laboratory it is widely used for solidifying microbiological culture media. The baking, confectionary, and meat-packing industries make use of agar, and pharmaceutical manufacturers utilize it as an emulsifying agent. Japan produced more than 95 per cent of the agar marketed prior to World War II, and in 1936 more than 5,500,000 pounds was produced.[5] This agar was extracted from various Gelidiales, especially *Gelidium* (see page 329). Because of war shortages when supplies were no longer available from Japan, factories were established in various countries for the extraction of

[1] Taylor, 1928. [2] Funk, 1927. [3] Printz, 1926.
[4] H. M. Smith, 1905; Yendo, 1919. [5] Tseng, 1944.

agar from agarophytes local to the region. In California[1] and New Zealand[2] the agarophytes used are various Gelidiales; on the East Coast of the United States,[3] in South Africa,[4] and in Australia[5] the chief agarophyte is *Gracilaria*, one of the Gigartinales. Agarophytes are dried immediately after collection and then sent to a factory for conversion into agar. This involves an extraction of the agar by boiling, a freezing of the agar solution, and removal of water after the agar ice is melted.

At one time *Chondrus crispus* (L.) Stack., familiarly known as Irish moss or carrageen, was widely used in home cookery for the preparation of the well-known dessert blancmange. The gel (carrageenin) in this alga has properties different from agar or from algin (see page 218). Carrageenin is produced commercially from *Chondrus* collected along the shores of Massachusetts, Nova Scotia, France, and Ireland. *Iridophycus*, a Pacific Coast alga that is a close relative of *Chondrus*, is also a commercial source of a gel quite similar to carrageenin. The chief use of carrageenin is as an emulsifying or stabilizing agent. Commercial dairymen use carrageenin to prevent settling of the ground chocolate in chocolate milk.

Cell Structure. Cells of a few Rhodophyta lack a central vacuole, but those of most species have a large central vacuole and the cytoplasm restricted to a thin layer next to the cell wall. The cell wall contains cellulose and various pectic compounds.[6] In species belonging to the subclass Florideae there is a relatively large pore-like opening in the wall between sister cells and a strand of cytoplasm connecting the two protoplasts. Cells of vegetative portions of the great majority of species are uninucleate at all times; but vegetative cells of certain species are multinucleate and sometimes[7] have 3,000 to 4,000 nuclei in the larger cells. Resting nuclei are generally small, and often the only structures discernible are a sharply defined nuclear membrane and a nucleolus separated from each other by an intervening hyaline area.

Cells of the more primitive Rhodophyta generally have a single, centrally located, stellate chromatophore (Fig. 171*B*, page 299). At the center of this chromatophore is a dense, colorless, proteinaceous body, the pyrenoid. These "naked" pyrenoids lack the encircling sheath of starch grains usually found around pyrenoids of Chlorophyta. The more advanced Rhodophyta generally have disciform chromatophores and generally more than one within a cell. These chromatophores lack pyrenoids.

Carbohydrate reserves of red algae are usually stored in the form of small granules that lie in the cytoplasm instead of in the chromatophores. When these granules are treated with an iodine–potassium iodide solution they become wine-red to reddish violet instead of taking on the deep

[1] Tseng, 1944. [2] Moore, 1944. [3] Humm, 1944. [4] Chapman, 1950.
[5] Wood, 1946. [6] Kylin, 1943. [7] Lewis, 1909.

blue-violet so characteristic of the iodine-starch reaction. On this account the insoluble carbohydrate food reserve of red algae is called **floridean starch.** It is considered[1] related to, but not identical with, the amylopectin of the starch of green plants. Many red algae also accumulate the soluble sugar **floridoside,**[2] a galactoside of glycerol.

Pigments. The pigments of chromatophores of Rhodophyta are shown in Table I (page 4). Variations in the amounts of the various pigments, especially *r*-phycoerythrin and *r*-phycocyanin, account for the diversity of shades and colors among Rhodophyta. Intense illumination seems to favor the formation of *r*-phycocyanin and retard that of *r*-phycoerythrin. Because of this, most fresh-water species, and marine species of the upper intertidal zone, rarely have the red color considered characteristic of Rhodophyta. Marine species from low in the intertidal zone and from levels never exposed by the tide are generally a pink or a bright red because *r*-phycoerythrin is present in quantity.

The chlorophylls, carotenes, and xanthophylls function in the same manner as in other algae. The *r*-phycoerythrin has been shown[3] to be a photosynthetic pigment, and one of much greater importance than are the other photosynthetic pigments. When light penetrates more than a few meters below the surface of water there is a screening out of practically all but the blue rays. When growing where blue rays predominate, red algae are more efficient photosynthetically than are green or brown algae because practically all photosynthesis of red algae is in the blue part of the spectrum.

The Thallus. Except for two genera, all the Rhodophyta are multicellular. Almost all the multicellular genera have a thallus that is fundamentally filamentous in structure (see page 302). Such thalli are generally of definite macroscopic shape and either radially symmetrical or markedly compressed. Species of red algae growing along the Atlantic Coast of the United States have small thalli that rarely attain a height of more than 10 cm. Those on the Pacific Coast of this country tend to be larger, but only a few of them have thalli growing to a height of more than a meter.

Reproduction. Red algae seldom reproduce vegetatively by a fragmentation of the thallus. All the Rhodophyta form one or more kinds of nonflagellated spores. The **carpospores** are formed directly or indirectly from the zygote. All other spores are asexual in nature. These include **neutral spores, monospores, bispores, tetraspores, polyspores,** and **paraspores.** For the differences between these various types of spores see pages 297 and 307–308.

[1] Kylin, 1943.
[2] Colin and Augier, 1933; Colin and Guéguen, 1930, 1933; Haas *et al.*, 1935.
[3] Haxo and Blinks, 1950.

Sexual reproduction of Rhodophyta is unlike that of any other algae, and a special terminology is applied to the structures involved in, and resulting from, gametic union. The male sex organ of a red alga is a **spermatangium** (sometimes it is called an **antheridium**) and it contains a single nonflagellated male gamete, the **spermatium.** The female sex organ, the **carpogonium,** is one-celled, and its distal end is prolonged into an outgrowth, the **trichogyne.** Spermatia liberated from spermatangia may be passively carried to, and may lodge against, the trichogyne. Fertilization is effected by an entrance of the spermatium into a trichogyne, and a downward migration of the spermatial nucleus to the female nucleus at the carpogonial base. Of the two subclasses into which the Rhodophyceae are divided, one has a direct division of the zygote into carpospores (see page 297). It is very probable that division of the zygote nucleus in these algae is meiotic. In the other subclass of algae, the carpospores are formed indirectly from the zygote (see page 305). Here, division of the zygote nucleus may be meiotic or mitotic.

Relationships. Rhodophyta, similar to the Chlorophyta, are known with certainty from as far back as the Ordovician.[1] They must have arisen long before this because the oldest known fossils are related to advanced Rhodophyta. However, the hypothesis[2] that Rhodophyta are older than all other algae but the Cyanophyta is based upon purely speculative assumptions.

All attempts to connect Rhodophyta with other algae have centered around the Bangiales, since this order is universally recognized as the most primitive among the red algae. Only two of the suggestions put forward merit serious consideration.

The stellate chloroplasts, thallus structure, and method of spore formation in *Prasiola* (page 65) and *Porphyra* (page 299) are so similar that it has been thought[3] that the Bangiales have come from the Chlorophyta via *Prasiola*. However, comparative study of pigments in the two makes this seem very improbable.[4]

Cyanophyta and Rhodophyta are alike in that both have phycoerythrin and phycocyanin, and both lack flagellated reproductive cells. The suggestion[5] that the Bangiales originated among the Cyanophyta has received some support,[6] but an evolution of Bangiales from the Cyanophyta would involve an introduction of too many new features to make such an origin probable. These features include sexual reproduction, localization of pigments in chromatophores, and true nuclei.

Although only a small minority of botanists think that the Rhodophyta are related to other algae, there are many who think that the Ascomycetale

[1] Pia, 1927. [2] Tilden, 1935. [3] Lagerheim, 1892; Setchell and Gardner, 1920.
[4] Kylin, 1930. [5] Cohn, 1867. [6] Ishikawa, 1921; Skuja, 1938.

have been derived from red algae. This question will be considered on a later page (see page 431).

Classification. All Rhodophyta are placed in a single class, the *Rhodophyceae*. This is divided into two subclasses, the *Bangioideae* and the *Florideae*.

SUBCLASS 1. BANGIOIDEAE

Thalli of Bangioideae (sometimes called the Protoflorideae) may be simple filaments, branched filaments, solid cylinders, or expanded sheets either one or two cells in thickness. Growth of a thallus is by intercalary cell division and there are no evident cytoplasmic connections between the cells. In most genera each cell contains a single central stellate chromatophore, but in a few genera each cell contains numerous parietal disciform chromatophores.

Asexual reproduction is by means of spores formed in **monosporangia** containing a single **monospore**; or by means of **neutral spores** that are not produced within sporangia and are formed by direct metamorphosis of vegetative cells. Sexual reproduction, when present, is by direct division of a vegetative cell into many spermatia, which may be carried to and fuse with a vegetative cell functioning as a carpogonium. The zygote thus formed divides directly into 4, 8, 16, 32, or 64 carpospores.

The Bangioideae include some 15 genera and about 70 species. Sexual reproduction has not been found in many of the genera, but their systematic position is unquestioned because of their intercalary growth and lack of cytoplasmic connection between the cells. All Bangioideae are usually placed in a single order, the Bangiales, divided into three or four families. Sometimes[1] the families are each given the rank of an order.

Asterocytis, a rare fresh-water genus in this country,[2] is representative of the simpler Bangiales. Its spherical to broadly ellipsoidal cells are joined end to end in branched filaments (Fig. 170*A*). Each cell contains a single bright blue-green stellate chromatophore with a single pyrenoid at its center; and each cell is surrounded by a broad gelatinous sheath, quite distinct from the colonial matrix (Fig. 170*B*). Cell division is always intercalary and always at right angles to the long axis of a cell. Now and then there is a change in orientation of an intercalary cell and a rapid division and redivision of it. This produces a lateral branch (Fig. 170*A*). In certain colonies all cells are globose and division takes place in all planes. This results in a palmelloid colony (Fig. 170*C*) similar to that of the blue-green alga *Stigonema*.

Asexual reproduction is by the direct functioning of the protoplast of a vegetative cell as a neutral spore. This spore is liberated[3] by a rupture

[1] Skuja, 1939. [2] G. M. Smith, 1933. [3] Geitler, 1924; Wille, 1900.

of the surrounding gelatinous sheath (Fig. 170*D*). A liberated neutral spore secretes a wall and grows into a new filament after it has lodged on a suitable substratum. Thick-walled akinetes are also formed.[1] They are surrounded by a wall at the time they are liberated from the thallus producing them.

Porphyra, a marine genus with a dozen or more species, is a common alga along both the Atlantic and Pacific Coasts of this country. Most of the species grow attached to rocks in the intertidal zone, but some species are epiphytic and restricted to a single host. For example, along the coast of California, *P. naiadum* Anderson grows only upon the marine angio-

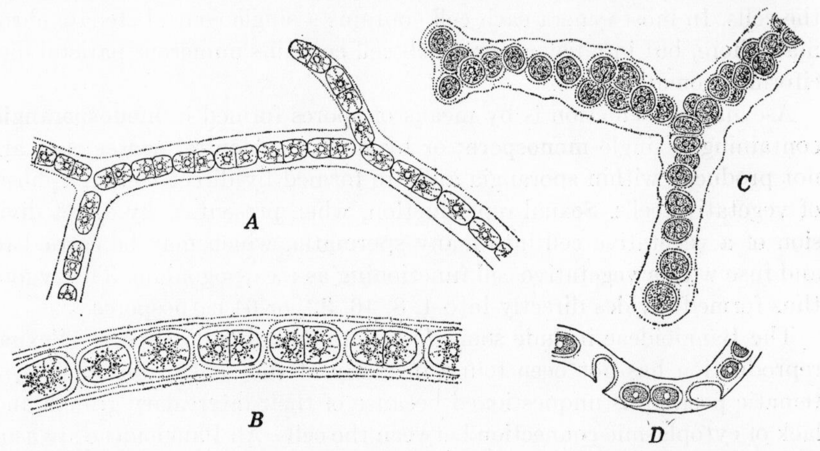

FIG. 170. *A–C, Asterocytis smaragdina* (Reinsch) Forti. *A–B*, portion of a filament. *C*, *Stigonema*-like filament. *D*, filament of *A. ramosa* (Thw.) Gobi after liberation of neutral spores. (*D, after Wille*, 1900.) (*A, C*, × 325; *B*, × 650; *D*, × 240.)

sperm *Phyllospadix;* and *P. nereocystis* Anderson grows only on the stipes of one of the giant kelps (*Nereocystis*). The thallus of *Porphyra* is a smooth to greatly convoluted blade that is attached to the substratum by a disciform or a cushion-like holdfast (Fig. 171*A*). Blades of most species do not grow to a height of more than 20 to 50 cm., but those of certain species, as *P. nereocystis*, may attain a height of more than 2 meters.

According to the species, the blade of a thallus is either one or two cells in thickness. The cells are cubical to broadly ellipsoidal and lie within a homogeneous gelatinous matrix of a very tough consistency (Fig. 171*B*). Cell division may take place anywhere in a blade but is always in a plane perpendicular to the surface of a blade. Cells of most species contain a single stellate chromatophore, but those of certain species contain two stellate chromatophores. The chromatophores always

[1] Kolderup-Rosenvinge, 1909–1924; Wille, 1900.

have a large centrally located pyrenoid (Fig. 171*B*). Chromatophores of species growing high in the intertidal zone may contain so much phycocyanin that the thallus is a deep olive-brown. Chromatophores of species growing low in the intertidal zone or below it have a predominance of phycoerythrin and a range of color of the thallus from pink to deep red. The single nucleus of a cell lies at one side of the chromatophore or between them if there are two in a cell. Nuclear division is mitotic and at

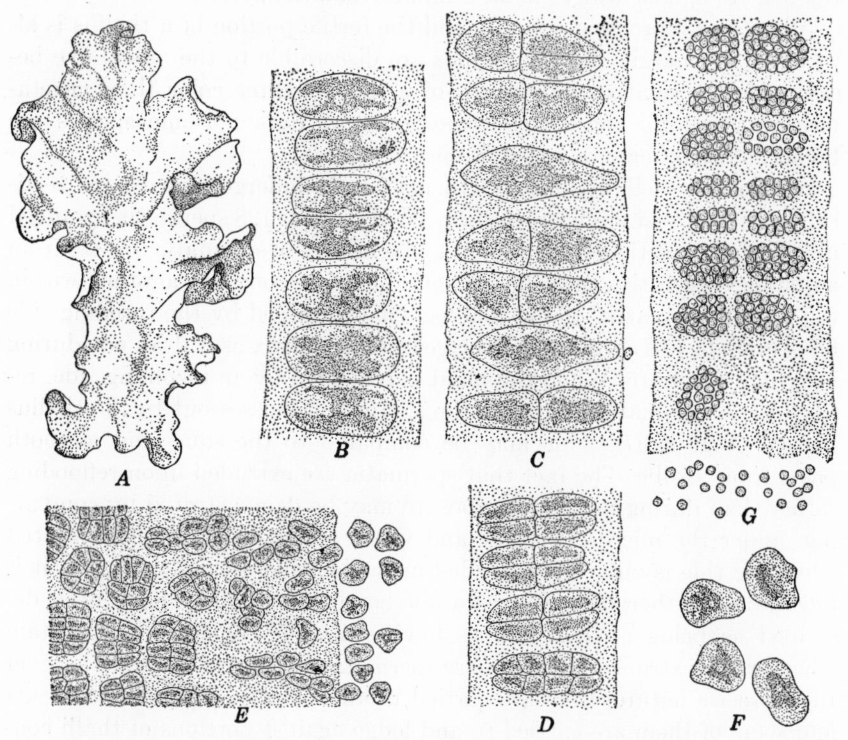

FIG. 171. *Porphyra perforata* J. G. Ag. *A*, thallus. *B*, vertical section of vegetative portion of a thallus. *C–D*, vertical sections of thalli with carpogonia and developing carpospores. *E*, surface view showing liberation of carpospores. *F*, amoeboid carpospores. *G*, vertical section through portion of thallus liberating spermatia. (*A*, × ½; *B–E*, *G*, × 325; *F*, × 650.)

metaphase two chromosomes have been observed in one species,[1] and four chromosomes in another.[2]

Conversion of vegetative cells into reproductive cells generally begins at the margin of a blade. Sometimes, as in *P. perforata* J.G.Ag., vegetative cell division keeps pace with conversion into reproductive cells, and the thalli remain approximately constant in size throughout the entire growing season. In other species, as *P. tenera* Kjellm., there is but little

[1] Dangeard, 1927. [2] Magne, 1952.

vegetative cell division after reproduction begins and after this the thalli gradually decrease in size and eventually disappear.

The formation of asexual neutral spores is of rather rare occurrence in *Porphyra* and generally is found only in vegetative cells intermingled with carpogonia.[1] Division of vegetative cells into neutral spores may be distinguished from division of carpogonia into carpospores because the former is always in a plane perpendicular to the thallus surface.[1] Hence the neutral spores always lie in a monostromatic layer.

All species reproduce sexually and the fertile portion of a thallus is always at the margin. Fertile regions are discernible to the naked eye because the spermatial masses are of a much lighter color than vegetative cells and the masses of carpospores are darker. Some species are homothallic; others are heterothallic.

A vegetative cell dividing to form spermatia undergoes successive vertical and transverse division to form 16, 32, 64, or 128 spermatia arranged in superimposed tiers of 4, 8, or 16. The masses of spermatia formed from adjoining vegetative cells lie a short distance from one another within the gelatinous matrix of the thallus. Thalli exposed by the receding tide have more or less shrinking of the gelatinous matrix as it dries out during intertidal exposure. When the plant is reflooded by an incoming tide, reswelling of the matrix squeezes the spermatial masses out to the thallus margin (Fig. 171*G*). This may be compared to the squeezing of tooth paste from a tube. The fact that spermatia are extruded upon reflooding rather than during intertidal exposure may be demonstrated by comparing, under the microscope, dry and water mounts of material collected when the tide is out. The extruded male elements are so small that it is uncertain whether they do or do not have a wall. They have been described as being naked,[2] and as having a wall.[1] Thus, it is uncertain whether the extruded elements are spermatangia or spermatia. Whatever their precise nature, they are carried in all directions by water currents and some of them are carried to and lodge against portions of thalli containing carpogonia.

Carpogonia are formed by a slight metamorphosis of vegetative cells. A mature carpogonium is ellipsoidal with a slight protuberance at one or both poles (Fig. 171*C*). The protuberance is in the nature of a trichogyne and it generally extends to the surface of the gelatinous matrix of a thallus.[3] If the carpogonium does not extend to the thallus surface, a spermatium sends out a thread-like extension that grows down to the carpogonium and establishes a connection between the two.[4] Both the spermatium and carpogonium are uninucleate at the time of union and

[1] Hus, 1902. [2] Knox, 1926.
[3] Berthold, 1882; Grubb, 1924; Ishikawa, 1921; Joffé, 1896; Knox, 1926.
[4] Dangeard, 1927; Magne, 1952.

the spermatial nucleus has been shown[1] to migrate into the carpogonium and fuse with its nucleus. Gametic union is followed by repeated vertical and transverse division of the zygote to form carpospores. According to the species, 2 or 4, 4 or 8, 8 or 16, 16 or 32 carpospores are produced by division of a zygote. Each carpospore contains a single stellate chromatophore somewhat darker in color than that of a vegetative cell. Division of the zygote nucleus has been found to be meiotic,[2] but all nuclear divisions from zygote to carpospore have also been described as mitotic.[3] Thus the place at which meiosis takes place in the life cycle is not definitely established.

Discharge of carpospores of littoral species is similar to that of spermatia, and it takes place when thalli are resubmerged by the incoming tide (Fig. 171*E*). The liberated carpospores are naked, and they move[4] about with an almost imperceptible amoeboid movement (Fig. 171*F*). Amoeboid movement continues for two or three days; then the carpospores become spherical, secrete a wall, and develop into uniseriate branched filaments. The filamentous structure developed from carpospores of *P. umbilicalis* (L.) J.G.Ag. has been shown[5] to produce monospores and has been considered identical with the alga known as *Conchocelis rosea* Batters. The function of the monospores is unknown. There are two possibilities. They may duplicate the *Conchocelis* stage in the same manner as do the monospores produced by the *Chantransia* stage of certain Nemalionales, including *Batrachospermum*. There is also the possibility that the monospores develop into the blade-like *Porphyra* thallus.

SUBCLASS 2. FLORIDEAE

Thalli of Florideae are filamentous in construction, with more or less evident cytoplasmic connections between sister cells, and in almost all cases with cell division restricted to apical cells of the filament. Cells of most genera contain more than one chromatophore, but those of certain of the more primitive genera have a single chromatophore that is stellate and at the center of the cell.

Carpogonia are borne terminally on special filamentous branches (**carpogonial filaments**) and carpospores are always formed on **gonimoblast filaments** that may or may not grow directly from the carpogonium. Carpospores are the only spores produced by certain genera. Other genera produce one or more types of spore in addition to carpospores.

The subclass contains some 375 genera and 2,500 species.

Vegetative Structure. All Florideae have a branched filamentous thallus. In some genera the various branches are free from one another; in other genera they lie more or less intermingled with one another within

[1] Dangeard, 1927; Magne, 1952. [2] Dangeard, 1927. [3] Magne, 1952.
[4] Grubb, 1924; Kylin, 1921. [5] Drew, 1949.

a common gelatinous matrix; in still other genera they are so closely applied to one another that the thallus seems to be parenchymatous.

Increase in number of cells is due to transverse division of apical cells at the tips of branches.[1] With the exception of a few anomalous genera,[2] there is no transverse division of the daughter cell cut off posterior to an apical cell. However, derivatives from an apical cell may increase to many times their original length and breadth. Apical organization of a plant body is according to one of two general types. In one case there is a **monoaxial**[3] or **central-filament**[4] type of organization, in which there is

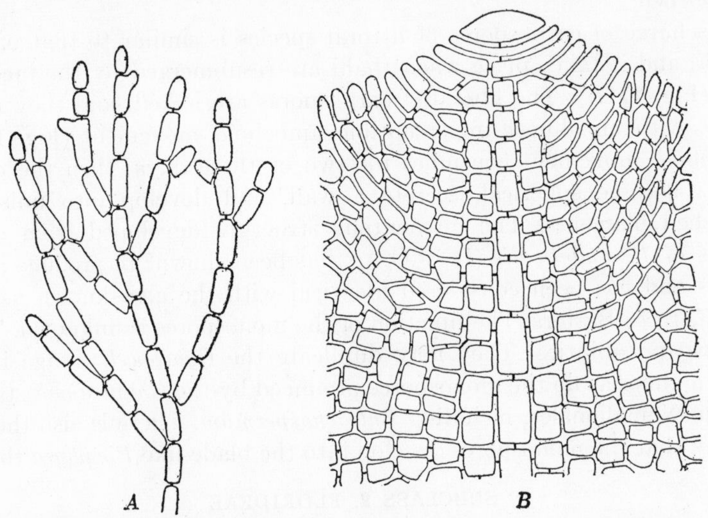

FIG. 172. Diagram of loosely branched monoaxial thallus of *Acrochaetium*. *B*, diagram of pseudoparenchymatous monoaxial thallus of *Grinnellia*.

a single axial filament that gives off filaments laterally or on all sides. In the other case there is a **multiaxial** or **fountain type** of organization with a central core of axial filaments, each giving off lateral filaments.

Growth of the monoaxial type is initiated by transverse division of the apical cell. After a derivative has come to lie one, two, or more cells back from the apical initial, it sends forth a lateral outgrowth that soon becomes cut off as a lateral cell (Fig. 172*A*). This cell is the apical initial of a lateral filament, and it functions in precisely the same manner as the apical initial of the central axis. Cells back from the apical initial of a lateral filament may cut off initials of secondary filaments; this may continue until there are filaments of tertiary, quaternary, or higher orders. Every derivative cut off from an apical initial is connected to it by a strand of cytoplasm. Thus, by following the arrangement of cytoplasmic

[1] Schmitz, 1883. [2] Kolderup-Rosenvinge, 1909–1924; Kylin, 1924, 1928.
[3] G. M. Smith, 1933. [4] Oltmanns, 1922.

connections, one may recapitulate the sequence of development in branching thalli. The arrangement of the cytoplasmic connections in relatively young portions of "parenchymatous" thalli (Fig. 172*B*) shows that they are filamentous in nature and generally of a monoaxial type. This cannot always be determined with certainty in older portions of a thallus because there are secondary cytoplasmic connections which obscure the sequence of development.

Multiaxial thalli grow in the same manner as monoaxial ones, except that each filament in the axial core has an apical cell. Lateral filaments

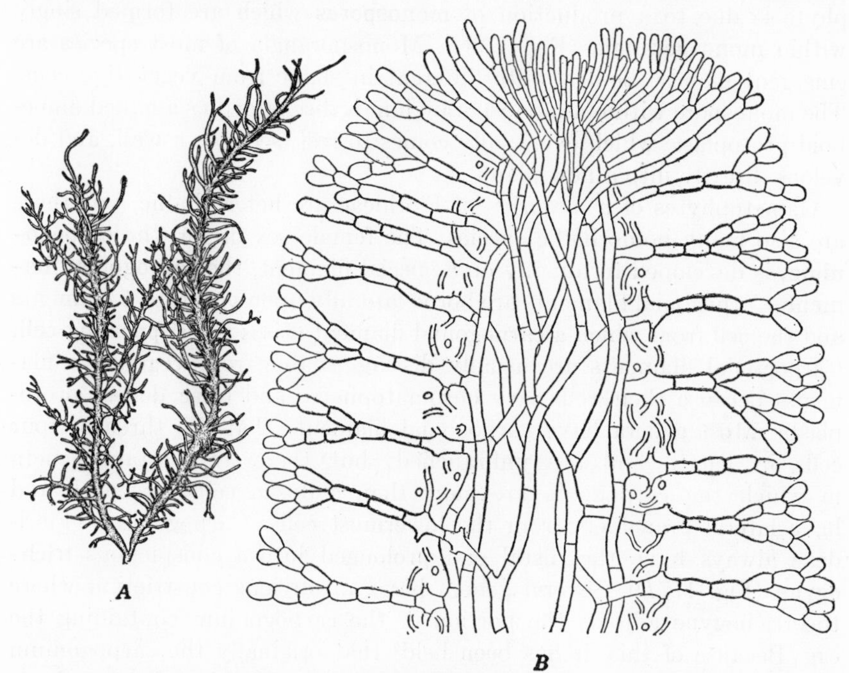

Fig. 173. *Cumagloia andersonii* (Farlow) Setchell and Gardner. *A*, thallus. *B*, semidiagrammatic vertical section of a multiaxial branch apex. (*A*, × ½; *B*, × 325.)

from an axial filament are developed only on the free face not in contact with other axial filaments. Therefore mature portions of such thalli have a central core of longitudinal filaments surrounded by an ensheathing layer of lateral filaments (Fig. 173*B*).

Thalli of some Florideae are perennial. The entire thallus may persist throughout the year, or the major portion of it may disappear during winter and the persistent basal portion proliferate new outgrowths the next year. Other Florideae are annual, with all thalli developed from sporelings each growing season. An all-year-round survey of the algal flora of the Isle of Man[1] has shown that the number of perennials is

[1] Knight and Parke, 1931.

considerably greater than that of the annuals. Most of the extratropical annuals develop and fruit during the summer. This tendency is not so marked in the perennials, and fruiting individuals of many species are present throughout the year. Florideae with free-living sexual and tetrasporic generations generally have the two fruiting at different seasons, but the periods of the two frequently overlap.

Reproductive Organs of the Gametophyte. The sexual plant (**gametophyte**) may produce sex organs only, or it may bear both sporangia and sex organs. In practically all cases asexual reproduction of the gametophyte is due to a production of **monospores** which are formed singly within **monosporangia** (Fig. 179*C*). Monosporangia of most species are emergent globose bodies quite different in shape from vegetative cells. The monospore within a monosporangium is discharged as a naked amoeboid protoplast[1] which eventually comes to rest, secretes a wall, and develops directly into a new plant.

Gametophytes of a majority of Florideae are heterothallic, but there are also many homothallic species. The female sex organ, the **carpogonium,** is developed terminally on a special filament, the **carpogonial filament.** Carpogonial filaments are borne laterally upon vegetative filaments and the cell from which a carpogonial filament arises is a **supporting cell.** Carpogonial filaments are usually distinguishable from vegetative filaments because their cells lack chromatophores and have denser protoplasts. Most genera have carpogonial filaments that are three or four cells in length and are unbranched; but there are certain genera in which the carpogonia are more than a dozen cells in length and have lateral branchlets from the lowermost cells. Carpogonia of Florideae always have the distal end prolonged into a conspicuous **trichogyne** (Fig. 177*D*). Several genera have an obvious constriction where the trichogyne adjoins the portion of the carpogonium containing the egg. Because of this, it has been held[2] that originally the carpogonium was a two-celled structure. Carpogonia of most Florideae have a single nucleus, but there is also a considerable number of species in which there is also a nucleus in the trichogyne.[3]

The male sex organ, the **spermatangium,** is developed terminally or subterminally upon a **spermatangia mother cell.** Spermatangial mother cells of the simpler Florideae are borne in special filaments of four or five cells (Fig. 177*B*). These filaments do not adjoin one another. More advanced Florideae have the spermatangial mother cell grouped in definite sori. A spermatangial mother cell is always uninucleate and with the nu-

[1] Svedelius, 1917. [2] Svedelius, 1917*A*.

[3] Grubb, 1923*A*; Kylin, 1914, 1916, 1916*A*; Svedelius, 1914, 1915, 1917, 1933, 1942; Yamanouchi, 1906, 1921.

cleus basal in position.[1] The first step in production of a spermatangium is a development of a protuberance at the distal end of the mother cell. This is accompanied by a division of the nucleus and a migration of one daughter nucleus into the protuberance. There then follows a ring-like ingrowth of the lateral wall in the region where protuberance and mother cell adjoin.[1] The resultant uninucleate cell, the spermatangium, may be globose or elongate. Many species regularly have the mother cell budding off additional spermatangia after the first is formed.

A **spermatium,** the uninucleate protoplast of a spermatangium, is usually colorless, but there are a few species[2] in which there is a chromatophore. Many species have been shown to have a rupture of the spermatangial wall and an escape of the spermatium. The liberated spermatium is surrounded by a delicate wall,[1] but it is uncertain whether this is the innermost layer of the spermatangial wall or entirely distinct from it. Discharge of the spermatium may be followed by development of another spermatangium within the old spermatangial wall (Fig. 177*I*, page 314) and this may be repeated until there are the remains of several spermatangial walls nested one inside another.

Fertilization. Spermatia carried by water currents may be transported to, and lodge against, trichogynes projecting beyond the thallus. The sticky gelatinous sheath around projecting portions of many trichogynes greatly increases the chances for adherence once a spermatium has lodged against it. Fertilization begins with a breaking down of spermatial and trichogyne walls at the point of mutual contact. The spermatial nucleus then migrates into the trichogyne and migrates down to the carpogonial base where it fuses with the carpogonial nucleus. In a few species[3] the spermatial nucleus divides as it migrates down the trichogyne, and one of its daughter nuclei then fuses with the carpogonial nucleus.

Certain genera, all belonging to the Nemalionales, have been shown[4] to have a meiotic division of the zygote nucleus. All members of orders other than the Nemalionales have a mitotic division of the zygote nucleus and have meiosis occurring in sporangia of the free-living diploid generation (**tetrasporophyte**).

Development of Carpospores. Gametic union, with or without an immediately succeeding meiosis, is followed by a development of **gonimoblast filaments.** Some Florideae have the zygote nucleus, or its haploid daughter nuclei, remaining in the carpogonium, and the gonimoblast filaments growing directly from the carpogonial base (Fig. 177). Other Florideae have the zygote nucleus, or one of its descendants, migrating

[1] Grubb, 1925. [2] Cleland, 1919; Dunn, 1917; Osterhout, 1900.
[3] Cleland, 1919; Kylin, 1916*B*, 1917.
[4] Cleland, 1919; Kylin, 1916*B*, 1917; Svedelius, 1915, 1933.

from the carpogonium into another cell of the thallus, and have an outgrowth of gonimoblast filaments from this **auxiliary cell.** The cell functioning as an auxiliary cell is not the same in different orders of the Florideae. In such Nemalionales as have an auxiliary cell it is a cell of the carpogonial filament. In Gigartinales the auxiliary cell is either the supporting cell of the carpogonial filament (Fig. 189, page 330); or is a vegetative cell near or remote from the carpogonial filament (Fig. 190, page 331). Other orders of Florideae have the auxiliary cell a member of a special filament that may be borne on the supporting cell of the carpogonial filament (Fig. 193, page 335); or the filament may be borne remote from the carpogonial filament (Fig. 184, page 324). When auxiliary cells and carpogonia are members of a common branch system this is called a **procarp.**

Establishment of a connection between carpogonium and auxiliary cell, except for genera where the auxiliary cell is a member of the carpogonial filament, is due to development of a tubular outgrowth (the **oöblast**) from the carpogonial base. This is very short when carpogonium and auxiliary cell adjoin each other, but is quite long when the two are remote. An oöblast serves as a passageway for migration of a zygote nucleus or one of its descendants from carpogonium to auxiliary cell. An auxiliary cell may send out secondary oöblasts to other auxiliary cells. Thus descendants of a single zygote nucleus may migrate into more than one auxiliary cell. An auxiliary cell sends out gonimoblast filaments after receiving a nucleus derived from the zygote nucleus. There may also be an establishment of a connection between carpogonium and vegetative cells, or between gonimoblast filaments and vegetative cells. The relationship in this case is one in which the vegetative cells furnish food and for this reason they have been called[1] **nurse cells.** Nurse cells may be solitary or they may adjoin one another to form a **nurse tissue.**

Gonimoblast filaments growing out from a carpogonium or from an auxiliary cell may lie free from one another, or they may be compacted into a pseudoparenchymatous mass. All the cells of a mature gonimoblast filament, or only the terminal cells of its branches, may enlarge to form what are usually termed "carpospores." When fully mature they generally, if not always, have an escape of the protoplast from the surrounding wall.[2] Hence the so-called carpospore is really a sporangium (**carposporangium**) and the liberated protoplast is really the carpospore. Sporangia developed on gonimoblast filaments of most Florideae contain but one spore; but there are certain genera[3] in which sporangia of some species contain one spore and those of other species contain four spores.

[1] Kylin, 1928. [2] Kylin, 1917*A*.
[3] Børgesen, 1927; Feldmann, 1939; Kylin, 1930.

These sporangia with four spores have been called[1] **carpotetrasporangia** and the spores within them **carpotetraspores.**

The mass of sporangia, the sterile cells of the gonimoblast filaments, and the cell or cells subtending them are often called the **cystocarp** and considered the fruiting body of the gametophyte. The cystocarp may be borne freely exposed, or it may be protected by surrounding vegetative tissues. In some cases, protection results from an upgrowth of adjoining vegetative parts that results in an embedding of the cystocarp in the thallus. In other cases upgrowth of vegetative tissue results in an urn-shaped sheath, the **pericarp** (Fig. 197*C*, page 340).

Nature of the Cystocarp. All the older and many of the present-day phycologists interpret the cystocarp as an integral portion of the thallus producing it. Over half a century ago Oltmanns[2] proposed an entirely different conception of the cystocarp. He suggested that, when interpreted from the morphological standpoint, the cystocarp is really an asexual spore-producing generation parasitic upon the thallus bearing the sex organs. Oltmann's theory was quite generally ignored when first proposed, but in recent years a number of phycologists have accepted it. Their adherence to the theory is best shown by their substitution of the term **carposporophyte** for the term cystocarp.

Germination of Carpospores. Carpospores produced by a carposporophyte may be haploid or diploid. Germinating carpospores with a haploid nucleus always develop into gametophytes which produce sex organs.

Diploid carpospores liberated from a carposporophyte develop into a free-living, asexual, diploid plant—the **tetrasporophyte.** This has been culturally demonstrated for a few species with diploid nuclei in the carpospore[3] and is universally assumed to be true for all of them. In most genera the gametophytic and tetrasporophytic generations are vegetatively identical and it is impossible to distinguish between the two when not in fruit. Cultural studies[4] have shown that in two species of *Bonnemaisonia* and in *Asparagopsis armata* Harv. there are marked vegetative differences between gametophyte and tetrasporophyte. In *Bonnemaisonia* the carpospores are diploid[5] and so there is a strong probability that meiosis occurs in the four-spored sporangium of the tetrasporophyte. Carpospores of *A. armata* are haploid,[6] and it is probable that the tetrasporophyte is also haploid.

Sporangia of Tetrasporophytes. A tetrasporophyte usually produces **tetrasporangia** containing four **tetraspores**; but it may produce **bisporangia** containing two **bispores,** or produce **polysporangia** containing **polyspores** in multiples of four. Usually a thallus bears but one kind of

[1] Feldmann, 1939. [2] Oltmanns, 1898. [3] Lewis, 1912, 1914.
[4] J. and G. Feldmann, 1942; Feldmann and Mazoyer, 1937; Harder and Koch, 1949.
[5] Svedelius, 1933. [6] Svedelius, 1942.

sporangium but instances are known where a thallus bears both tetrasporangia and bisporangia,[1] or tetrasporangia and polysporangia.[2] When, as is usually the case, meiosis immediately precedes formation of bispores, tetraspores, or polyspores, these develop into gametophytes when they germinate.

Tetrasporangia are the typical sporangia of tetrasporophytes. They are at first usually uninucleate, and in the cases where they are at first multinucleate all the nuclei but one degenerate.[3] According to the genus, the arrangement of the four tetraspores is either **zonate** and one above the other (Fig. 191*C*, page 333), or **cruciate** and two above two (Fig. 188*C*, page 329), or **pyramidate** and with all touching at a common central point (Fig. 198*B*, page 341). Frequently there is but one type of spore arrangement throughout an entire family.

In all but one of the cytologically investigated species, division of the single nucleus in a young tetrasporangium is meiotic. The species with an apomeiotic instead of a meiotic division of the primary nucleus produces diploid tetraspores.[4] The absence of sexual individuals of this species indicates that diploid tetraspores give rise to tetrasporophytes. Presumably the tetraspores are also diploid in another species where tetraspores have been found developing into tetrasporophytes.[5]

Bisporangia and polysporangia (Fig. 194, page 336) are modifications of tetrasporangia. Cytological investigation of Corallinaceae has shown[1] that when division of the primary nucleus is meiotic both bispores have two haploid nuclei. On the other hand, when division of the primary nucleus is apomeiotic each bispore contains a single diploid nucleus. Abnormal cases showing the beginning of a cleavage of the bisporangia into four parts indicate that bisporangia have been derived from tetrasporangia. In the only species where development of polysporangia has been studied cytologically[6] there is a cleavage into uninucleate polyspores after each of the two to nine nuclei in the young sporangium has divided meiotically into four nuclei.

There are many recorded cases where tetrasporophytes have been found bearing carpogonia and spermatangia in addition to tetrasporangia. Cytological investigation[7] of *Spermothamnion turneri* (Mert.) Aresch. sheds light on the question of whether or not sex organs on diploid thalli are functional. Triploid and tetraploid plants have been found, presumably resulting from union of a diploid and a haploid gamete, or from union of two diploid gametes. Triploid and tetraploid individuals of this species are sterile. In another red alga, *Plumaria elegans* (Bonnem.) Schmitz, triploid individuals bear only the clustered masses of spores known as **paraspores.** These paraspores give rise to new triploid plants. Paraspores

[1] Suneson, 1950. [2] Drew, 1951. [3] Svedelius, 1914*A*. [4] Svedelius, 1935.
[5] J. and G. Feldmann, 1952. [6] Drew, 1937. [7] Drew, 1934, 1943.

have also been found on several other Ceramiales, but nothing is known concerning the chromosome numbers in thalli bearing them.

Alternation of Generations in Florideae. Some of the Florideae have a biphasic alternation in which a sexual generation (the gametophyte) alternates with an asexual generation (the carposporophyte). Others are triphasic with three generations or somatic phases (gametophyte, carposporophyte, tetrasporophyte) successively following one another. The Florideae also differ from other plants in that alternation of sexual and

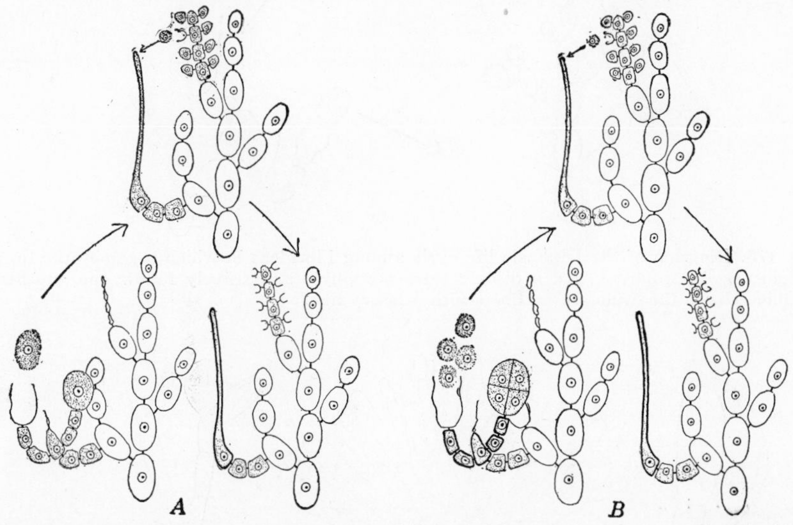

Fig. 174. Diagrams showing the two types of diphasic life cycle found among the Florideae. Diploid cells in the cycle are outlined with a heavy line. *A*, the cycle in which a haploid carposporophyte alternates with the gametophyte. *B*, the cycle in which a diploid carposporophyte alternates with the gametophyte.

asexual generations (somatic phases) is not always accompanied by an alternation in number of chromosomes. Consequently, the following three types of life cycle may be recognized among the Florideae: (1) a biphasic alternation of a haploid gametophyte and a haploid carposporophyte (Fig. 174*A*), (2) a biphasic alternation of a haploid gametophyte and a diploid carposporophyte (Fig. 174*B*), and (3) a triphasic cycle in which both the carposporophyte and tetrasporophyte are diploid (Fig. 175).

A diphasic alternation of a haploid gametophyte and a haploid carposporophyte has been demonstrated cytologically[1] for certain Nemalionales and probably occurs in many other members of the order.

One species of *Liagora*[2] and one of *Helminthocladia*[3] (Fig. 176) have

[1] Cleland, 1919; Kylin, 1916*B*, 1917; Svedelius, 1915, 1933.
[2] Kylin, 1930*A*. [3] Feldmann, 1939.

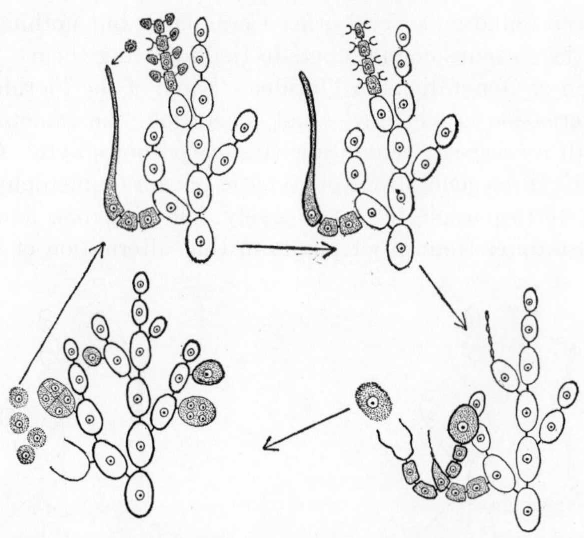

FIG. 175. Diagram of the triphasic life cycle among Florideae in which a gametophyte, a diploid carposporophyte, and a diploid tetrasporophyte successively follow one another. Diploid cells in the cycle are outlined with a heavy line.

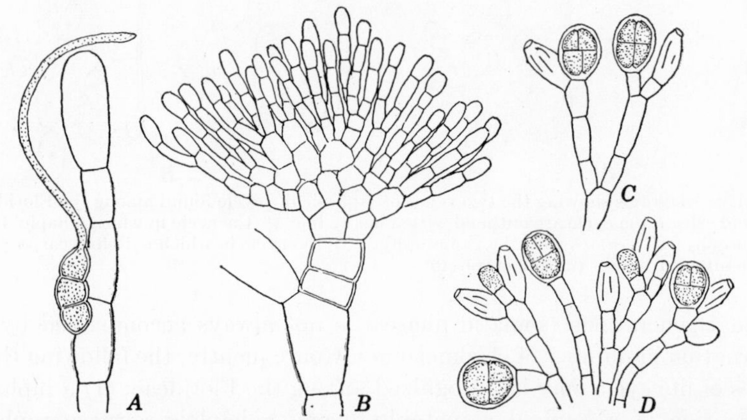

FIG. 176. *Helminthocladia hudsonii* (C.Ag.) J. Ag. *A*, portion of a vegetative filament bearing a carpogonial filament. *B*, carposporophyte. *C–D*, gonimoblast filaments with carpotetrasporangia. (*After Feldmann*, 1939.)

carposporophytes with carpotetrasporangia, whereas those of all other species in these two genera have carposporangia. It is believed,[1] although not demonstrated cytologically, that these carposporophytes with carpotetrasporangia are diploid and that meiosis occurs immediately prior to formation of carpotetraspores. Thus these two species have a diphasic life cycle of a haploid gametophyte and a diploid carposporo-

[1] Feldmann, 1939; Kylin, 1930*A*; Svedelius, 1931.

phyte. It is also believed that this is immediately derived from a diphasic cycle in which the carposporophyte is haploid.

Other Florideae with a diphasic alternation of a haploid gametophyte and a diploid carposporophyte seem to have been evolved from genera with a triphasic cycle. *Phyllophora* is an example of this. Most species of this genus have a triphasic cycle with a haploid gametophyte, a diploid carposporophyte producing diploid carpospores, and a free-living diploid tetrasporophyte. *P. brodiaei* (Turn.) J.G.Ag. has a gametophyte with normal sex organs and a development of filaments from an auxiliary cell that is the supporting cell of the carpogonial filament.[1] Cells toward the end of many of the filaments become sporangia, each containing four spores, and it has been shown[2] that spore formation is immediately preceded by meiosis. The diploid nature of the filaments is unquestioned, but this plexus of filaments has been considered a reduced parasitic tetrasporophyte rather than a carposporophyte.[3] The warty, excrescent mass produced by the filaments does not look like a carposporophyte but it should be considered one because the filaments are in organic connection with an auxiliary cell that is an integral part of the gametophyte. According to such an interpretation the filaments are gonimoblastic and the sporangia borne on them are carpotetrasporangia. *Gymnogongrus griffithsiae* Mart.[4] and *Schizymenia epiphytica* (Setchell and Lawson) Smith and Hollenberg[5] seem to be of a similar type.

Florideae with a triphasic cycle are readily recognized by their free-living tetrasporophytes. Cytological study[6] of numerous genera with free-living tetrasporophytes has shown that they have diploid carposporophytes and tetrasporophytes. It is very probable that other genera with free-living tetrasporophytes are similar.

Evolution among the Florideae. From the standpoint of vegetative organization there are two distinct types, the monoaxial and the multiaxial (see page 302). Since the multiaxial has undoubtedly been derived from the monoaxial type, it might be argued that the two are two divergent series established early in evolution of the Florideae. But the occurrence of both types in conjunction with reproductive features typical of Nemalionales, Gigartinales, and Cryptonemiales, indicates very strongly that evolution from a monoaxial to a multiaxial organization has occurred more than once within the Florideae.

On the basis of structures associated with development of the carposporophyte together with phases in the life cycle, the Florideae can be

[1] Kolderup-Rosenvinge, 1929. [2] Claussen, 1929.

[3] Drew, 1951; Feldmann, 1952; Kolderup-Rosenvinge, 1929; Svedelius, 1931.

[4] Gregory, 1934. [5] Smith and Hollenberg, 1943.

[6] Drew, 1934, 1943; Kylin, 1914; Suneson, 1950; Svedelius, 1911*A*, 1914; Westbrook, 1928, 1935; Yamanouchi, 1906, 1921.

arranged in a progressive series. There is a widespread belief that diphasic Florideae with a meiotic division of the zygote nucleus and an outgrowth of a haploid carposporophyte from the carpogonium are the most primitive known members of the subclass. The fundamental feature in an advance from this condition has been a postponement of the time at which meiosis takes place.[1] The first step in advance was a postponement of meiosis to the time spores were formed in sporangia of the carposporophyte. This resulted in a diphasic alternation of haploid gametophyte and a diploid carposporophyte. That this undoubedly took place more than once is shown by the occurrence of this type in both *Liagora* and *Helminthocladia*. The next step was an omission of meiosis in sporangia of the carposporophyte and a resultant production of diploid carpospores. This evolution of diploid carpospores did not necessarily involve an introduction of new genes for thallus structure, and as a result the free-living diploid thalli developed from liberated diploid carpospores were identical in vegetative structure with those developing from haploid carpospores. The sporangia of diploid plants can be considered homologous with monosporangia of gametophytes.[2] Sporangia of diploid thalli differed from monosporangia of gametophytes in that there was a meiotic division of the nucleus and a division of the protoplast to form four spores (tetraspores) that grew into gametophytes after liberation.

The most primitive of such triphasic Florideae with a free-living tetrasporophyte probably had (as in present-day Gelidiales) the carposporophyte growing directly from the carpogonium. When the carposporophyte develops upon a carpogonium the amount of available food is limited. A much greater supply of food is available when the carposporophyte is borne upon other cells of the thallus. Thus the evolution of auxiliary cells must be looked upon as a secondary feature and one that arose in connection with nutrition of the developing carposporophyte.

The evolutionary relationships between the various orders of the Florideae are obscure. From the reproductive standpoint, the Nemalionales are generally believed to be the most primitive of the subclass, and the Ceramiales to be the most advanced. One suggestion concerning relationships of the remaining four orders is that they represent four divergent series from primitive types.[3]

Classification. The Florideae were classified according to various bases until Schmitz[4] showed that the most important characters in a natural classification of them are the structure and development of the cystocarp (carposporophyte). It is largely through the efforts of Kylin and his students[5] that the system proposed by Schmitz has been refined into the

[1] Cleland, 1919; Svedelius, 1927, 1931. [2] Cleland, 1919.

[3] Kylin, 1930*A*. [4] Schmitz, 1889.

[5] Bliding, 1928; Kylin, 1923, 1928, 1930*A*, 1935; Sjöstedt, 1926.

widely adopted system which divides the Florideae into the following six orders: Nemalionales, Gelidiales, Cryptonemiales, Gigartinales, Rhodymeniales, and Ceramiales.

ORDER 1. NEMALIONALES

Most Nemalionales have a meiotic division of the zygote nucleus and a production of haploid carpospores by the carposporophyte, and have no free-living tetrasporophytic generation. Almost all genera have the carposporophyte developing from the carpogonium but there are also genera in which a vegetative cell of the carpogonial filament functions as an auxiliary cell.

The order contains some 35 genera and 250 species. These have been divided[1] into seven families. The systematic position of certain families referred to the order is open to question. This is particularly true of the Bonnemaisoniaceae where there is a free-living tetrasporophytic generation, and on this account the family has been thought[2] to be sufficiently distinct to be placed in a separate order, the Bonnemaisoniales.

Nemalion is a marine summer annual which grows in the middle portion of the intertidal zone. It is rather local in distribution, but there are usually many individuals at stations where it does grow. The thallus (Fig. 177*A*) is cylindrical, sparingly to profusely branched, and of a reddish-brown color. The generic name is based upon the distinctly wormlike appearance of thalli as they lie clinging to rocks when the tide is out.

The carpospore is naked when liberated from a carposporangium, but it becomes invested with a wall about the time it becomes affixed to a rock or some other firm substratum. Its germination begins with a protrusion of a germ tube and a migration of the chromatophore and most of the cytoplasm into the tube. The nucleus moves to the base of the tube and there divides. One daughter nucleus remains within the old spore wall; the other migrates into the tube.[3] A cross wall is then formed at the base of the tube, and the cell thus formed functions as an apical cell. Division and redivision of the apical cell produce a protonema-like, sparingly branched, monoaxial filament with a dozen or more cells.[4] As growth continues, lateral branches of the filament become intertwined with one another and develop into the adult portion of the thallus. This is multiaxial in organization and with many apical cells at the growing tip. Except for the looser arrangement of filaments, the structure of the thallus is quite similar to that of *Cumagloia* (Fig. 173*B*).

Mature portions of the plant body are differentiated into a colorless axial core and a colored ensheathing layer. The mature portion of the

[1] Kylin, 1932. [2] J. and G. Feldmann, 1942.
[3] Cleland, 1919: Lewis. 1912*A*. [4] Chester. 1896; Kylin, 1917*A*.

axial core is composed of closely intertwined longitudinal filaments of elongate cells without chromatophores or nuclei.[1] The ensheathing layer, often called the cortex, consists of short, erect, densely branched, lateral filaments terminating in elongate hyaline hairs. Median cells of lateral

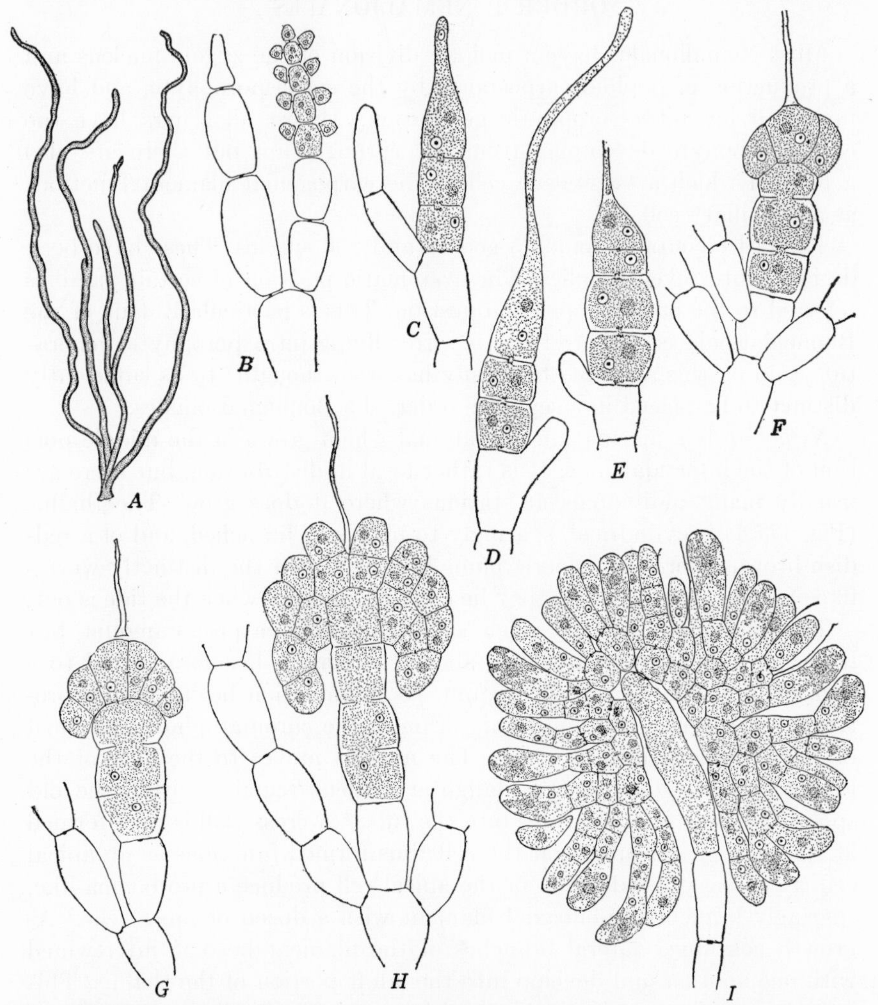

FIG. 177. *Nemalion multifidum* (Weber and Mohr) J. Ag. *A*, gametophyte. *B*, filament with spermatangia. *C–D*, young and mature carpogonial filaments. *E–H*, early stages in development of carposporophyte. *I*, mature carposporophyte. (*A*, × ⅓; *B–H*, × 975; *I*, × 650.)

filaments are barrel-shaped, uninucleate, and have a single stellate chromatophore containing a conspicuous pyrenoid.

Nemalion is homothallic, but many plants appear to be heterothallic because there is not a simultaneous production of the two kinds of sex

[1] Cleland, 1919.

organs. The initial of a spermatangial branch is an ordinary vegetative cell terminating a lateral filament from the central core. This initial cuts off a chain of four to seven derivatives each of which is a spermatangial mother cell. Spermatangial branches are easily distinguishable from vegetative ones because their cells are colorless or have feebly developed chromatophores. Each spermatangial mother cell[1] generally buds off four radially disposed spermatangia (Fig. 177*B*). The spermatium within a spermatangium contains a single nucleus and a rudimentary chromatophore. It is liberated by a rupture of the spermatangial wall, and, after its escape, a new spermatangium may develop within the old spermatangial wall.

The carpogonial filament is developed from an initial cell borne near the base of a lateral filament from the central core. The initial functions as an apical cell that usually cuts off three daughter cells, but the number formed may range from one to five. The apical cell of a carpogonial filament becomes the carpogonium after it stops forming daughter cells. The carpogonium has an elongate protuberance, the trichogyne, at the distal end (Fig. 177*C–D*). Most carpogonia of *Nemalion* are uninucleate, but occasional ones are binucleate, with an ephemeral nucleus in the trichogyne.[2]

Spermatia carried about by water currents may lodge against a trichogyne. A spermatium is uninucleate at the time of lodgment but shortly afterward its nucleus divides into two daughter nuclei.[2] This is followed by a dissolution of spermatial and trichogynal walls at the point of mutual contact and a migration of one or both spermatial nuclei into the trichogyne. One of the spermatial nuclei migrates to the carpogonial base, where it unites with the female nucleus.

The zygote nucleus increases in size and then divides meiotically into two daughter nuclei which lie one above the other. There is next a formation of a horizontal wall between the two nuclei (Fig. 177*E*). The nucleus within the inferior daughter cell eventually disintegrates. That within the superior daughter cell of the carpogonium divides equationally, and one daughter nucleus moves into a lateral protuberance growing out from the cell. A vertical wall is formed across the base of the protuberance, and the cell thus cut off is the initial of a gonimoblast filament. In the same manner several additional initials are successively developed lateral to the superior cell (Fig. 177*F–G*). Each initial gives rise to a short, compactly branched, gonimoblast filament in which the terminal cell of each branchlet eventually enlarges and becomes a carposporangium. The gonimoblast filaments jointly constitute the carposporophyte. Food for development of the carposporophyte is obtained from an elongate **placental cell** produced by terminal fusion of carpogonial filament

[1] Cleland, 1919; Kylin, 1916*B*; Wolf, 1904. [2] Cleland, 1919.

cells and the inferior daughter cell formed by division of the carpogonium (Fig. 177*G–I*). The wall of a mature carposporangium ruptures at the distal end, and the carpospores escape. Liberation of a carpospore may be followed by proliferation of a new carposporangium within the old empty carposporangial wall (Fig. 177*I*), and successive sporangia may be proliferated as the season progresses.[1]

Thalli of *Nemalion* disappear completely late in the autumn, and new ones do not reappear until late in the next spring. The prostrate protonematal stage has been found during the winter,[2] and it is very probable that the plant remains in this stage of development until the spring.

Scinaia is one of the few Nemalionales in which the carposporophyte is surrounded by a pericarp. It is also of interest because it is the genus

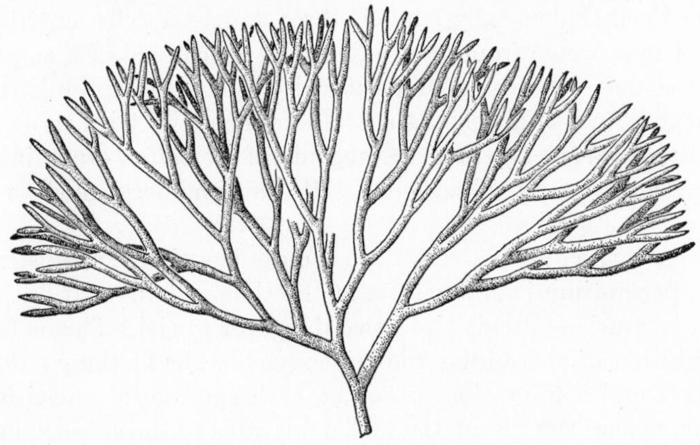

FIG. 178. Gametophyte of *Scinaia furcellata* (Turn.) Bivona. (Natural size.)

where meiosis was first demonstrated among the Nemalionales.[3] *Scinaia* is a marine genus of world-wide distribution. There are about a dozen species.[4] Two of them have been recorded from the Atlantic Coast of this country and one from the Pacific Coast. All three are rare algae.

The thallus is erect, is cylindrical to subcylindrical, and has several successive dichotomous branchings (Fig. 178). The growing points are multiaxial and have many apical cells. Mature regions of a thallus have an axial core of colorless longitudinal filaments. The axial core is surrounded by an encircling layer of corymbosely branched filaments that stand vertical to it. The outermost branchlets of the corymbose filaments are compacted into a pseudoparenchymatous tissue whose cells contain chromatophores. Terminal cells of many of the branchlets enlarge to several times their original size and become colorless (Fig. 179*A*).

[1] Cleland, 1919; Kylin, 1916*B*; Wolf, 1904. [2] Kolderup-Rosenvinge, 1909–1924.
[3] Svedelius, 1915. [4] Setchell, 1914.

These cells constitute the colorless epidermis-like layer at the surface of a thallus.[1]

The gametophyte of *Scinaia* reproduces asexually by means of monospores.[2] They are formed in monosporangia borne at the tips of branchlets which have grown out between the "epidermal" cells. The terminal cell of a branchlet is a mother cell which buds off either one or two monosporangia (Fig. 179*C*). A monosporangium contains a single haploid nu-

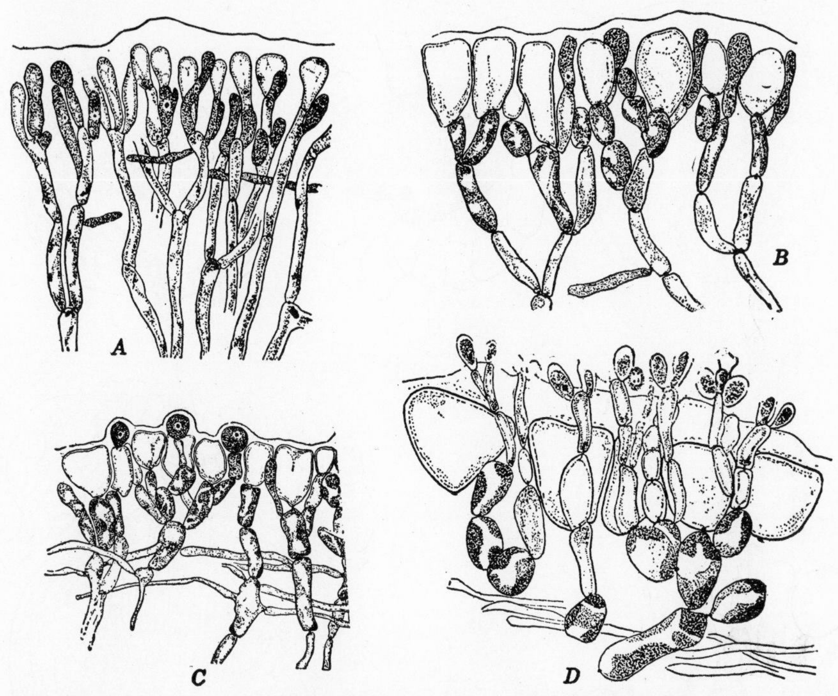

FIG. 179. *Scinaia furcellata* (Turn.) Bivona. *A*, section of vegetative region with young epidermal cells. *B*, the same with mature epidermal cells. *C*, monosporangia. *D*, spermatangia. (*From Svedelius*, 1915.) (*A–B*, × 615; *C*, × 510; *D*, × 600.)

cleus, and the entire protoplast becomes the naked monospore that is liberated by rupture of the sporangial wall. Liberation of the monospore may be followed by proliferation of a new monosporangium within the old sporangial wall.[2] The method of germination of monospores is unknown.

Gametophytes of *Scinaia* may be homothallic or heterothallic. The spermatangia lie in large or small sori scattered over the thallus surface. They are borne upon branchlets of filaments which grow up between and project beyond the "epidermal" cells.[2] The terminal cell of each projecting branchlet is a spermatangial mother cell that bears two or three spermatangia at the distal end. Each spermatangium contains a single

[1] Setchell, 1914; Svedelius, 1915. [2] Svedelius, 1915.

spermatium which is liberated by a rupture of the spermatangial wall (Fig. 179*D*). Development of spermatangia may continue for some time, because new spermatangia may be proliferated within walls of old empty ones.

Carpogonial filaments are formed close to the growing apex and upon vertical filaments from the central axis (Fig. 180*A*). A carpogonial fila-

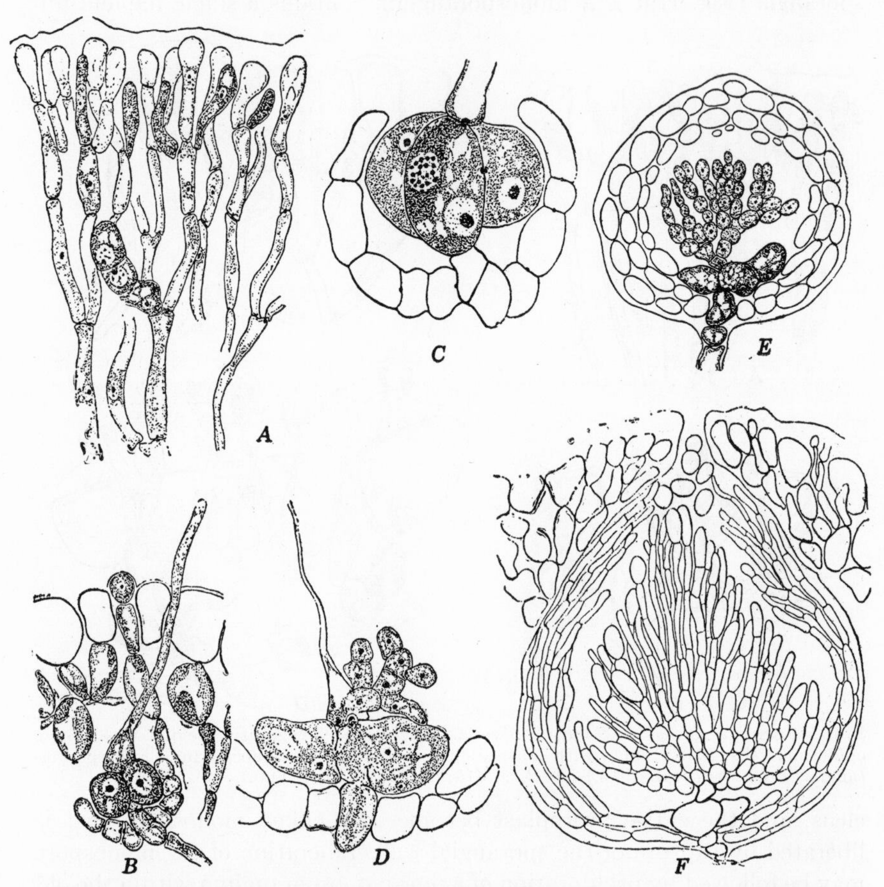

FIG. 180. *Scinaia furcellata* (Turn.) Bivona. *A–B*, young and mature carpogonial filaments. *C*, after migration of the zygote nucleus into one of the auxiliary cells. *D–E*, early stages in development of carposporophytes. *F*, mature carposporophyte with its surrounding pericarp. (*From Svedelius*, 1915.) (*A–B*, × 615; *C*, × 1,150; *D*, × 840; *E–F*, × 345.)

ment is three-celled and has the terminal cell metamorphosing into a carpogonium with a long trichogyne. *Scinaia* is one of the few Florideae where there is a nucleus both in the trichogyne and in the carpogonial base.[1] Shortly before fertilization the median cell of a carpogonial fila-

[1] Svedelius, 1915.

ment cuts off four large cruciately disposed **auxiliary cells,** each densely filled with protoplasm (Fig. 180*B*). At the same time there is a development of upwardly curved sterile filaments from the lowermost carpogonial filament cell. These curved filaments become the urn-shaped pericarp which surrounds the mature carposporophyte. A mature pericarp lies embedded just within the thallus surface, and it has an opening, the ostiole, at the distal end.

Immediately after fertilization there is a migration of the zygote nucleus into one of the auxiliary cells (Fig. 180*C*). There it divides meiotically into four haploid daughter nuclei.[1] One of these nuclei migrates into the gonimoblast primordium which grows up through the old empty carpogonium (Fig. 180*D–E*). The gonimoblast primordium develops into an outwardly divergent and profusely branched system of gonimoblast filaments which fill most of the space within the pericarp. Three or four of the outermost cells of certain branchlets develop into carposporangia. Other branches remain sterile and develop into paraphyses (Fig. 180*F*). The nucleus within the single carpospore of a carposporangium has the haploid number of chromosomes. Eventually there is a liberation of the carpospores by an apical rupturing of the carposporangial wall. Although not demonstrated by cultures, there is every reason for believing that liberated carpospores develop directly into gametophytes.

ORDER 2. GELIDIALES

The Gelidiales are the only tetrasporophytic Florideae in which the carposporophyte develops directly from the carpogonium. There is but one family, the Gelidiales, and it contains about half a dozen genera.

The type genus, *Gelidium,* is a widely distributed marine alga with many species. It is a perennial plant in which new shoots are proliferated from the persisting basal portion each growing season. The thallus is cylindrical or flattened, pinnately branched, and of a tough consistency. In many species the branchlets bend away from the axis in a geniculate fashion and are constricted in the basal portion (Fig. 181*A*).

Thalli of *Gelidium* have a single apical cell at each branch apex. Derivatives are cut off at the posterior face of an apical cell and they mature into a single axial filament of the adult portion (Fig. 181*B*). Cells of the axial filament, one or two back from the apical cell, cut off four quadrately arranged pericentral cells and each of them produces a short branched lateral filament.[2] The tips of these lateral filaments are compacted into the pseudoparenchymatous tissue which forms the surface of the thallus.

Gelidium differs from most other American Florideae in that the thalli, both sexual and tetrasporic, usually fruit during the late autumn and winter months. Gametophytes of *G. cartilagineum* Gaill. are heterothallic.

[1] Svedelius, 1915. [2] Kylin, 1928.

The spermatangia are borne in elliptical sori (nemathecia) on the flattened sides of branchlets of male plants (Fig. 181*F*). A spermatangial mother cell usually bears two spermatangia which become transversely divided after they are cut off.[1]

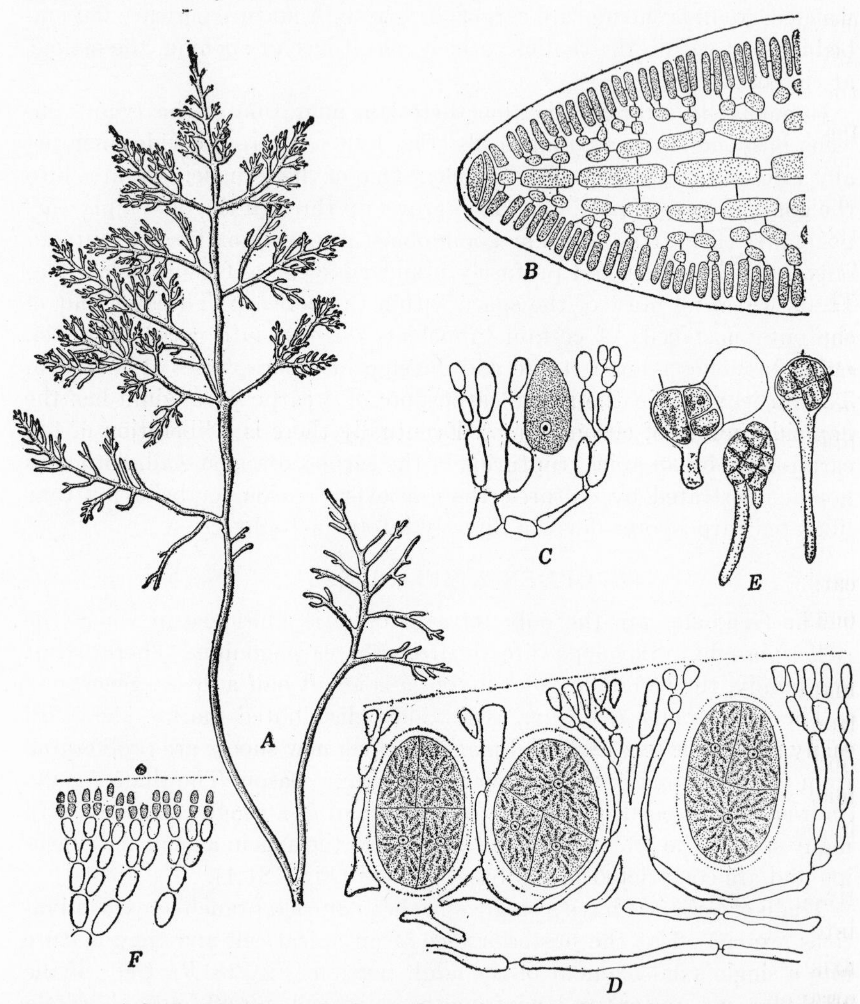

Fig. 181. *A–D*, *F*, *Gelidium cartilagineum* Gaill. *A*, thallus. *B*, diagrammatic section of a thallus apex. *C–D*, young and mature tetrasporangia. *E*, germinating tetraspores of *G. capillaceum* (Gmel.) Kütz. *F*, spermatangia. (*E*, *after Killian*, 1914.) (*A*, × ½; *B–D*, × 650; *F*, × 430.)

Fertile branches of female gametophytes are macroscopically distinguishable from vegetative branches on account of their indented apices. Carpogonial filaments are developed on the flattened sides of fertile

[1] Kylin, 1928.

branches and close to the growing point. The carpogonial filament is one-celled, and it is borne upon the lowermost cells of a vegetative filament growing out from the central axis. The single cell of a carpogonial filament metamorphoses into a carpogonium with an elongate trichogyne that is inflated in the distal portion (Fig. 182*A*). Carpogonial development is accompanied by an outgrowth of small-celled filaments from the basal (pericentral) cells[1] of vegetative filaments. The cells of these special filaments are densely packed with protoplasm, and they serve as a nurse tissue for the growing carposporophyte. The gonimoblast filament growing out from the base of a carpogonium is many-celled and sparingly branched. It grows longitudinally along the axial filament and between

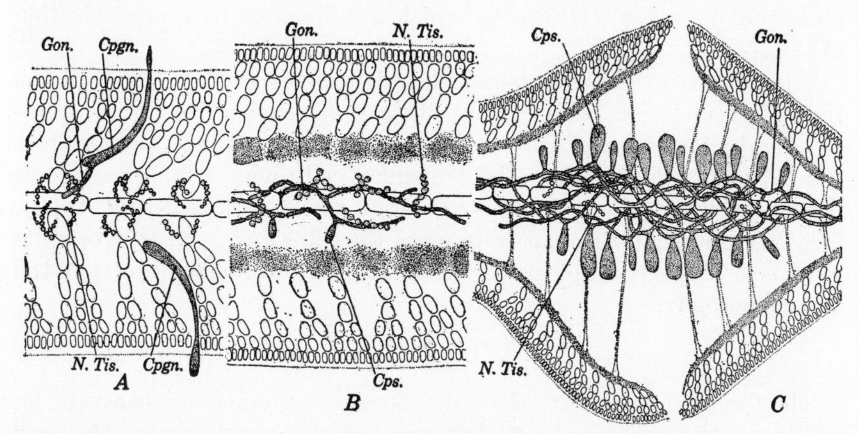

Fig. 182. *Gelidium cartilagineum* Gaill. Diagrammatic longitudinal sections of thalli with developing carposporophytes. *A*, with a carpogonium and a carpogonium producing the first gonimoblast filament. *B*, carposporophyte with very young carposporangia. *C*, carposporophyte with mature carposporangia. (*Cpgn.*, carpogonium; *Cps.*, carposporangia; *Gon.*, gonimoblast filament; *N. Tis.*, nurse tissue.) (*A–B*, × 300; *C*, × 210.)

the nurse filaments (Fig. 182*B*). Eventually it forms numerous erect, one-celled, lateral branchlets which develop into carposporangia (Fig. 182*C*). It is very probable that the interwoven mass of gonimoblast filaments about an axial filament has grown out from several carpogonia. Thus the "cystocarp" of *Gelidium* is to be interpreted as an aggregation of carposporophytes rather than as a single one. Development of the carposporangia is accompanied by an upward arching of the overlying tissues and differentiation of an opening (ostiole) in one or in both of the flattened sides. Carpospores liberated from the carposporangia float out through these pores and are carried about by water currents.

Germlings produced by germination of carpospores have not been grown to maturity, but there is no doubt that they develop into tetrasporophytes. Mature tetrasporophytes of *Gelidium* are indistinguishable

[1] Kylin, 1928.

from mature gametophytes when the two are in a sterile condition. Fruiting tetrasporophytes may be distinguished by their swollen fertile branchlets. The tetrasporangia lie close to one another along the flattened side of fertile branchlets, but they are not organized into nemathecia. The tetrasporangia are superficial in position when first differentiated, but they gradually become embedded in the thallus through an upgrowth of adjoining vegetative tissue (Fig. 181*C–D*). A young tetrasporangium enlarges to several times its original size, and the nucleus within it divides to form four daughter nuclei. Undoubtedly, as is known for several other tetrasporophytic Florideae, this nuclear division is reductional. The four-nucleate protoplast within a tetrasporangium divides cruciately into four tetraspores which are liberated by a gelatinization of the sporangial wall.

The liberated tetraspore is naked, but it is enclosed by a wall at the time of germination. This begins with a protrusion of the entire protoplast and a formation of a transverse wall separating the protrusion from the old empty spore wall.[1] The protruded cell divides transversely and one of the daughter cells sends out a long colorless rhizoid (Fig. 181*E*). The two successive diagonal divisions of the cell with the rhizoid, or of its sister cell, produce an apical cell which continues all further growth of the new gametophyte.

ORDER 3. CRYPTONEMIALES

The Cryptonemiales are the only tetrasporophytic Florideae with an auxiliary cell borne in a special filament of the gametophyte. Auxiliary cell filaments may be borne remote from or upon the supporting cell of a carpogonial filament.

The order has some 85 genera and 650 species. These have been divided[2] into nine families, differing from one another in position of auxiliary cells, in thallus structure, and in position of the carposporophyte.

Auxiliary cell filaments resemble carpogonial filaments in that their cells lack chromatophores and are densely packed with protoplasm. Thus they appear to be modified carpogonial filaments. The carpogonium and an auxiliary cell cannot be considered homologous because the former is always terminal in position and the latter is always intercalary.[3]

Dudresnaya, a genus with about five species, is an alga of warmer portions of the Atlantic Ocean. Along the shores of North America it has not been found north of Florida, but in Europe it ranges as far north as the southern shores of England and Ireland. The soft gelatinous thalli of *Dudresnaya* are especially favorable for studying the characteristic reproductive structures of Cryptonemiales.

[1] Killian, 1914. [2] Kylin, 1932. [3] Kylin, 1930*A*.

The thallus is monoaxial and with derivatives from the single apical cell each cutting off four lateral cells that are initials of branched lateral filaments whose cells contain chromatophores (Fig. 183*A–B*). Cells of the axial filament increase somewhat in diameter and increase greatly in length. Because of this the lateral filaments tend to be borne in successive transverse whorls along the axial filament. In older portions of a

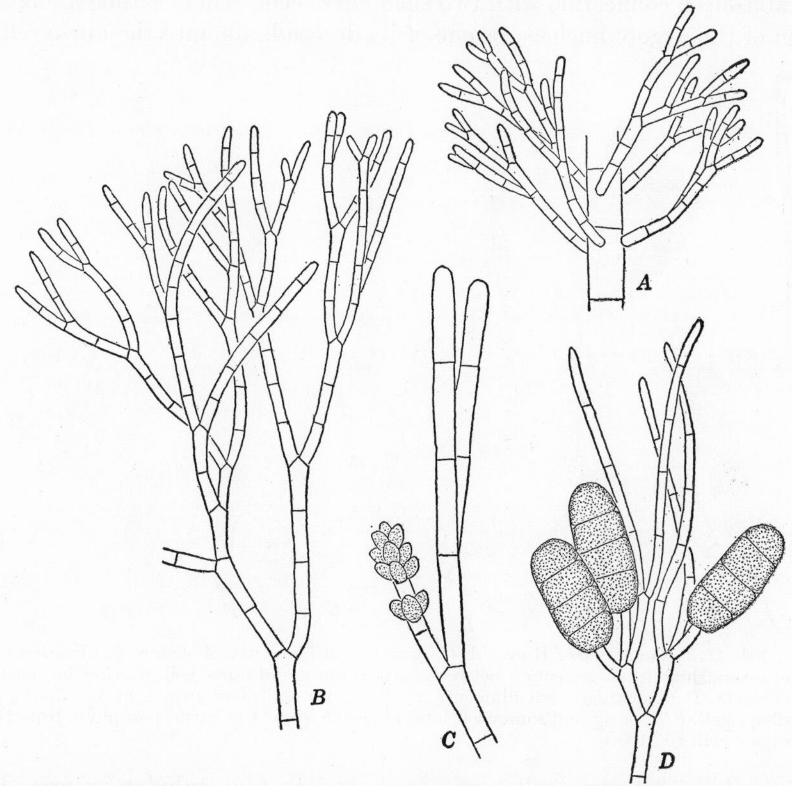

FIG. 183. *A–C*, *Dudresnaya crassa* Howe. *A*, segment of upper portion of axial filament with each cell bearing four immature lateral filaments. *B*, distal portion of a mature lateral filament. *C*, spermatangia at tip of a lateral filament. *D*, *D. verticillata* (Wither.) Le Jolis. Lateral filament with tetrasporangia. (*A–B*, × 225; *C*, × 800; *D*, × 400.)

thallus the lowermost cell of lateral filaments gives rise to descending filaments that form a corticating sheath around the axial filament.

Most species are heterothallic. Male thalli are somewhat smaller than female thalli, and when in fruit are paler. Spermatangia (Fig. 183*C*) are produced in abundance on cells toward the tips of lateral filaments.[1]

Carpogonial filaments (Fig. 184*A–C*) are borne near the base of lateral filaments. They are 6 to 10 cells in length and terminate in a carpogo-

[1] Kylin, 1928; Taylor, 1950.

nium with a trichogyne much longer than the carpogonial filament. The apex of a carpogonial filament is recurved in such a manner that the carpogonial base lies near the third or fourth cell below the carpogonium. After fertilization the base of a carpogonium sends out a tubular outgrowth that establishes a connection with a carpogonial filament cell lying three or four cells below the carpogonium.[1] Sometimes the outgrowth establishes a connection with two such nurse cells. There is then a migration of the zygote nucleus, or one of its descendants, into the nurse cell.[2]

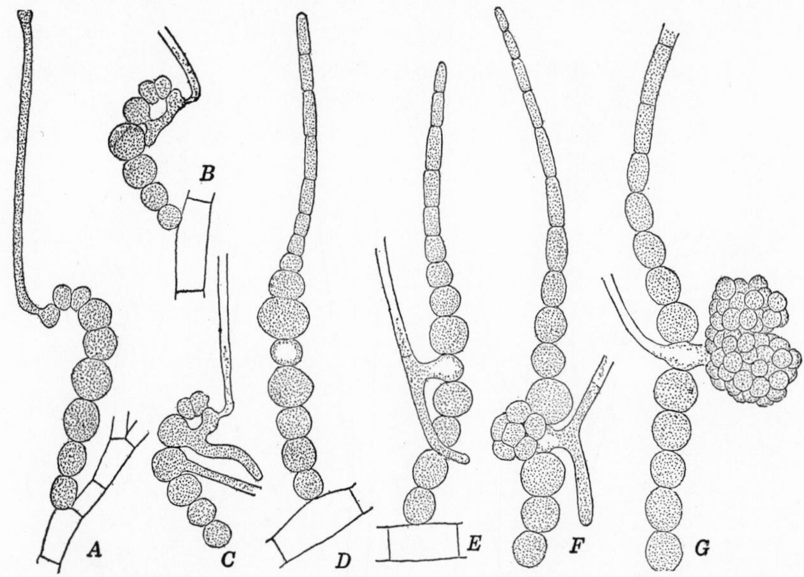

Fig. 184. *Dudresnaya crassa* Howe. *A–C*, carpogonial filaments. *A*, before fertilization. *B*, after establishment of connection between carpogonium and nurse cell. *C*, after formation of oöblasts. *D–G*, auxiliary cell filaments. *D–E*, before and after growth of an oöblast to auxiliary cell. *F–G*, early and somewhat later stages in growth of carposporophyte from the auxiliary cell. (× 400.)

After this, the nurse cell sends forth one to four tubular outgrowths (**oöblasts**) which grow to and fuse with a cell of an auxiliary cell filament.

Auxiliary cell filaments (Fig. 184*D–G*) are borne in the same manner as carpogonial filaments. They are not recurved at the upper end, are up to 15 or more cells in length, and are with or without lateral branches from cells near the base. The auxiliary cell lies about midway between base and apex of the filament. It is the median of three successive cells with denser protoplasts in *D. coccinea* (C.A.Ag.) Crouan;[3] in *D. crassa* Howe it is smaller in diameter and with a less dense protoplast than abutting cells.[4]

[1] Kylin, 1928; Oltmanns, 1898; Taylor, 1950. [2] Kylin, 1928; Oltmanns, 1898.
[3] Kylin, 1928. [4] Taylor, 1950.

Fusion of the oöblast tip with an auxiliary cell is followed by a migration of a diploid nucleus into the auxiliary cell. There is then a growth of gonimoblast filaments from the auxiliary cell. Frequently, before or shortly after beginning of development of gonimoblast filaments, the auxiliary cell sends out a secondary oöblast that grows to another auxiliary cell filament whose auxiliary cell then forms gonimoblast filaments. In turn, this auxiliary cell may send out tertiary oöblasts (Fig. 185). Thus several carposporophytes may be produced as a result of a single gametic

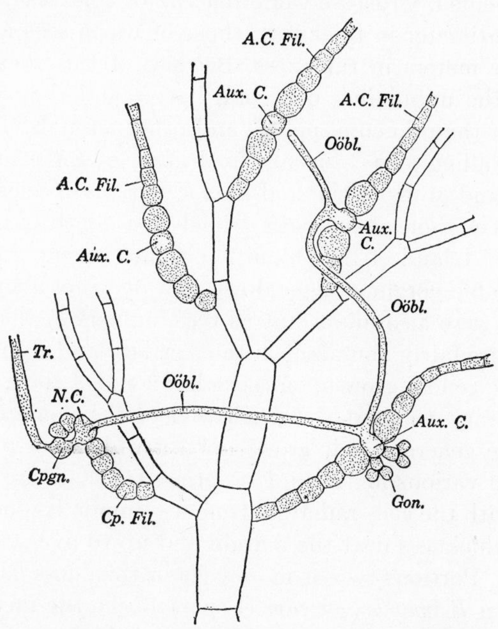

Fig. 185. *Dudresnaya crassa* Howe. Diagram of base of a lateral filament bearing a carpogonial filament and four auxiliary cell filaments. The base of the carpogonium has fused with a nurse cell from which an oöblast has grown to an auxiliary cell filament and thence to another auxiliary cell filament. (*A.C. Fil.*, auxiliary cell filament; *Aux. C.*, auxiliary cell; *Cp. Fil.*, carpogonial filament; *Cpgn.*, carpogonium; *Gon.*, gonimoblast filaments; *N.C.*, nurse cell; *Oöbl.*, oöblast; *Tr.*, trichogyne.) (× 225.)

union. The carposporophyte formed by each auxiliary cell consists of a compactly branched mass of gonimoblast filaments in which each cell eventually develops into a carposporangium.

Tetrasporophytes are of infrequent occurrence and phycologists who have examined hundreds of plants on the coast of France[1] and in Bermuda[2] report the finding of many fertile gametophytes but not a single fruiting tetrasporophyte. Tetrasporophytes of *D. verticillatum* (Wither.) Le Jolis have been found fruiting in the Mediterranean.[3] Its tetrasporan-

[1] Kylin, 1928. [2] Taylor, 1950. [3] Feldmann, 1942.

gia are borne on lateral filaments of the axis and they are zonately divided into four tetraspores (Fig. 183*D*).

The Corallinaceae differ from other Cryptonemiales in two distinctive features. One is in the production of sex organs (and in some genera the production of tetrasporangia) in conceptacles opening externally by a circular ostiole. The second feature is the heavy calcification of the thallus. Some genera have a crustose thallus that is entirely calcified; other genera have an erect jointed thallus in which the internodes are calcified and the nodes uncalcified. Crustose Corallinaceae of cold seas rarely become more than a centimeter in thickness; those of warm seas may produce a calcareous layer meters in thickness. Because of this they are of great importance in the upbuilding of "coral" reefs and they contribute far more to the reef than do coral polyps and other animals. The reef-building crustose coralline alga is usually identified as *Lithothamnion* but in certain islands and atolls of the mid-Pacific various species of *Porolithon* predominate.[1] Test holes have been drilled to a depth of more than 800 meters on Bikini Island of the Bikini Atoll, and corings from them contained recognizable coralline algae down to a depth of about 125 meters. Coralline algae were also important as reef builders in the past, and remains of them are fairly abundant in the Tertiary and Upper Cretaceous.

Most crustose genera grow upon rocks but some of them are epiphytic. *Epilithon*, contrary to what the derivation of the name implies, is one of the epiphytic genera and it grows upon a wide variety of other Florideae and upon various marine angiosperms. Its thalli are 3 to 8 mm. in diameter and with the cells radiating from a common center. Sterile thalli are one cell in thickness near the margin and up to five cells in thickness near the center. Portions two or more cells in thickness have the cells in vertical rows. In *E. membranaceum* (Esper) Foslie the increase in thickness has been shown[2] to be due to division of the lowermost cell. Thus growth of the vertical rows (filaments) is intercalary and not terminal.

The gametophytes are heterothallic. Spermatangia and carpogonial filaments are borne in **nemathecia** (sori) which lie in conceptacles produced by an upgrowth and overarching of the adjoining vegetative tissue. The conceptacles, both male and female, open externally by a single opening (ostiole). The ostioles of conceptacles are the minute pinpricks one sees when a thallus is viewed from above with a hand lens.

Every basal cell in a spermatangial nemathecium produces an upright spermatangial filament in which most of the cells cut off two spermatangial mother cells. Several successive crops of spermatangia are produced by the spermatangial mother cells.[3] Unlike most other Florideae,

[1] Setchell, 1929; Taylor, 1950*A*.
[2] Kolderup-Rosenvinge, 1909–1924; Kylin, 1928; Suneson, 1937.
[3] Kylin, 1928.

the entire spermatangium and not the spermatium within it is liberated.[1] Spermatangia breaking away from the cells bearing them may accumulate in such numbers that they completely fill the conceptacle (Fig. 186*A*).

At the base of a female conceptacle is a layer one cell in thickness in which each cell functions as a supporting cell. The procarp (see page 306) consists of a basal auxiliary cell from which arises a single two-celled carpogonial filament. Other Corallinaceae may have the single auxiliary

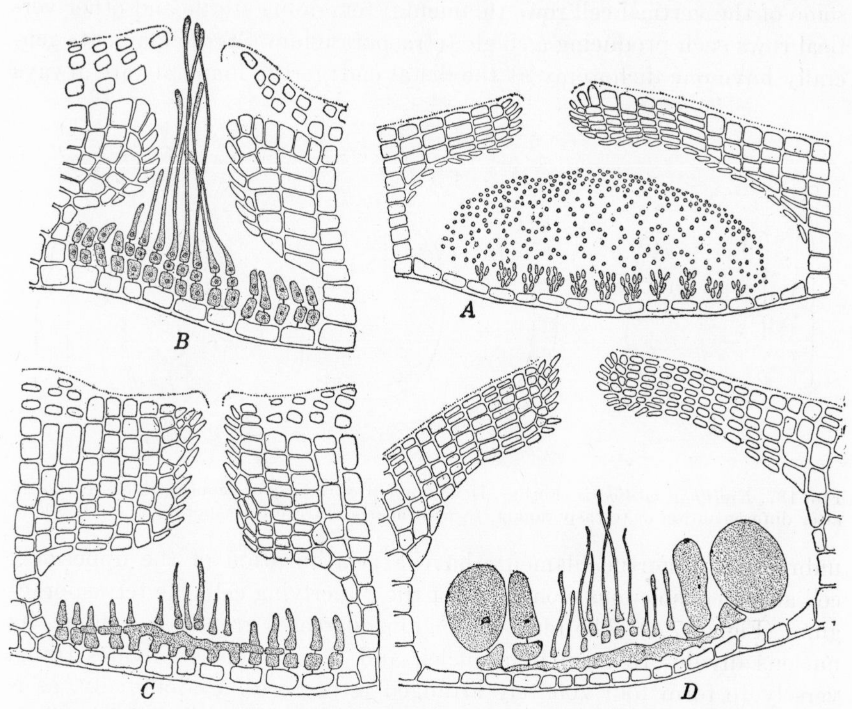

FIG. 186. *Epilithon mediocris* (Foslie). Semidiagrammatic vertical sections of conceptacles, *A*, spermatangial conceptacle. *B–D*, stages in development of cystocarpic conceptacles. *B*, with carpogonial filaments before fertilization. *C*, during fusion of auxiliary cells into the placental cell. *D*, placental cell with gonimoblast filaments producing carposporangia. (× 650.)

cell bearing two carpogonial filaments, and the condition found in *Epilithon* is thought[2] to have been derived from it. Carpogonial filaments at the center of a conceptacle terminate in a carpogonium with a long trichogyne projecting through the ostiole (Fig. 186*B*). Carpogonial filaments lateral to them are of an abortive type and do not have a trichogyne. Fertilization is followed by a development of a short oöblast from the base of the carpogonium. It grows directly downward and unites with the auxiliary cell bearing the carpogonial filament.[3]

[1] Suneson, 1937, 1943*A*. [2] Suneson, 1937.
[3] Kylin, 1928; Suneson, 1937, 1943.

All auxiliary cells of the conceptacle, including those with abortive carpogonial filaments, then fuse laterally with one another to form a large disk-shaped **placental cell.** Two- or three-celled gonimoblast filaments grow out from the periphery of the placental cell and the terminal cell of each gonimoblast filament develops into a large carposporangium (Fig. 186*C–D*).

Portions of tetrasporophytes destined to produce tetrasporangia have some of the vertical cell rows (filaments) remaining sterile and other vertical rows each producing a single tetrasporangium. Sterile filaments generally have one dichotomy at the distal end; fertile filaments are always

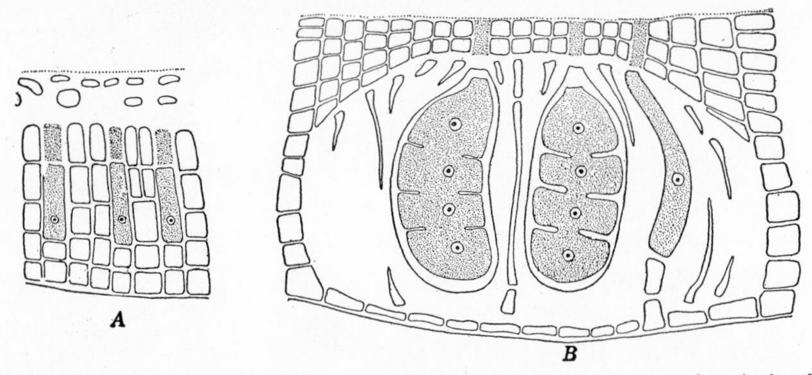

Fig. 187. *Epilithon mediocris* (Foslie). Development of tetrasporic conceptacles. *A*, shortly after differentiation of tetrasporangia. *B*, with nearly mature tetrasporangia. (× 650.)

unbranched.[1] Fertile filaments have a gelatinization of the uppermost cell and a conspicuous elongation of the underlying cell, the tetrasporangium (Fig. 187*A*). The tetrasporangium increases greatly in volume, its nucleus divides to form four nuclei, and the protoplast divides transversely to form four zonately arranged tetraspores. Undoubtedly, as is definitely established for certain other Corallinaceae,[2] the division into four nuclei is meiotic. Enlargement of tetrasporangia is accompanied by a disintegration of laterally adjoining portions of sterile filaments (Fig. 187*B*). There is no disintegration of the uppermost portions of sterile filaments, and they persist and constitute the roof of the cavity (conceptacle) containing the mature tetrasporangia. Tetrasporic conceptacles differ from conceptacles of the gametophyte in that they have several pore-like openings, each formed by disintegration of a terminal cell of a fertile filament.

Bispores are not known for *Epilithon* but they are known[3] for several other genera of Corallinaceae. In some cases a single thallus produces both tetraspores and bispores; in other cases a single thallus produces

[1] Kylin, 1928. [2] Suneson, 1950. [3] Suneson, 1943, 1950.

but one kind of spore. Bispores may be uninucleate or binucleate. When uninucleate the nuclei are diploid and when binucleate the nuclei are haploid.[1]

ORDER 4. GIGARTINALES

The Gigartinales are the only tetrasporophytic Florideae in which the auxiliary cell is a vegetative cell of the gametophyte. In some genera the auxiliary cell is the supporting cell of a carpogonial filament; in other genera it lies in vegetative filaments remote from the carpogonial filaments. The order includes some 65 genera and 500 species. These have been divided into 20 families.[2]

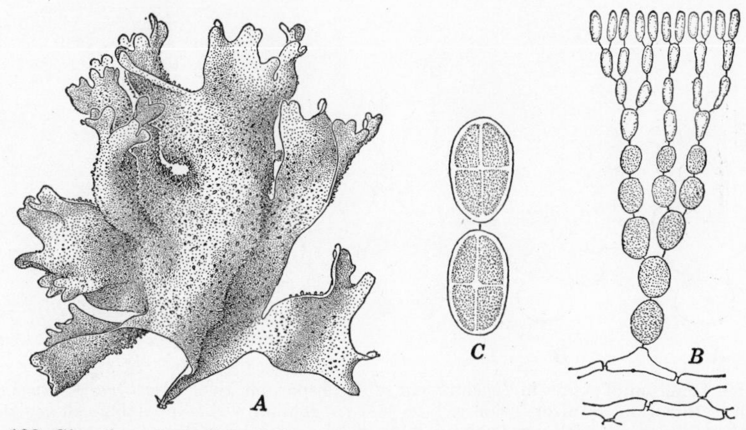

FIG. 188. *Gigartina. A*, thallus of *G. papillata* (C.Ag.) J. Ag. *B–C*, young and mature tetrasporangia of *G. leptorhynchos* J. Ag. (*A*, × ½; *B–C*, × 650.)

Gigartina, the type genus, exemplifies the genera in which the auxiliary cell is a supporting cell of a carpogonial filament. *Gigartina* is widely distributed in extratropical portions of the Atlantic and Pacific Oceans. There are about 90 species, each with a more or less definite geographical range. Along the shores of North America there are 28 species on the Pacific Coast[3] and but one species on the Atlantic Coast.[4] A thallus has a more or less disciform holdfast bearing one or more erect shoots. Most species have a perennial holdfast that gives rise to new shoots each spring. According to the species, the shoots are cylindrical or foliaceous; and undivided to dichotomously, irregularly, or pinnately divided. When mature, a shoot bears many small papillate or ligulate outgrowths (Fig. 188*A*).

A shoot has a multiaxial growing point. At the center of mature portions is a medulla composed of numerous parallel, colorless, longitudi-

[1] Suneson, 1950. [2] Kylin, 1932.
[3] Setchell and Gardner, 1933. [4] Taylor, 1937.

nal filaments. External to the medulla is a cortex composed of erect filaments with progressively smaller cells toward the exterior. The cortex is compacted into a pseudoparenchymatous tissue containing many chromatophores.

The gametophytes are heterothallic. Male plants bear their spermatangia in irregularly shaped sori. Spermatangial mother cells are superficial cells of a thallus and each of them generally cuts off more than one spermatangium.

Female gametophytes form their procarps (see page 306) on small papillate or laminate outgrowths from the surface of the thallus. Procarps

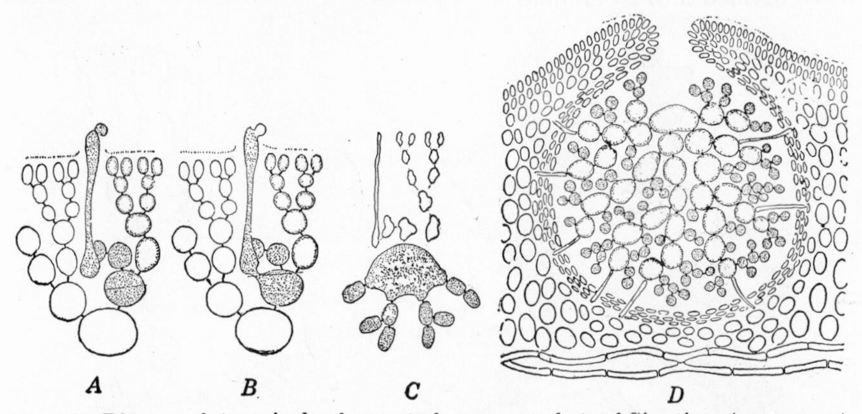

Fig. 189. Diagram of stages in development of carposporophyte of *Gigartina*. *A*, procarp at time of fertilization. *B*, after fusion of base of carpogonium with supporting cell (auxiliary cell). *C*, auxiliary cell with young gonimoblast filaments and remains of rest of procarp. *D*, carposporophyte with young carposporangia and haustorial filaments penetrating the nurse tissue.

are borne near the base of cortical filaments. A procarp (Fig. 189*A*) consists of a supporting cell bearing a three-celled carpogonial filament and a short sterile filament.[1] The sterile filament is erect and the carpogonial filament is so bent that the base of the carpogonium lies near the supporting cell. Fertilization is followed by an establishment of a tubular connection between the carpogonial base and the supporting cell which now becomes the auxiliary cell (Fig. 189*B*). There is then a migration of a diploid nucleus into the auxiliary cell.[1] The auxiliary cell next sends forth several gonimoblast filaments that grow toward the thallus interior. The carposporophyte thus formed is freely branched and with many short lateral branchlets in which each cell develops into a carposporangium (Fig. 189*C–D*). All food for early development of a carposporophyte is derived from the auxiliary cell. Later on, vegetative cells adjoining the carposporophyte differentiate into a nurse tissue (see page 306) which furnishes additional food. The carposporophyte obtains this food by

[1] Sjöstedt, 1926.

means of long tubular haustorial filaments that grow into the nurse tissue (Fig. 189*D*). Development of a carposporophyte is accompanied by a thickening of cortical tissue external to it and a development of an opening through which the carpospores escape.

Tetrasporophytes develop tetrasporangia internally and in sori (Fig. 188*B–C*). The tetrasporangia are formed from the inner half of the cortex and each cell in this portion develops into a tetrasporangium whose protoplast becomes cruciately divided into four tetraspores.[1]

Agardhiella, a genus with three species, is representative of the Gigartinales in which a vegetative cell remote from a carpogonial filament be-

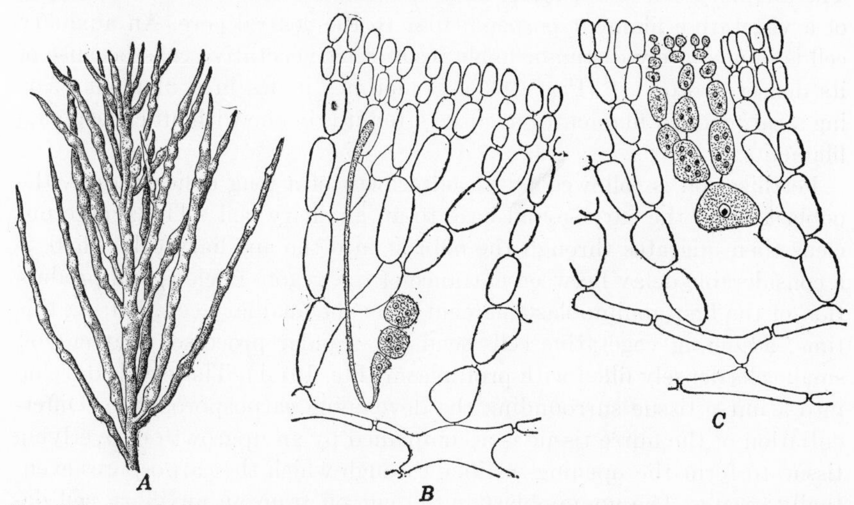

FIG. 190. *Agardhiella coulteri* (Harv.) Setchell. *A*, fruiting female gametophyte. *B*, portion of thallus with carpogonial filament. *C*, portion of thallus with auxiliary cell filament. (*A*, × ½; *B–C*, × 430.)

comes an auxiliary cell. *Agardhiella* is a rather common alga along both the Atlantic and Pacific Coasts of this country.

Agardhiella has a cylindrical branched thallus which is attached to the substratum by a discoid holdfast. The erect portion has numerous alternate branches tapering at both apex and base (Fig. 190*A*). The growing points are multiaxial. At the center of mature portions of a branch is a medulla composed of more or less parallel, colorless, longitudinal filaments. The medulla is ensheathed by a cortex composed of erect, dichotomously branched filaments whose cells are progressively smaller from base to apex.

Gametophytes of *Agardhiella* are heterothallic. Male thalli produce spermatangia in sori of varying size that are borne upon young branches.[2]

[1] Kylin, 1928. [2] Kylin, 1928; Osterhout, 1898.

A superficial cell of the branch bears three to five spermatangial mother cells, each of which cuts off two or three spermatangia.

Carpogonial filaments are differentiated less than 1 mm. back from growing tips of branches of female gametophytes. They are borne adaxially upon the corticating filaments and generally upon the next to the lowermost cell. The carpogonial filaments are three-celled and at first grow toward the center of the thallus. As the trichogyne elongates, it bends through an arc of 180 degrees, and its distal end grows to the thallus surface (Fig. 190*B*). The carpogonium is always uninucleate; the other two cells of a carpogonial filament contain two to five nuclei each. The auxiliary cell[1] is an intercalary cell midway between base and apex of a vegetative filament perpendicular to the central core. An auxiliary cell is immediately distinguishable from other vegetative cells because of its denser protoplast (Fig. 190*C*). Sometimes it lies in a filament bearing a carpogonial filament, but more often it is in one without carpogonial filaments.

Fertilization is followed by an outgrowth of a long delicate tube, the oöblast, from the carpogonial base to an auxiliary cell.[1] The zygote nucleus then migrates through the oöblast into the auxiliary cell. There is a considerable delay between entrance of the zygote nucleus and production of the first gonimoblast filament from the auxiliary cell. During this time, adjoining vegetative cells send out tubular processes that cut off small cells densely filled with protoplasm (Fig. 191*A*). These cells develop into a nurse tissue surrounding the developing carposporophyte. Differentiation of the nurse tissue is accompanied by an upgrowth of overlying tissue to form the opening, ostiole, through which the carpospores eventually escape. The gonimoblast initial cut off from an auxiliary cell develops into a radiately branched spherical mass of intertwined gonimoblast filaments (Fig. 191*B*). Most of the filaments lie internal to the nurse tissue, but some of them are haustorial in nature and penetrate the nurse tissue. Carposporangia are developed from terminal cells of branch tips at the periphery of a carposporophyte. Carpospores liberated from the carposporangia float out through the ostiole.

Agardhiella is one of the genera in which there is some cultural evidence[2] that carpospores develop into tetrasporophytes, hence gives evidence that tetraspores give rise to sexual plants. Tetrasporangia are differentiated from superficial cells of a tetrasporophyte (Fig. 191*C*). Development of tetrasporangia is accompanied by an upgrowth of adjoining vegetative tissues. Thus the mature tetrasporangia lie embedded a short distance beneath the thallus surface. At the time of spore formation the protoplast divides zonately into four tetraspores.

[1] Kylin, 1928; Osterhout, 1898. [2] Lewis, 1912.

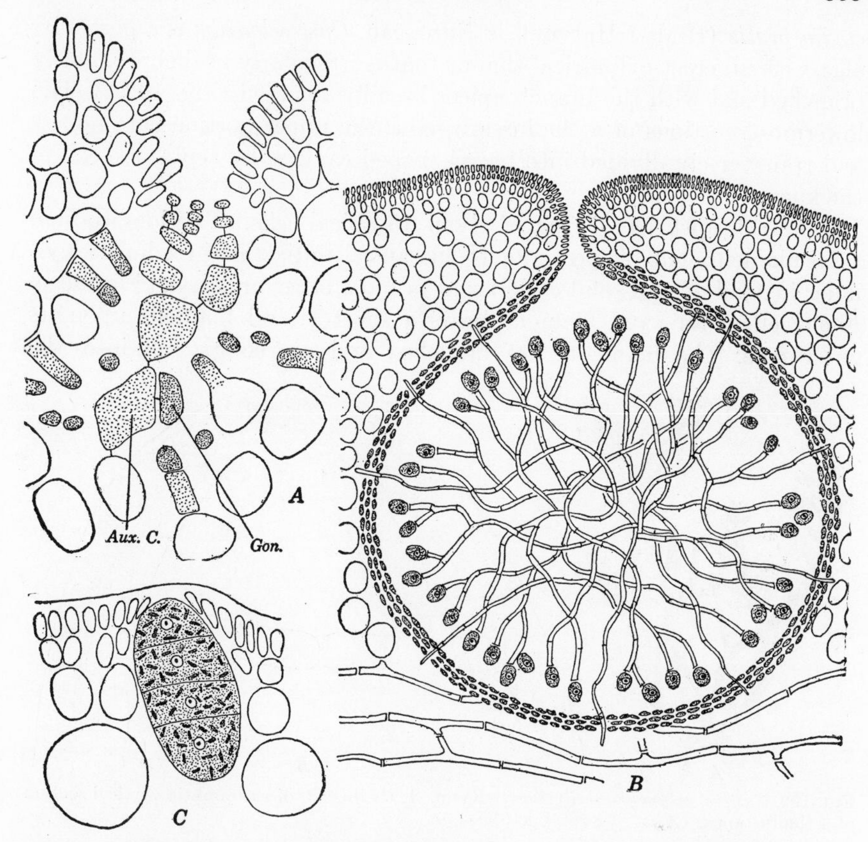

FIG. 191. *Agardhiella coulteri* (Harv.) Setchell. *A*, portion of a female gametophyte containing an auxiliary cell (*Aux. C.*) that has formed the first cell (*Gon.*) of a gonimoblast filament. *B*, diagrammatic vertical section of a carposporophyte with young carposporangia. *C*, tetrasporangium. (*A*, × 430; *B*, × 80; *C*, × 325.)

ORDER 5. RHODYMENIALES

The Rhodymeniales are tetrasporophytic Florideae in which the auxiliary cell is a special cell of the procarp and one differentiated before fertilization. The auxiliary cell is the terminal member of a two-celled filament borne upon the supporting cell of a carpogonial filament. According to the genus a procarp has either one or two filaments terminating in an auxiliary cell. The order includes about 25 genera and 130 species.[1] These are placed in two families.[2]

Gastroclonium, here selected to exemplify the order, has three species. The only species of the United States is *G. coulteri* (Harv.) Kylin, a common species along the Pacific Coast. The best-known species, *G. ovale* (Huds.) Kütz. [often called *Lomentaria ovalis* (Huds.) J.G.Ag. or *Chylo-*

[1] Kylin, 1931*A*. [2] Bliding, 1928; Kylin, 1931*A*.

cladia ovalis (Huds.) Harvey], is European. *Gastroclonium* is a perennial alga with an erect cylindrical thallus that is irregularly or dichotomously branched and with the branch apices broadly rounded (Fig. 192*A*). The lowermost portions of a thallus are solid; the upper portions are hollow and transversely divided into barrel-shaped cavities by septa one cell in thickness.

A branch apex has a ring of about 15 apical cells.[1] The longitudinal axial filaments cut off posterior to the apical initials lie in a hollow cylinder instead of in a solid cylinder as in most other multiaxial Florideae. Each cell of an axial filament bears a short lateral filament upon its outer face. The filaments are branched and are compacted into the

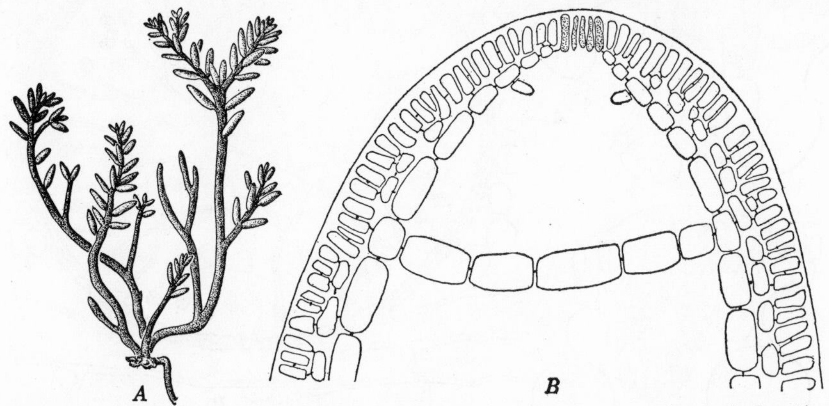

FIG. 192. *Gastroclonium coulteri* (Harv.) Kylin. *A*, thallus. *B*, diagrammatic vertical section of a thallus apex. (*A*, × ½; *B*, × 215.)

pseudoparenchymatous tissue which surrounds the central cavity of mature portions of a thallus (Fig. 192*B*). Septation of the central cavity is due to a development of horizontal unbranched filaments on the internal face of axial filaments. They are formed simultaneously at the same level upon all axial filaments, and they grow inward until they meet one another at the center of the thallus.

Gametophytes of *Gastroclonium* are heterothallic, but male plants are much scarcer than female ones.[2] The spermatangia lie in irregularly shaped sori borne upon the bladder-like branchlets at the distal end of a thallus. The spermatangial mother cells are borne at tips of lateral filaments from the axial filaments. Each spermatangial mother cell generally bears three spermatangia.[2]

The supporting cell of a carpogonial filament is differentiated very close to the thallus apex, and it is borne directly upon a cell of an axial filament. The supporting cell gives rise to a four-celled carpogonial filament in which the lowermost cell is binucleate and the other cells

[1] Bliding, 1928. [2] Grubb, 1925.

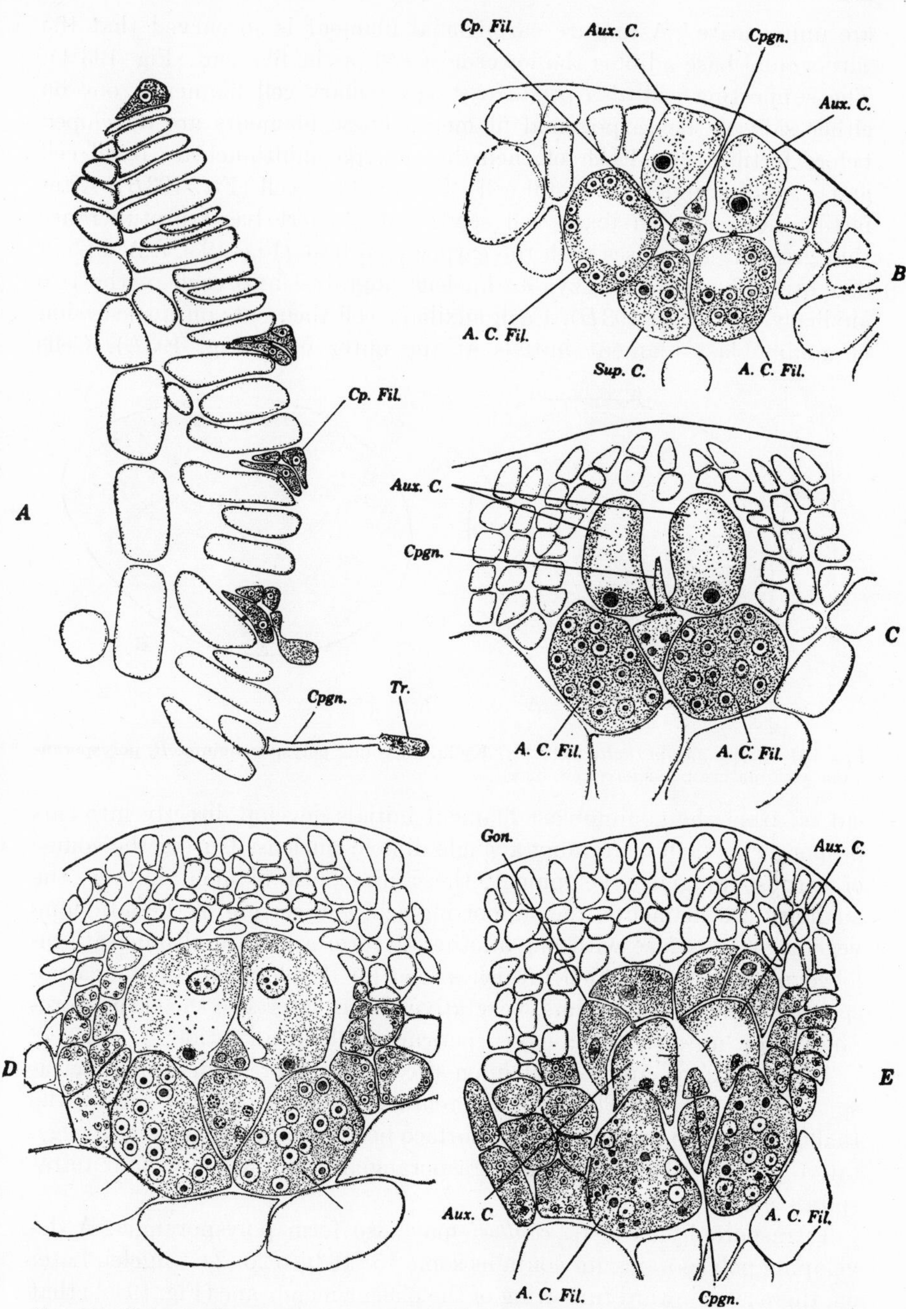

FIG. 193. *Gastroclonium ovale* (Huds.) Kylin. *A*, vertical section of a thallus apex with young carpogonial filaments. *B*, transverse section of a carpogonial filament and the adjacent auxiliary cell filaments before fertilization. *C*, the same after fusion of the carpogonial base with the auxiliary cells. *D*, the same after migration of a diploid nucleus into each auxiliary cell. *E*, after the auxiliary cells have cut off initials of gonimoblast filaments. (*After Bliding*, 1928.) (*Aux. C.*, auxiliary cell; *A. C. Fil.*, auxiliary cell filament; *Cpgn.*, carpogonium; *Cp. Fil.*, carpogonial filament; *Gon.*, gonimoblast; *Sup. C.*, supporting cell; *Tr.*, trichogyne.) (*A–B*, × 500; *C–E*, × 400.)

are uninucleate.[1] A mature carpogonial filament is so curved that the carpogonial base adjoins the lowermost cell of the filament (Fig. 193*A*). The supporting cell also produces two auxiliary cell filaments, one on either side of the carpogonial filament. These filaments are developed before fertilization. Each of them has a large multinucleate basal cell and a small uninucleate distal cell—the auxiliary cell (Fig. 193*B*). After fertilization each auxiliary cell sends out a short basal protuberance that grows to and fuses with the carpogonial base (Fig. 193*C*). A diploid daughter nucleus of the zygote nucleus migrates[1] into each of the two auxiliary cells (Fig. 193*D*). Each auxiliary cell then cuts off a succession of gonimoblast filament initials at the outer face (Fig. 193*E*). Cells

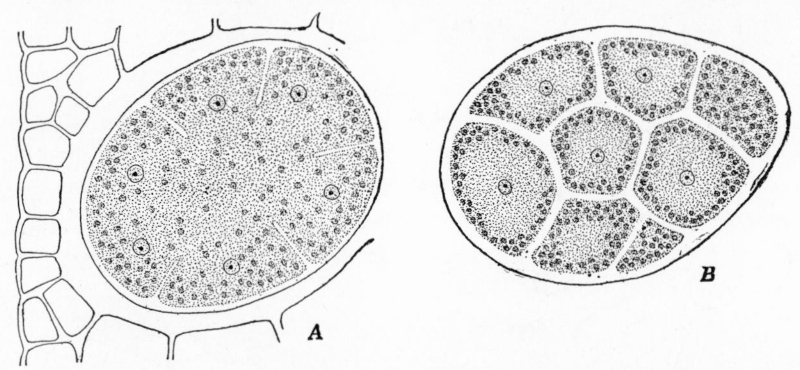

FIG. 194. *Gastroclonium coulteri* (Harv.) Kylin. *A*, young polysporangium. *B*, polysporangium with mature polyspores. (× 325.)

cut off from the gonimoblast filament initials develop directly into carposporangia, each containing a single diploid nucleus. During the course of carposporangial development, the gonimoblast filament initials, the auxiliary cell filaments, the supporting cell, and certain of the adjoining vegetative cells fuse with one another to form a large multinucleate bilobed placental cell which furnishes food for development of the carposporangia. At the same time, vegetative tissues lateral to the carposporophyte grow upward into a closed pericarp without an ostiole.

Tetrasporangia are formed upon the ultimate branchlets of a tetrasporophytic thallus. They are differentiated from superficial cells of the thallus but come to lie below the surface because of an upgrowth of vegetative portions. Division of a tetrasporangial protoplast into four tetraspores is pyramidate.[1]

Tetrasporophytes of *G. coulteri* may also form polysporangia. A developing polysporangium contains some 15 (16?) to 20 (24?) nuclei. Later on, there is an inward furrowing of the plasma membrane (Fig. 194*A*) that divides the sporangial contents into uninucleate polyspores (Fig. 194*B*).

[1] Bliding, 1928.

ORDER 6. CERAMIALES

The Ceramiales are the only tetrasporophytic Florideae in which the procarp has an auxiliary cell that is produced after fertilization. The auxiliary cell is borne directly upon the supporting cell of a carpogonial filament. The order includes about 160 genera and 900 species. These are divided into three families.[1]

Polysiphonia is one of the few genera in which there has been a demonstration[2] that carpospores grow into tetrasporophytes and that tetraspores grow into gametophytes. The nuclear behavior throughout the entire life cycle is also definitely known.[3] *Polysiphonia* is a common alga along both the Atlantic and Pacific Coasts of this country.

Germinating carpospores and tetraspores divide transversely into a small lower cell and a large upper cell, both of which also divide transversely.[4] The lowermost of the four cells develops into a long unicellular rhizoid whose distal end expands into an irregularly lobed attachment disk. The uppermost cell becomes an apical cell that cuts off a linear file of axial cells at its posterior face. Cell division in a vertical plane begins when the plantlet is six or seven cells in length, and each axial cell in the basal portion of the file cuts off an encircling layer of **pericentral cells** (Fig. 195*A*). The number of encircling pericentral cells is fairly constant for any given species and ranges from 4 to 24. Many of the first-formed pericentral cells send out secondary rhizoids which help anchor the thallus. Each axial cell two or three removed from the apical cell may divide diagonally at the upper end and cut off a small **trichoblast initial.** Repeated division of the trichoblast initial produces a uniseriate dichotomously forked gradually tapering multicellular filament—the **trichoblast.** Cells of a trichoblast are uninucleate and colorless or with very faintly colored chromatophores. The trichoblasts are generally borne in a spiral succession along the thallus. Some species have an early abscission of the trichoblast; other species retain all or certain of them for a considerable time. The cells of the axial filament cut off an encircling layer of pericentral cells after they have cut off the trichoblast initial. Each cell of the transverse tier thus formed elongates to several times its original length (Fig. 195*B*). Mature portions of thalli of most species retain this "polysiphonous" organization, but there are certain species in which older portions of the thallus may also become "corticated" through the formation of a layer of small cells external to the pericentral cells.

Lateral branches are generally differentiated close to the growing apex and before the formation of pericentral cells. An initial of a lateral branch

[1] Schmitz and Hauptfleisch, 1896–1897. [2] Lewis, 1912, 1914.
[3] Iyengar and Balakrishnan, 1949; Yamanouchi, 1906.
[4] Derick, 1899; Kylin, 1917*A*.

is formed in the same manner as that of a trichoblast. In some cases, as in *P. nigrescens* (J. E. Smith) Grev., they develop axillary to and from the basal cell of a trichoblast.[1] In other cases they replace certain trichoblasts, and sometimes there is a development of branches upon mature portions of a thallus.

Gametophytes of most, if not all, species of *Polysiphonia* are heterothallic. The spermatangia are produced upon fertile trichoblasts borne near the thallus apex. A developing, fertile trichoblast branches dichotomously after it has become two or three cells in length. Both arms

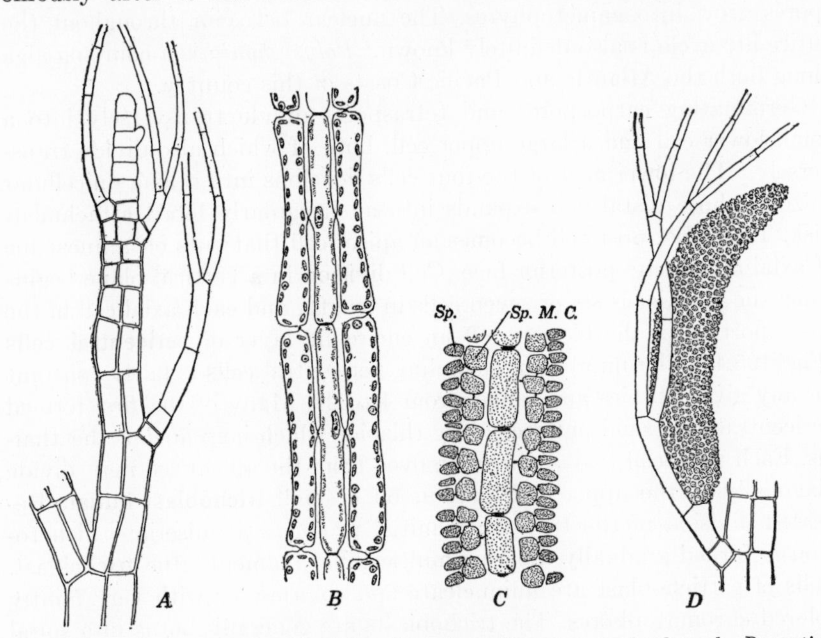

Fig. 195. *Polysiphonia flexicaulis* Harv. *A*, surface view of apex of a branch. *B*, vertical section of mature portion of a branch. *C–D*, *Polysiphonia* sp. *C*, optical section of a fertile trichoblast with spermatangial mother cells (*Sp. M. C.*) bearing spermatangia (*Sp.*). *D*, surface view of a fertile spermatangial trichoblast. (*A*, × 430; *B–C*, × 650; *D*, × 325.)

of the dichotomy may develop into a fertile axis [*P. lanosa* (L.) Tandy[2]], but in most species[3] one arm develops into a short fertile axis and the other into a long, repeatedly branched, sterile axis (Fig. 195*D*). A fertile axis is several cells in length and unbranched. The two lowermost cells are sterile; the others each cut off a variable number of encircling pericentral cells. Each pericentral cell cuts off one or more spermatangial mother cells at the free face.[2] According to the species,[3] the spermatangial mother cell bears two, three, or four spermatangia (Fig. 195*C*). The spermatium is liberated by a rupture of the spermatangial wall, and, after it has been discharged, there may be a proliferation of a new spermatangium within the old empty spermatangial wall.

[1] Kolderup-Rosenvinge, 1909–1924. [2] Grubb, 1925. [3] Grubb, 1925; Kylin, 1923.

The procarps are borne upon a greatly reduced, fertile trichoblast of a female gametophyte. The initial cell of a fertile female trichoblast is cut off from an axial filament cell three or four cells back from the thallus apex. The axial filament cell also cuts off an encircling ring of pericen-

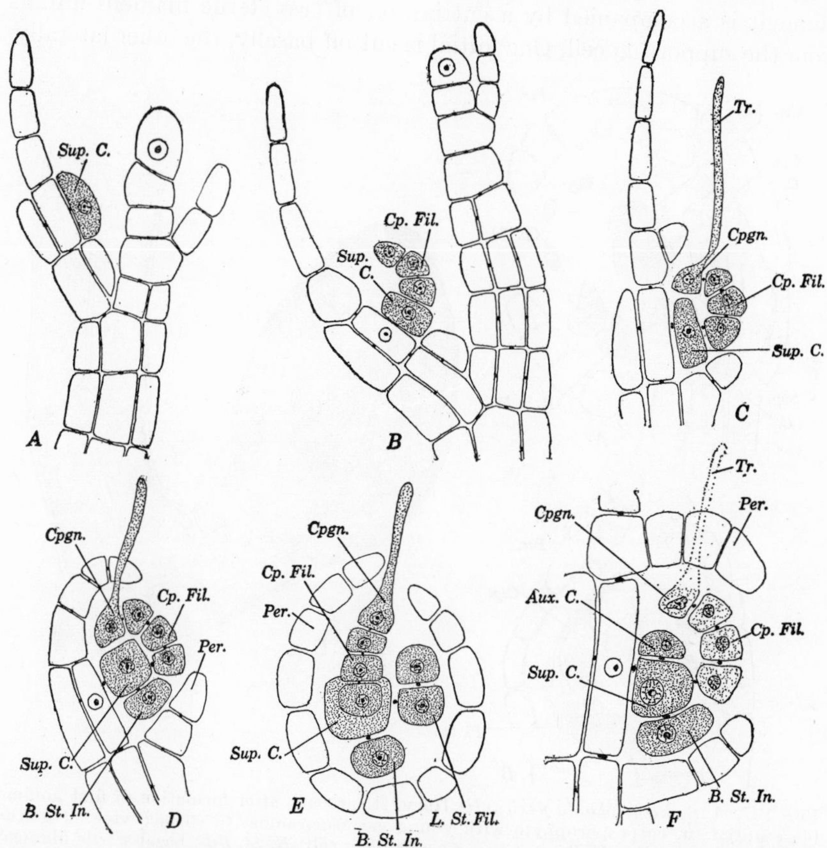

FIG. 196. *Polysiphonia flexicaulis* Harv. *A–E*, longitudinal sections showing the development of the procarp up to the time of fertilization. *A*, before development of carpogonial filament. *B–C*, developing and mature carpogonial filaments. *D*, after the cutting off of sterile filament initials. *E*, tangential section of *D*, showing the basal and lateral sterile filaments. *F*, after fertilization and formation of the auxiliary cell. (*Aux. C.*, auxiliary cell; *B. St. In.*, basal sterile initial; *Cpgn.*, carpogonium; *Cp. Fil.*, carpogonial filament; *L. St. Fil.*, lateral sterile filament; *Per.*, pericarp; *Sup. C.*, supporting cell; *Tr.*, trichogyne.) (× 875.)

tral cells about the same time it cuts off the trichoblast initial. The trichoblast initial looks so much like one of the pericentral cells that it is often called the **fertile pericentral cell.**

The trichoblast initial grows into a trichoblast five to seven cells in length, and one in which the two lowermost cells each cut off an ensheathing layer of pericentral cells (Fig. 196*A*). One of the adaxial cells in the upper tier of pericentral cells is the supporting cell of the future carpogonial filament. This supporting cell cuts off an initial at its free face, and this initial produces a curved, four-celled, carpogonial filament in which the terminal cell metamorphoses into a carpogonium with a long erect trichogyne (Fig. 196*B–C*). Development of the carpogonial filament is accompanied by a cutting off of two **sterile filament initials** from the supporting cell. One initial is cut off basally, the other laterally.

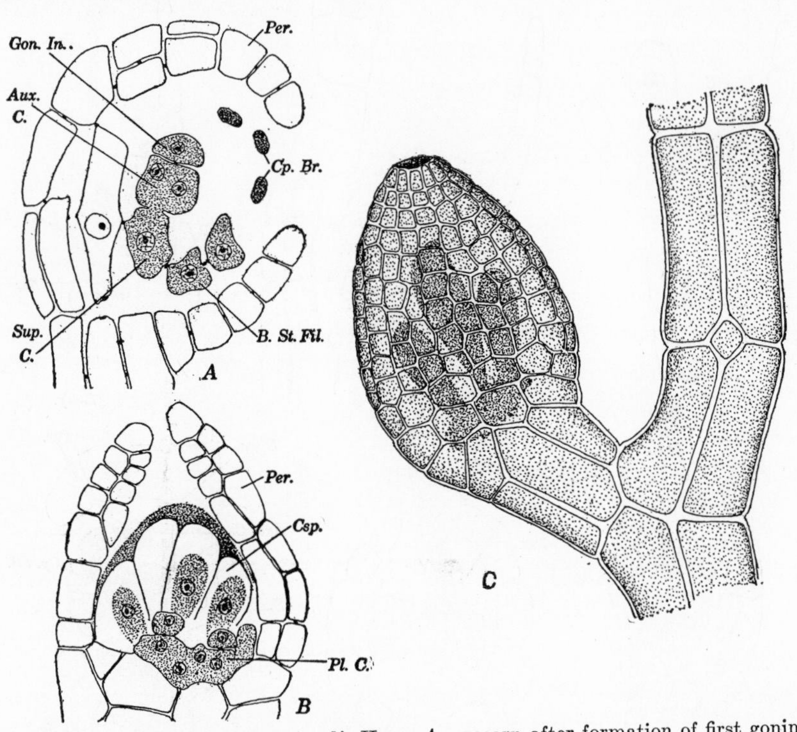

Fig. 197. *A–B*, *Polysiphonia flexicaulis* Harv. *A*, procarp after formation of first gonimoblast initial. *B*, carposporophyte with young carposporangia. *C*, surface view of mature pericarp of *P. pacifica* Hollenb. (*Aux. C.*, auxiliary cell; *B. St. Fil.*, basal sterile filament; *Cp. Br.*, remains of carpogonial filament; *Csp.*, carposporangium; *Gon. In.*, gonimoblast initial; *Per.*, pericarp; *Pl. C.*, placental cell; *Sup. C.*, supporting cell.) (*A*, × 875; *B*, × 430; *C*, × 215.)

The basal sterile filament initial remains undivided for a time; the lateral one divides[1] immediately (Fig. 196*D–E*).

Fertilization takes place at this stage of development and is effected in the usual manner.[2] Shortly afterward the lateral sterile filament becomes 4- to 10-celled, and the basal sterile initial develops into a 2-celled filament. Following this the supporting cell buds off a daughter cell at the upper side (Fig. 196*F*). This cell (the auxiliary cell) lies below, and

[1] Kylin, 1923. [2] Yamanouchi, 1906.

soon establishes a tubular connection with, the carpogonial base. A diploid daughter nucleus of the zygote nucleus next migrates into the auxiliary cell.[1] The gonimoblast grows from the upper side of the auxiliary cell (Fig. 197*A*). It consists of a densely compacted mass of gonimoblast filaments in which each cell is uninucleate and has a diploid nucleus. The carposporangia are elongate and are developed only from terminal cells of gonimoblast filaments. The single carpospore within each carposporangium has a diploid nucleus. Development of the carposporophyte is accompanied by a gradual fusion of the supporting cell, the auxiliary cell, and cells of the sterile filaments into a single large, irregularly shaped, placental cell (Fig. 197*B*). The carpogonial filament withers and does not contribute to the placental cell. The mature carposporophyte is surrounded by a large urn-shaped pericarp with a conspicuous ostiole at the distal end (Fig. 197*C*). Development of the pericarp begins before fertilization, and it is developed from pericentral trichoblast cells adjacent to the supporting cell.

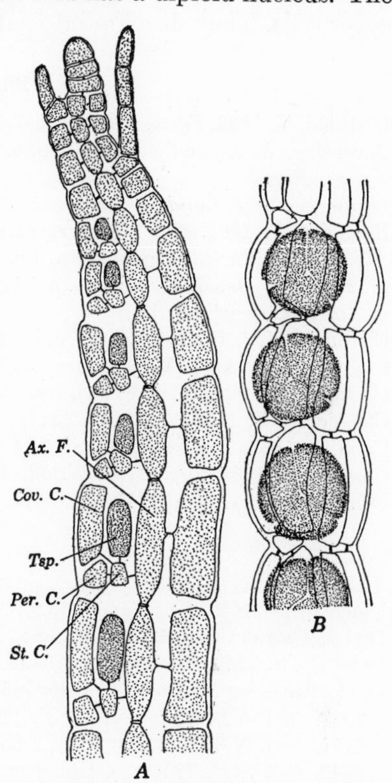

FIG. 198. *Polysiphonia* sp. *A*, optical section of apex of tetrasporophyte with young tetrasporangia. *B*, surface view of older portion containing mature tetrasporangia. (*Ax. F.*, axial filament; *Cov. C.*, cover cell; *Per. C.*, peripheral cell; *St. C.*, stalk cell; *Tsp.*, tetrasporangium.) (*A*, × 650; *B*, × 215.)

Carpospores liberated from the carposporangia develop into tetrasporophytes.[2] Only one pericentral cell of any transverse tier in a fruiting tetrasporophyte produces a tetrasporangium. However, tetrasporangia are usually developed in several successive tiers. The fertile pericentral cell of a tier is smaller than the other pericentral cells. It first cuts off a daughter cell at its outer face. In some species, as *P. nigrescens*, the daughter cell cuts off two **cover cells** at the upper face;[3] in other species, as *P. violacea* (Roth) Grev.,[4] the daughter cell cuts off two large cover cells and a small **peripheral cell** (Fig. 198*A*). In either case the fertile pericentral cell then divides transversely. The lower daughter cell is a

[1] Yamanouchi, 1906. [2] Lewis, 1912, 1914.
[3] Kolderup-Rosenvinge, 1909–1924; Kylin, 1923.
[4] Kolderup-Rosenvinge, 1904–1924.

stalk cell; the upper is the tetrasporangium. The sporangial cell increases to several times its original size; its single nucleus divides meiotically,[1] and the protoplast divides to form four pyramidately disposed tetraspores (Fig. 198*B*). The tetraspores are liberated by a rupture of the sporangial wall and a longitudinal spreading apart of the two elongate cover cells. They develop into gametophytes.[2]

Bibliography

Berthold, G. **1882.** *Fauna u. Flora d. Golfes von Neapel* **8:** 1–28. 1 pl. [*Porphyra.*]

Beveridge, W. A., and V. J. Chapman. **1950.** *Pacific Sci.* **4:** 188–201. 14 figs. [Vertical zonation.]

Bliding, C. **1928.** *Lunds. Univ. Ärsskr.* N.F. **24,** Nr. 3: 1–74. 52 figs. [*Gastroclonium.*]

Børgesen, F. **1905.** The algae-vegetation of the Faeröese coasts. In Botany of the Faeröes. Part 3. Copenhagen. Pp. 683–834. 12 pl. 14 figs.

1927. *Kgl. Danske Videnskab. Selskab. Biol. Meddel.* **6,** Nr. 6: 1–97. 49 figs. [Algae of Canary Islands.]

Chapman, V. J. **1950.** Seaweeds and their uses. London. 287 pp. 20 pl. 52 figs.

Chester, Grace D. **1896.** *Bot. Gaz.* **21:** 340–347. 2 pl. [*Nemalion.*]

Claussen, H. **1929.** *Ber. Deutsch. Bot. Ges.* **47:** 544–547. 4 figs. [*Phyllophora.*]

Cleland, R. E. **1919.** *Ann. Bot.* **33:** 324–351. 3 pl. 3 figs. [*Nemalion.*]

Cohn, F. **1867.** *Arch. mikr. Anat.* **3:** 1–60. 2 pl. [Relationships of Rhodophyta.]

Coleman, J. **1933.** *Jour. Marine Biol. Assoc.* **18:** 435–476. 15 figs. [Vertical zonation.]

Colin, H., and J. Augier. **1933.** *Compt. Rend. Acad. Sci. Paris* **196:** 1042–1043. [Floridoside.]

Colin, H., and E. Guéguen. **1930.** *Ibid.* **191:** 163–164. [Floridoside.]

1933. *Ibid.* **197:** 1688–1690. [Floridoside.]

Dangeard, P. **1927.** *Le Botaniste* **18:** 183–244. 5 pl. 12 figs. [*Porphyra.*]

Derick, Carrie M. **1899.** *Bot. Gaz.* **28:** 246–263. 3 pl. 5 figs. [Holdfasts.]

Doty, M. S. **1946.** *Ecology* **27:** 315–328. 6 figs. [Vertical zonation.]

Drew, Kathleen M. **1934.** *Ann. Bot.* **48:** 549–573. 2 pl. 2 figs. [Diploid gametophytes.]

1937. *Ibid.* N.S. **1:** 463–476. 1 pl. 12 figs. [Polyspores.]

1939. *Ibid.* N.S. **3:** 347–367. 1 pl. 35 figs. [Paraspores.]

1943. *Ibid.* N.S. **7:** 23–30. 1 pl. 1 fig. [Triploid thalli.]

1949. *Nature* **164:** 748. 2 figs. [*Porphyra.*]

1951. Rhodophyta. In G. M. Smith (editor), Manual of phycology. Waltham, Mass. Pp. 167–191. 4 figs.

Dunn, Grace A. **1917.** *Bot. Gaz.* **63:** 425–467. 4 pl. 7 figs. [Cryptonemiales.]

Feldmann, J. **1938.** *Rev. Algologique* **10:** 1–339. 19 pl. 26 figs. [Algae of Mediterranean.]

1939. *Bull. Soc. Hist. Nat. Afrique du Nord* **30:** 87–97. 4 figs. [Carpotetraspores.]

1942. Les Algues marines de la côte des Albères. IV. Rhodophycées. Paris. Pp. 199–372. 61 figs.

1952. *Rev. Cytol. et Biol. Veg.* **13:** 1–49. 6 figs. [Life cycles.]

Feldmann, J., and G. Feldmann. **1942.** *Ann. Sci. Nat. Bot.* Ser. 11. **3:** 75–175. 26 figs. [Alternation of generations.]

1952. *Rev. Gen. Bot.* **59:** 313–323. 24 figs. [Reduplication of tetrasporophyte.]

Feldmann, J., and G. Mazoyer. **1937.** *Compt. Rend. Acad. Sci. Paris* **205:** 1085–1086. [Alternation of generations.]

[1] Yamanouchi, 1906. [2] Lewis, 1912, 1914.

Funk, G. **1927.** *Pubbl. Stazione Zool. Napoli* **7** (supplemento): 1–507. 20 pl. 50 figs. [Algae of Gulf of Naples.]

Geitler, L. **1924.** *Rev. Algologique* **1:** 357–375. 11 figs. [*Asterocytis.*]

Gregory, Beryl D. **1924.** *Jour. Linn. Soc. Bot. London* **49:** 531–551. 26 figs. [*Gymnogongrus.*]

Grubb, Violet M. **1923.** *Ann. Bot.* **37:** 131–140. 1 pl. 8 figs. [*Porphyra.*]

1923A. *Ibid.* **37:** 151–152. 2 figs. [Binucleate carpogonia.]

1924. *Rev. Algologique* **1:** 223–234. 4 figs. [*Porphyra.*]

1925. *Jour. Linn. Soc. Bot. London* **47:** 177–255. 36 figs. [Spermatangia.]

Haas, P., T. G. Hill, and W. H. K. Karstens. **1935.** *Ann. Bot.* **49:** 609–619. 6 figs. [Floridoside.]

Harder, R., and W. Koch. **1949.** *Nature* **163:** 106. 2 figs. [Alternation of generations.]

Haxo, F. T., and L. R. Blinks. **1950.** *Jour. Gen. Physiol.* **33:** 389–422. 22 figs. [Photosynthesis.]

Hoyt, W. D. **1920.** *Bull. U.S. Bureau of Fisheries* **36:** 371–556. 36 pl. 47 figs. [Algae of Beaufort, N.C.]

Humm, H. J. **1944.** *Science* **100:** 209–212. [Agar.]

Hus, H. T. A. **1902.** *Proc. Calif. Acad. Sci.* 3 ser. *Botany* **2:** 173–240. 3 pl. [*Porphyra.*]

Isaac, W. E. **1937.** *Trans. Roy. Soc. S. Africa* **25:** 115–152. 2 pl. 6 figs. [Vertical zonation.]

Ishikawa, M. **1921.** *Bot. Mag. Tokyo* **35:** 206–218. 1 pl. 14 figs. [*Porphyra.*]

Iyengar, M. O. P., and M. S. Balakrishnan. **1949.** *Proc. Indian Acad. Sci.* **29:** 105–108. 1 pl. 8 figs. [*Polysiphonia.*]

Joffé, Rachel. **1896.** *Bull. Soc. Bot. France* **43:** 143–146. 1 pl. [*Porphyra.*]

Killian, K. **1914.** *Zeitschr. Bot.* **6:** 209–278. 18 figs. [Spore germination.]

Knight, Margery, and Mary W. Parke. **1931.** *Mem. Liverpool Marine Biol. Comm.* **30:** 1–147. 19 pl. [Algae of Isle of Man.]

Knox, Elizabeth. **1926.** *Publ. Puget Sound Biol. Sta.* **5:** 125–135. 2 pl. [*Porphyra.*]

Kolderup-Rosenvinge, L. **1909–1924.** *Kgl. Danske Videnskab. Selsk. Skr.* **7** *Raekke, Naturvidenskab. og Math.* Afd. 7, Nr. 1–3: 486 pp. 7 pl. 453 figs. [Rhodophyta of Denmark.]

1929. *Kgl. Danske. Videnskab. Selsk. Biol. Meddel.* **8,** Nr. 4: 1–40. 1 pl. 18 figs. [*Phyllophora.*]

Kylin, H. **1914.** *Svensk Bot. Tidsskr.* **8:** 33–69. 2 pl. 12 figs. [Binucleate carpogonia.]

1916. *Zeitschr. Bot.* **8:** 97–123. 1 pl. 11 figs. [Binucleate carpogonia.]

1916A. *Ibid.* **8:** 545–586. 11 figs. [Binucleate carpogonia.]

1916B. *Ber. Deutsch. Bot. Ges.* **34:** 256–271. 7 figs. [*Nemalion.*]

1917. *Ibid.* **35:** 155–164. 7 figs. [Nemalionales.]

1917A. *Ark. Bot.* **14,** Nr. 22: 1–25. 12 figs. [Spore germination.]

1921. *Ibid.* **17,** Nr. 5: 1–12. 7 figs. [*Porphyra.*]

1923. *Kgl. Svensk. Vetenskab.-Ak. Handl.* **63,** Nr. 11: 1–139. 82 figs. [Development of various Florideae.]

1924. *Lunds Univ. Ärsskr.* N.F. **20,** Nr. 6: 1–111. 80 figs. [Ceramiales.]

1928. *Ibid.* **24,** Nr. 4: 1–127. 64 figs. [Development of various Florideae.]

1930. *Bot. Notiser* **1930:** 417–420. [Pigments.]

1930A. *Lunds Univ. Ärsskr.* N.F. **26,** Nr. 6: 1–104. 56 figs. [Development of various Florideae.]

1931. *Hoppe-Seyler's Zeitschr. Physiol. Chem.* **197:** 1–6. 2 figs. [Pigments.]

1931A. *Lunds Univ. Ärsskr.* N.F. **27,** Nr. 11: 1–48. 20 pl. 8 figs. [Rhodymeniales.]

1932. *Ibid.* **28,** Nr. 8: 1–88, 28 pl. 22 figs. [Gigartinales.]

1935. *Bot. Rev.* **1:** 138–148. [Classification of Florideae.]

1937. Anatomie der Rhodophyceen. In K. Linsbauer, Handbuch der Pflanzenanatomie. Vol. 6, Bd. 2. Pp. 1–347. 250 figs.

1943. *Föhr. Kgl. Fysiograf. Salls. i Lund* **13,** Nr. 6: 1–13. [Biochemistry.]

Lagerheim, G. **1892.** *Ber. Deutsch. Bot. Ges.* **10:** 366–374. 1 pl. [*Porphyra.*]

Lewis, I. F. **1909.** *Ann. Bot.* **23:** 639–690. 5 pl. 2 figs. [Multinucleate cells.]

1912. *Bot. Gaz.* **53:** 236–242. [Alternation of generations.]

1912A. *Science* N.S. **35:** 154. [*Nemalion.*]

1914. *Plant World* **17:** 31–35. [Alternation of generations.]

Magne, F. **1952.** *Compt. Rend. Acad. Sci. Paris* **234:** 986–988. 5 figs. [*Porphyra.*]

Moore, Lucy B. **1944.** *New Zealand Jour. Sci. and Tech.* **25:** 183–209. 16 figs. [Agar.]

Oltmanns, F. **1898.** *Bot. Zeitg.* **56:** 99–140. 4 pl. [Nature of cystocarp.]

1922. Morphologie und Biologie der Algen. 2d ed. Bd. 2. Jena. 439 pp. 150 figs.

Osterhout, W. J. V. **1898.** *Ann. Bot.* **10:** 403–427. 2 pl. [*Agardhiella.*]

1900. *Flora* **87:** 109–115. 1 pl. [Carpogonium.]

Pia, J. **1927.** Thallophyta. In M. Hirmer, Handbuch der Paläobotanik. Munich. Bd. 1. Pp. 31–136. 116 figs.

Printz, H. **1926.** *Skr. Norske Videnskab. Akad. i Oslo* (Mat.-Nat. Kl.) **1926,** Nr. 5: 1–273. 10 pl. 29 figs. [Algae of Norway.]

Schmitz, F. **1883.** *Sitzungsber. Preussisch. Akad. Wiss. Berlin* **1883:** 215–258. 1 pl. [Reproduction of Florideae.]

1889. *Flora* **47:** 435–456. 1 pl. [Classification of Florideae.]

Schmitz, F., and P. Hauptfleisch. **1896–1897.** Rhodophyceae. In A. Engler and K. Prantl. Die natürlichen Pflanzenfamilien. Teil 1, Abt. 2. Pp. 298–544. 97 figs.

Setchell, W. A. **1914.** *Univ. Calif. Publ. Bot.* **6:** 79–152. 7 pl. [*Scinaia.*]

1915. *Ann. Missouri Bot. Gard.* **2:** 287–305. [Temperature and geographical distribution.]

1926. *Proc. Amer. Phil. Soc.* **65:** 136–140. [Coral reefs.]

1929. *Proc. Fourth Pacific Sci. Congr. Java.* Pp. 265–286. [Coral reefs.]

Setchell, W. A., and N. L. Gardner. **1920.** *Univ. Calif. Publ. Bot.* **8:** 139–374. 31 pl. [Marine Chlorophyta of Pacific Coast.]

1933. *Ibid.* **17:** 255–340. 20 pl. [*Gigartina.*]

Sjöstedt, L. G. **1926.** *Lunds Univ. Årsskr.* N.F. **22,** Nr. 4: 1–94. 41 figs. [Development of various Florideae.]

Skuja, H. **1938.** *Acta Biol. Latvica* **8:** 1–26. [Relationships of Rhodophyta.]

1939. *Acta Hort. Bot. Univ. Latviensis* **11:** 23–38. [Classification of Bangioideae.]

Smith, G. M. **1933.** The fresh-water algae of the United States. New York. 716 pp. 449 figs.

Smith, G. M., and G. J. Hollenberg. **1943.** *Amer. Jour. Bot.* **30:** 211–222. 30 figs. [Carpotetrasporophytes.]

Smith, H. M. **1905.** *Bull. U.S. Bureau of Fisheries* **24:** 135–165. 4 pl. 24 figs. [Economic uses.]

Suneson, S. **1937.** *Lunds Univ. Årsskr.* N.F. **33,** Nr. 2: 1–101. 4 pl. 42 figs. [Corallinaceae.]

1943. *Ibid.* **39,** No. 9: 1–65. 9 pl. 26 figs. [Corallinaceae.]

1943A. *Bot. Notiser* **1943:** 372–381. 1 fig. [Spermatia.]

1950. *Ibid.* **1950:** 429–450. 8 figs. [Bispores.]

Svedelius, N. **1911.** Rhodophyceae. In A. Engler and K. Prantl, Die natürlichen Pflanzenfamilien. Teil 1. Abt. 2 (Nachträge). Pp. 191–276. 64 figs.

1911A. *Svensk. Bot. Tidsskr.* **5:** 264–324. 2 pl. 16 figs. [Meiosis.]

1914. *Ibid.* **8:** 1–32. 2 pl. 22 figs. [Binucleate carpogonia.]

1914A. *Ber. Deutsch. Bot. Ges.* **32:** 48–57. 1 pl. 1 fig. [Multinucleate tetrasporangia.]

1915. *Nova Acta Reg. Soc. Sci. Upsaliensis* 4 ser. **4,** Nr. 4: 1–55. 32 figs. [*Scinaia.*]
1917. *Ber. Deutsch. Bot. Ges.* **35:** 212–224. 7 figs. [Binucleate carpogonia.]
1917A. *Ibid.* **35:** 225–233. 4 figs. [Homologies of sex organs.]
1927. *Bot. Gaz.* **83:** 362–384. [Alternation of generations.]
1931. *Beih. Bot. Centralbl.* **48:** 38–59. 5 figs. [Alternation of generations.]
1933. *Nova Acta Reg. Soc. Sci. Upsaliensis* 4 ser. **9,** Nr. 1: 1–61. 49 figs. [Auxiliary cells.]
1935. *Ber. Deutsch. Bot. Ges.* **53:** (19)–(26). [Diploid tetraspores.]
1942. *Nova Acta Reg. Soc. Sci. Upsaliensis* 4 ser. **13,** Nr. 4: 1–154. 79 figs. [Auxiliary cells.]
Taylor, W. R. *Carnegie Inst. Wash. Publ.* **379:** 1–219. 37 pl. [Algae of Florida.]
1937. Marine algae of the Northeastern Coast of North America. Ann Arbor, Mich. 427 pp. 60 pl.
1950. *Biol. Bull.* **99:** 272–284. 52 figs. [*Dudresnaya.*]
1950A. Plants of Bikini and other Northern Marshall Islands. Ann Arbor, Mich. 227 pp. 79 pl.
Tilden, Josephine E. **1935.** The algae and their life relations. Minneapolis. 550 pp. 9 pl. 257 figs.
Tseng, C. K. **1944.** *Sci. Monthly* **58:** 24–32. 7 figs. [Agar.]
Westbrook, M. Alison. **1928.** *Ann. Bot.* **42:** 149–172. 1 pl. 8 figs. [Meiosis.]
1935. *Beih. Bot. Centralbl.* **53:** 564–585. 2 pl. [Meiosis.]
Wille, N. **1900.** *Nyt. Mag. Naturvidenskab.* **38:** 7–10. 1 pl. [*Asterocytis.*]
Wolfe, J. J. **1904.** *Ann. Bot.* **18:** 607–630. 2 pl. 1 fig. [*Nemalion.*]
Wood, E. J. F. **1946.** *Commonwealth of Australia. Council Sci. and Indust. Res. Bull.* **203:** 1–43. 4 pl. [Agar.]
Yamanouchi, S. **1906.** *Bot. Gaz.* **42:** 401–449. 10 pl. 3 figs. [*Polysiphonia.*]
1921. *Ibid.* **72:** 90–96. [Corallinaceae.]
Yendo, K. **1919.** *Bot. Mag. Tokyo* **33:** 73–93. 1 pl. 2 figs. [*Porphyra.*]

CHAPTER 9

MYXOMYCOPHYTA

The Myxomycophyta, the slime molds, resemble true fungi (Eumycophyta) in their lack of photosynthetic pigments and in their food reserves. They differ from Eumycophyta in that the plant body is a naked protoplast throughout all stages of vegetative development. The vegetative phase may be a single large multinucleate naked protoplast (**plasmodium**); or it may be a **pseudoplasmodium** resulting from aggregation of many small naked uninucleate protoplasts, each of which retains its individuality. Reproduction of Myxomycophyta is by a formation of small uninucleate spores, each with a distinct wall. In a majority of the genera the spores are borne within or upon a fructification of definite form; but there are genera where there is a production of a more or less amorphous mass of spores. According to the genus, a germinating spore gives rise to biflagellate swarmers or produces nonflagellate amoeboid cells (**myxamoebae**). Some genera have the swarmers fusing in pairs to form a zygote that develops directly into a plasmodium; other genera have the swarmers developing directly into plasmodia. Thus a plasmodium may be diploid or haploid. When haploid there is eventually a production of swarmers that fuse in pairs to form a zygote that is diploid. A number of genera have been shown to have a meiotic division of diploid nuclei immediately preceding spore formation.

Classification. Although certain mycologists[1] place the myxomycetes and chytridiaceous phycomycetes in a class equal in rank with other classes of fungi, most mycologists place the myxomycetes in a group by themselves and give the taxon the rank either of a class or of a division. All are agreed that the free-living plasmodial myxomycetes belong in the same taxon, but there is disagreement as to whether certain other organisms should be placed in it. The traditional association of the parasitic plasmodial forms (Plasmodiophorales) with plasmodial myxomycetes has been questioned during the past quarter century and several mycologists[2] think that they are in a more logical position when placed among the

[1] Gäumann, 1949; Langeron and Vanbreuseghem, 1952.

[2] Ainsworth and Bisby, 1950; Fitzpatrick, 1930; Martin, 1950; Sparrow, 1943.

Phycomycetae. The pseudoplasmodial genera are generally considered sufficiently related to the free-living plasmodial myxomycetes to be put in the same primary taxon, but there are those[1] who reject this association of the two.

There is also a small imperfectly known group of parasitic organisms without chromatophores whose cells are connected by cytoplasmic strands to form what is called a **net plasmodium.** Because of this they (the Labyrinthulae) are sometimes ranged alongside the plasmodial and pseudoplasmodial groups, but with a realization that the relationship is not a close one. The Labyrinthulae show considerable resemblance to such rhizopodial Xanthophyceae as *Chlorarachnion* (Fig. 96, page 172). There are also rhizopodial Chrysophyceae of a similar nature and among them are genera[2] without chromatophores but with typical chrysophycean cysts. The occurrence of such net plasmodial forms obviously related to algae seems to indicate that the Labyrinthulae may be more closely related to algae than to myxomycetes.

Exclusive of the Labyrinthulae the Myxomycophyta fall into three distinct groups each of which is here given the rank of a class. These classes are: the *Myxomycetae*, the *Plasmodiophoreae*, and the *Acrasieae*.

CLASS 1. MYXOMYCETAE

The vegetative phase of members of this class is a naked, amoeboid, multinucleate, free-living plasmodium that may be up to several centimeters in diameter. At the time of fruiting a plasmodium heaps up to form one or more sessile or stalked sporangia that generally have a wall-like layer (**peridium**) at the outside. The protoplast of a sporangium becomes divided into a large number of spores, each surrounded by a definite wall. A germinating spore gives rise to one to four biflagellate swarmers in which one flagellum is markedly shorter than the other. There may be an immediate union of the swarmers in pairs, or they may multiply vegetatively for one or more generations before fusion in pairs takes place. Gametic union is followed by union of the two gamete nuclei. The resultant zygote soon becomes amoeboid and develops into a multinucleate plasmodium with diploid nuclei. Meiosis generally takes place immediately before spore formation.

There are about 60 genera and 400 species.[3] These are divided into two subclasses; the *Endosporeae* and the *Exosporeae*.

SUBCLASS 1. ENDOSPOREAE

The Endosporeae produce their spores internally within a fruiting body of definite shape. This subclass includes all but one genus of the Myxomycetae.

[1] Jahn, 1928*A*; Martin, 1950. [2] Pascher, 1940. [3] Ainsworth and Bisby, 1950.

Plasmodia. All genera have a well-developed plasmodium (Fig. 199). Plasmodia are generally found creeping over moist decaying vegetable matter including rotting logs, old wood piles, and decaying leaves. The Endosporeae are an important constituent of the microflora of soil[1] but their presence in soil is not usually evident and can be demonstrated only by culture methods.

A plasmodium is differentiated into an inner granular portion containing many nuclei, and an outer hyaline portion without nuclei. Some plasmodia are colorless; others are colored, and taken collectively the

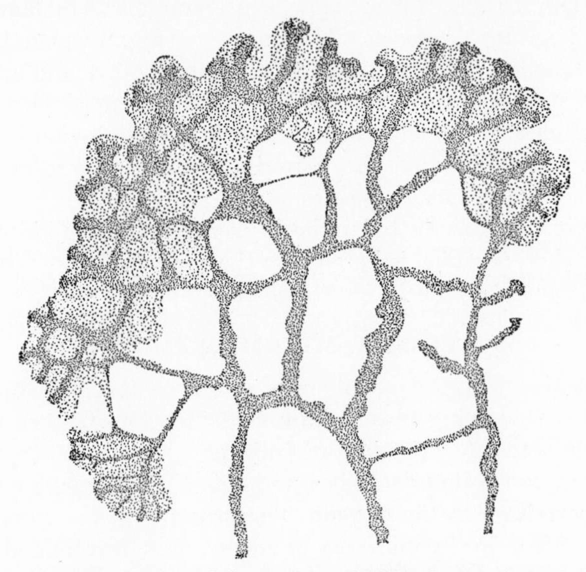

Fig. 199. Portion of plasmodium of *Didymium* sp. (× 30.)

range of color covers the entire spectrum. The color is generally due to a pigment produced by the plasmodium, but it may be due to pigments from organisms ingested by the plasmodium. The color of some species is quite constant; that of others is quite variable.[2] Among species varying in color, the variation may be due to the pH of the substratum. *Physarum polycephalum* Schw. is a species so sensitive to changes in the pH that its change in color makes it a living pH indicator.[3]

A plasmodium moves in an amoeboid manner and at times the rate of flow may be 1.35 mm. per second.[4] The anterior end of a moving plasmodium is a solid sheet with many small lobes projecting forward; elsewhere the plasmodium is a reticulate mass. The meshwork may be formed either by anastamosis of projecting lobes at the anterior end, or by develop-

[1] Thom and Raper, 1930. [2] Kambly, 1939.
[3] Seifritz and Zetzmann, 1935. [4] Kamiya, 1950.

ment of perforations in the plasmodial sheet.[1] As a plasmodium flows along it may fragment into two or more parts that continue growth as independent plasmodia. Conversely, two plasmodia may fuse to form a single plasmodium. There is rarely a fusion between plasmodia of two species, and even in the same species there may be physiological races that do not fuse with each other.[2]

Bacteria and fungus spores are the chief sources of food for growth of a plasmodium. They are ingested in the same manner as an amoeba ingests its food. The plasmodium of any species does not feed upon particular species of bacteria, but feeds upon a wide variety of them.[3] Plasmodia of a number of species have been isolated in pure (bacteria-free) culture,[4] but they cannot be cultured on any of the media successfully used for the cultivation of fungi. Autoclaved yeast must be added to the medium before the plasmodium will grow.

If conditions of moisture, temperature, or food supply become unfavorable, a plasmodium may become concentrated into one or more thick, horny, resting stages (**sclerotia**) that generally revert to the plasmodial condition with a return of favorable conditions. The length of time sclerotia remain viable depends upon the species; for example, sclerotia of *Badhamia foliicola* Lister remain viable for about a month[4] whereas those of *Physarum polycephalum* may remain viable for about three years.[5]

Sporangia. A plasmodium generally migrates to a more brightly illuminated and drier side of the substratum just before it fruits. Most genera have the plasmodium producing many stalked sporangia, which tend to lie grouped together upon the substratum (Fig. 200*C*). Other genera have all or the major portion of a plasmodium developing into a single sessile sporangium. If this sporangium is flattened and biscuit-shaped it is an **aethalium** (Fig. 200*A*); if it retains more or less of the reticulate outline of the plasmodium it is a **plasmodiocarp** (Fig. 200*B*).

Fruiting is affected by environmental conditions. When plasmodia are cultured in the laboratory, a diminution in the food supply frequently induces fruiting. Light is essential for fruiting of yellow-pigmented plasmodia and in *Physarum polycephalum* the shorter wave lengths of the visible spectrum are the only ones inducing fruiting.[6] Nonpigmented plasmodia do not need light to induce fruiting. The ratio between temperature and pH also has its effect on fruiting.[7]

Development of fructifications of species with stipitate sporangia begins with an aggregation of a plasmodium into a denser mass and a downward growth of furrows that cut it into many small fragments. Each fragment rounds up into a small knob that soon becomes a pillar in which

[1] Camp, 1937. [2] Gray, 1945. [3] Cohen, 1941. [4] Cohen, 1939.
[5] Gehenio, 1944. [6] Gray, 1938. [7] Gray, 1939.

the stipe of the fructification is first differentiated as an internal axial column of alveolate protoplasm.[1] The stipe gradually increases in height and eventually secretes a wall. While this is taking place the protoplasm of denser consistency flows upward along the outer face of the fructification and accumulates in a mass at the apex of the stipe. This apical mass of protoplasm, the young sporangium, eventually secretes a wall—the **peridium.** A large number of Myxomycetae have cellulose in their peridia.[2] Many genera also have the peridium becoming heavily impregnated with lime. During development of fruiting bodies a remnant of

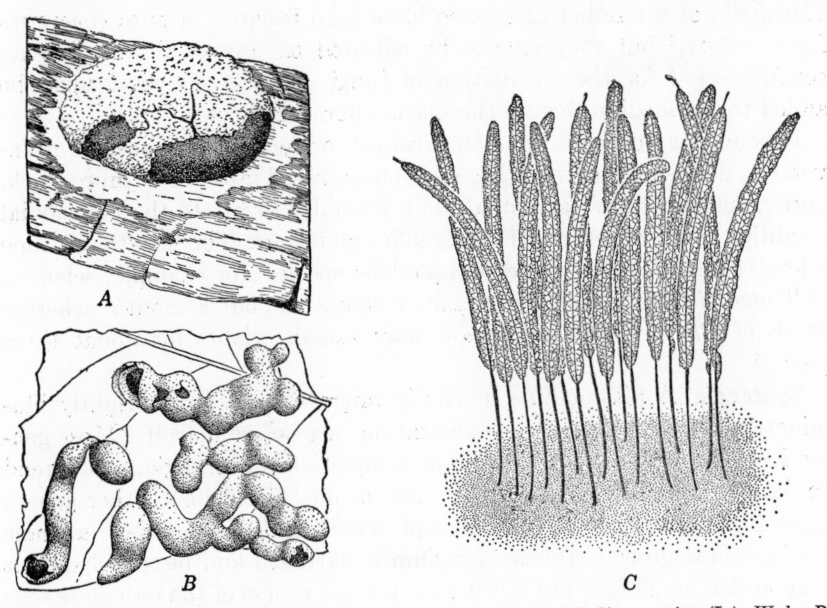

FIG. 200. Fruiting bodies of Myxomycetae. *A*, aethalium of *Fuligo septica* (L.) Web. *B*, plasmodiocarp of *Physarum alpinum* G. List. *C*, stalked sporangia of *Stemonitis splendens* Rost. (*A*, × ¾; *B*, × 10; *C*, × 5.)

protoplasm remains at the base of the stipe or stipes and develops into a sheet-like **hypothallus.**

The protoplasm of a young sporangium is multinucleate and with the nuclei uniformly distributed throughout the cytoplasm (Fig. 201*A*). Sooner or later after differentiation of the peridium there is an appearance of furrows at various points in the plasma membrane of the cytoplasm.[3] They become deeper, branch and rebranch, and finally cut the protoplasm into small uninucleate protoplasts (Fig. 201*C*). Each uninucleate protoplast formed by this **progressive cleavage** rounds up, secretes

[1] Howard, 1931. [2] Nederczky, 1937. [3] Harper, 1900, 1914; Howard, 1931.

a cellulose wall, and becomes a spore. A number of species are known[1] to have a meiotic division of the nuclei just prior to or during cleavage into uninucleate protoplasts, and it is very probable that nuclei in spores of all Myxomycetae are haploid.

Members of certain genera have a development of numerous branched or unbranched canals in the protoplasm before the beginning of progressive cleavage.[2] These canals become filled with materials and the threads thus cast in molds of living protoplasm (Fig. 201*B*) persist after spore formation and constitute the **capillitium.** Some genera have the capillitial

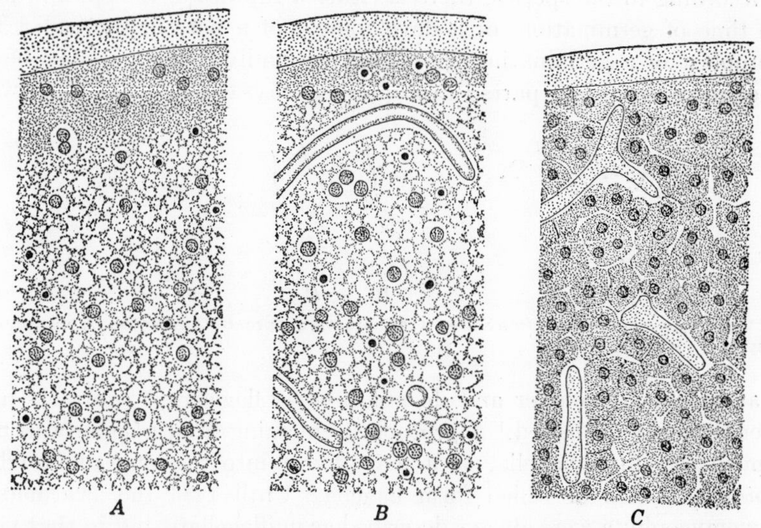

FIG. 201. *Physarum* sp., development of sporangium. *A*, before formation of capillitium. *B*, after formation of capillitium. *C*, cleavage into spores. (× 430.)

threads attached to the peridium; other genera have them attached to an extension of the stipe into the sporangium (Fig. 200*C*). Rupture of the peridium exposes the intermingled spores and capillitium. In some species the expanded or unexpanded capillitium is a meshwork that favors a gradual instead of an immediate escape of spores. In other species the capillitial threads are hygroscopic and coil and uncoil with changes in the humidity. Thus, similar to elaters of liverworts, they are structures facilitating the escape of spores.

Germination of Spores. Spore germination may take place shortly after spores are liberated. On the other hand, it may be long delayed if conditions are unfavorable, and spores of certain species are known[3] to remain

[1] Cadman, 1931; Jahn, 1933; Schünemann, 1930; Schure, 1949; Wilson and Cadman, 1928.

[2] Harper and Dodge, 1914; Howard, 1931. [3] Smith, 1929.

viable for more than 25 years. The longest record for viability of spores is 62 years.[1] When germinated in liquids the percentage of germination is greatly increased after treatment with wetting agents.[1] The nature of the liquid, its pH, and its temperature all have their effect on the percentage of germination. There is also a mutual relationship in germination of spores. When a single spore is placed in a drop of water it will not germinate, but germination frequently takes place if several spores are added to the drop or if the spore is transferred to the filtrate from a medium in which many spores have germinated.[2]

According to the species, there is either a rupture of the spore wall at the time of germination, or a development of a pore in the wall.[3] The protoplast of a germinating spore may be undivided, or it may be divided into two or four parts.[4] Protoplasts always emerge from spore walls

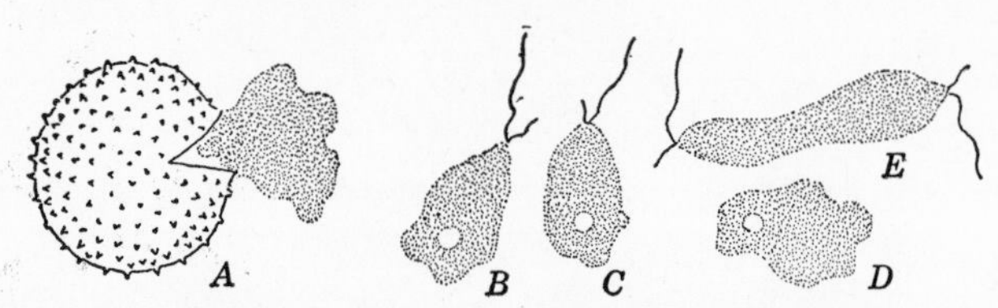

FIG. 202. *Physarum polycephalum* Schw. *A*, germinating spore. *B–C*, gametes. *D*, myxamoeba. *E*, zygote. (× 1,300.)

in an amoeboid manner and do not become flagellated swarmers until after they have emerged.[1] A protoplast emerging from a spore wall may immediately form flagella, or it may divide into two or four daughter protoplasts each of which form flagella.[5] Until 1934 the swarmers of Myxomycophyta were always described as uniflagellate, but in that year[6] those of certain Plasmodiophorales were shown to be biflagellate and with one flagellum very much shorter than the other. Since then, this has been found[7] to be true for all critically examined swarmers of Myxomycophyta (Fig. 202*B–C*). Swarmers may remain motile or they may become nonflagellate amoeboid myxamoebae (Fig. 202*D*). Division into two daughter cells may take place in either the flagellated or myxamoeboid state, but this rarely continues for more than a few cell generations. If conditions are unfavorable a swarmer or a myxamoeba may assume a spherical shape and secrete a thin wall. Such spore-like bodies (**cysts**) germinate to form a single swarmer upon return of favorable conditions.[8]

Both swarmers and myxamoebae are potential gametes. Both of a fusing pair of swarmers (Fig. 202*E*) are actively motile at the time of union

[1] Elliott, 1949. [2] Smart, 1937. [3] F. A. Gilbert, 1928.
[4] F. A. Gilbert, 1928; Smith, 1929.
[5] Jahn, 1904; Howard, 1931; F. A. Gilbert, 1928. [6] Ledingham, 1934.
[7] Elliott, 1949; Ellison, 1945. [8] Howard, 1931.

and their fusion is by an apposition of their posterior poles.[1] The zygote formed by union of flagellated swarmers remains motile for a few hours before the flagella disappear and it becomes a myxamoeba. Zygotes produced by gametic union of swarmers, or of myxamoebae, soon have a union of the gametes. The diploid nucleus in a myxamoeba resulting from gametic union divides and redivides mitotically for an indefinite number of nuclear generations as the myxamoeba grows into a plasmodium.

SUBCLASS 2. EXOSPOREAE

The Exosporeae have their "spores" borne externally and in considerable numbers upon an erect, branching, fruiting pillar. There is but one genus (*Ceratiomyxa*) with but one or two species.

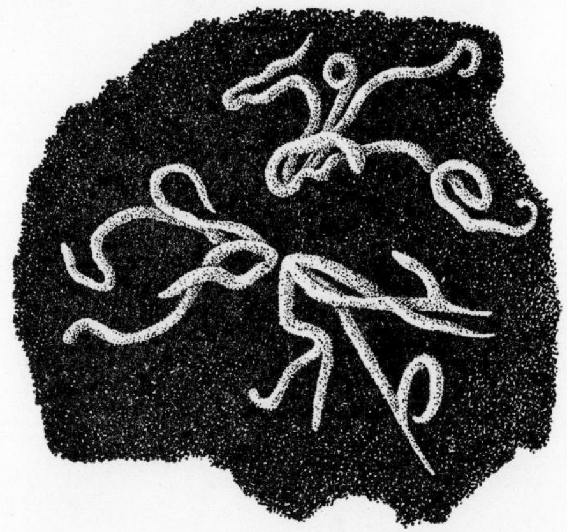

FIG. 203. Dried fruiting bodies of a species of *Ceratiomyxa*. (× 20.)

The entire vegetative development takes place within the substratum, usually a rotting log, and the plasmodium does not migrate to the surface of the substratum until the time of fruiting. Then minute papillate masses of plasmodial protoplasm appear upon the surface of the substratum within which the plasmodium has completed its vegetative development. Each papillate portion of the plasmodium becomes differentiated into a central gelatinous core of nonliving material (the **sporophore**) and an ensheathing layer of protoplasm (Fig. 203). The sporophore is thought to be homologous with the hypothallus of Endosporeae rather than homologous with the stipes and sporangia.[2] As the sporophore increases in height, the ensheathing protoplasm becomes restricted to the upper portion of it. The protoplasm covering a developing sporophore may have a doubling of the number of nuclei by an equational

[1] Abe, 1934; Cayley, 1929; Howard, 1931; Wilson and Cadman, 1928.
[2] H. C. Gilbert, 1935.

division of each nucleus.[1] When growth of the sporophore ceases, there is a progressive cleavage (Fig. 204*A*) of the multinucleate protoplasmic sheath into uninucleate protoplasts.[2] These protoplasts lie in a single or double layer around the upper portion of the upper end of a sporophore. They lie side by side and are polygonal in outline because of mutual pressure (Fig. 204*B*). Each protoplast soon becomes broadly ellipsoidal and secretes a thin wall (Fig. 204*C*). One pole of the enclosing wall is attached to a short stalk-like projection from the sporophore. The walled uninucleate bodies borne on stalks are usually called spores. In reality they are

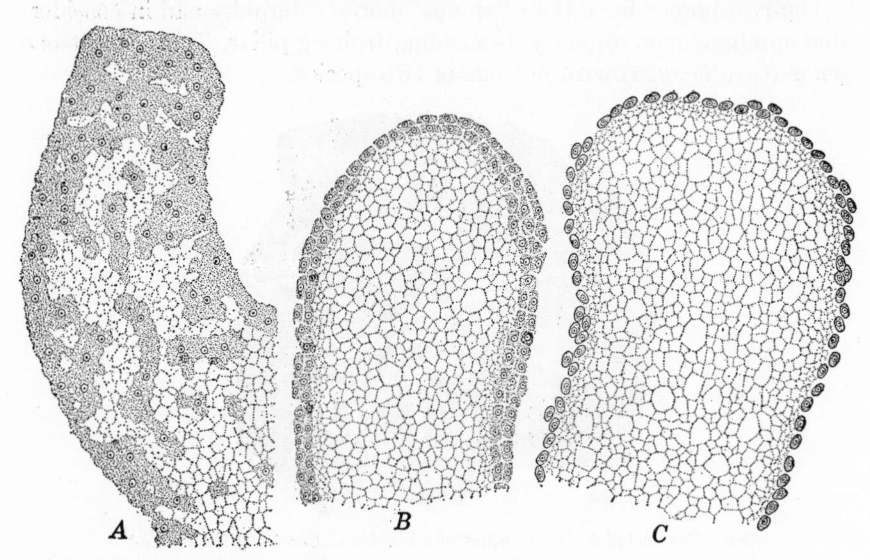

FIG. 204. Development of fructification of *Ceratiomyxa*. *A*, young fruiting pillar. *B*, after cleavage of the protoplast. *C*, after formation of "spores." (× 325.)

sporangia.[1] Hence, one may homologize *Certiomyxa* with the Endosporeae by considering the fructification of *Ceratiomyxa* as an elevated hypothallus (the sporophore) that bears an immense number of minute stalked uninucleate sporangia.

The stalk of a sporangium elongates to several times its original length and pushes the sporangium out from the sporophore (Fig. 205). During the course of this elongation the orientation of the sporangium is so changed that its long axis lies parallel to the stalk.[1] There are two conflicting accounts concerning the stage at which meiosis occurs. According to one account it is during the last nuclear divisions before formation of the sporangia;[3] according to the other, the single nucleus within a sporangium is diploid and it divides meiotically into four daughter nuclei.[2]

[1] H. C. Gilbert, 1935. [2] H. C. Gilbert, 1935; Olive, 1907. [3] Jahn, 1936.

The latter account appears the more probable. Division to form four nuclei within a sporangium is not followed by cytokinesis.

Succeeding stages in sporangial development are completed after detachment and dispersal of the sporangia (Fig. 206). The detached spo-

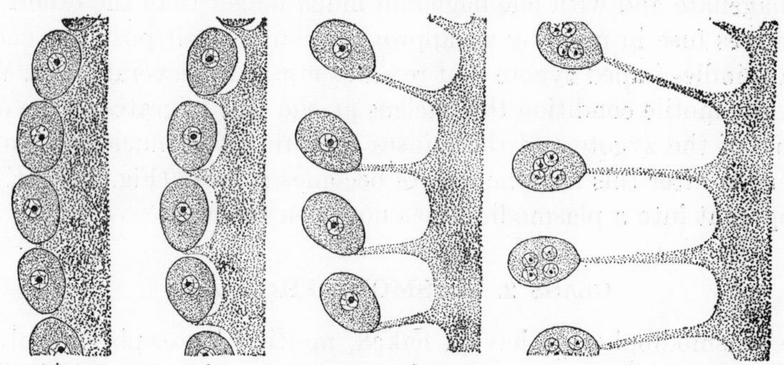

Fig. 205. Diagram showing progressive elevation of the "spores" of *Ceratiomyxa* above the sporophore. (*Based upon H. C. Gilbert*, 1935.)

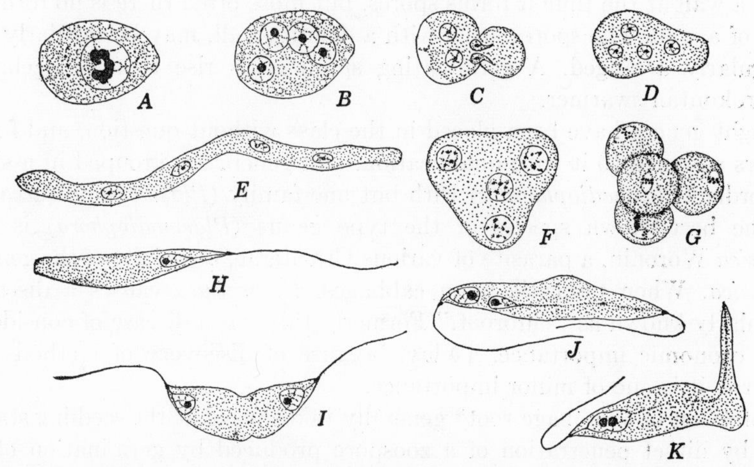

Fig. 206. *Ceratiomyxa* sp., "spore" germination and gametic union. *A*, uninucleate "spore." *B*, quadrinucleate "spore." *C*, germination. *D–E*, protoplasts shortly after emerging from wall. *F–G*, rounding up of protoplast and cleavage into uninucleate protoplasts. *H*, gamete. *I–K*, successive stages in union of gametes. (*After H. C. Gilbert*, 1935.) (*A–B*, *F–K*, × 2,250; *C–E*, × 1,500.)

rangium behaves like a germinating spore in that it develops a pore in the sporangial wall, and the protoplast moves out through the pore. The protoplast is globose immediately after emergence, but it soon becomes vermiform and with the four nuclei evenly spaced in a linear series.[1] Within a few hours the protoplast again becomes globose and with the

[1] H. C. Gilbert, 1935.

four nuclei tetrahedrally arranged. There is then a division into four tetrahedrally arranged uninucleate protoplasts (Fig. 206*F–G*). These uninucleate protoplasts are the true spores. They remain apposed to each other, and each divides into two zoogametes (Fig. 206*H*). The zoogametes are biflagellate and with one flagellum much longer than the other.[1] The zoogametes fuse in pairs by an approximation at their posterior ends to form a spindle-shaped zygote that remains motile for several hours. While still in the motile condition the nucleus at one pole migrates to the opposite pole of the zygote and there fuses with the other nucleus.[2] Motility ceases soon after this and the zygote becomes globose (Fig. 206*I–K*). Its development into a plasmodium has not been followed.

CLASS 2. PLASMODIOPHOREAE

The Plasmodiophoreae have a naked, multinucleate, plasmodial type of thallus in which all vegetative development takes place within living tissues of a host plant. Sometimes the vegetative body becomes invested with a wall at the time it forms spores, but more often there is no formation of a wall. The spores, each with a definite wall, may be regularly or irregularly arranged. A germinating spore gives rise to a biflagellate heterokontan swarmer.

Eight genera have been placed in the class without question, and four others assigned to it with qualification.[3] All genera are grouped in a single order (*Plasmodiophorales*) with but one family (*Plasmodiophoraceae*).

The best-known species of the type genus (*Plasmodiophora*) is *P. brassica* Woronin, a parasite of various Cruciferae, especially of the genus *Brassica*. When parasitic upon cabbages, *P. brassica* causes a disease popularly known as "clubroot." Formerly this was a disease of considerable economic importance. Today, because of discovery of methods of control, it is one of minor importance.

Infection of a cabbage root* generally takes place at the seedling stage and by direct penetration of a zoospore produced by germination of a resting spore. The zoospores are of a biflagellate heterokontan type[4] and probably with both of the whiplash type.[5] They enter the root by penetrating the cell wall of a root hair or of an epidermal cell. Immediately after, and sometimes even before, penetration of the host cell the zoospore becomes a myxamoeba. The nucleus of the myxamoeba divides and redivides mitotically to form a plasmodium that may have up to 30

[1] Elliott, 1949. [2] H. C. Gilbert, 1935. [3] Karling, 1942.

* The account of the life cycle as given here is that of Cook and Schwartz (1930). For a summary of stages where other investigators are not in accord with them see Karling (1942).

[4] Ledingham, 1934. [5] Ellison, 1945.

nuclei[1] (Fig. 207*A–J*). At any time in development of this haploid plasmodium it may fragment into uninucleate protoplasts, each of which becomes surrounded by a wall. These cells are gametangia whose protoplasts divide to form four or eight flagellated gametes.[2]

The zoogametes fuse in pairs to form an amoeboid zygote (myxamoeba) with a diploid nucleus (Fig. 207*K–M*). Thus gametic union may take place within the root hair or after a migration of zoogametes to adjoining cortical cells.[3] The diploid myxamoeba thus formed increases in size and its nucleus divides and redivides a few times. Diploid myxamoebae and young diploid plasmodia migrate from cell to cell of the host, and some of them

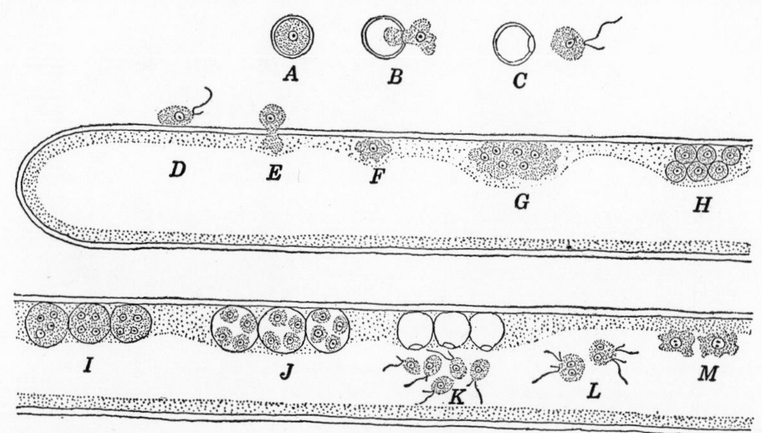

Fig. 207. *Plasmodiophora brassicae* Woronin. *A–C*, diagram of portion of life cycle in soil. *A*, spore. *B–C*, germination of spore. *D–M*, diagram of portion of life cycle in root hair. *D–E*, entrance into root hair. *F*, myxamoeba. *G*, plasmodium. *H–J*, gametangia. *K*, gametes. *L–M*, zygotes. (*Diagrams based in large part upon Cook and Schwartz*, 1930.)

migrate inward to the cambium and thence up and down the root. Movement from cell to cell is by a direct perforation of cell walls.[4] After migrating upward or downward through the cambium, the myxamoebae and young plasmodia then migrate outward through the cortex. Upon reaching a cortical cell containing an abundance of food the plasmodium remains within it and increases greatly in size. Up to this time the parasite has had no pronounced effect upon roots of the host. Shortly after outward migration of myxamoebae or young plasmodia from the cambium, the cortical cells in an infected region are stimulated to divide rapidly and this increases the number of cells containing plasmodia. The cells containing plasmodia enlarge to several times their original size, and this causes the greatly enlarged roots from which the disease gets its popular

[1] Chupp, 1917; Cook and Schwartz, 1930. [2] Cook and Schwartz, 1930.
[3] Cook, 1933. [4] Chupp, 1917; Kunkel, 1918; Lutman, 1913.

name. Increase in size of a plasmodium within a cortical cell is accompanied by repeated simultaneous division of its nuclei (Fig. 208*C*). Nuclear division is mitotic up to the penultimate series of division. The last two divisions are meiotic and halve the number of chromosomes in each nucleus.[1] Numerous vacuoles of large and small size appear in the cytoplasm after completion of meiosis. They become joined to one another and thus cut the plasmodium into small uninucleate fragments, each of which becomes a spherical spore with a distinct wall (Fig. 208*D*).

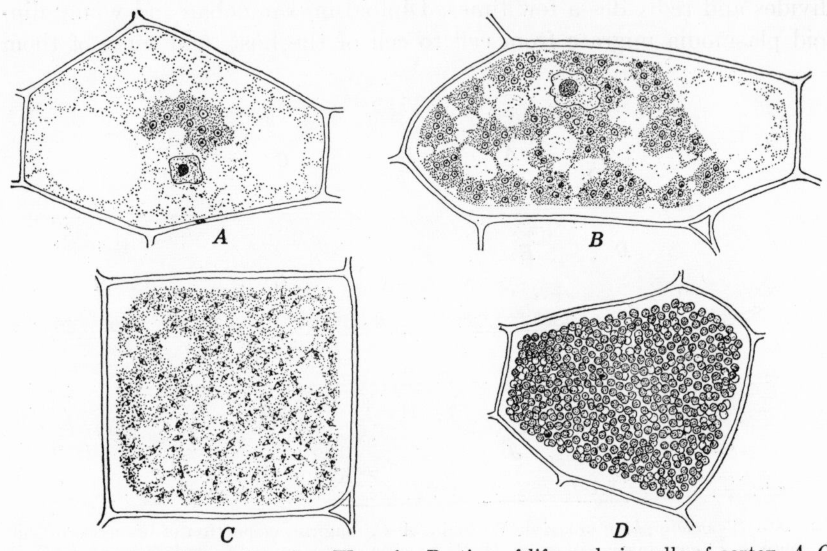

FIG. 208. *Plasmodiophora brassicae* Woronin. Portion of life cycle in cells of cortex. *A–C*, increase in size of plasmodium. *D*, after division of plasmodium into a mass of spores.

The spores remain within the host until the latter decays. Infection of a new host takes place after germination of a spore that has remained *in situ* in the soil, and it has been shown[2] that infection does not take place unless the spore lies within a few centimeters of a seedling.

CLASS 3. ACRASIEAE

The Acrasieae resemble the Myxomycetae in being free-living. They differ from Myxomycetae in that there is never a development of a multinucleate plasmodium or of flagellated swarmers. Reproduction is preceded by an aggregation of large numbers of uninucleate myxamoebae into a mass, the **pseudoplasmodium,** in which each myxamoeba retains its individuality. The pseudoplasmodium then changes into a fruiting body (**sorocarp**) that is generally differentiated into a sterile and a fertile portion.

[1] Cook, 1933; Cook and Schwartz, 1930; Lutman, 1913. [2] Chupp, 1917.

As they occur in nature, the sorocarps of Acrasieae are generally found upon dung of various animals, but when isolated by means of suitable media[1] Acrasieae may be obtained from a considerable percentage of soils rich in decaying vegetable matter. The single order of the class, the *Acrasiales*, contains 9 genera and about 25 species. These are divided into three families.[2]

Dictyostelium (Fig. 209), a genus with about nine species, is the most thoroughly investigated member of the class. A spore germinates to form a myxamoeba that regularly contains a single nucleus and a contractile

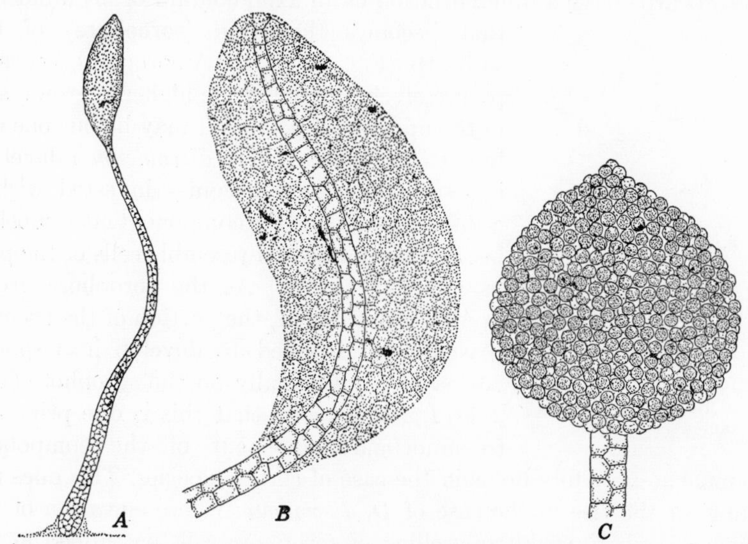

Fig. 209. *Dictyostelium* sp. *A*, entire fructification. *B*, optical section of apex of a young sorophore. *C*, surface view of apex of a mature fructification. (*A*, × 30; *B–C*, × 325.)

vacuole (Fig. 210*B*). Nutrition of myxamoebae is exclusively by ingestion of bacteria; and they feed upon a wide variety of species, except for those whose cells are encased by gum or slime.[3] Depending upon the particular species of *Dictyostelium* and the size of the inoculum, cultures produce sorocarps within two to four days when cultured on agar.

In a scattered population of myxamoebae, development of a sorocarp begins with the establishment of linear strands of myxamoebae which converge toward, stream toward, and fuse with a small central pseudoplasmodial mass of myxamoebae (Fig. 211*A–C*). Somewhat inconclusive evidence has been presented[4] to show that there is at first a streaming toward a single "initiator cell." There is much more conclusive evidence[5] that the pseudoplasmodium thus formed excretes a chemotactic sub-

[1] Raper, 1951. [2] Olive, 1902; Raper, 1940.
[3] Raper, 1937: 1939. [4] Sussmann, 1952. [5] Bonner, 1947, 1949.

stance (**acrasin**) and that in later stages the acrasin is not uniformly distributed throughout a developing pseudoplasmodium.

As more and more myxamoebae join the pseudoplasmodium it becomes an erect cylinder with a rounded apex (Fig. 211*D*). This cylinder, which is the young sorocarp, is sessile in all species except *D. discoideum* Raper. At this stage of development of *D. discoideum* the young sorocarp may fall to its side and become a "migrating pseudoplasmodium" that moves at the rate of about 1 mm. per hour. After moving for a short distance the "migrating pseudoplasmodium" again becomes erect.[1] Young erect sorocarps have a differentiation of an axial column of myxamoebae that becomes the stipe (**sorophore**) of the sorocarp (Fig. 211*F–H*). A sorophore becomes progressively narrower the higher it grows, and in the uppermost portion it may be but one cell broad (Fig. 209*B*). In *D. discoideum* a developing sorophore soon becomes invested with a cellulose sheath and the component myxamoebae become vacuolate and resemble cells of the pith of vascular plants.[2] As the sorophore grows upward the **sorogen,** the portion of the pseudoplasmodium destined to develop into spores, begins to rise vertically on the sorophore (Fig. 211*I–L*). The view[3] that this is due primarily to amoeboid movement of the component myxamoebae probably holds in the case of certain species. This does not account for the rise in the case of *D. discoideum* where elevation of the sorogen is due primarily to swelling of sorophore cells entrapped in the vertically elongating cellulose sheath around the sorophore.[2] Each myxamoeba in a sorogen at the top of a sorophore rounds up, secretes a wall, and becomes a spore. Collectively they constitute the fertile portion (**sorus**) of a sorocarp (Fig. 209*C*).

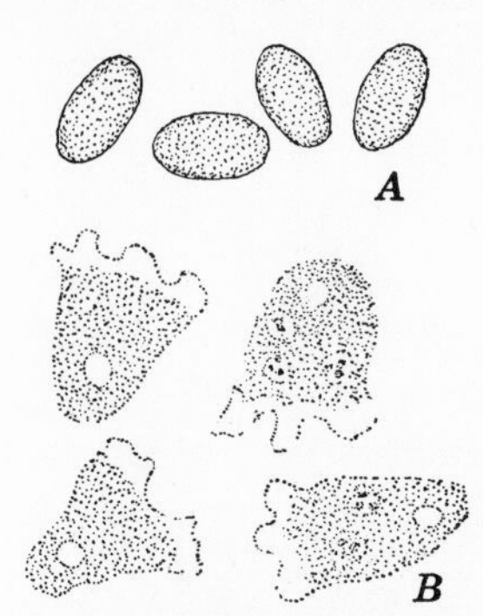

FIG. 210. *Dictyostelium discoideum* Raper. *A*, spores. *B*, myxamoebae. (× 950.)

The pseudoplasmodium of *D. discoideum* shows a differentiation into parts destined to develop into sorogen, stalk, and basal disk as early as the "migrating plasmodium" stage. This has been demonstrated[4] by feeding some pseudoplasmodia with red bacteria, feeding other pseudoplasmodia with colorless bacteria, and then grafting colorless anterior portions of pseudoplasmodia upon red posterior portions, or vica versa. This shows that the anterior portion of a "migrating pseudoplasmodium" gives rise to the stalk and that the posterior portion gives rise to the sorogen and basal disk of a sorocarp. Differentiation has also been dem-

[1] Bonner, 1944; Raper, 1935, 1939, 1940*A*, 1941; Raper and Fennell, 1952.
[2] Raper and Fennell, 1952. [3] Harper, 1926; Olive, 1902. [4] Raper, 1940*A*.

onstrated[1] by means of vital stains. This investigation has shown that, if the anterior portion of a "migrating pseudoplasmodium" is arbitrarily considered as consisting of three successive parts, the part nearest the apex gives rise to the base of the sorophore and the part adjoining the future sorogen gives rise to the apex of the sorophore (Fig. 211*M–N*).

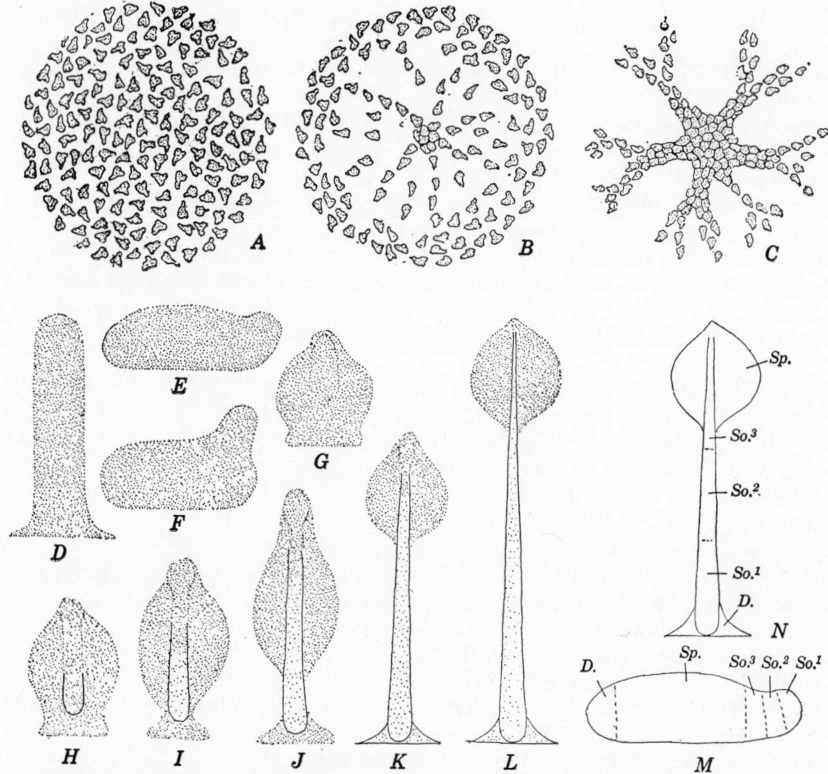

Fig. 211. Diagram of successive stages in development of sorocarp of *Dictyostelium discoideum* Raper. *A*, myxamoebae before aggregation. *B*, early in aggregation of myxamoebae into a pseudoplasmodium. *C*, later in aggregation into a pseudoplasmodium. *D–L*, vertical sections showing development of pseudoplasmodium into a sorocarp. *D*, before migration. *E*, migrating pseudoplasmodium. *F*, beginning of return to erect condition. *G–H*, before and after beginning of formation of cellulose sorophore sheath. *I-L*, elevation of sorogen due to expansion of myxamoebae within sheath of sorophore. *M–N*, diagrams showing relation of spores (*Sp.*), sorophore ($So.^1$, $So.^2$, $So.^3$), and disk (*D*) of a mature sorocarp to regions of a migrating pseudoplasmodium. (*D–L, based upon Raper and Fennell*, 1952; *M–N, based on J. T. Bonner*, 1944.)

The disk at the base of the sorophore is derived from the extreme posterior portion of a "migrating pseudoplasmodium."

A gametic union of myxamoebae occurs during early stages in development of a pseudoplasmodium.[2] The zygotes thus formed are the only diploid myxamoebae in the life cycle and their nuclei divide meiotically early

[1] Bonner, 1944. [2] Skupienski, 1918; Wilson, 1952.

in development of a sorocarp.[1] Cultures thought[2] to be derived from single spores or single myxamoebae of *Dictyostelium* do not shed light upon the question as to whether a pseudoplasmodium is homothallic or heterothallic.

Bibliography

Abe, S. **1934.** *Sci. Repts. Tokyo Bunrika Daigaku.* Sect. **B, 18:** 193–202. 1 fig. [Gametic union.]

Ainsworth, G. C., and G. R. Bisby. **1950.** A dictionary of the fungi. 3d ed. Kew. 447 pp. 138 figs.

Bonner, J. T. **1944.** *Amer. Jour. Bot.* **31:** 175–182. 3 figs. [*Dictyostelium.*[

1947. *Jour. Exper. Zool.* **106:** 1–26. 4 figs. [*Dictyostelium.*]

1949. *Ibid.* **110:** 259–272. 3 figs. [*Dictyostelium.*]

Cadman, Elsie L. **1931.** *Trans. Roy. Soc. Edinburgh* **57:** 93–142. 5 pl. [Structure and development Myxomycetae.]

Camp, W. G. **1937.** *Bull. Torrey Bot. Club* **64:** 307–335. 10 figs. [Plasmodia.]

Cayley, Dorothy M. **1929.** *Trans. Brit. Mycol. Soc.* **14:** 227–248. 2 pl. 3 figs. [Gametic union.]

Chupp, C. **1917.** *Cornell Univ. Agr. Exper. Sta. Bull.* **387:** 421–452. 16 figs. [*Plasmodiophora.*]

Cohen, A. L. **1939.** *Bot. Gaz.* **101:** 243–275. 4 figs. [Nutrition of plasmodia.]

1941. *Ibid.* **103:** 205–224. 1 fig. [Nutrition of plasmodia.]

Cook, W. R. I. **1933.** *Arch. Protistenk.* **80:** 79–254. 7 pl. 14 figs. [Plasmodiophoreae.]

Cook, W. R. I., and E. J. Schwartz. **1930.** *Phil. Trans. Roy. Soc.* London *B.* **218:** 283–314. 3 pl. 1 fig. [*Plasmodiophora.*]

Elliott, E. W. **1949.** *Mycologia* **41:** 141–170. 25 figs. [Motile cells.]

Ellison, B. R. **1945.** *Ibid.* **37:** 444–459. 4 figs. [Motile cells.]

Fitzpatrick, H. M. **1930.** The lower fungi. Phycomycetes. New York. 331 pp. 112 figs.

Gäumann, E. **1949.** Die Pilze. Basel. 382 pp. 440 figs.

Gehenio, P. M. **1944.** *Biodynamica* **4:** 359–368. [Sclerotia.]

Gilbert, F. A. **1928.** *Amer. Jour. Bot.* **15:** 345–353. 2 pl. [Spore germination.]

Gilbert, H. C. **1935.** *Ibid.* **22:** 52–74. 3 pl. 1 fig. [*Ceratiomyxa.*]

Gray, W. D. **1938.** *Amer. Jour. Bot.* **25:** 511–522. 13 figs. [Factors affecting fruiting.]

1939. *Ibid.* **26:** 709–714. 2 figs. [Factors affecting fruiting.]

1945. *Ibid.* **32:** 157–160. [Factors affecting fruiting.]

Harper, R. A. **1900.** *Bot. Gaz.* **30:** 217–251. 1 pl. [Mitosis.]

1914. *Amer. Jour. Bot.* **1:** 117–144. 2 pl. [Sporogenesis.]

1926. *Bull. Torrey Bot. Club* **53:** 229–268. 3 pl. [*Dictyostelium.*]

Harper, R. A., and B. O. Dodge. **1914.** *Ann. Bot.* **28:** 1–18. 2 pl. [Development of sporangia.]

Howard, F. L. **1931.** *Amer. Jour. Bot.* **18:** 116–133. 8 pl. 1 fig. [Development of Myxomycetae.]

1932. *Ann. Bot.* **46:** 461–477. 1 pl. 3 figs. [Development of Myxomycetae.]

Jahn, E. **1904.** *Ber. Deutsch. Bot. Ges.* **22:** 84–92. 1 pl. [Mitosis.]

1928. *Ibid.* **46:** 8–17. 1 pl. [Classification.]

1928A. Myxomycetes. In A. Engler and K. Prantl, Die natürlichen Pflanzenfamilien. 2d ed. Bd. 2. Pp. 304–337. 22 figs.

1933. *Ber. Deutsch. Bot. Ges.* **51:** 377–385. 1 pl. [Meiosis.]

1936. *Ibid.* **54:** 517–528. 1 pl. [*Ceratiomyxa.*]

[1] Wilson, 1952. [2] Sussman, 1951, 1952.

Kambly, P. E. **1939.** *Amer. Jour. Bot.* **26:** 386–390. [Color of plasmodia.]
Kamiya, N. **1950.** *Cytologia* **15:** 194–204. 10 figs. [Movement of plasmodia.]
Karling, J. S. **1942.** The Plasmodiophorales. New York. 144 pp. 17 pl.
Kunkel, L. O. **1918.** *Jour. Agr. Res.* **14:** 543–572. 20 pl. 2 figs. [*Plasmodiophora.*]
Langeron, M., and R. Vanbreuseghem. **1952.** Précis de mycologie. Paris. 703 pp. 460 figs.
Ledingham, G. A. **1934.** *Nature* **133:** 534. 1 fig. [Flagella.]
Lutman, B. F. **1913.** *Vt. Agr. Exper. Sta. Bull.* **175:** 1–27. 4 pl. 6 figs. [*Plasmodiophora.*]
Martin, G. W. **1950.** Outline of the fungi. Dubuque, Iowa. 82 pp.
Nederczky, A. **1937.** *Acta Soc. Bot. Poloniae* **14:** 68–87. [Cell walls.]
Olive, E. W. **1902.** *Proc. Boston Soc. Nat. Hist.* **30:** 451–513. 4 pl. [Acrasieae.]
1907. *Trans. Wis. Acad.* **15:** 753–774. 1 pl. [*Ceratiomyxa.*]
Pascher, A. **1940.** *Arch. Protistenk.* **94:** 295–309. 12 figs. [Net plasmodial algae.]
Raper, K. B. **1935.** *Jour. Agr. Res.* **50:** 135–147. 3 pl. [*Dictyostelium.*]
1937. *Ibid.* **55:** 289–316. 4 figs. [*Dictyostelium.*]
1939. *Ibid.* **58:** 157–198. 10 figs. [*Dictyostelium.*]
1940. *Amer. Jour. Bot.* **27:** 436–448. 10 figs. [*Dictyostelium.*]
1940A. *Jour. Elisha Mitchell Sci. Soc.* **56:** 241–282. 12 figs. [*Dictyostelium.*]
1941. *Growth* **5** (Suppl.): 41–76. 8 figs. [*Dictyostelium.*]
1951. *Quart. Rev. Biol.* **26:** 169–190. 8 figs. [*Dictyostelium.*]
Raper, K. B., and Dorothy I. Fennell. **1952.** *Bull. Torrey Bot. Club* **79:** 25–52. 12 figs. [*Dictyostelium.*]
Schünemann, E. **1930.** *Planta* **9:** 645–672. 1 pl. 3 figs. [Gametic union.]
Schure, P. S. J. **1949.** *Antonio van Leeuwenhoek Jour. Microbiol. u. Serol.* **15:** 143–161. 2 pl. [Meiosis.]
Seifritz, W., and Marie Zetzmann. **1935.** *Protoplasma* **23:** 175–179. [Plasmodia.]
Skupienski, F. **1918.** *Compt. Rend. Acad. Sci. Paris* **167:** 960–962. [*Dictyostelium.*]
Smart, R. F. **1937.** *Amer. Jour. Bot.* **24:** 145–159. 3 figs. [Spore germination.]
Smith, E. C. **1929.** *Amer. Jour. Bot.* **16:** 645–650. 1 pl. [Spore germination.]
1929A. *Mycologia* **21:** 321–323. 1 pl. (Longevity of spores.)
Sparrow, F. K. **1943.** Aquatic Phycomycetes exclusive of Saprolegniaceae and Pythium. Ann Arbor, Mich. 785 pp. 69 figs.
Sussman, M. **1951.** *Jour. Exper. Zool.* **118:** 407–417. 2 figs. [*Dictyostelium.*]
1952. *Biol. Bull.* **103:** 446–457. 4 figs. [*Dictyostelium.*]
Thom, C., and K. B. Raper. **1930.** *Jour. Wash. Acad. Sci.* **20:** 362–370. [Acrasieae of soil.]
Wilson, C. M. **1952.** *Proc. Nat. Acad. Sci. U.S.A.* **38:** 659–662.
Wilson, M., and Elsie J. Cadman. **1928.** *Trans. Roy. Soc. Edinburgh* **55:** 555–608. 6 pl. 4 figs. [Development and reproduction.]

CHAPTER 10

EUMYCOPHYTA—INTRODUCTION

The Eumycophyta include all fungi with a definite cell wall throughout all stages of vegetative development. Most genera have the branching filamentous type of thallus known as a **mycelium** and one in which a single filament or branch is termed a **hypha.** The mycelium may consist of a single multinucleate cell (a **coenocyte**) in which there are no transverse septa; or it may be multicellular and composed of uni-, bi-, or multinucleate cells. The various hyphae of a mycelium may lie in an amorphous felt-like mass, or they may be intertwined to form a macroscopic mass of definite form. In the latter case, the mycelium is generally multicellular and with all or some of the hyphae compacted into a pseudoparenchymatous tissue. There are no photosynthetic pigments and the mycelium is either a saprophyte or a parasite.

Some of the simpler unicellular genera have the entire thallus producing spores or gametes. The great majority of genera have only a portion of the thallus producing spores or gametes and the rest of the thallus remaining vegetative. Spores are generally formed within sporangia of distinctive shape; and gametes are formed within gametangia of the same or different shape from sporangia of the species.

According to a conservative estimate[1] there are approximately 3,700 genera and 36,000 species. Some species are strictly parasitic, some strictly saprophytic, some are parasitic at one stage of development and saprophytic at another, and still other species may grow either saprophytically or parasitically. When parasitic, the host may be a plant or an animal. Plants parasitized by Eumycophyta range from the simplest algae to the most advanced angiosperms. In some cases a particular species of fungus is restricted to a single host species; in others it may be parasitic upon several distantly related hosts. A few saprophytic species are aquatic in habit, but the great majority are terrestrial and grow either in the soil or upon the remains of plants or animals.

Spores. Asexual reproduction is effected by a wide variety of spores. Some spores are formed directly upon or within specialized or unspe-

[1] Ainsworth and Bisby, 1950.

cialized hyphae; others are formed within sporangia and in definite or indefinite numbers. Certain kinds of spores (as ascospores and basidiospores) are formed at a specific time in the life cycle and their formation is immediately preceded by meiosis. Discussion of the various types of spores will be postponed until succeeding chapters.

Sexual Reproduction. All Eumycophyta except the Deuteromycetae (Fungi Imperfecti) are known or presumed to have a life cycle in which there is a union of gametes or of gamete nuclei. Similar to other plants, the sexual reproduction of Eumycophyta involves two distinct processes. There is first a fusion (**plasmogamy**) of two uninucleate or multinucleate protoplasts of opposite sex. In the second process (**karyogamy**) two nuclei of opposite sex unite in pairs to form a nucleus with a diploid number of chromosomes. Some Eumycophyta have karyogamy taking place in the protoplast produced by plasmogamy; in other Eumycophyta there is no karyogamy in the protoplast produced by plasmogamy and it gives rise to a sequence of binucleate cell generations in which there are two nuclei of opposite sex. Eventually such Eumycophyta give rise to a special cell in which karyogamy takes place.

In sexual reproduction of all Phycomycetae and certain Ascomycetae, karyogamy takes place in the protoplast produced by plasmogamy. In these fungi the two fusing protoplasts are usually known as **gametes.** The phycomycetes show the same progressive differentiation of gametes as is found in such algae as Chlorophyta and Phaeophyta. The most primitive type of gametic union is **isogamy**—the fusion of two gametes of equal size. In isogamous phycomycetes the gametes are usually flagellated **zoogametes,** but they may be nonflagellated **aplanogametes.** A condition somewhat in advance of isogamy is a union of two motile gametes of unequal size (**anisogamy**). Among anisogamous fungi the larger of the two gametes is female and the smaller is male. The most advanced condition in differentiation of gametes is **oögamy.** Here, the female gamete (the **egg**) is always large, nonflagellated, and immobile. The male gamete is always much smaller than the egg, and either a flagellated motile gamete (**antherozoid**) or an amoeboid nonflagellated aplanogamete. As is the case with green and brown algae, an evolution from isogamy to oögamy has occurred in independent phyletic lines among phycomycetes.

Gametes of phycomycetes are usually formed within special cells, the sex organs. Strictly speaking, all such cells should be called gametangia, but the term gametangium is generally applied to the sex organs of isogamous and anisogamous species. Among the oögamous species the male gametangium is called an **antheridium** and the female called an **oögonium.**

In Phycomycetae, the cell formed by union of two gametes is a **zygote***

* Some botanists, especially mycologists, prefer the term **zygospore** for isogamously and anisogamously produced zygotes, and **oöspore** for oögamously produced zygotes.

and it is a cell in which plasmogamy is followed by karyogamy. Most phycomycetes have thick-walled zygotes that enter upon a period of rest before germinating. Although demonstrated for but relatively few of them, it is very probable that the diploid nucleus in such zygotes divides meiotically before or at the time a zygote germinates. Some phycomycetes form thin-walled zygotes that germinate immediately, and in at least one case (*Allomyces*, see page 385) the diploid nucleus does not divide meiotically.

Ascomycetes do not form motile gametes. In most of them there is a plasmogamy between a small male gamete and a large female gamete. Male gametes are usually **spermatia** produced singly within male sex organs (**antheridia**), but protoplasts of certain spores may also function as male gametes. The female sex organs of these ascomycetes is an **ascogonium.** In these ascomycetes plasmogamy is not followed by karyogamy. Instead, there is a production of a sequence of binucleate cells which eventually give rise to a special cell (**ascus**) in which karyogamy and meiosis take place (for further details see page 429).

Basidiomycetes do not form sex organs, however, there is what in effect is gametic union. In their gametic union there is a plasmogamy between protoplasts of two vegetative cells or between the protoplast of a spore and a vegetative cell. Here, also, plasmogamy is not followed by karyogamy in the two united protoplasts. Similar to the ascomycetes, the binucleate cell thus formed gives rise to a sequence of binucleate cells which eventually give rise to a special cell (**basidium**) in which karyogamy and meiosis take place (for further details see page 472).

Origin of the Eumycetae. There are two conflicting schools of thought concerning the origin of the Eumycetae. According to one school they have been evolved from algae; according to the other school they are derived from protozoa.

Those believing in an algal origin hold that Eumycophyta are algae that have lost their photosynthetic pigments and thus have changed from an autotrophic to a heterotrophic mode of nutrition. They think that this change in metabolism has also been accompanied by some modification of the sexual and asexual reproductive organs of the algal ancestry. Proponents of an algal origin think that this has been polyphyletic, the phycomycetes coming from one class of algae and the ascomycetes from another. The basidiomycetes are usually thought to have been derived from the ascomycetes. The presumed algal origin of phycomycetes is shown in the literal translation (algal fungi) of the name given the Phycomycetae when the class was established by DeBary.[1]

Many botanists favoring an algal origin think that the Phycomycetae are derived from the Chlorophyceae of the Chlorophyta, and probably

[1] DeBary in Fuckel, 1869–1875.

from a siphonaceous member of that class. Those who postulate an origin from Chlorophyceae overlook the fact that there are fundamental differences between phycomycetes and the known Chlorophyceae which regularly lack chlorophyll. Saprophytic and parasitic colorless Chlorophyceae regularly have an accumulation of reserve carbohydrates as starch, just as do Chlorophyceae with chlorophyll. On the other hand, phycomycetes never form starch. There are also fundamental differences in position and structure of flagella of the two groups. Swarmers of Chlorophyceae always have their flagella borne at the anterior end and their biflagellate swarmers have both flagella morphologically alike (see page 16). Swarmers of some phycomycetes are uniflagellate and those of others are biflagellate. Most phycomycetes whose swarmers have a single flagellum have it borne at the posterior end and those with an anterior flagellum seem to have one of the tinsel type. Phycomycetes producing biflagellate swarmers have the two borne at the anterior but they are morphologically different (see page 373). Since metabolism and type of flagellation are considered characters of deep significance among algae it is not unlikely that the same holds for fungi. For these reasons an origin of the Phycomycetae from the Chlorophyceae seems very improbable.

Because of the great similarity in their sex organs, the oögamous phycomycetes (**"oömycetes"**) have been thought[1] to be related to such oögamous Xanthophyceae as *Vaucheria*. It has also been held[2] that the first phycomycetes evolved were "oömycetes" and that they, in turn, gave rise to the chytrids and to the **"zygomycetes"** (aplanogamic isogamous phycomycetes). According to another interpretation[3] of an algal origin, the phycomycetes arose from some unicellular coccoid member of the Xanthophyceae. This ancestral form soon gave rise to two divergent types of phycomycete, one producing uniflagellate swarmers, the other producing biflagellate swarmers. The similarity in distinctive structure of swarmers of Xanthophycetae and biflagellate swarmers of biflagellate phycomycetes and the presence of cellulose in cell walls of the two are strong arguments for this theory. On the other hand the posterior position of the single flagellum of uniflagellate phycomycetes and the lack of cellulose in their cell walls seem to indicate that the two types are not divergent from a common ancestor. Thus there is a possibility that the phycomycetes are polyphyletic and include a series derived from an algal ancestor and a series derived from a protozoan ancestor.

Many of those believing in an algal origin of Eumycophyta think that the ascomycetes are immediately derived from the red algae. This view is based upon the striking similarities in the structure of sex organs and the structures developed subsequent to gametic union in Ascomycetae

[1] DeBary, 1881; Gäumann, 1949; von Tavel, 1892.
[2] DeBary, 1881. [3] Bessey, 1942.

and Florideae. However, there are equally good reasons for thinking that the distinctive reproductive features common to the two have been evolved along independent phyletic lines (for further details see page 431).

A considerable number[1] of students of phylogeny of fungi think that they arose from protozoa. Evolution of a protozoan into a fungus (phycomycete) involved a change in the dominant phase in the life cycle. Among protozoa the naked flagellate phase is dominant and the walled immobile phase (cyst) is more or less transitory. Among fungi, the walled immobile phase is of long duration and the naked flagellated stage is transitory. It is thought that the first phycomycetes evolved from protozoa were of a nonhyphal type (chytrids) and that these evolved into hyphal types with an extensive mycelium. The idea that an evolution from protozoa has been polyphyletic was first clearly enunciated by Scherffel[2] when he held that uniflagellate protozoa gave rise to one series among phycomycetes, and biflagellate protozoa gave rise to another series. As far as posteriorly uniflagellate phycomycetes are concerned the lack of such swarmers among algae and their frequent occurrence among protozoa are arguments in favor of this view. Anteriorly biflagellate protozoa may have given rise to phycomycetes with biflagellate swarmers but there is also the possibility that these may have arisen from Xanthophyceae. All those believing in a protozoan origin of phycomycetes think that the ascomycetes have been derived from phycomycetes.

Evolution among the Eumycophyta. The Eumycophyta are a series of considerable antiquity and indubitable phycomycetes have been found as far back as the Devonian.[3] Many fossil fungi are known from periods later than the Devonian but, as in the case of algae, the fossil record does not shed any light on evolution among the fungi.

Regardless of their views concerning the origin of fungi, mycologists are almost unanimous in placing the chytrids (in the broad sense) at the bottom of the phycomycete series. Chytrids are mostly aquatic fungi with a more or less globose unicellular thallus, and often with the entire thallus becoming fertile and producing swarmers. Mycelial phycomycetes whose uniflagellate swarmers have a single posterior flagellum are thought to have evolved from chytrids with swarmers of a similar type; and phycomycetes with anteriorly biflagellated swarmers are thought to have arisen from chytrids with this type of swarmer. In both series of mycelial phycomycetes there has been a progressive evolution to oögamy. The aplanogamic isogamous phycomycetes ("zygomycetes") are probably retrogressive from aplanogamic oögamous forms.

[1] Atkinson, 1909; Cavers, 1915; Cook, 1928; Dangeard, 1886, 1903; Fischer, 1892; Scherffel, 1925.

[2] Scherffel, 1925. [3] Kidston and Lang, 1921.

If one rejects a derivation of ascomycetes from red algae, an origin of the ascomycetes is to be sought among the aplanogamic phycomycetes. According to such an origin the most primitive ascomycetes are those with a fusion of two cells to form a solitary ascus (see page 433). More advanced ascomycetes have a branched binucleate hypha or hyphae growing out from a zygote and a production of an ascus at the tip of each branch.

The basidium, the characteristic feature of Basidiomycetae, probably arose by modification of an ascus (for further details see page 477). It is probable, also, that this modification took place among ascomycetes with binucleate (dikaryotic) hyphae producing asci. The most primitive of basidiomycetes appear to be those in which the basidium is undivided. Evolution from this type seems to have been in two directions, one characterized by a vertically divided basidium, the other by a transversely divided basidium.

Classification. For a long time the Eumycetae have been divided into four classes. These are the *Phycomycetae*, the *Ascomycetae*, the *Basidiomycetae*, and the *Deuteromycetae* (*Fungi Imperfecti*). There is no disagreement about genera to be assigned to the last three, but there is some disagreement about those that should be placed in the Phycomycetae. Most mycologists include all the so-called "lower fungi" in the Phycomycetae, but there are some who place certain of them in a separate class called the *Archimycetae*. As first delimited[1] this class included the uni- and biflagellate chytrids in which the entire plant body forms swarmers, and the Plasmodiophorales. Others[2] also include in the Archimycetae the Myxomycophyta and certain of the hyphal phycomycetes. The customary practice of including all chytrids in the Phycomycetae shows their relationships better than a segregation of them in a special class.

Bibliography

Ainsworth, G. C., and G. R. Bisby. **1950.** A dictionary of the fungi. Kew. 447 pp. 138 figs.

Atkinson, G. F. **1909.** *Ann. Mycol.* **7:** 441–472. [Phylogeny.]

Bessey, E. A. **1942.** *Mycologia* **34:** 355–379. 5 figs. [Phylogeny.]

Cavers, F. **1915.** *New Phytol.* **14:** 94–104, 164–168, 223–227, 275–280, 302–304. 6 figs. [Classification.]

Cook, W. R. I. **1928.** *New Phytol.* **27:** 230–260, 298–320. 3 pl. 111 figs. [Classification.]

Dangeard, P. A. **1886.** *Ann. Sci. Nat. Bot.* 7 ser. **4:** 243–341. 4 pl. [Chytrids.]

1903. *Le Botaniste* **9:** 157–303. 18 pl. 9 figs. [Phylogeny of fungi.]

DeBary, A. **1881.** *Bot. Zeitg.* **39:** 1–17, 33–36. [Classification.]

Fischer, A. **1892.** Phycomycetes. In L. Rabenhorst, Kryptogamen-Flora Deutschlands, Österreichs und der Schweiz. 1 Bd., Abt. 4. Pp. 1–505. 74 figs.

[1] Gäumann, 1926; Gäumann and Dodge, 1928. [2] Cook, 1928; Langeron, 1952.

Fuckel, L. **1869–1875.** Symbolae mycologicae. I-III. Wiesbaden. 39 + 459 pp. 6 pl.
Gäumann, E. A. **1926.** Vergleichende Morphologie der Pilze. Jena. 626 pp. 398 figs.
1949. Die Pilze. Basel. 382 pp. 440 figs.
Gäumann, E. A., and C. W. Dodge. **1928.** Comparative morphology of fungi. New York. 701 pp. 406 figs.
Kidston, R., and W. H. Lang. **1921.** *Trans. Roy. Soc. Edinburgh* **52**: 855–901. 10 pl. 1 fig. [Fossil phycomycetes.]
Langeron, M. **1952.** Précis de mycology. Paris. 703 pp. 460 figs.
Scherffel, A. **1925.** *Arch. Protistenk.* **52**: 1–141. 5 pl. [Phylogeny.]
Tavel, F. von. **1829.** Vergleichende Morphologie der Pilze. Jena. 208 pp. 90 figs.

CHAPTER 11

PHYCOMYCETAE

Phycomycetae differ from other classes of Eumycophyta in that their sporangia contain an indefinite number of spores. Sexual reproduction is also distinctive. Unlike other Eumycophyta, the zygote formed by union of two gametes has a fusion of the two gamete nuclei and develops a wall. In most genera the zygote is thick-walled and does not germinate immediately; but there are genera where it is thin-walled and germinates soon after it is formed. The thallus of most phycomycetes is a single multinucleate cell, but there are genera where it is regularly multicellular.

According to a recent estimate,[1] there are about 240 genera and 1,100 species.

Occurrence. Some phycomycetes are strictly saprophytic, some are strictly parasitic, and still others are facultatively saprophytic or parasitic. A majority of the genera are aquatic fungi. Most aquatic parasitic species parasitize algae or other aquatic phycomycetes, and in the great majority of cases each species is limited to a specific host. Aquatic saprophytes are most frequently encountered on vegetative debris, or on the dead remains of fishes and insects.

Nonaquatic saprophytic phycomycetes grow in the soil or on dead remains of plants and animals. Parasitic nonaquatic species are found on various angiosperms. Saprophytic terrestrial forms are rarely evident in nature and become evident only when isolated from soil by appropriate techniques. A considerable number of species which at one time were thought to be strictly aquatic have also been isolated from soil.

Vegetative Structure. Thalli of most phycomycetes are unicellular and multinucleate. They range from small globose cells to profusely branched tubular mycelia capable of indefinite extension. Some unicellular genera are **holocarpic**—with the entire protoplast dividing into spores or gametes; others are **eucarpic**—with the fertile portion distinct from the vegetative portion. Eucarpic forms may have the old vegetative portion forming cross walls and thus becoming multicellular, or may have a formation of cross walls in vegetative portions early in the development of a mycelium.

[1] Ainsworth and Bisby, 1950.

Protoplasts of all phycomycetes are completely or incompletely surrounded by a definite wall. When determined by microchemical tests, the wall seems to be composed exclusively either of **fungus chitin** or of cellulose, but chemical analyses show that walls with fungus chitin may also contain cellulose.[1] Fungus chitin is an acetylglucosamine[1] with the empirical formula $(C_{22}H_{54}N_4O_{21})_x$. Studies by means of microchemical tests and X rays show that the type of cell wall is characteristic for an order. Blastocladiales, Chytridiales, Mucorales, and Entomophthorales have fungus chitin walls; Lagenidiales, Saprolegniales, Leptomitales, and Peronosporales have cellulose walls.[2] The nature of the cell wall has been considered[3] of significance in determining phylogenetic relationships among Phycomycetae.

The protoplast within the cell wall is usually vacuolate; and either with numerous small vacuoles, or with a large central vacuole and the cytoplasm restricted to a layer just internal to the cell wall. Food reserves accumulating in a protoplast are usually minute droplets of oil lying in the cytoplasm. Most genera are multinucleate and with a large number of small nuclei. Nuclei are similar in structure to those in other divisions of the plant kingdom and their mode of division is the same.

Asexual Reproduction. Asexual reproduction of phycomycetes is by means of either zoospores or aplanospores. Usually a thallus produces but one kind of spore, but there are cases where it produces both kinds of them. Holocarpic genera have the entire protoplast dividing into a large and indefinite number of spores. Eucarpic genera have their spores formed within sporangia that are frequently borne terminally on special hyphae (**sporangiophores**). The number of spores within a sporangium is always indefinite and according to the genus either large or small.

Zoospores of phycomycetes are without walls and are either uniflagellate or biflagellate. Most uniflagellate genera have the flagellum borne at the posterior end, but there are also genera where it is anterior. Biflagellate genera may bear their flagella at the anterior end, or may bear them laterally. In either case, one flagellum (the anterior) points forward and the other (posterior) flagellum points backward. Special staining techniques, dark-field illumination, and the electron microscope show that a flagellum may be of the whiplash type or the tinsel type (see page 142). Posteriorly uniflagellate zoospores have a whiplash flagellum and anteriorly uniflagellate ones have a tinsel flagellum.[4] The anterior flagellum of biflagellate zoospores is of the tinsel type and the posterior flagellum is of the whiplash type[5] (Fig. 212).

[1] Foster, 1949.
[2] Frey, 1950; Nabel, 1939; von Wettstein, 1921; van Wisselingh, 1898.
[3] Nabel, 1939; von Wettstein, 1921. [4] Couch, 1941.
[5] Couch, 1941; Manton *et al.*, 1951; Vlk, 1939.

Asexual reproductive bodies of Peronosporales and of Entomophthorales superficially resemble the conidia of ascomycetes and are frequently called conidia. They become detached and dispersed in the same manner as ascomycete conidia but germinating conidia of many Peronosporales have the protoplast dividing into zoospores. Such conidia are essentially sporangial in nature and more properly called **conidiosporangia.** Swollen ends of sporangiophores of certain Mucorales also bear globose to cylindrical outgrowths that resemble conidia. However, in the cases where these outgrowths contain one or a few aplanospores they are evidently sporangial in nature and therefore called **sporangiola** (Fig. 235, page 410).

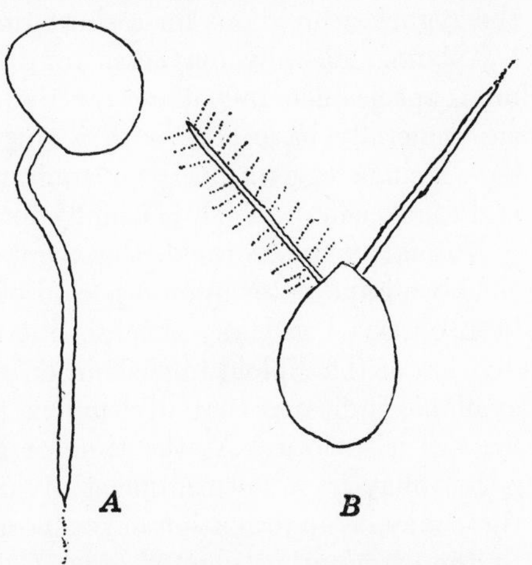

FIG. 212. Zoospores of Phycomycetae. *A*, *Nowakowskiella elegans* (Nowak.) Schroeter. *B*, *Saprolegnia ferax* (Gruith.) Thur. (*After Couch*, 1941.) (× 1,620.)

Sexual Reproduction. Sexual reproduction of phycomycetes is effected by a union of gametes. The Phycomycetae differ from other classes of Eumycophyta in that **karyogamy** (fusion of gamete nuclei) takes place soon after **plasmogamy** (fusion of gametes).

A phycomycete may be **homothallic** and with a single thallus producing both male and female gametes; or it may be **heterothallic** and with a single thallus producing only male gametes or only female gametes. The question as to whether a particular species is homothallic or heterothallic can be settled only by means of pure cultures, each derived from a single spore.

Some chytrids are holocarpic and with the entire thallus producing gametes. Other chytrids and all mycelial phycomycetes are eucarpic and with the production of gametes restricted to sex organs (**gametangia**) of distinctive form. No matter how formed, the types of gametic union fall into two general categories; those in which one or both gametes of a uniting pair are flagellated **zoogametes,** and those in which there is a union of two nonflagellated **aplanogametes.**

In species with zoogametes, the most primitive type of gametic union is a fusion of two gametes of equal size. A condition somewhat in advance of this **isogamy** is a union of two zoogametes of unequal size (**anisogamy**). Zoogametes of isogamous and anisogamous species usually retain their flagella when they unite and the zygote remains motile for a short time before disappearance of the flagella and a secretion of a wall. In exceptional cases, as in *Rhizophydium* (Fig. 217*A–B*, page 382), one gamete of a fusing pair loses its flagellum before the two unite and so the zygote is immobile from the beginning. The most advanced type of gametic union (**oögamy**) is a union of a small flagellated male gamete (**antherozoid**) with a large nonflagellated female gamete (**egg**). Among zoogametic phycomycetes, oögamy is known only for certain genera of the Monoblepharidales. In them, as in other oögamous phycomycetes, the male gametangium is called an **antheridium** and the female is called an **oögonium.** In oögamous Monoblepharidales the flagellum of an antherozoid may disappear at the time of gametic union[1] or it may persist[2] and the zygote swim about for a short time.

Aplanogamic phycomycetes may be isogamous or oögamous. Isogamous species generally have multinucleate gametes, and oögamous species generally have eggs with a single nucleus. Oögamous species may have a single egg within the oögonium; or an oögonium may contain several eggs, each of which is usually fertilized.

No matter how formed, the zygotes of most phycomycetes develop a thick wall and enter upon a period of rest. A union of gamete nuclei has been observed in many species, but there has been cytological study of division of the diploid nucleus in only a few of them. Such evidence as is available indicates that division of the diploid nucleus of thick-walled zygotes is meiotic.[3] At the time of germination, a resting thick-walled zygote may have its protoplast dividing into a number of zoospores, or there may be no formation of zoospores and a direct formation of a hypha by the germinating zygote.

There are a few zoogametic species where the zygote is thin-walled and germinates immediately. Cytological study of one of them shows that division of the diploid nucleus is mitotic and that meiosis takes place at another place in the life cycle.[4]

Life Cycle of Phycomycetae. It is very probable that most phycomycetes have a meiotic division of diploid nuclei of zygotes before or at the time zygotes germinate. If these species have a multinucleate mycelium and a uninucleate zygote, the life cycle is comparable to that of green algae in which a many-celled haploid generation alternates with a one-celled diploid phase. Similar to these green algae, the haploid generation of phycomycetes may be reduplicated by means of spores; and the life cycle may consist of a succession of haploid generations before there is a formation of the diploid phase.

Certain of the Blastocladiales and Monoblepharidales have a definite alternation of multinucleate sexual and asexual generations. Species with

[1] Sparrow, 1933. [2] Sparrow, 1940; Springer, 1945.

[3] Blackwell, 1943; Claussen, 1908; Cutter, 1942; Kusano, 1912; Laibach, 1927; Ziegler, 1953.

[4] Wilson, 195?

the *Euallomyces* type of life cycle (page 385) have an isomorphic alternation of identical gametophyte and sporophyte, and one in which there may be a reduplication of the sporophyte.[1] The species of *Allomyces* with this type of life cycle have a diploid sporophyte that may produce either haploid or diploid zoospores.[2] Haploid zoospores develop into gametophytes and diploid zoospores develop into sporophytes.[3] In the *Cystogenes* type of life cycle (page 386) there is a heteromorphic alternation of a large many-nucleate sporophyte and a small cyst-like gametophyte producing a small number (generally four) of gametes. Species of *Allomyces* with the *Cystogenes* type of life cycle have a nuclear cycle similar to that of the *Euallomyces* type.[2]

Evolution among the Phycomycetae. There seems to have been early establishment of two divergent lines among phycomycetes with flagellated reproductive bodies. Both lines are alike in showing a progression from a chytridiaceous to a mycelial type of thallus. They differ as follows: One line has posteriorly uniflagellate swarmers, cell walls with fungus chitin predominating, and with sexual reproduction usually by means of zoogametes. The other line has anteriorly biflagellate swarmers with dimorphic flagella, cell walls composed exclusively of cellulose, and aplanogametes that are always oögamous. Phylogenetic progress in the uniflagellate series is primarily that of an advance from isogamy to oögamy. Phylogenetic progress in the biflagellate series is primarily that of a differentiation of sporangia to a conidial type, and a reduction in number of eggs within an oögonium.

There is a third series of phycomycetes where there is never a formation of flagellated swarmers, and where sexual reproduction is isogamous and aplanogamic. The aplanogamy suggests a derivation from aplanogamic members of the biflagellate series, but the fact that the cell walls are composed of fungus chitin instead of cellulose makes this seem questionable.

Classification. Brefeld's system[4] with a primary segregation of the Phycomycetae into the Oömycetae and Zygomycetae was quite generally followed until about a quarter century ago. Even today, some mycologists still recognize these two groups and give them the rank of subclasses. When this is done, the usual practice is to include all aplanogamic isogamous forms in the Zygomycetae; and to include all other phycomycetes in the Oömycetae, or to segregate the chytrids from the Oömycetae. The placing of all oögamous phycomycetes in the same subclass is decidedly artificial and obscures the fact that the primary character (oögamy) has originated in independent phyletic lines among the phycomycetes. The

[1] Emerson, 1950. [2] Wilson, 1952.
[3] Couch, 1945; Couch and Whiffen, 1942; McCranie, 1942; Teter, 1944.
[4] Brefeld, 1881.

same is true, but to a more limited extent, when all aplanogamic isogamous forms are placed in the same subclass.

According to the structure of the reproductive cells, the phycomycetes may be segregated into three major groups: one with posteriorly uniflagellate swarmers, another with anteriorly biflagellate swarmers, and a third group in which there are no flagellated swarmers. These three groups differ sufficiently to be considered subclasses. The group with posteriorly uniflagellate swarmers has been called the Uniflagellatae, and that with biflagellate swarmers called the Biflagellatae.[1] The group lacking flagellated spores or gametes has been called[2] the Aplanatae, but a name more consistent with that given other groups would be Aflagellatae.

There are also a few chytrids, the Hyphochytriales (Anisochytridiales), in which there is a single anterior flagellum of the tinsel type. Since the relationship of this order to other phycomycetes with flagellated swarmers is obscure it is best to consider it an order of doubtful systematic position (see page 418).

SUBCLASS 1. UNIFLAGELLATAE

Thalli of Uniflagellatae have cell walls in which fungus chitin predominates but in which there may be some cellulose. The thalli may be holocarpic or eucarpic. Most genera form zoospores and these are always uniflagellate, and always with a flagellum of the whiplash type that is always borne posteriorly. Sexual reproduction may be isogamous, anisogamous, or oögamous. Motile gametes are uniflagellate and with the flagellum borne in the same manner as in zoospores.

There are about 85 genera and 450 species. These are segregated into the following three orders: Chytridiales, Blastocladiales, and Monoblepharidales. On pages to follow the Chytridiales are delimited according to those who exclude from the order the chytrids whose swarmers have two flagella[3] and the chytrids whose swarmers have a single anterior flagellum.[4]

ORDER 1. CHYTRIDIALES

The Chytridiales include those Uniflagellatae in which the thallus is never a true mycelium. The thalli may be holocarpic or eucarpic, and when eucarpic may have the vegetative portion consisting of a branched rhizoidal system (**rhizomycelium**) without a cell wall. Cell walls are of fungus chitin and at times with some cellulose. Asexual reproduction is by means of posteriorly uniflagellate zoospores with a flagellum of the whiplash type. Sexual reproduction is either by an isogamous union of zoogametes, or by an isogamous or anisogamous union of aplanogametes.

[1] Sparrow, 1943. [2] Alexopoulos, 1952.
[3] Couch, 1941; Scherffel, 1925; Sparrow, 1942. [4] Karling, 1943.

The order includes about 75 genera and 400 species. According to opinion concerning relationships, these have been segregated into nine[1] or into seven[2] families.

The Chytridiales are predominantly aquatic, but there are species parasitic upon vascular land plants. Aquatic species may be parasitic or saprophytic. If parasitic they are mostly parasitic upon algae or upon other aquatic phycomycetes. In relation to the host, a thallus may be **epibiotic** and lie external to the host, or it may be **endibiotic** and lie wholly within a cell or cells of the host. The thallus may be **monocentric** and with a single reproductive body, or it may be **polycentric** and with more than

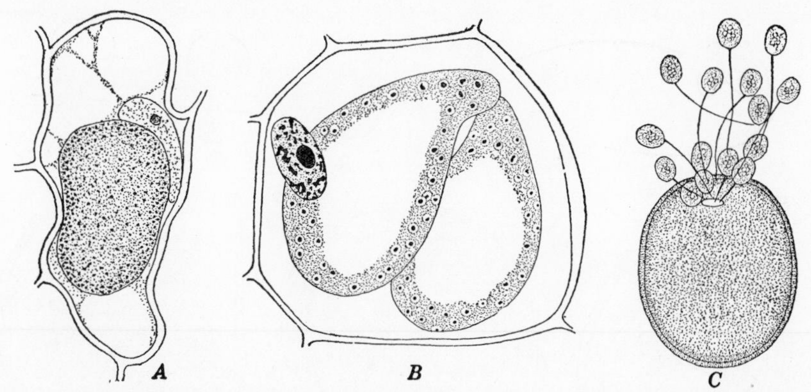

FIG. 213. *Olpidium viciae* Kusano. *A–B*, stages in development of "summer sporangia." *C*, liberation of zooids from a "summer spore." (*After Kusano*, 1912.) (*A*, × 300; *B*, × 900; *C*, × 800.)

one reproductive body. The first two chytrids described on pages to follow exemplify monocentric and polycentric holocarpic genera; the second two exemplify monocentric and polycentric eucarpic genera.

Olpidium, a genus with about 25 species, grows on a wide variety of hosts; including algae, aquatic fungi, pollen grains, and epidermal cells of vascular plants. The thallus is endobiotic, holocarpic, and monocentric. The most thoroughly investigated species is *O. viciae* Kusano, a parasite infecting epidermal cells of leaves and stems of *Vicia unijuga* A. Br. Successive generations of thalli formed during the summer are thin-walled and are generally called "summer sporangia." At first, the thallus within a host cell is a naked globose mass of protoplasm. If there has been but a single infection of a host cell, the fungus may enlarge until it fills almost all of the host cell (Fig. 213*A*). During enlargement the fungus becomes multinucleate (Fig. 213*B*) and a wall surrounding it becomes plainly evident.[3] After a few days, and when the fungus is nearly mature, there is a formation of a small beak-like outgrowth, the future

[1] Sparrow, 1943. [2] Whiffen, 1944. [3] Kusano, 1912.

exit tube, that grows through the wall of the host cell. Soon after this the entire protoplast becomes divided into posteriorly uniflagellate swarmers. The tip of the beak-like exit tube ruptures suddenly, and the swarmers swim out with their flagella trailing (Fig. 213*C*). Under favorable conditions all swarmers escape within two or three minutes. At the end of the swarming period, a swarmer creeps over the surface of the host in an amoeboid fashion, comes to rest, assumes a spherical shape, and secretes a thin wall. The protoplast of this cell soon sends forth a naked haustorial outgrowth that grows through the underlying host-cell wall; and this is followed by the entire protoplast migrating into the host cell and there

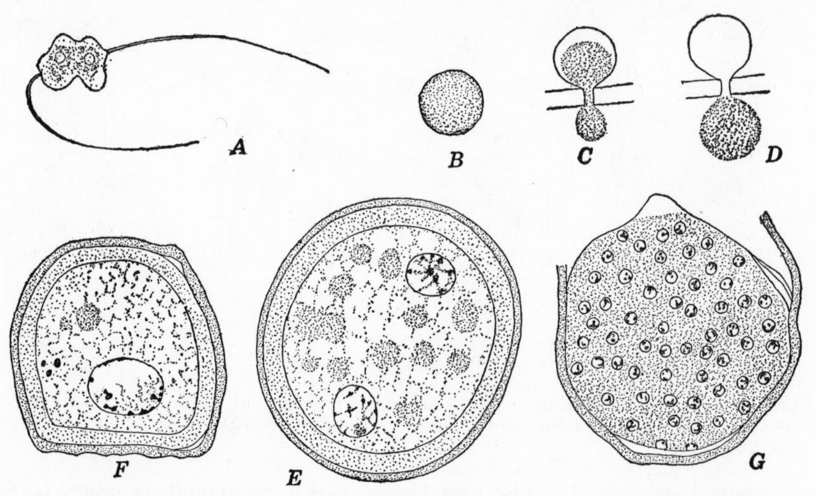

FIG. 214. *Olpidium viciae* Kusano, gametic union and development of "winter sporangia." *A*, gametic union. *B–D*, germination of zygotes. *E–F*, overwintering stages before and after union of the nuclei. *G*, multinucleate stage just before germination. (*After Kusano*, 1912.) (*A–D*, × 1,200; *E–G*, × 1,350.)

developing into a one-celled globose thallus. Since they develop into new thalli, the swarmers are generally considered asexual in nature and called zoospores. However, since those formed at the end of the summer unite in pairs it is more probable that the swarmers are gametic in nature and that their direct development into thalli is due to parthenogenesis.

At the end of the growing season there is regularly a fusion of the zoogametes in pairs instead of a parthenogenetic development of them into thalli. Union of a pair of zoogametes takes place while both are motile,[1] and the resultant biflagellate zygote remains motile for some time (Fig. 214*A*). It eventually comes to rest upon the host and becomes invested with a thin wall. The zygote's protoplast also sends out a haustorium that perforates the host-cell wall, and this is followed by a migration of

[1] Kusano, 1912.

the protoplast into the host cell (Fig. 214*B–D*). After entering a host cell the zygote enlarges considerably, secretes a thick wall, and enters upon a rest period that lasts until the following spring. This thick-walled stage of the zygote is usually called a "winter sporangium." Karyogamy is long delayed and does not take place until early in the following spring (Fig. 214*E–F*). Karyogamy is soon followed by a repeated division and redivision of the fusion nucleus (Fig. 214*G*), and it is very probable that the first two divisions are meiotic. When nuclear division ceases there is

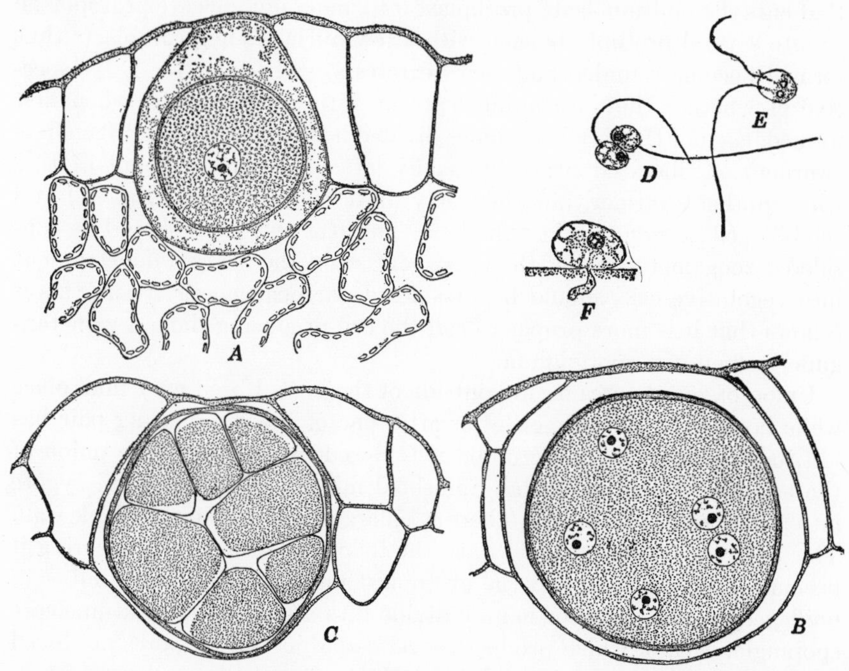

FIG. 215. *A–C*, "summer sporangia" of *Synchytrium* sp. *A*, uninucleate stage. *B*, multinucleate stage. *C*, after cleavage of cell contents. *D–F*, *S. endobioticum* (Schillb.) Perc. *D–E*, gametic union. *F*, germination of zygote. (*D–F*, *after Curtis*, 1921.) (*A–C*, × 325; *D–F*, × 2,000.)

a cleavage of the multinucleate protoplast into uniflagellate swarmers. These are liberated by a cracking of the old zygote wall, and after swarming for a time they infect the host and develop into new thalli.

Synchytrium, a genus with about 50 species, is a widely distributed parasite in epidermal cells of various terrestrial angiosperms. It is endobiotic, holocarpic, and polycentric. Most species cause a gall-like swelling of infected host cells (Fig. 215*A*). In some species the globose one-celled thallus is always surrounded by a thick wall; in others it may be surrounded by either a thin or a thick wall. For certain of these latter species it is definitely established[1] that production of thick-walled cells (the so-

[1] Curtis, 1921; Kusano, 1930; Köhler, 1931.

called "winter spores" or "winter sporangia") is preceded by gametic union, and that production of thin-walled cells (the so-called "summer spores" or "summer sporangia") is not preceded by gametic union.

The thin-walled, unicellular, globose stage of *Synchytrium* is uninucleate until it has grown nearly to full size, but enlargement of the fungus is accompanied by a conspicuous increase in size of the nucleus (Fig. 215*A*). Then the nucleus divides and redivides as the fungus is attaining its maximum size (Fig. 215*B*). This is followed by a progressive cleavage that cuts the multinucleate protoplast into many uninucleate protoplasts[1] or into several protoplasts each with a few nuclei.[2] The protoplasts thus formed become rounded and each secretes a wall (Fig. 215*C*). Irrespective of whether they are uninucleate or with several nuclei when first formed, each of these cells becomes divided into a number of uniflagellate swarmers. A liberated swarmer usually infects the host without uniting with another swarmer, but they may unite in pairs (Fig. 215*D–E*) and the biflagellate zygote infect the host. Thus the swarmers should be considered zoogametes rather than zoospores, and their direct development into vegetative cells should be considered parthenogenesis. From this it follows that it is more proper to call the cell producing them a gametangium instead of a sporangium.

Union of zoogametes occurs outside of the host. Union may take place while both gametes are motile[3] or after one of the conjugating pair has lost its flagellum.[2] Gametic union is followed by an immediate union of the two gamete nuclei and an amoeboid migration of the naked zygote into a host cell (Fig. 215*F*). There it enlarges and develops a thick wall. This cell remains uninucleate until the following spring. In the spring it becomes multinucleate and the protoplast may divide into a number of uniflagellate zoospores; or it may divide into a number of multinucleate sporangia, each of which produces several zoospores. Zoospores produced by a zygote infect the host and develop into new thalli.

Rhizophydium is a genus with about 45 species. Most of the species are parasitic upon fresh-water algae but certain of them, as *R. graminis* Ledingham, are parasitic upon angiosperms. The thallus is eucarpic and monocentric. The fertile portion of a thallus is more or less globose, surrounded by a distinct wall, and lies external to the host cell. The vegetative portion is a naked rhizomycelium consisting of attenuated rhizoidal branches that grow into the protoplast of the host cell (Fig. 216*A–C*).

Asexual reproduction is by the monocentric fertile portion becoming a sporangium producing zoospores. In *R. ovatum* Couch the contents of the sporangium cleave into many angular protoplasts (Fig. 216*D–E*), each of which is metamorphosed into a posteriorly uniflagellate zoospore.[4] These escape through one or more pores in the wall. All zoospores may

[1] Harper, 1899. [2] Curtis, 1921. [3] Kusano, 1930. [4] Couch, 1932.

swim out within a few seconds after the pore opens,[1] or they may creep out slowly in an amoeboid manner and then swim away. At the end of the swarming period a zoospore comes to rest upon a host cell and lies with the flagellated end upward. The flagellum soon disappears and a delicate rhizoidal outgrowth grows into the host and becomes a rhizomycelium (Fig. 216*A*). The portion external to the host secretes a wall, increases rapidly in size, and becomes the sporangium. Development to maturity may be completed within 20 hours by *R. ovatum*.[1] There are also species where the sporangium becomes thick-walled and enters upon a dormant stage. When such resting sporangia ("resting spores") resume activity there is a protrusion of the protoplast surrounded by a thin wall, and then a division of the contents of the protruded portion into zoospores.[2]

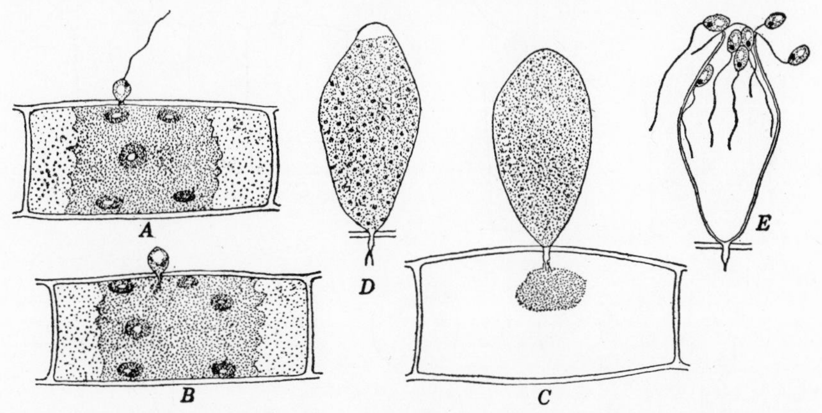

Fig. 216. *Rhizophydium ovatum* Couch. *A–B*, early stages in germination. *C*, mature thallus. *D*, cleavage into zoospores. *E*, liberation of zoospores. (*After Couch*, 1935.) (× 1,250.)

Sexual reproduction of *R. ovatum* is by means of uniflagellate zoogametes of equal size. A male gamete comes to rest upon the host, loses its flagellum, and sends a delicate rhizoid into the host in the same manner as a germinating zoospore.[1] Shortly afterward a female gamete becomes applied to the male gamete and loses its flagellum (Fig. 217). Both the apposed gametes increase greatly in size and secrete a wall. As enlargement continues, the contents of the male cell migrate into the female cell, and the two nuclei unite. The spherical zygote borne upon the empty male cell secretes a fairly thick wall. This zygote may germinate to form zoospores within two or three days.[1] Certain other species[3] have the zoogametes coming to rest side by side upon the host. In these species the male cell is always smaller than the female and there is a lateral migration of the male protoplast into the female cell.

[1] Couch, 1935. [2] Hanson, 1945; Karling, 1939.
[3] Sparrow, 1933*A*, 1936, 1939.

Cladochytrium, with about half a dozen species, is representative of the eucarpic polycentric genera. It is generally found on decaying tissues of angiosperms but also occurs in the gelatinous envelope of various fresh-water algae. The thallus is a much branched rhizomycelium and when growing in plant tissues may extend through several adjoining cells (Fig. 218*A*). Here and there in a rhizomycelium are more or less spindle-shaped portions, the **spindle organs** or **turbinate organs.** They are purely vegetative in nature, but their precise function is uncertain. One suggested function is that of a center for reduplication of the rhizomycelium.[1]

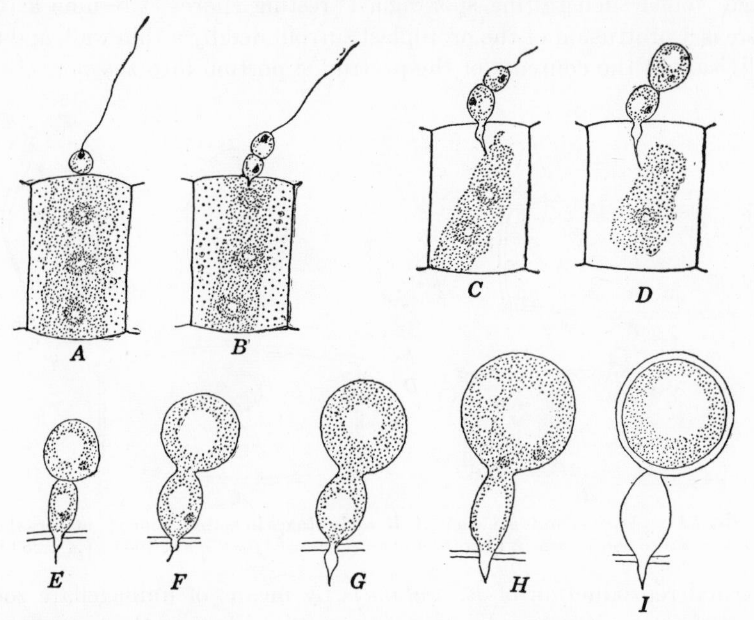

FIG. 217. *Rhizophydium ovatum* Couch. *A*, male gamete. *B–D*, gametic union. *E–H*, stages in gradual enlargement of zygote. *I*, mature zygote. (*After Couch*, 1935.) (× 1,875.)

A turbinate organ is usually blocked off from the remainder of the thallus by transverse walls, and it may be divided into two or more cells by transverse walls.

A mature rhizomycelium generally forms several sporangia. These may develop either at the tips of branches or some distance from a branch tip (Fig. 218*A*). Sporangial development begins with a localized swelling of the rhizomycelium.[1] Enlarging sporangia are club-shaped, but fully developed ones are globose and with one or more tubular outgrowths, the future exit tubes.[2] A mature sporangium is invested with a thin wall that delimits it from the remainder of the rhizomycelium. The protoplast within a sporangium cleaves progressively to form a number of uniflagel-

[1] Karling, 1931. [2] Karling, 1937.

late zoospores that are discharged through the exit tubes (Fig. 218*B–C*). Sometimes[1] the sporangium develops a very thick wall and enters upon a dormant period. When these resting sporangia resume activity there is a production of zoospores that are discharged through a newly formed exit tube.[2] Sexual reproduction has never been observed in *Cladochytrium*.

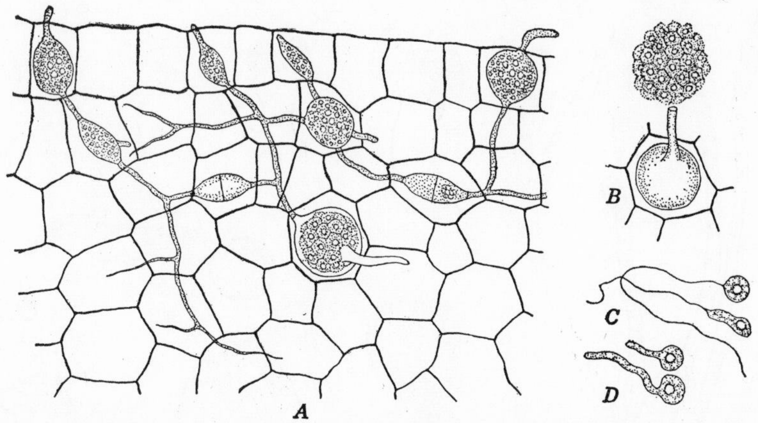

FIG. 218. *Cladochytrium replicatum* Karling. *A*, thallus in leaf of *Eriocaulon septangulare* With. *B*, discharge of zoospores from a sporangium. *C*, zoospores. *D*, germinating zoospores. (*After Karling*, 1931.)

ORDER 2. BLASTOCLADIALES

The Blastocladiales have a more or less extensive true mycelium and one with cell walls of fungus chitin. Asexual reproduction is by means of posteriorly uniflagellate zoospores produced within sporangia. Most species have two kinds of sporangia; one with thin walls, the other with thick walls. Sexual reproduction is isogamous or anisogamous and by a fusion of posteriorly uniflagellate zoogametes. Certain species have an isomorphic or heteromorphic alternation of generations.

The Blastocladiales differ from other mycelial phycomycetes in that sexual reproduction is by an isogamous or anisogamous union of zoogametes. Another distinctive feature is the production of thick-walled **resistant sporangia.** The order includes 5 genera and about 40 species. These have been segregated into three families.[3] Some species are saprophytic, and either aquatic or terrestrial. Other species are parasitic upon other fungi, insects, worms, or rotifers.

Allomyces, a saprophytic terrestrial genus with five species, has been studied more extensively than other genera of the order. It is world-wide in distribution, but among the hundreds of stations where it has been found almost all are in tropical or warm temperate regions.[4] The myce-

[1] Karling, 1935; Sparrow, 1931. [2] Karling, 1935.
[3] Bessey, 1950; Martin, 1950. [4] Emerson, 1941; Wolf, 1941.

lium grows erect from a rhizoidal system of delicate hyphal branches (Fig. 219*A*). A single stout hypha arises from the rhizoidal system, and it generally has several successive dichotomous branchings that tend to become progressively narrower at each dichotomy. There is an incomplete transverse wall at each dichotomy.

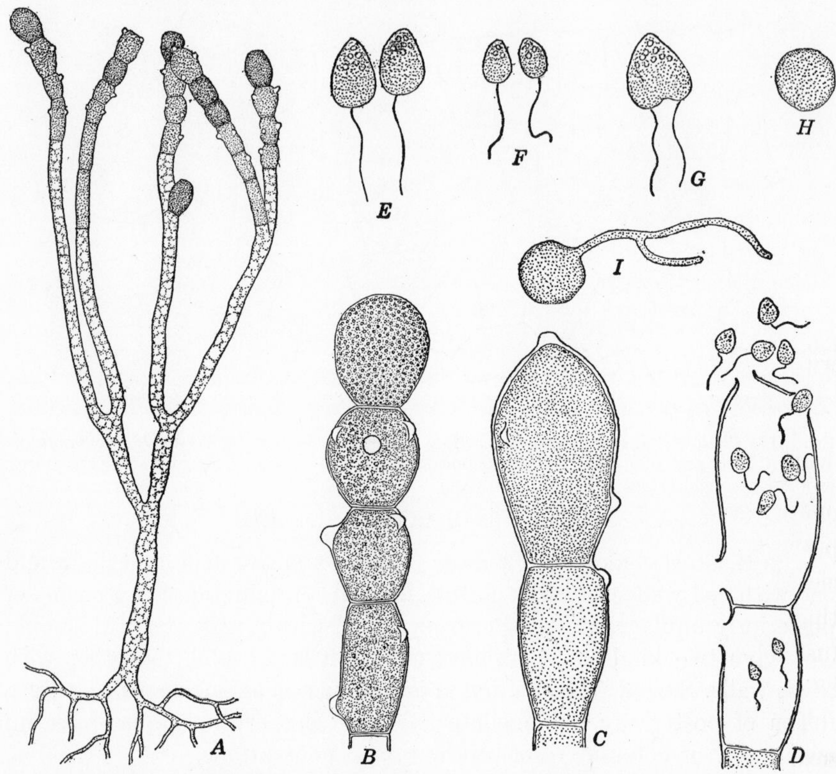

FIG. 219. *Allomyces arbuscula* Butler. *A*, sporophyte. *B*, resistant sporangia and zoosporangia. *C*, gametangia. *D*, liberation of gametes. *E*, female gametes. *F*, male gametes. *G*, union of gametes. *H*, zygote. *I*, germination of zygote. (*A*, × 120; *B*, × 485; *C–D*, × 400; *E–I*, × 800.)

The genus has been divided[1] into three subgenera on the basis of the life cycle. *A. arbuscula* Butler and *A. javanicus* Kniep belong to the subgenus *Euallomyces* in which there is an isomorphic alternation of generations. A sporophyte produces ovoid sporangia singly or in catenate series at the tips of the ultimate dichotomies (Fig. 219*A–B*). The sporangia are of two types: **zoosporangia** with thin walls, and **resistant sporangia** (**meiosporangia**) with thick walls. Early stages in development of the two are similar. Development begins with a

[1] Emerson, 1941.

swelling of the multinucleate tip of a hypha and a formation of a transverse wall that separates the swollen portion from the remainder of the hypha. During further development of a zoosporangium there is an increase in number of the nuclei.[1] This is followed by an inward furrowing of the plasma membrane that eventually divides the sporangial contents into uninucleate protoplasts, each of which is metamorphosed into a uniflagellate zoospore. The zoospores are liberated through one or more pores developed in the sporangial wall. All nuclear divisions in a developing zoosporangium are mitotic and it has been shown[2] that zoospores from them develop into sporophytes.

During development of a resistant sporangium there is a formation of a thick pitted wall internal to the original sporangial wall (Fig. 219*B*). Resistant sporangia must remain dormant for a time before the protoplast divides into zoospores. Desiccation is an important factor in maturation of resistant sporangia but it is not absolutely essential. The time required for ripening varies from a few days to six weeks.[3] Just prior to "germination" of a resistant sporangium there is a meiotic division of the nuclei[4] and a cleavage of the protoplast into uniflagellate zoospores. Zoospores are liberated by a cracking of the sporangial wall. After swimming for a time, they retract their flagella, secrete a wall, and develop into gametophytes.

Gametophytes of the subgenus *Euallomyces* are homothallic, and with the gametangia borne terminally on the hyphae. The gametangia lie in catenate series of two or more, and with male and female alternating with each other (Fig. 219*C*). According to the species, female gametangia lie above male gametangia, or vica versa.[5] The two kinds of gametangia may be distinguished from each other by differences in shape and by the deep orange color of male gametangia. Young gametangia have approximately the same number of nuclei, but the number in a male gametangium eventually becomes two to three times that in a female gametangium.[6] Zoogametes are formed by progressive cleavage of the protoplast, and escape singly through one or more exit papillae in the gametangial wall (Fig. 219*D*). Members of the subgenus *Euallomyces* are anisogamous,[5] and free-swimming female zoogametes have a length and breadth about double that of male zoogametes (Fig. 219*E–F*). The biflagellate zygote formed by union of two gametes moves sluggishly for 5 or 10 minutes and then becomes immobile, secretes a wall, and immediately begins developing into a sporophyte (Fig. 219*G–I*).

The isomorphic alternation of generations in the subgenus *Euallomyces* is not obligatory in the sense that one generation is always succeeded by

[1] Barrett, 1912*A*; Lugg, 1929. [2] Emerson, 1941; Sörgel, 1937.
[3] Emerson, 1941; Kniep, 1930. [4] Emerson and Wilson, 1949; Wilson, 1952.
[5] Emerson, 1941; Hatch, 1933; Kniep, 1929. [6] Hatch, 1935.

the alternate generation, and the life cycle (Fig. 220*A*) may involve a succession of sporophytes or of gametophytes. The sporophyte is reduplicated by means of zoospores from zoosporangia. Precociously "germinating" resistant sporangia may give rise to zoospores which develop into sporophytes instead of into gametophytes.[1] Reduplication of the gametophyte is by parthenogenesis of female zoogametes.[2]

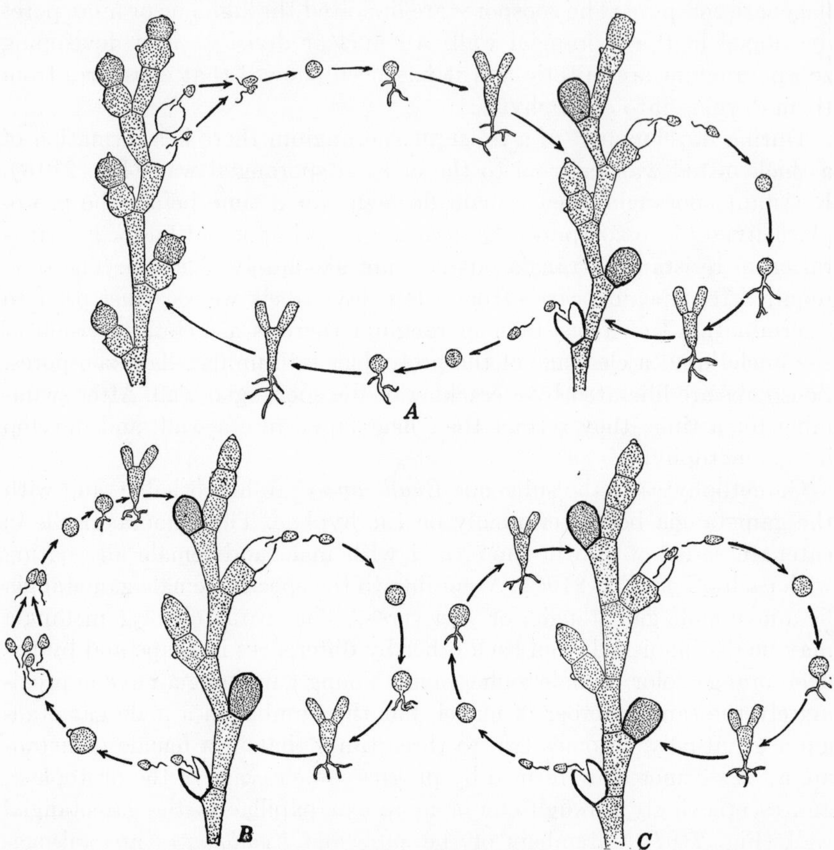

FIG. 220. Diagrams of types of life cycle in *Allomyces*. *A*, *Euallomyces* type. *B*, *Cystogenes* type. *C*, *Brachyallomyces* type. (*Based upon Emerson*, 1941.)

A. cystogenus Emerson and *A. moniliformis* Coker and Braxton, the two species of the subgenus *Cystogenes*, have a heteromorphic alternation of generations (Fig. 220*B*). The sporophytes are similar to those in the subgenus *Euallomyces* and it has been shown[3] that meiosis immediately precedes zoospore formation in resistant sporangia. Zoospores from resistant sporangia develop into minute globose gametophytes that usu-

[1] Emerson, 1941; Hatch and Jones, 1944; Sörgel, 1937.
[2] Emerson, 1941; Kniep, 1930; Sörgel, 1937. [3] Wilson, 1952.

ally produce but four zoogametes whose gametic union is isogamous.[1] The zygote formed by union of zoogametes develops into a sporophyte.

A. anomalus Emerson, the sole member of the subgenus *Brachyallomyces,* lacks an alternation of generations except for certain aberrant individuals. In this species, zoospores from both the zoosporangia and the resistant sporangia develop into mycelia producing both kinds of sporangia (Fig. 220*C*).

ORDER 3. MONOBLEPHARIDALES

Members of this order have a well-developed mycelium that produces sporangia and sex organs. Sporangia are elongate, formed terminally on hyphae, and produce posteriorly uniflagellate zoospores. Sexual reproduction is oögamous, with a single egg in an oögonium and with motile male gametes.

Monoblepharidales are the only oögamous phycomycetes with motile antherozoids. The order is also unique in that the naked zygote may emerge from the oögonium before forming a wall. There is but one family, the Monoblepharidaceae. It contains 3 genera and about 10 species, some of which are aquatic and others of which are soil-inhabiting.

There are about seven species in the type genus, *Monoblepharis.* These are usually found in clear waters and growing on dead twigs of various trees, but they have also been found on other substrata. The mycelium is usually attached to the substratum by rhizoidal hyphae. According to the species, the remainder of a thallus consists of rigid sparingly branched hyphae that tend to lie free from one another (Fig. 221*A*), or it consists of freely branched hyphae that lie interwoven in a felted mat. The hyphae are without cross walls during vegetative growth. The cytoplasm is alveolate and with a uniseriate row of nuclei that lie equidistant from one another. Reproductive organs are developed at the tips of hyphae, and the type of organ developed is contingent upon the temperature. If it is 8 to 11°C. reproduction is asexual; if the temperature is raised to about 20°C. sexual organs are formed.[2]

Asexual reproduction (Fig. 221*B–E*) is by means of uniflagellate zoospores produced within narrowly cylindrical sporangia separated from the remainder of the mycelium by transverse walls. The protoplast within a sporangium may contain a uniseriate or a multiseriate row of nuclei.[3] In either case, there is a cleavage of the sporangial contents into angular uninucleate protoplasts that become metamorphosed into zoospores. The zoospores are uniflagellate, with the flagellum borne at the posterior end and of the whiplash type.[4] A mature sporangium has a circular pore at its apex, and one by one the zoospores creep out through it in an amoe-

[1] McCranie, 1942; Teter, 1944. [2] Sparrow, 1933.
[3] Laibach, 1927. [4] Couch, 1941.

boid fashion. The flagellum of an emerging zoospore remains attached to the pore for some time, and the body of the spore oscillates back and forth. Eventually the zoospore becomes free and swims through the water for some time before coming to rest, withdrawing its flagellum, and secreting a wall. When this cell begins to develop into a mycelium it forms two hyphae, one growing into the rhizoidal system of the new plant, the

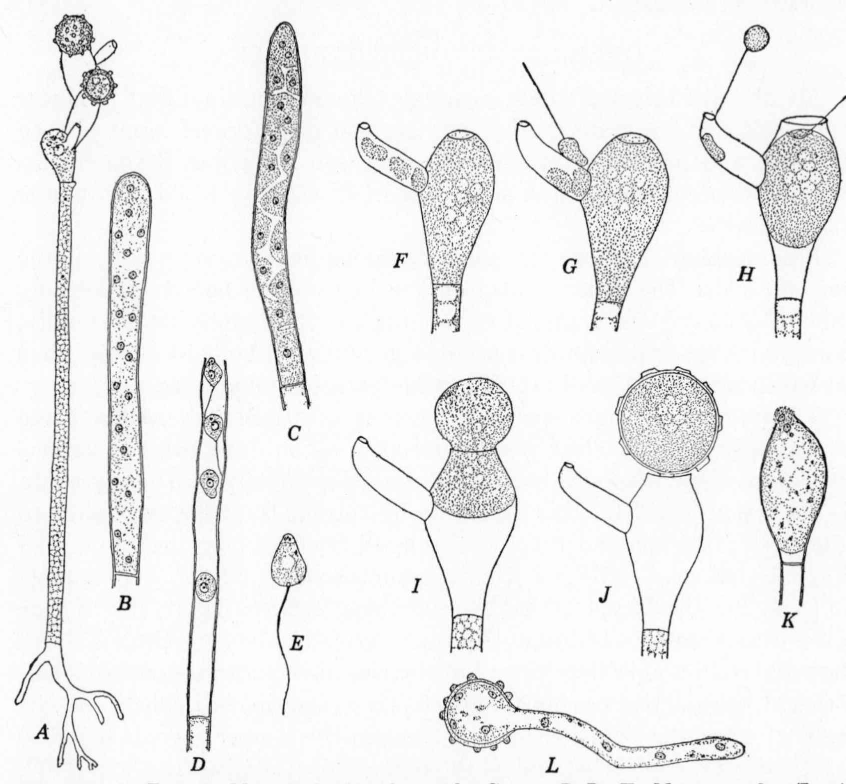

FIG. 221. *A*, *E–J*, *L*, *Monoblepharis polymorpha* Cornu. *B–D*, *K*, *M. macrandra* (Lag.) Woronin. *A*, thallus with mature sex organs. *B–D*, development of sporangia. *E*, zoospore. *F–J*, diagrams of successive stages in fertilization and development of zygote. *K*, union of gametes. *L*, germination of zygote. (*A*, *E–J*, *after Sparrow*, 1933; *B–D*, *K–L*, *after Laibach*, 1927.) (*A*, × 185; *B–D*, × 440; *E*, × 630; *F–J*, × 675; *K–L*, × 440.)

other into the remainder of the thallus. In rare cases the entire contents of a sporangium may develop into a chlamydospore.[1]

Development of sex organs is preceded by a formation of several transverse walls in the distal portion of a hypha. The cells thus formed alternately mature into antheridia and oögonia. In some species the oögonia lie above the antheridia; in others antheridia lie above oögonia. Antheridial development, except for the smaller number of uniflagellate

[1] Sparrow, 1933.

swarmers, is similar to that of sporangia. The oögonial protoplast is uninucleate from the beginning[1] and during the course of oögonial development there is a formation of a pore in the apical portion of the oögonial wall.

At the time of fertilization (Fig. 221*F–J*) an antherozoid swims to an oögonium and then crawls, in an amoeboid fashion, over the oögonial wall until it reaches the pore.[2] It then crawls through the pore and fuses with the egg. The resultant zygote may remain within the oögonium, or it may migrate out from the oögonium and remain attached to the pore in the oögonial wall. In either case there is a formation of a thick zygote wall. The two gamete nuclei do not unite until the zygote wall is formed and maturation of a zygote takes several months. During this time there is a meiotic division of the fusion nucleus,[1] and each of the four daughter nuclei may divide once or twice. At the time of germination the zygote wall cracks open and a hypha grows out through the crack in the zygote wall (Fig. 221*L*).

SUBCLASS 2. BIFLAGELLATAE

Thalli of Biflagellatae have cell walls composed in large part of cellulose. Almost all of them have a definitely mycelial thallus. The thalli may be holocarpic or eucarpic. Asexual reproduction is by means of zoospores. In the eucarpic genera the zoospores may be formed within sporangia permanently attached to the thallus, or formed within sporangia (conidiosporangia) that become detached. Zoospores are biflagellate, with one flagellum of the tinsel type and the other of the whiplash type. Sexual reproduction is aplanogamic, oögamous, and with one or more than one egg within an oögonium.

There are about 50 genera and 400 species. A majority of the species are aquatic or terrestrial saprophytes. The remainder are parasitic and most of them are parasitic on land plants.

The Biflagellatae have a number of distinctive features not found in other subclasses. They are the only phycomycetes in which the cell wall is composed entirely or in large part of cellulose. The flagella of a zoospore are dimorphic, one being of the whiplash type and the other of the tinsel type.[3] Most genera also have a production of zoospores of two different morphological types (**diplanetism**). The primary zoospores, those liberated from a sporangium, are more or less pyriform and have the two flagella borne at the anterior end. After swimming for a time a primary zoospore retracts its flagella, rounds up, and secretes a thin wall. If environmental conditions are favorable, the cyst thus formed germinates by sending out a hypha which grows into a mycelium. If conditions are

[1] Laibach, 1927. [2] Sparrow, 1933; Thaxter, 1895.
[3] Couch, 1941; Manton *et al.*, 1951; Vlk, 1939.

less favorable, the germinating cyst gives rise to a single zoospore (secondary zoospore) that is reniform and with the two flagella inserted on the concave side. After swarming for a time, a secondary zoospore usually develops into a mycelium, but it may become encysted and give rise to another secondary zoospore. A formation of as many as five successive secondary zoospores has been noted in *Achlya*.[1]

Of the orders into which the Biflagellatae may be divided the Lagenidiales (formerly known as the Ancylistales), the Saprolegniales, and the Peronosporales have long been recognized. The proposal[2] that certain families formerly placed in the Saprolegniales be segregated into a separate order, the Leptomitales, has received widespread support.

ORDER 1. LAGENIDIALES

The Lagenidiales are holocarpic and with a chytridiaceous or a simple mycelial type of thallus. The cell walls are composed of cellulose. Asexual reproduction is by means of biflagellate zoospores with the two flagella unlike in structure. Sexual reproduction is aplanogamic and with a sufficient differentiation in size of gametes to be considered oögamous.

The order includes some 10 genera and 45 species. Most of the species are aquatic and parasitic on fresh-water algae or fresh-water phycomycetes.

The primary feature distinguishing this from other orders of the subclass is the holocarpic thallus. At the time when a thallus forms reproductive cells it may become a single reproductive organ or divide into several. For a long time only the mycelial genera were referred to the order but the extension of ordinal limits to include biflagellate chytridiaceous phycomycetes[3] is now generally accepted. Of the two genera described on pages to follow, *Olpidiopsis* is representative of the chytridiaceous types, and *Lagenidium* is representative of the mycelial types.

Olpidiopsis is a parasitic genus with about 15 species. The majority of species are parasitic on fresh-water phycomycetes; the remainder are parasitic on fresh-water or marine algae. The thallus is an ellipsoidal to globose protoplasmic mass that lies wholly within a host cell. Growth of a thallus is accompanied by a continuous increase in number of nuclei,[4] and it does not become invested with a cellulose wall until it is almost mature (Fig. 222*A*).

Asexual reproduction is by means of zoospores and with a holocarpic development of the thallus into a single sporangium. A cell becoming a sporangium develops one or more cylindrical projections, the future exit tubes, extending to and through the wall of the host cell (Fig. 222*B*). The multinucleate protoplast within a developing sporangium cleaves into uninucleate protoplasts by progressive furrowing from one or more

[1] Salvin, 1940. [2] Kanouse, 1927. [3] Sparrow, 1943. [4] Barrett, 1912.

vacuoles at the center of the sporangium.[1] Each of the uninucleate protoplasts is metamorphosed into a biflagellate zoospore, and the zoospores escape through a pore developed at the apex of the exit tube (Fig. 222*C*). A zoospore has one flagellum of the tinsel type and one of the whiplash type.[2] Some species are diplanetic and with a formation of secondary zoospores; other species are not.

Instead of producing zoospores, a thallus may develop into a gametangium containing a single aplanogamete. Thalli developing into male and

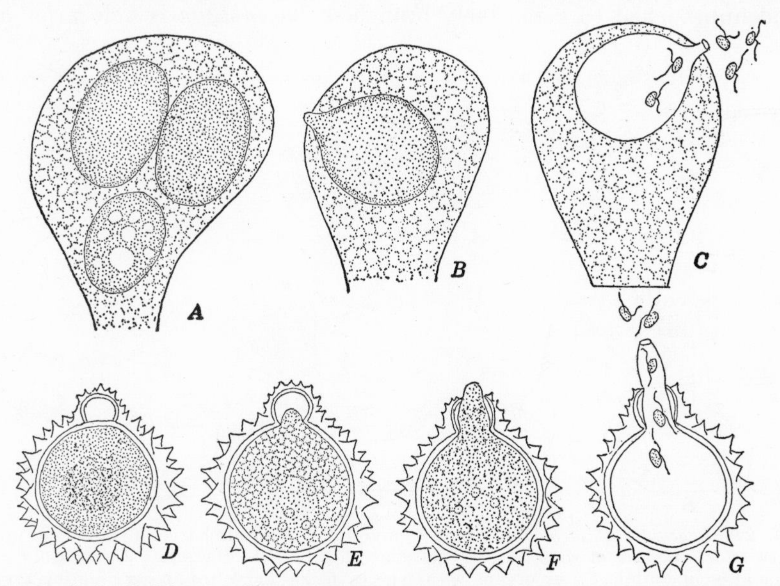

FIG. 222. *A–C*, *Olpidiopsis achlyae* McLarty in hyphae of *Achlya* sp. *A*, vegetative cells. *B*, young sporangium. *C*, liberation of zoospores from a mature sporangium. *D–G*, *Olpidiopsis* sp. *D*, zygote. *E–G*, germination of zygote. (*D–G*, *after Shanor*, 1939.) (*A–C*, × 90; *D–G*, × 240.)

female gametangia lie adjacent to one another. A male (antheridial) gametangium is surrounded by a wall and the aplanogamete within it is multinucleate. A female (oögonial) gametangium is larger than a male gametangium, and the aplanogamete (egg) within it contains many more nuclei. At the time of gametic union the cell walls disappear in the region of mutual contact and the male gamete migrates into the oögonium. Sometimes the contents of more than one antheridium migrate into an oögonium. A fusion of nuclei from the two gametes has been affirmed[3] and denied.[4] Gametic union is followed by a development of a thick spiny wall layer around both the oögonium and the empty antheridium ("companion cell") (Fig. 222*D*). Zygotes must ripen for a considerable time

[1] Barrett, 1912; McLarty, 1941. [2] Couch, 1941.
[3] Barrett, 1912. [4] McLarty, 1941.

before germinating. At the time of germination a cylindrical exit tube grows out through the empty antheridial wall and the enclosing zygote wall.[1] There is then a cleavage of the protoplast into numerous biflagellate zoospores which are liberated through a pore at the apex of the exit tube (Fig. 222*E–G*).

Lagenidium (Fig. 223*A*) is a widely distributed fungus with some 15 species, all but one of which are parasitic. Most of the parasitic species are parasitic upon fresh-water algae. The thallus of *Lagenidium* is tubular and unbranched to extensively branched. *Lagenidium* is holocarpic and

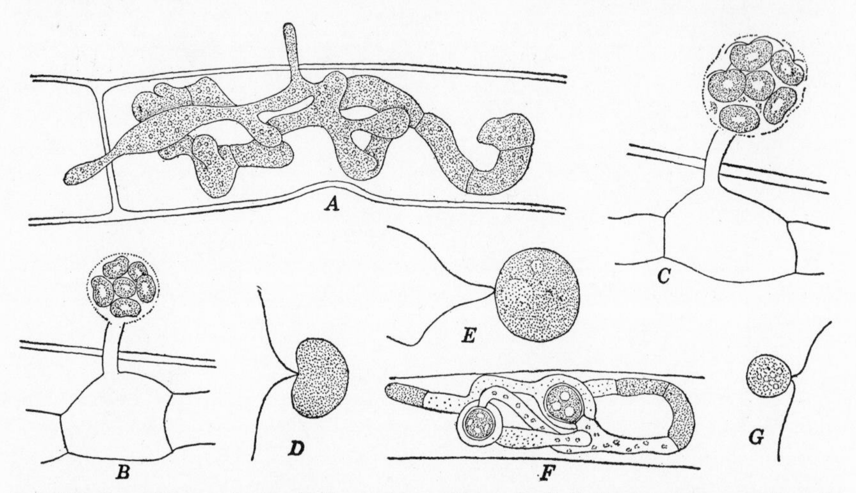

FIG. 223. *Lagenidium rabenhorstii* Zopf. *A*, mycelium. *B–C*, discharge of sporangial protoplast and formation of zoospores. *D*, zoospore shortly after liberation. *E*, zoospore some time after liberation. *F*, sex organs with zygotes. *G*, zoospore from a germinating zygote. (*After Cook*, 1935.) (*A–B*, × 540; *C*, × 790; *D–E*, × 1,300; *F*, × 385; *G*, × 790.)

with the entire thallus remaining one-celled or dividing into several cells immediately before reproduction.

The only evident change in a cell developing into a sporangium is a formation of a tubular outgrowth, the exit tube, that projects through the host-cell wall. Formation of the tube is followed by a discharge of the protoplast through it.[2] The globose mass of protoplasm remains attached to the tip of the tube and there cleaves into several zoospores (Fig. 223*B–C*). The zoospores are reniform and with the two flagella inserted on the concave side. Within a short time they swim away from one another and become pear-shaped (Fig. 223*D–E*). Swarming of zoospores may continue for hours or days. At the end of the swarming period a zoospore comes to rest, with the flagellated end downward, upon a host cell and digests its way directly through the host-cell wall.

At the time of sexual reproduction an entire thallus may develop into

[1] Shanor, 1939. [2] Cook, 1935.

a single sex organ or may divide into several cells each of which becomes a sex organ. Sexual reproduction is aplanogamic and oögamous. A cell developing into an oögonium becomes rounded, and its protoplast becomes a globose egg that lies some distance inward from the oögonial wall. A cell developing into an antheridium remains the same shape and sends forth a slender tubular outgrowth (the **fertilization tube**) that grows through the oögonial wall.[1] The protoplast of the antheridium then migrates through the fertilization tube into the oögonium and there unites with the egg. The zygote formed by this gametic union generally secretes a thick wall (Fig. 223*F*). The protoplast of a host cell begins to disappear when the sex organs are being formed and completely disappears by the time the zygotes are mature. A germinating zygote gives rise to a single zoospore. Zoospores liberated from germinating zygotes (Fig. 223*G*) are discharged into the empty host cell and continue swimming around within it until there is a breaking or disintegration of the host-cell wall.

ORDER 2. SAPROLEGNIALES

The Saprolegniales have an extensive mycelial thallus that is without incipient cross walls and is without a conspicuous holdfast portion. The thalli are holocarpic or eucarpic. Asexual reproduction is by means of biflagellated zoospores and those of most genera are diplanetic. Zoospores of eucarpic genera are formed within more or less cylindrical sporangia that do not become detached from the mycelium. Sexual reproduction is aplanogamic and oögamous. The oögonia are globose and generally with more than one egg.

The order includes some 20 genera and 150 species. Almost all members of the order are saprophytic and grow in water or in damp soil. When aquatic, the mycelia are of frequent occurrence on dead bodies or eggs of fishes, and for this reason the Saprolegniales are sometimes called the "fish molds."

Saprolegnia, the type genus, has about 25 species. Its mycelium is much branched and multinucleate. When growing as an aquatic saprophyte upon dead plant or animal remains, some of the hyphae are short and penetrate the substratum and others are long and extend in all directions from the substratum. The thalli are eucarpic and with reproductive organs borne at the tips of hyphae.

Sporangial development begins with a slight enlargement of the terminal portion of a hypha (Fig. 224*A*). After there has been a considerable streaming of cytoplasm and nuclei into the inflated portion, there is a formation of a transverse wall that separates the inflated portion (the sporangium) from the remainder of the hypha. Following this there is a progressive cleavage of the multinucleate contents into uninucleate pro-

[1] Cook, 1935.

toplasts (Fig. 224*B*). Cleavage is generally effected by furrows developing from the plasma membrane. The uninucleate protoplasts are then metamorphosed into biflagellate zoospores that are liberated through a broad pore developed at the sporangial apex (Fig. 224*C–D*). After the escape of zoospores, the sporangial base may bulge up into the empty sporangium and there develop into a new sporangium. This may be repeated three or four times, the successively formed sporangial walls lying nested one within the other.

Zoospores of *Saprolegnia* are often diplanetic (see page 389). The primary zoospores are more or less pyriform and with the two flagella at the anterior end. The secondary zoospores are reniform and with the two flagella laterally inserted on the concave side. *Saprolegnia* is one of the Biflagellatae definitely known[1] to have zoospores with one flagellum of the tinsel type and the other of the whiplash type.

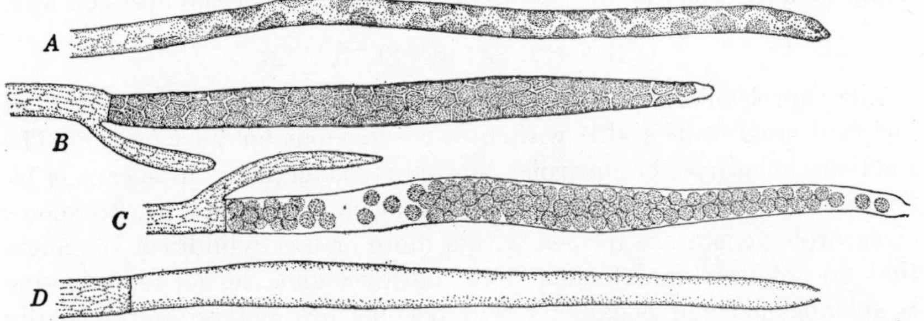

Fig. 224. *Saprolegnia ferax* (Gruith.) Thur. *A–C*, stages in development of sporangia. *D*, empty sporangium. (× 160.)

Asexual reproduction may also be effected by a direct division of a hypha into spore-like cells. These "gemmae" generally lie in a catenate series at the end of a hypha, but they may be intercalary. They are comparable to the oïdia formed by many ascomycetes.

Thus far all critically investigated species of *Saprolegnia* have been found to be homothallic. There is the possibility that there may be heterothallic species in the genus since this has been demonstrated[2] for certain species of other genera of the order.

Sex organs generally develop singly at the tips of hyphae, but sometimes several oögonia develop successively posterior to one another. The sex organs may be borne at the tips of long hyphae or upon short lateral ones. In some species an antheridial and an oögonial branch arise near each other (Fig. 225); in other species they do not.

Oögonial development begins with an enlargement of a hyphal tip to form a globose body several times the diameter of the hypha (Fig. 226*A*). The enlarging oögonium is filled with alveolar cytoplasm and many nuelci

[1] Couch, 1941; Manton *et al.*, 1951; Vlk, 1939.

[2] Coker, 1927; Coker and Leitner, 1938; Couch, 1926; Raper, 1939.

that lie equidistant from one another. Sooner or later a transverse septum is formed between the enlarging oögonium and the subtending hypha. As enlargement continues, there is a formation of a large central vacuole within the multinucleate protoplast (Fig. 226*B–C*). Blunt furrows growing centrifugally from the vacuolar membrane eventually cut the protoplasm into a number of fragments each of which may develop into an egg.[1] In most cases the egg is multinucleate when first formed, but there is soon a degeneration of all but one of the nuclei (Fig. 226*D*). The number of eggs within a mature oögonium is variable and ranges from 1 to 20 in most species.

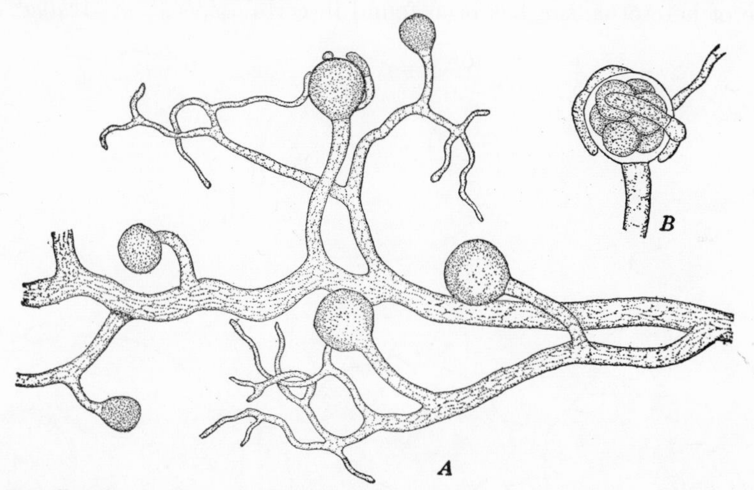

Fig. 225. *Saprolegnia ferax* (Gruith.) Thur. *A*, portion of a mycelium with young sex organs. *B*, mature sex organs. (× 160.)

Antheridia develop singly at the tips of slender hyphae that have grown toward and become applied to, developing oögonia. The terminal portion of each of these hyphae enlarges slightly and becomes filled with a nonvacuolate mass of protoplasm in which there are a dozen or more nuclei. Antheridia are delimited by a formation of a cross wall between the inflated portion and the remainder of the hypha. In certain species, as *S. ferax* (Gruith.) Thur., no antheridia are developed next to a large percentage of the oögonia. If no antheridia lie next to an oögonium, the eggs within it develop into **parthenospores** that are identical in appearance with zygotes. If there is an antheridium next to an oögonium, it sends out one or more delicate filamentous outgrowths, **fertilization tubes,** that penetrate the oögonial wall and come in contact with one or more eggs (Fig. 226*D*). Fertilization is effected by a migration of an antheridial nucleus, and possibly some of the cytoplasm into the egg. The two gamete nuclei unite with each other and the zygote secretes a thick wall (Fig. 226*E–F*).

Zygotes must ripen for a considerable time before they are capable of germinating.[2] Germination begins with a meiotic division of the fusion nucleus[3] and this is followed by several mitotic divisions. The zygote then sends forth a short unbranched hypha-like **germ tube.** The protoplast of the zygote then moves to the tip of the germ tube and becomes a sporangium whose protoplast divides into a number of zoospores.[4]

Sexuality of Saprolegniales. Sexuality has been more extensively studied in Saprolegniales than in other Biflagellatae. Many Saprolegniales have been found to be homothallic or heterothallic according to the manner in which these terms were originally defined.[5] A more complicated type of heterothallism has been found in certain species of *Achlya*[6] and

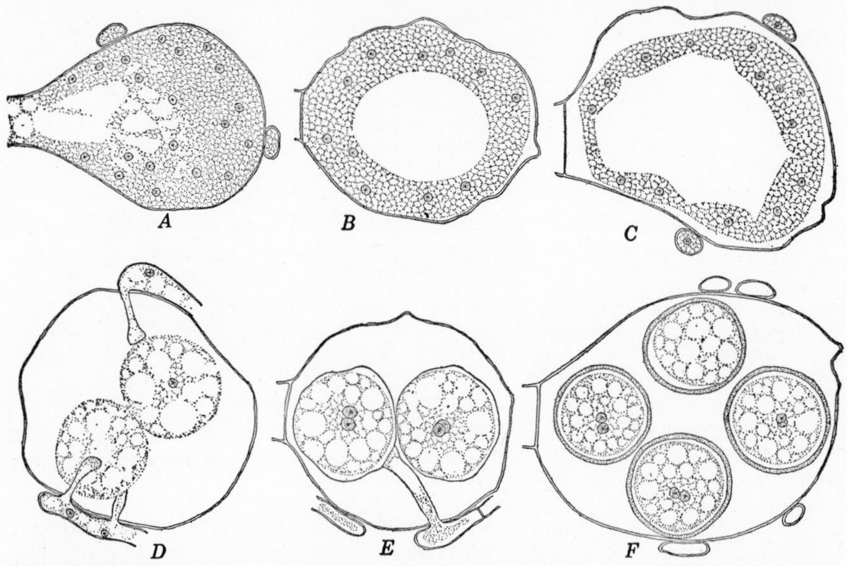

FIG. 226. Development of sex organs of *Saprolegnia* sp. *A–B*, oögonia before cleavage of protoplast. *C*, oögonium at the beginning of cleavage of protoplast. *D–E*, oögonia just before and just after fertilization. *F*, ripening zygotes. (× 650.)

Dictyuchus.[7] In these species there is no formation of sex organs when a mycelium is grown alone but there is a formation of sex organs when mycelia are grown in contact with mycelia of opposite sex. These species have the following four different types of thalli: (1) **pure male** thalli, (2) **predominantly male** thalli with a latent capacity for producing oögonia, (3) **pure female** thalli, and (4) **predominantly female** thalli with a latent capacity for producing antheridia. Although each of the foregoing four types does not form sex organs when grown alone it does form sexual

[1] Claussen, 1908; Davis, 1903; Mäckel, 1928; Trow, 1895.
[2] Klebs, 1899; Trow, 1895; Ziegler, 1948. [3] Ziegler, 1953. [4] Ziegler, 1948.
[5] Blakeslee, 1904. [6] Raper, 1936, 1940. [7] Couch, 1926.

organs with functional gametes and fertilization occurs when grown in contact with (mated with) any of the other three types (Fig. 227). This kind of heterothallism has been called **gynandromictic.**[1] Species in which gynandromixis occurs may also have two other additional types of thalli,[2] homothallic thalli, and sterile thalli which never form sex organs even when mated with any of the other types.

Studies on certain heterothallic species of *Achlya* show that development of sex organs consists of a series of steps, each governed by a particular hormone or group of hormones.[3] When grown by themselves neither male nor female thalli form sex organs, but when the two are grown together and come in contact with each other there is a formation of sex

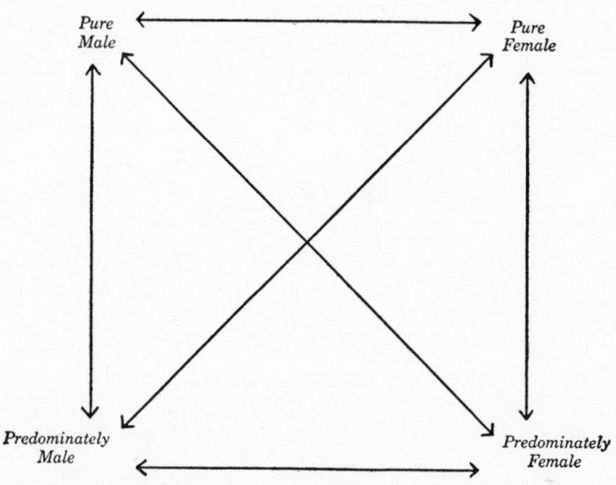

Fig. 227. Diagram showing the possible cross matings in the gynandromictic heterothallic *Achlya bisexualis* Raper. (*After J. R. Raper*, 1940.)

organs. The first step in their formation is a production of antheridial hyphae by the male mycelium. This is controlled by the four hormones comprising the *A* complex. The female mycelium secretes hormones *A* and A^2 which singly or together induce the formation of antheridial hyphae by the male mycelium (Fig. 228). At the same time the male mycelium secretes hormone A^1 which augments the activity of hormones *A* and A^2. The male mycelium also secretes hormone A^3 which depresses the activity of the responses induced by the other hormones. The antheridial hyphae secrete hormone *B* which induces step 2—the formation of oögonial initials by the female mycelium. The oögonial initials then begin to secrete hormone *C*. This hormone induces step 3—the growth of antheridial hyphae to the oögonial initials and the delimitation of antheridia at the tips of the antheridial hyphae. The final hormone, hor-

[1] Raper, 1940. [2] Couch, 1926; Raper, 1940.
[3] Raper, 1939, 1940, 1940*A*, 1942, 1942*A*, 1950.

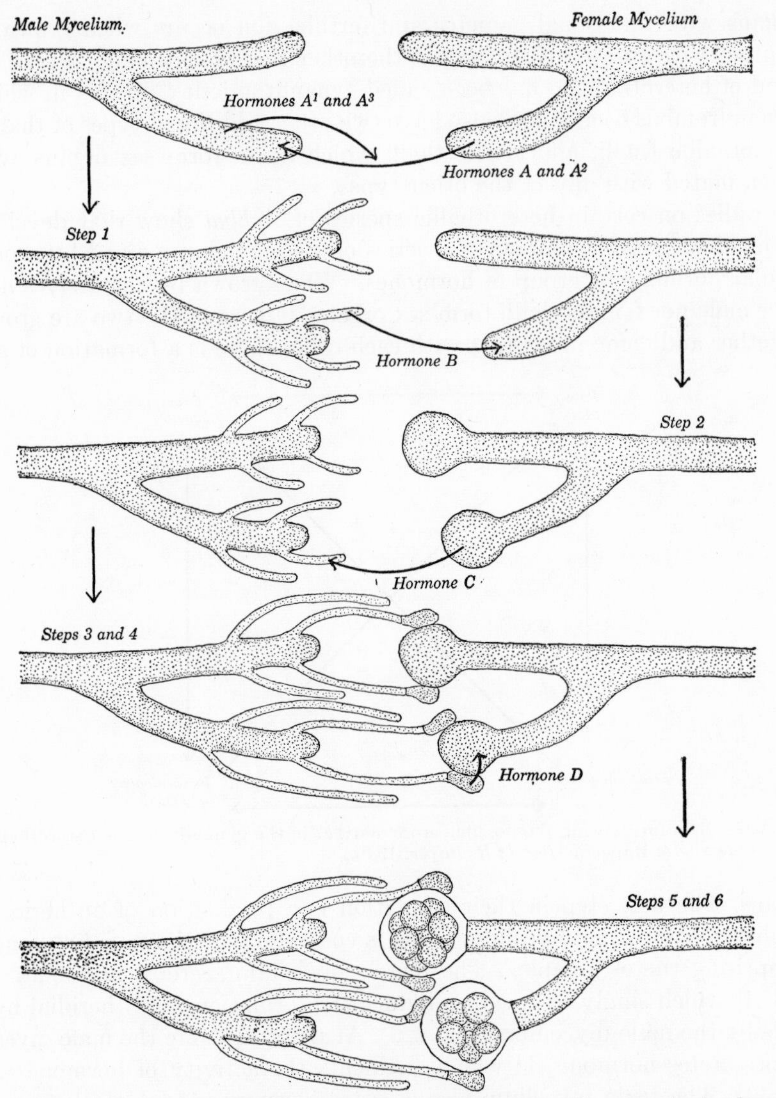

FIG. 228. *Achlya bisexualis* Raper. Diagram showing the successive steps in development of sex organs and source of successively formed hormones inducing the steps.

mone *D*, is secreted by the antheridia. It causes a formation of oögonia by the oögonial initials, and causes a differentiation of eggs within the oögonia. The presence of these various hormones and their formation in sequence was demonstrated[1] by their diffusion through permeable cellophane membranes and by other ingeniously devised experiments.

[1] Raper, 1939, 1940, 1940*A*, 1942, 1942*A*, 1950.

ORDER 3. LEPTOMITALES

The Leptomitales have a mycelial thallus that is generally with a basal holdfast bearing erect hyphae constricted at regular intervals into segments that are completely or incompletely separated from one another by cellulose plugs. Asexual reproduction is by means of biflagellate zoospores produced within sporangia borne upon distinctly constricted pedicels. Sexual reproduction is aplanogamic and oögamous. The antheridia and oögonia are pedicellate, and oögonia of most genera contain a single egg surrounded by periplasm.

There are about 7 genera and 20 species. All members of the order are fresh-water aquatic saprophytes.

For a long time the Leptomitales were placed in the Saprolegniales and as the family Leptomitaceae. The segregation of the family into a separate order has been generally accepted ever since it was first proposed.[1] Features in which the Leptomitaceae differ from Saprolegniales are segmentation of the mycelium into pseudocells, the pedicellate reproductive organs, and the periplasm around the single egg within an oögonium.

Sapromyces, a genus with two species, grows in fresh water and upon submerged twigs and fruits. The mycelium has a single basal cell that may or may not be attached to the substratum by a few rhizoids. The basal cell bears two or more erect hyphae at its apex. Each hypha is constricted at its point of origin and with the constriction partly plugged with cellulose. The hyphae are repeatedly di- or trichotomously branched and with a constriction at each forking (Fig. 229*A*).

Asexual reproduction is by means of biflagellate zoospores produced within subcylindrical pedicellate sporangia borne in tufts at the ends of the ultimate hyphal branches (Fig. 229*B*). Development of sporangia is accompanied by an inflow of cytoplasm and nuclei from the subtending portion of the hypha. At first the nuclei are evenly distributed within a sporangium; later on, they migrate to the periphery of the cytoplasm as a large central vacuole develops in the center of the protoplast.[2] The protoplasm then cleaves into uninucleate protoplasts by means of furrows that develop centrifugally from the membrane of the central vacuole. Each uninucleate protoplast is metamorphosed into a biflagellate zoospore, and the zoospores are liberated through a circular pore formed at the apex of the sporangium. Zoospores are of the secondary type and with the two flagella inserted on the concave side.

Oögonia and antheridia of *Sapromyces* arise adjacent to one another[3] on the tip of the same hypha (Fig. 229*C*). A young oögonium contains 10 to 12 nuclei evenly distributed throughout the cytoplasm.[2] These undergo one mitotic division. The cytoplasm soon becomes differentiated

[1] Kanouse, 1927. [2] Kevorkian, 1935. [3] Thaxter, 1896.

into a densely granular peripheral portion and an alveolar central portion (Fig. 229*D–E*). All but one of the nuclei migrate to the peripheral portion and begin to show signs of disintegration. The nucleus remaining in the central portion enlarges. Sometimes there is a disintegration of all but one nucleus without any preceding outward migration of the other nuclei. In either case, there then follows a cytokinesis that cuts off the outer portion (the **periplasm**) from the central uninucleate portion (the egg).

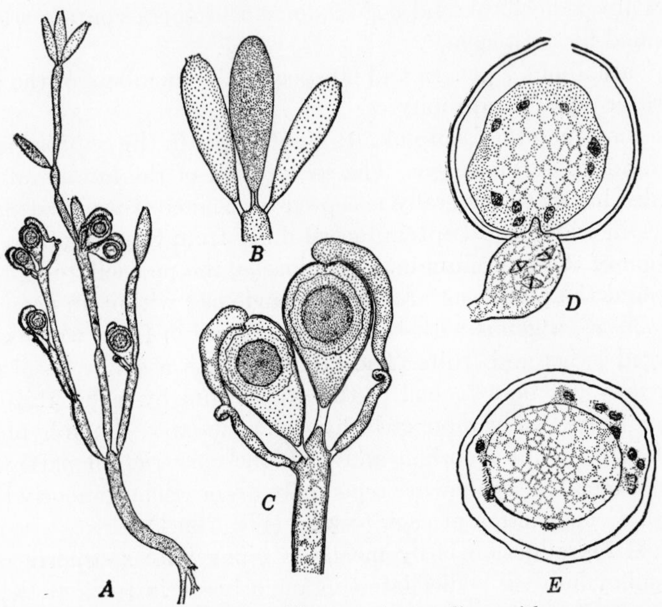

FIG. 229. *A–C, Sapromyces androgynus* Thaxter. *A*, mycelium with sex organs and sporangia. *B*, sporangia. *C*, sex organs. *D–E*, development of sex organs of *S. reinschii* (Schröter) Fritsch. (*A–C, after Thaxter*, 1896; *D–E, after Kevorkian*, 1935.) (*A*, × 70; *B–C*, × 320; *D–E*, × 500.)

Antheridial hyphae are club-shaped, pedicellate, and elongate (Fig. 229*C*). Apparently there is no formation of a transverse wall that cuts off the distal portion as a distinct antheridium. There are four to six nuclei in an antheridial hypha[1] and they undergo one mitotic division (Fig. 229*D*). Following this, one of them enlarges and the others degenerate. Prior to gametic union an antheridial hypha sends forth a fertilization tube that pushes through the oögonial wall to the egg. This is followed by a migration of the male nucleus into the egg and a fusion of it with the egg nucleus. The zygote is known to develop a thick wall but its germination has not been observed.

Similar to certain Saprolegniales, *Sapromyces reinschii* (Schroter)

[1] Kevorkian, 1935.

Fritsch has been found[1] to be gynandromictic (see page 397) and with four different types of heterothallic mycelia.

ORDER 4. PERONOSPORALES

The Peronosporales differ from other Biflagellatae in that most of them produce sporangia (conidiosporangia) which become detached from the mycelium, and in which formation and liberation of zoospores do not take place until after the conidiosporangia are shed. Sexual reproduction is aplanogamic and oögamous. Oögonia regularly contain a single egg surrounded by periplasm.

The order includes some 12 genera and 325 species. Many species are parasitic on aerial portions of land plants. Other species are saprophytic. Distinctions between the various genera are chiefly in the manner in which conidiosporangia are borne and according to this the Peronosporales fall into three general types. In one type the conidiosporangia are produced in succession at the apex of a special unbranched hypha (**sporangiophore**). In another type the sporangiophore is branched and with the conidiosporangia borne singly at the tips of the ultimate branchlets. In a third type the hyphae bearing sporangia are similar to other hyphae and the sporangium is rarely a conidiosporangium.

Albugo (*Cystopus*) is one of the genera with conidiosporangia produced in succession at the apex of an unbranched sporangiophore. It is a parasite on land plants and there are about 25 species. *A. candida* (Pers.) Kuntze, parasitic on several Cruciferae, is one of the species that was first thought to belong to *Uredo*, a form genus of the rusts. Because of its color it was called the "white rust," and this name has remained in common usage ever since. The white rust may infect stems, leaves, flowers, or fruits of the host. Its mycelium is multinucleate, generally without cross walls, and with numerous branches that grow between the host cells. The hyphae bear numerous globular outgrowths (**haustoria**) that penetrate walls of the host cells and absorb food from their protoplasts. After growing throughout tissues adjoining the point of infection, the mycelium produces a dense mat of hyphae just beneath the epidermis of the host. Numerous short thick-walled hyphae (sporangiophores) grow erect from the mat (Fig. 230*A*). The protoplast within a sporangiophore contains about a dozen nuclei. The distal portion of a sporangiophore is enclosed by a thin wall; the lower portion is surrounded by a greatly thickened wall. The upper end of a sporangiophore enlarges slightly and is then cut off as a five- to eight-nucleate conidiosporangium by the formation of a transverse wall. The portion of the sporangiophore just beneath the conidiosporangium soon enlarges and becomes cut off as a second conidiosporangium. This may be repeated indefinitely. The ac-

[1] Bishop, 1940.

cumulating mass of conidiosporangia pushes out and eventually bursts the overlying epidermis. These exposed conidiosporangia are the white, mealy patches evident on the host. Division of the conidiosporangial protoplast into zoospores and their subsequent liberation take place within 2 to 10 hours after they are shed (Fig. 230*B–D*). The optimum temperature for germination is around 10°C.[1] The zoospores are reniform and with two flagella (Fig. 230*E*) inserted on the concave side. Sometimes[2] there is a direct germination without a production of zoospores. Zoo-

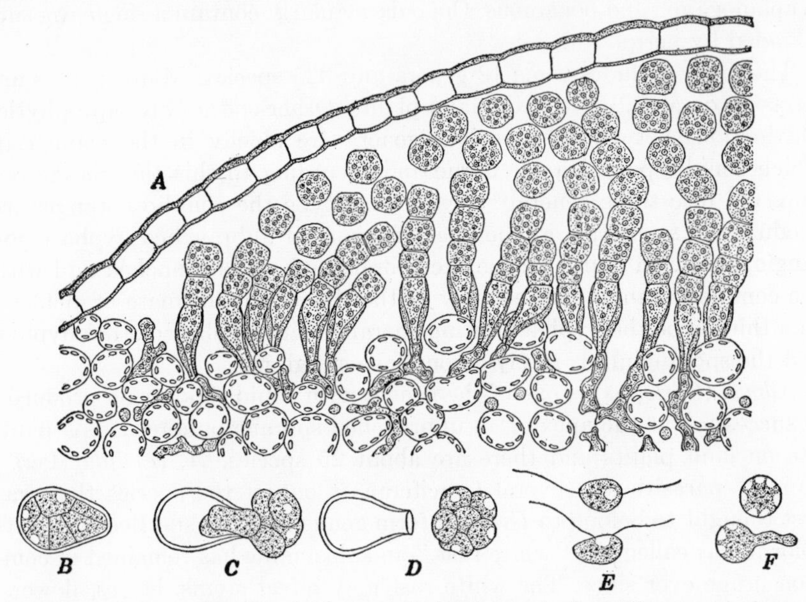

FIG. 230. *Albugo candida* (Pers.) Kuntze. *A*, development of conidiosporangia beneath epidermis of host. *B–D*, "germination" of conidiosporangia. *E*, zoospores. *F*, germination of zoospores. (*B–F*, *after DeBary*, 1863.) (*A*, × 325; *B–F*, × 400.)

spores that have ceased to swarm become spherical, secrete a wall, and send out a hypha (Fig. 230*F*) that grows through a stoma of the host.[3]

Toward the end of the growing season of the host, certain of the hyphae penetrate the deeper lying tissues of stem or petiole and there form sex organs. In *A. candida*[4] an inflated hyphal tip developing into an oögonium forms a cross wall just below the inflation. At first the cytoplasm within the young oögonium is uniformly vacuolate and with the nuclei evenly distributed (Fig. 231*A*). Later on, the central portion of the cytoplasm becomes denser, and all nuclei migrate to the periphery of it. Here the nuclei divide mitotically, and many of the spindles are so oriented that one daughter nucleus lies within the dense central cytoplasm

[1] Melhus, 1911. [2] Palm, 1932. [3] DeBary, 1863.
[4] Davis, 1900; Stevens, 1901; Wager, 1896.

and the other within the more vacuolate outer cytoplasm (Fig. 231*B*). There then follows a cytokinesis that divides the dense and vacuolate portions into egg and periplasm. An egg contains several nuclei when first delimited, but all but one of them soon disintegrate. In certain other species of *Albugo*,[1] the multinucleate egg has no degeneration of nuclei. Meanwhile, tips of other hyphae lying against the oögonium have formed cross walls that cut off small antheridia, each containing a few nuclei. The antheridium of *A. candida* forms a slender fertilization

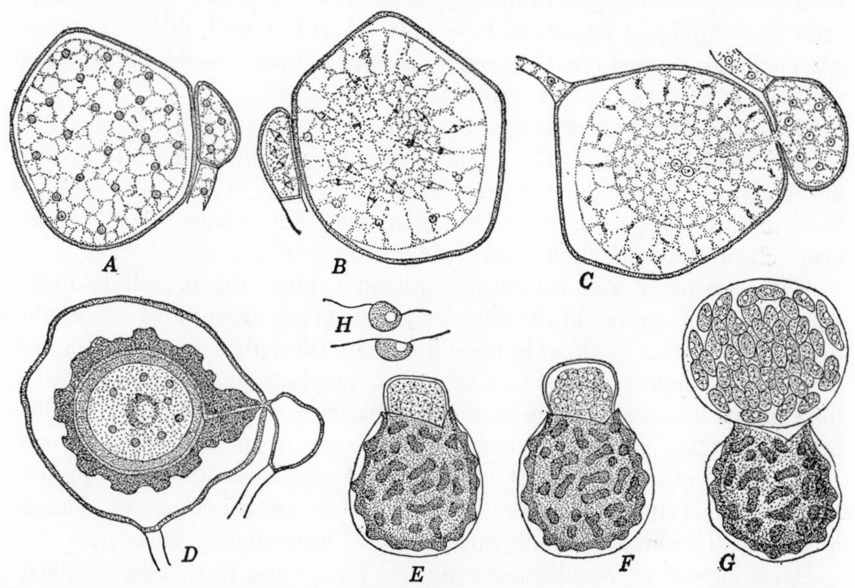

Fig. 231. Sexual reproduction of *Albugo candida* (Pers.) Kuntze. *A*, oögonium before differentiation of egg. *B*, oögonium at the beginning of differentiation of egg. *C*, oögonium just after fertilization. *D*, old zygote. *E–G*, germination of zygote. *H*, zoospores from a germinating zygote. (*E–H*, *after DeBary*, 1863.) (*A–D*, × 650; *E–H*, × 400.)

tube that grows through the oögonial wall, through the periplasm, and penetrates rather deeply into the egg (Fig. 231*C*). A male gamete nucleus then enters the egg and fuses with its nucleus. In the species with multinucleate eggs, several male nuclei enter an egg and each unites with an egg nucleus.

The zygote of *A. candida* soon secretes a thick wall with three distinct layers (Fig. 231*D*). Parthenogenesis has not been observed in *A. candida* but it has been noted in certain other species.[2] The zygote nucleus divides within a relatively short time and simultaneous nuclear divisions continue until there are 32 nuclei.[3] Meiosis has not been observed in *A. candida* but it has been recorded for another species.[2] The zygote

[1] Stevens, 1899, 1901. [2] Thirumalacher *et al.*, 1949. [3] Wager, 1896.

usually overwinters in the 32-nucleate stage. When it germinates the following spring there is a formation of more than a hundred biflagellate zoospores.[1] Then the wall cracks open and the zoospores are extruded in a mass surrounded by a thin vesicle (Fig. 231*E–H*). The vesicle soon disappears and the zoospores swim freely in all directions. Those reaching a suitable host are able to infect it.

The Peronosporales with branched sporangiophores projecting beyond the host are called "downy mildews." *Plasmopara* is a downy mildew with about 20 widely distributed species. From the economic standpoint, the most important species is *P. viticola* (B. & C.) Berl. & Det., a parasite of the grape and one that caused serious damage to vineyards before methods of control were discovered.

The downy mildew of grapes grows as an intercellular parasite within leaves and young branches. The mycelium is multinucleate, freely branched, and with the branches varying greatly in size. The hyphae bear numerous lateral outgrowths (**haustoria**) that penetrate walls of the host cells and absorb food from their protoplasts.

After becoming well established within a host, the mycelium forms dense mats of hyphae in the cavities just beneath stomata of leaves and branches. Several of these hyphae grow out through a single stoma and develop into sporangiophores. Each sporangiophore has three to six fairly long lateral branches borne in monopodial succession (Fig. 232*A*). The lateral branches lie more or less at right angles to the axis bearing them and each bears several short branchlets. A single conidiosporangium is formed at the tip of each branchlet, and when mature is readily detachable from the narrow branch tip (**sterigma**) immediately below it.

Development of conidiosporangia has been most thoroughly studied[2] in *P. halstedii* (Farl.) Berl. & Det. When very young they are uninucleate. As a conidiosporangium increases in size the original nucleus divides and redivides to form a number of nuclei. Immediately after nuclear division ceases the nuclei are spherical and equidistant from one another. Later, they become pyriform (Fig. 232*B*), migrate to just within the plasma membrane, and come to rest with the narrow end pointing outward. There then follows an inward furrowing of the plasma membrane that cuts the multinucleate protoplast into uninucleate protoplasts (Fig. 232*C–D*). The conidiosporangia are shed at this stage of development.

Detached conidiosporangia float around through the air until they fall to earth. "Germination" of a conidiosporangium (metamorphosis of the uninucleate protoplasts into zoospores and their liberation) takes place soon after it has lodged upon a suitable substratum. A "germinating" conidiosporangium develops a circular pore in the distal end of its wall and the uninucleate protoplasts within it are extruded through the wall

[1] DeBary, 1863. [2] Gregory, 1912.

(Fig. 232*E–F*). Immediately after extrusion each protoplast develops a pair of flagella (Fig. 232*G*). The zoospores thus formed swarm for about half an hour and then come to rest, round up, and secrete a thin wall (Fig. 232*H*). When a conidiosporangium "germinates" upon leaves of the host, the zoospores show a marked tendency to come to rest in the immediate vicinity of stomata. The globose cell formed by rounding up of a zoospore soon sends out a germ tube that grows directly through a stoma.[1]

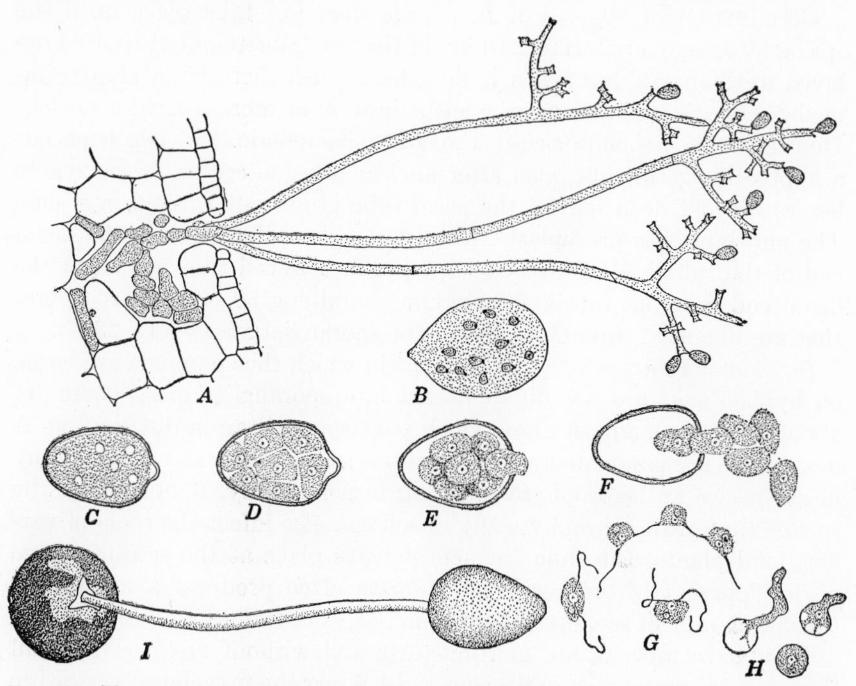

Fig. 232. *Plasmopara viticola* (Berk. & Curt.) Berl. & Det. *A*, sporangiophore *B*, multinucleate conidiosporangium *C–F*, "germination" of conidiosporangium. *G*, zoospores. *H*, germination of zoospores. *I*, germination of zygote. (*C–H*, *after Gregory*, 1912; *I*, *after Arens*, 1929.) (*A*, × 160; *B*, × 975.)

Development of sex organs is essentially the same in all three species where it has been investigated.[2] They are formed within tissues of the host and at the tips of hyphae. A hyphal tip developing into an oögonium enlarges greatly and contains many nuclei that lie approximately equidistant from one another. After formation of a transverse wall that separates an oögonium from the subtending hypha, all but one of the oögonial nuclei accumulate in a layer a short distance in from the plasma membrane. Sometimes there is an increase in the number of nuclei after they migrate to this layer. Sooner or later there is a cytokinesis that divides

[1] Gregory, 1912. [2] Nishimura, 1926; Rosenberg, 1903; Ruhland, 1903.

the oögonial protoplast into a central uninucleate egg and a peripheral multinucleate periplasm. Meanwhile, a hyphal tip adjacent to an oögonium has developed into an antheridium by forming a cross wall. The protoplast within an antheridium contains about a dozen nuclei. An antheridium sends forth a fertilization tube that grows through the oögonial wall, through the periplasm, and into the cytoplasm of the egg. A male gamete nucleus migrates through the fertilization tube into the egg and the zygote thus formed soon secretes a thick wall.

Germination of zygotes of *P. viticola* does not take place until the spring after they are formed. Union of the two gamete nuclei is often delayed until spring, but when it does take place there is an almost immediate division of the fusion nucleus into 50 or more daughter nuclei.[1] Division of the fusion nucleus is thought to be meiotic. A zygote sends out a hypha-like germ tube soon after nuclear division ceases. If the zygote lies within old dead leaves, the germ tube grows out through a stoma. The multinucleate protoplast within the zygote migrates into the distal end of the tube and a cross wall is formed. The cell thus cut off at the distal end develops into a sporangium containing 50 or more zoospores that are liberated through a pore in the sporangial apex[2] (Fig. 232*I*).

Pythium is representative of the type in which the sporangia are borne on hyphae that are not differentiated into sporangiophores. There are about 65 species, almost all of which are cosmopolitan in distribution. A few species are true aquatics and parasitic upon fresh-water algae. Many more species are saprophytes growing in soil. Many, if not all, of the species that grow saprophytically in soil can also infect the roots of various land plants. Infection frequently takes place at the seedling stage of development of the host, and *Pythium* often produces a widespread "damping off" of seedlings in greenhouses, cold frames, and seedbeds.

Vegetative mycelia are multinucleate and without cross walls at all times, or are with cross walls when old.[3] When the mycelium is parasitic some of the hyphae may lie within and others lie external to the host, or all may lie within it.

Asexual reproduction is generally by means of biflagellate zoospores. These are usually formed in sporangia that remain attached to the mycelium, but they may be formed in detachable conidiosporangia. The sporangia are of two types, elongate simple or branched sporangia of the same diameter as the hyphae bearing them; and globose sporangia much broader than the hyphae (Fig. 233). Sporangia are formed at the tips of hyphae and they usually have an apical papilla through which the undivided sporangial contents are discharged in a globose mass. There are species in which the apical papilla is prolonged into a definite exit tube.[4]

[1] Arens, 1929. [2] Arens, 1929; Gregory, 1912. [3] Butler, 1907.
[4] Drechsler, 1939, 1941.

The globose mass of protoplasm discharged from a sporangium is generally surrounded by a delicate vesicle (Fig. 233*B–C*, *G*). The mass of protoplasm soon divides into a number of biflagellate zoospores that escape from the vesicle. Free-swimming zoospores are reniform and with the flagella inserted on the concave side (Fig. 233*D*). At the end of the swarming period, a zoospore assumes a spherical shape and secretes a wall. In most cases this cell sends forth a single hypha, but the cell contents may develop into a single zoospore that escapes from the cell wall.[1] Strictly speaking, this is not diplanetism because both primary and secondary zoospores are morphologically alike. As in *Saprolegnia*, the spo-

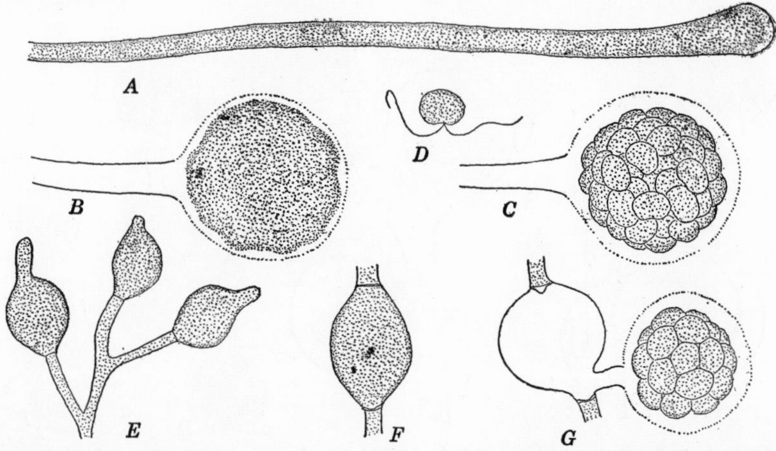

FIG. 233. Sporangia of *Pythium*. *A–D*, *P. periilum* Drechsler. *A*, apex of sporangium. *B*, the same after discharge of protoplast. *C*, after formation of zoospores. *D*, zoospore. *E*, terminal sporangia of *P. helicoides* Drechsler. *F–G*, *P. paroecandrium* Drechsler. *F*, intercalary sporangium. *G*, intercalary sporangium after discharge of protoplast and its cleavage into zoospores. (*A–D*, *F–G*, *after Drechsler*, 1940; *E*, *after Drechsler*, 1939.) (*A–D*, *F–G*, × 500; *E*, × 250.)

rangial base may bulge up into an empty sporangium and there develop into a new sporangium.[2] Asexual reproduction may also be accomplished by an intercalary formation of globose gemmae that at times have very thick walls. When gemmae germinate there is a formation of a long hypha-like exit tube whose length may be several times the diameter of the gemma.[3] A sporangium develops at the distal end of the exit tube and forms zoospores in the same manner as sporangia borne on mycelia.

Sexual reproduction of *Pythium* is aplanogamic and oögamous (Fig. 234*A–C*). All species grown in cultures derived from a single zoospore have been found to be homothallic.[4] Oögonial development begins with a globose enlargement of a hyphal tip and a migration of cytoplasm and

[1] Höhnk, 1932. [2] Drechsler, 1939, 1941.
[3] Drechsler, 1939, 1940, 1941, 1946. [4] Vanterpool, 1939.

nuclei into the enlarging portion. Soon after this there is a formation of a transverse wall setting off the inflated portion—the oögonium. Oögonia of most species have smooth walls but those of certain species have spiny walls. The number of nuclei within an oögonium may[1] or may not[2] be increased by division. In either case, the oögonial protoplast becomes divided into a uninucleate egg surrounded by a multinucleate periplasm in which the nuclei eventually disintegrate. Delicate antheridial hyphae arise adjacent to or remote from an oögonium. They become slightly inflated at the distal end and a cross wall is formed just back of the inflated portion. The cell thus formed is an antheridium (Fig. 234*A*). Antheridia

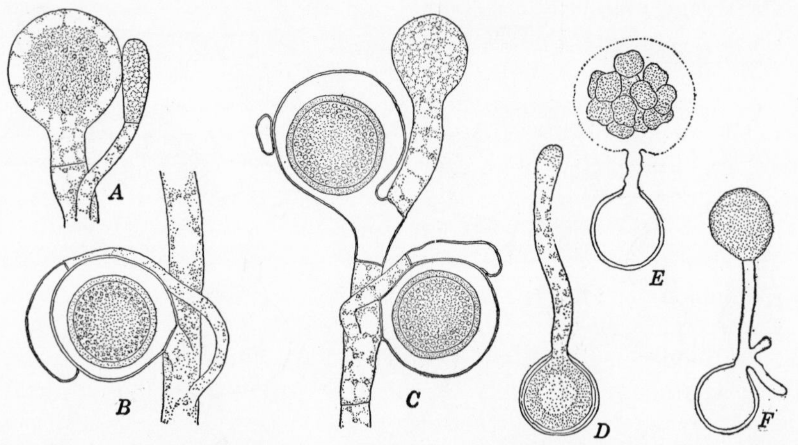

FIG. 234. *A–C*, development of sex organs of *Pythium intermedium* DeBary. *D–F*, germination of zygote of *P. salpingophorum* Drechsler. *D*, after formation of germ tube. *E*, after discharge of protoplast from germ tube and its cleavage into zoospores. *F*, formation of a sporangium at the apex of a germ tube. (*D–F*, *after Drechsler*, 1946.) (*A–C*, × 650; *D–F*, × 250.)

of most species form an evident fertilization tube that grows through the oögonial wall and the periplasm to the egg. *P. aphanidermatium* (Edson) Fitzpatrick is exceptional in having a formation of a wide pore where oögonial and antheridial walls adjoin.[2] In this species all but one of the antheridial nuclei degenerate as the antheridial protoplast migrates to and fuses with the egg. A parthenogenetic development of eggs into parthenospores may occur in *Pythium* and more than 50 per cent of the eggs of certain species[3] are parthenogenetic.

Zygotes and parthenospores develop thick walls that may be smooth or spiny. According to the species, zygotes germinate immediately after they are mature,[4] or must remain dormant for three to six months after becoming mature before they will germinate. During maturation of a zy-

[1] Miyake, 1901; Trow, 1901. [2] Edson, 1915. [3] Drechsler, 1946.
[4] Drechsler, 1939.

gote the two gamete nuclei unite, and the nucleus thus formed divides and redivides to form several nuclei. When germination takes place, a zygote sends out an unbranched or basally branched hypha whose length may be several times the diameter of the zygote (Fig. 234*D–F*). The protoplast may be discharged in a rounded mass from the apex of the hypha and then cleave into zoospores; or the apex of the hypha may develop into a sporangium which forms zoospores in the same manner as in sporangia produced by mycelia.[1]

SUBCLASS 3. AFLAGELLATAE (ZYGOMYCETAE, APLANATAE)

The Aflagellatae have cell walls composed of fungus chitin. The thalli are eucarpic, and have multinucleate mycelia that may be regularly with or without cross walls. There is no formation of flagellated reproductive bodies. Asexual reproduction may be by means of aplanospores produced in indefinite numbers within sporangia, or the entire sporangium may function as a single spore and behave in the manner of a conidium. Sexual reproduction is aplanogamic and generally isogamous, but in certain cases the two aplanogametes are regularly unequal in size.

There are about 70 genera and 350 species, the great majority of which are saprophytic.

The two most distinctive features of the subclass are the lack of flagellated reproductive bodies and the isogamous aplanogametes. The zygotes of Aflagellatae are frequently called **zygospores** because they are isogamously produced. The relationships of this to the other two subclasses are obscure. The nature of the cell wall suggests a relationship to the Uniflagellatae, but the aplanogamy found throughout the Aflagellatae is unlike that found in any of the Uniflagellatae. The Aflagellatae are divided into two orders.

ORDER 1. MUCORALES

Mycelia of Mucorales are generally capable of indefinite growth and, at least when young and growing vigorously, are without cross walls. Asexual reproduction is by means of aplanospores produced within globose sporangia borne on sporangiophores. A sporangium usually contains a large and indefinite number of aplanospores, but in some cases it contains a few or only one of them. Sexual reproduction is by means of aplanogametes produced singly within gametangia. A gametangium is borne terminally on a hypha and the portion of the hypha immediately subtending it is inflated to form a **suspensor.** Gametic union of most species is isogamous but there are a few species where it is anisogamous.

The Mucorales, often called the "black molds," are divided into about 45 genera and 250 species. A majority of the species are saprophytes

[1] Drechsler, 1946.

growing on substrata rich in soluble organic matter; a few species are parasitic on other fungi, and some species are parasites causing diseases of plants and animals.

Generic distinctions are based in large part upon the structure of sporangia and sporangiophores. Sporangiophores of some genera are unbranched, and either with a single terminal sporangium or with an in-

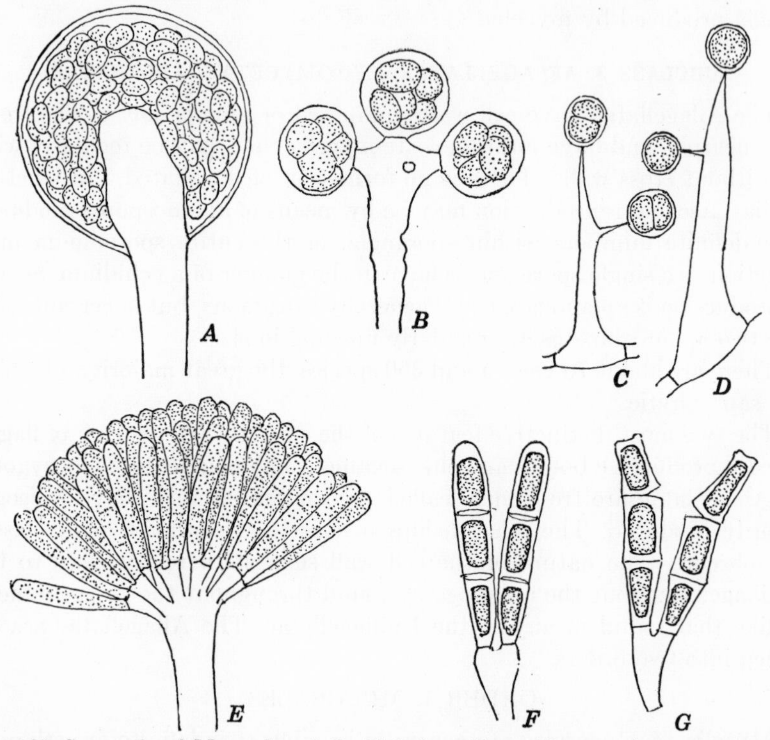

Fig. 235. Sporangia of Mucorales. *A–B*, *Blakeslea trispora* Thaxter. *A*, sporangium. *B*, sporangiola. *C–D*, *Haplosporangium bisporale* Thaxter. *C*, two-spored sporangiola. *D*, one-spored sporangiola. *E–G*, *Syncephalis pycnospora* Thaxter. *E*, immature sporangiola. *F–G*, mature sporangiola. (*A–D*, *after Thaxter*, 1914; *E–G*, *after Thaxter*, 1897.)

flated apex bearing several sporangia. Those of other genera are branched and with one to several sporangia at the tip of each ultimate branch. Some genera have sporangia containing a large number of spores; others have sporangia (**sporangiola**) with but few spores, two spores, or only a single spore (Fig. 235). Sometimes a species may produce both kinds of sporangia. Thus, according to the conditions under which it is cultured,[1] *Blakesleya* may produce sporangia with many spores or produce sporangiola with but few spores. Sporangiola with but a few spores are generally

[1] Thaxter, 1914.

believed to be derived from sporangia with many spores—the end product of such a series being a sporangiola with a single spore.

Rhizopus is one of the most thoroughly investigated of the Mucorales. There are about 35 species, all of which are saprophytic. *R. nigricans* Ehr. is of such frequent occurrence on bread that it is often called the "bread mold." It is so frequently a contaminant of cultures of bacteria and fungi that it is considered a weed of the laboratory. A young mycelium of *R. nigricans* is multinucleate, is without cross walls, and has all hyphae alike. Later on, a mycelium becomes differentiated into hyphae

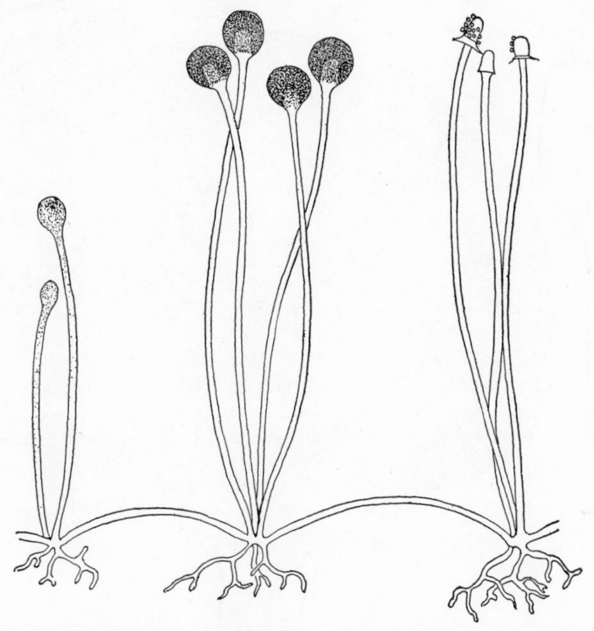

FIG. 236. Portion of a fruiting mycelium of *Rhizopus nigricans* Ehr. (diagrammatic). (× 30.)

of three types: repeatedly branched **rhizoids** that penetrate the substratum, **stolons** that grow horizontally above the substratum for some distance and then bend down to the substratum and form a tuft of rhizoids, and the erect **sporangiophores** that grow upward in tufts where the stolons form rhizoids (Fig. 236).

A sporangiophore of *Rhizopus* is unbranched, and after it has elongated to a certain height its tip begins to enlarge into a sporangium (Fig. 237*A*). Cytoplasm, many nuclei, and a considerable amount of reserve food flow into the enlarging sporangium. Most of the protoplasm accumulates in a thick layer just inside the enlarging sporangial wall, leaving the center occupied by a vacuolate protoplasm in which there are but a few nuclei. A dome-shaped layer of vacuoles then appears between the dense and the vacuolate portions of the protoplasm. These vacuoles flatten and fuse laterally with one another to form a dome-shaped cleft between the two portions of the protoplasm (Fig. 237*B*). There is next a secretion of a wall between the recently divided protoplasts. This completely separates the dome-shaped sterile portion (the **columella**) of a sporangium from the outer fertile portion.[1] The plasma membrane of the protoplast within a fertile portion next develops numerous branching inwardly growing furrows (Fig. 237*C*). These divide the protoplasm into smaller and smaller

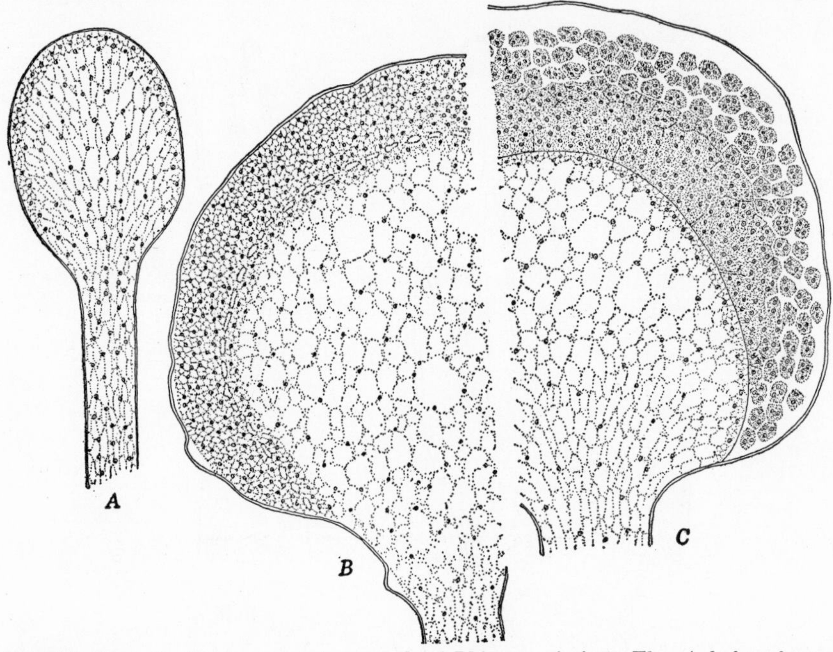

Fig. 237. Stages in development of sporangia of *Rhizopus nigricans* Ehr. *A*, before formation of columella. *B*, during formation of columella. *C*, during spore formation by progressive cleavage. (× 325.)

fragments. With continuation of this progressive cleavage, there is ultimately a division of the fertile protoplasm into irregularly shaped protoplasts each with 2 to 10 nuclei. The protoplasts then round up, secrete walls, and become aplanospores. The sporangial wall dries out after the aplanospores are mature and is so fragile that any slight disturbance ruptures it. The stalk of a sporangiophore and the columella persist after liberation of the spores by rupture of the sporangial wall.

Rhizopus may also reproduce asexually by means of chlamydospores. These are rarely, if ever, formed in *R. nigricans*, but they are of frequent occurrence in certain other species.[2] They are produced in old mycelia

[1] Swingle, 1903. [2] Lendner, 1908.

that have become transversely septate and are due to a thickening of walls in certain intercalary cells.

Some species are homothallic and others are heterothallic. For example, *R. sexualis* (Smith) Callen is homothallic[1] and *R. nigricans* is heterothallic.[2] When heterothallic species are cultured so that two thalli of opposite sex adjoin there is only a formation of sex organs in the region where the two meet each other. In this region hyphae of both sexes produce short side branches (**progametangia**) whose distal ends are inflated and densely filled with protoplasm (Fig. 238*A–B*). Progametangia of opposite sex lie end to end in pairs. Each divides transversely some

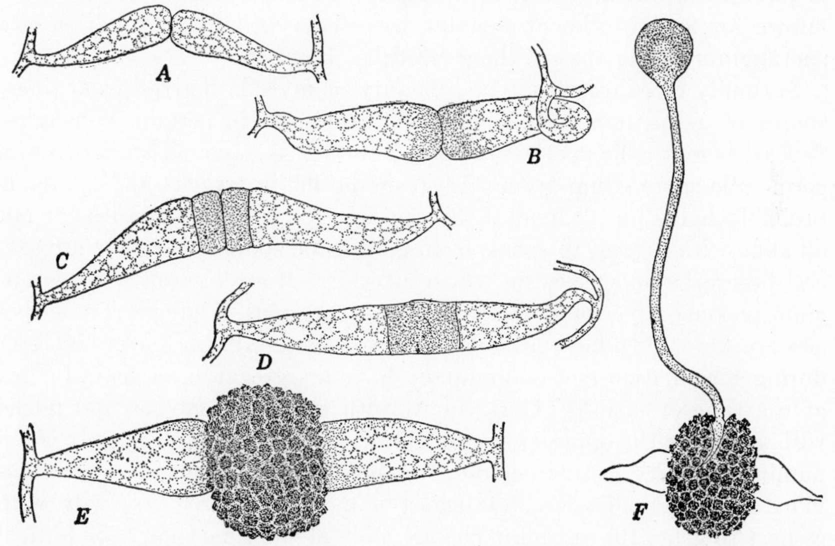

Fig. 238. Sexual reproduction of *Rhizopus nigricans* Ehr. *A–B*, progametangia. *C*, after formation of gametangia. *D–E*, young and mature zygotes. *F*, germination of zygote (diagrammatic). (*A–E*, × 160; *F*, × 80.)

distance back from its apex. The cell cut off at the distal end (the **gametangium**) has a densely granular multinucleate protoplast, and the portion beneath the gametangium (the **suspensor**) has a more vacuolate protoplast (Fig. 238*C*). Both gametangia of a pair increase in size and the number of nuclei in their protoplasts increases. There is considerable variation in size in the two members of the various pairs. In some pairs the two gametangia are equal in size; in other pairs the two are markedly unequal. As development continues there is a formation of a large pore where the two gametangia adjoin. The two gametangial protoplasts (**aplanogametes**) then fuse to form a zygote that soon becomes surrounded by a thick, black, warty wall (Fig. 238*D–E*). Nuclei contributed by the aplan-

[1] Callen, 1940. [2] Blakeslee, 1904.

ogametes increase in number during early stages in development of a zygote and then many fuse in pairs.[1] A zygote becomes mature and enters upon a dormant stage in about 10 days. During maturation the diploid nuclei remain undivided and the supernumerary haploid nuclei degenerate. Zygotes must remain dormant for many months before they can be induced to germinate. When this does occur the wall develops a lateral crack and a hypha-like germ tube grows out through the crack. There is a rapid increase in number of nuclei and there is some evidence that, as is definitely established for several other Mucorales, the first nuclear divisions are meiotic.[1] Germination of the zygote has not been followed beyond the germ-tube stage in *Rhizopus* but it is thought that, as is well known for several other Mucorales, there is eventually a formation of a sporangium at the apex of the germ tube (Fig. 238*F*).

Sexuality of Mucorales. The sexuality of mycelia derived from single spores of germ-tube mycelia has been analyzed in certain Mucorales. Several homothallic species have been shown[2] to have all spores from a germ-tube sporangium giving rise to homothallic mycelia and the same probably holds for all homothallic species. Heterothallic species are not all alike with respect to spores from germ-tube sporangia. There are several heterothallic species[2] in which all spores from a germ-tube sporangium produce mycelia of the same sex, either plus or minus. These species are known[1] to have a meiotic division of the fusion nuclei before or during germination and undoubtedly have a segregation of genes for sex at the time of meiosis. Thus, nuclei with genes for one sex and nuclei with genes for the opposite sex should be present in approximately equal numbers in a germ-tube sporangium before its protoplast becomes divided into spores. To date, no suggestion has been offered as to why, with respect to genes for sex, all nuclei are alike at the time spores are formed in germ-tube sporangia. In two heterothallic species of *Phycomyces*[3] and a heterothallic species of *Pilobolus*[4] there are three kinds of spores in each germ-tube sporangium: those producing plus mycelia, those producing minus mycelia, and those producing mycelia of a homothallic type. *Phycomyces* is known[1] to have a meiotic division of fusion nuclei, but some of them may not divide until the time of spore formation.

Multinucleate mycelia of Mucorales and of other fungi may be **homokaryotic** and with all nuclei alike in genetic composition, or they may be **heterokaryotic** and unlike in generic composition. Species in which all spores from a germ-tube sporangium develop into homothallic mycelia are homokaryotic as far as genes for sex are concerned and each nucleus has the genes for both sexes. These species are genotypically homothallic. The homothallism in mycelia from certain spores of a germ-tube sporan-

[1] Cutter, 1942. [2] Blakeslee, 1906; Cutter, 1942.
[3] Blakeslee, 1906; Burgeff, 1915; Cutter, 1942. [4] Krafczyk, 1935.

gium of *Phycomyces* is phenotypic. Here a mycelium is heterokaryotic as far as genes for sex are concerned, some nuclei containing genes for one sex and other nuclei containing genes for the opposite sex.

ORDER 2. ENTOMOPHTHORALES

Mycelia of Entomophthorales are generally of limited growth and with transverse walls dividing them into cells each with but a few nuclei. Asexual reproduction is by means of conidiosporangia that are usually violently discharged from the underlying sporangiophore. Discharged conidiosporangia may develop directly into mycelia; or their protoplasts may divide into aplanospores, each of which develops into a mycelium. Sexual reproduction is isogamous or anisogamous and by means of aplanogametes formed singly within gametangia. The gametangia are modified or unmodified cells without suspensors.

There are about 25 genera and 100 species. Many species are parasitic on insects; others are saprophytic.

Empusa is a genus parasitic on insects and one of the commonest species is *E. muscae* Cohn, a parasite of the common housefly. Houseflies infected with *Empusa* are most abundant in late summer and early autumn. Experiments[1] show that the fungus usually develops to maturity within five to eight days after a fly is infected. Infected flies may be recognized by their sluggishness, lighter coloration of the abdomen, and the peculiar dirty brick-red color of the eyes.[2] Flies dying from effects of the fungus crawl slowly over the ceiling or high on the side walls of a room. At the time of death they are firmly affixed by their proboscides to the object over which they were crawling. Here they remain after death, and the fungus develops conidiosporangia that shoot from the sporangiophores at maturity. These discharged conidiosporangia are the smoky halo that one sees beneath flies that have died on window panes or on mirrors.

During the early stages of vegetative development within a housefly, *E. muscae* consists of small, globose, multinucleate **hyphal bodies.** These multiply rapidly. In another species of *Empusa* the hyphal bodies are regularly four-nucleate and reproduce by transverse constriction after the nuclei have divided into two groups of four daughter nuclei each.[3] Among certain species, including *E. muscae,* the vegetative stage consists entirely of hyphal bodies. In certain other species there is a development of a true vegetative mycelium. The mycelium of one of these species has been grown in artificial culture.[4] The hyphal bodies become distributed throughout the body of the host, and it is thought[5] that their dispersal is due to a transporation in the blood stream. Multiplication of hyphal

[1] Thaxter, 1888. [2] Güssow, 1917. [3] Rees, 1932.
[4] Sawyer, 1929. [5] Speare, 1922.

bodies continues until they have replaced most of the tissues within the integument of a fly.

Shortly before the death of the host, each hyphal body of *E. muscae* sends forth an unbranched tubular outgrowth, the immature sporangiophore, that grows toward the chitinous integument covering the abdomen of the fly (Fig. 239*B*). The elongating sporangiophores lie in tufts that push through the thin places between segments of the integument (Fig. 239*A*). Sporangiophores growing toward the integument are densely filled

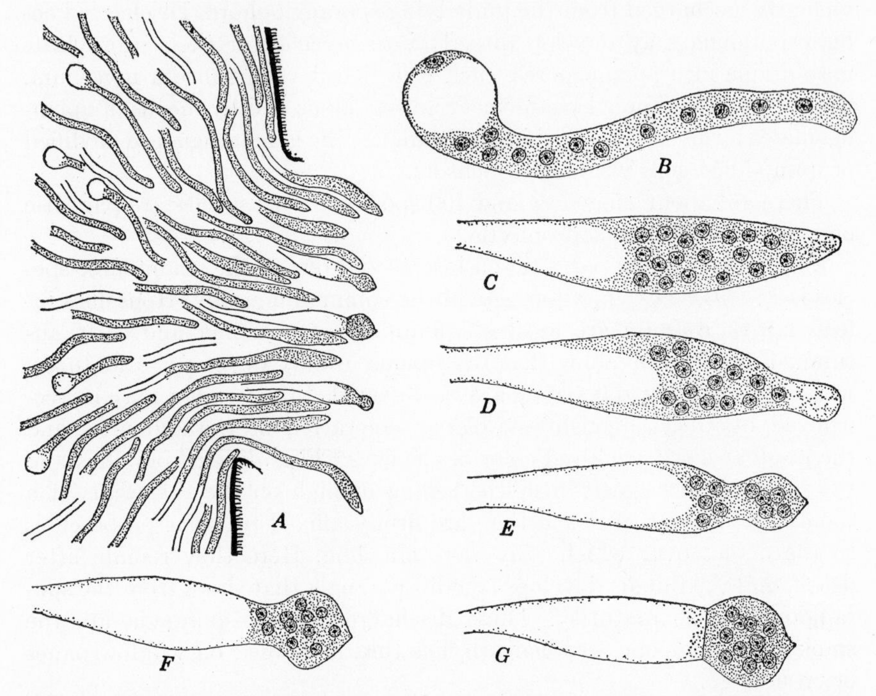

FIG. 239. *Empusa muscae* Cohn. *A*, portion of host with developing fructifications of the fungus. *B*, hyphal body elongating to form a sporangiophore. *C*, sporangiophore apex just before formation of conidiosporangium. *D–G*, successive stages in formation of a conidiosporangium. (*A*, × 160; *B–G*, × 650.)

with cytoplasm and contain 10 to 20 nuclei. The nuclei often lie equidistant from one another and in a linear series. After growing through the opening in the integument, the distal end of a sporangiophore inflates to three or four times its original diameter and all the protoplasm moves into the inflated portion (Fig. 239*C*). It is uncertain whether or not there is an increase in the number of nuclei during elongation of sporangiophores of *E. muscae.* Certainly this is not the case in another species of *Empusa* where a four-nucleate hyphal body produces a conidiosporangium containing four nuclei.[1]

[1] Rees, 1932.

Development of a conidiosporangium of *E. muscae* begins with a formation of a small mammilate outgrowth at the distal end of an inflated sporangiophore (Fig. 239*D–F*). The apex of the outgrowth swells, and most of the cytoplasm and all of the nuclei move into the swelling.[1] There is then a formation of a cross wall that separates the globose outgrowth, the conidiosporangium, from the underlying sporangiophore (Fig. 239*G*). A lens-shaped, water-filled cavity next appears between the cyto-

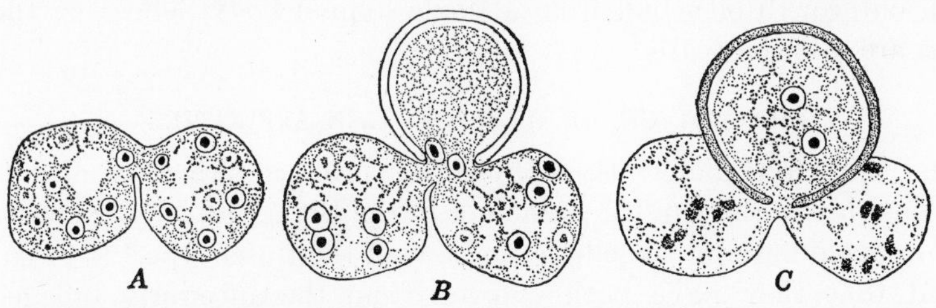

FIG. 240. Sexual reproduction of *Empusa*. *A*, hyphal bodies at the beginning of conjugation. *B–C*, young and nearly mature zygotes. (*After Rees*, 1932.) (× 1,900.)

plasm of the conidiosporangium and the transverse wall. Possibly, as in another closely related genus,[2] there is a secretion of a second transverse wall immediately next to the conidiosporangial protoplast. In any case, accumulation of water in the cavity eventually results in a hydrostatic pressure that bursts the lateral wall and suddenly squirts the conidiosporangium outward for a few millimeters. This forcible discharge of a conidiosporangium does not involve any rupture of the sporangiophore apex.

If the discharged conidiosporangium comes in contact with a suitable host it adheres to it and soon infects the host. If a conidiosporangium lodges upon an unsuitable substratum, it sends out a short protuberance that becomes swollen at its apex and develops into a conidiosporangium similar to that producing it. Formation of secondary conidiosporangia may be indefinitely repeated until a secondary conidiosporangium lodges upon a suitable host or until the reserve food is exhausted.

E. muscae may also form thick-walled resting spores within the body of the host. These have been considered parthenospores.[3] It is more probable that they are chlamydospores[4] since they are formed in old dead flies where the production of conidiosporangia is no longer possible. The chlamydospores are produced upon immature sporangiophores within the host and may be terminal or intercalary in position.

Sexual reproduction is by conjugation of two adjoining hyphal bodies.[5] In a species where the cells have four nuclei those in each of the two hyphal bodies divide once.[6] The walls of the two adjoining hyphal bodies

[1] Olive, 1906; Goldstein, 1927. [2] Sawyer, 1931. [3] Thaxter, 1888.
[4] Goldstein, 1923. [5] Rees, 1932; Speare, 1922. [6] Rees, 1932.

break down in the region of mutual contact and the two become joined by a narrow isthmus (Fig. 240*A*). One nucleus from each protoplast comes to lie very close to the isthmus. There is then a development of a globular outgrowth from the isthmus, and after it has attained approximately the size of a hyphal body, the two nuclei move into it (Fig. 240*B*). The binucleate protoplast of the outgrowth, now the zygote, then secretes a thick wall (Fig. 240*C*). Some species of *Empusa* form parthenospores by an outgrowth of a bud from a single hyphal body. These parthenospores are multinucleate.[1]

PHYCOMYCETAE OF UNCERTAIN AFFINITIES

The Anisochytridiales (Hypochytriales) produce swarmers of a type found neither in the Uniflagellatae nor in the Biflagellatae. The swarmers have a single anterior flagellum[2] and one of the tinsel type.[3] It might be argued that they have been evolved from the anteriorly biflagellate swarmers found in the Biflagellatae by a retention of the tinsel flagellum and an obliteration of the whiplash flagellum. However, the fact that cell walls of Anisochytridiales do not show a cellulose reaction[4] makes this seem improbable. Thus it is better to consider the order one whose relationships are uncertain.

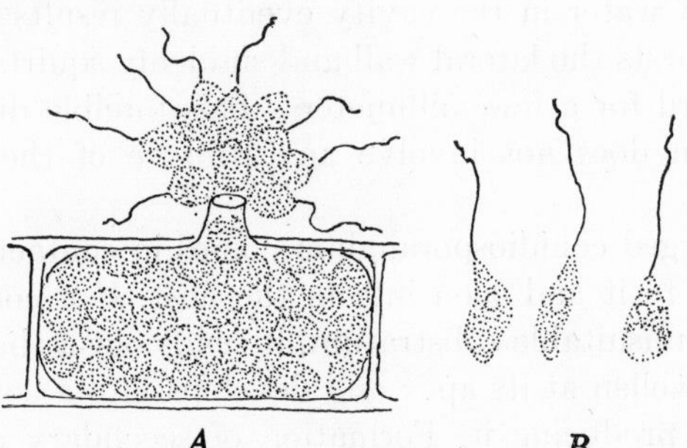

FIG. 241. *Anisolpidium ectocarpii* Karling. *A*, discharge of zoospores. *B*, free-swimming zoospores. (*After Karling*, 1943.)

The Anisochytridiales are nonmycelial, holocarpic or eucarpic, and monocentric or polycentric. Asexual reproduction is by means of zoospores with a single anterior flagellum of the tinsel type. Sexual reproduction is unknown for the order.

There are about 6 genera and 15 species, most of which are parasitic upon algae or upon aquatic phycomycetes.

Anisolpidium, a genus with three species, is parasitic upon marine Phaeophyta. The more or less globose thallus is holocarpic and lies within a single host cell or two adjoining host cells. At maturity the thallus is multinucleate, nearly filling the host cell or cells, and with one or two

[1] Riddle, 1906. [2] Karling, 1943. [3] Couch, 1941. [4] Karling, 1939, 1943.

exit tubes extending through the host-cell walls. At the time of reproduction the entire thallus becomes a single sporangium. The protoplast develops a large irregularly shaped central vacuole and forms zoospores by an outwardly directed progressive cleavage from the central vacuole. The uninucleate protoplasts thus formed are metamorphosed into zoospores that are liberated through a circular pore at the apex of the exit tube (Fig. 241*A*). The zoospores are pyriform and with a relatively long flagellum (Fig. 241*B*). Instead of developing an exit tube, a sporangium may form a thick wall and thus become a resting sporangium. Sexual reproduction has never been observed in this or in any other member of the order.

Bibliography

Ainsworth, G. C., and G. R. Bisby. **1950.** A dictionary of the fungi. Kew. 445 pp. 105 figs.

Alexopoulos, C. J. **1952.** Introductory mycology. New York. 482 pp. 187 figs.

Arens, K. **1929.** *Jahrb. Wiss. Bot.* **70:** 57–92. 17 figs. [Gametogenesis, *Plasmopara.*]

Barrett, J. T. **1912.** *Ann. Bot.* **26:** 209–238. 4 pl. [*Olpidiopsis.*]

1912A. *Bot. Gaz.* **54:** 353–371. 3 pl. [*Allomyces.*]

Bessey, E. A. **1950.** Morphology and taxonomy of fungi. Philadelphia. 791 pp. 210 figs.

Bishop, H. **1940.** *Mycologia* **32:** 505–529. 6 figs. [*Sapromyces.*]

Blackwell, Elizabeth. **1943.** *Trans. Brit. Mycol. Soc.* **28:** 71–89. 7 figs. [Peronosporales.]

Blakeslee, A. F. **1904.** *Proc. Amer. Acad. Arts and Sci.* **40:** 205–319. 4 pl. 6 figs. [Sexual reproduction, Mucorales.]

1906. *Ann. Mycol.* **4:** 1–28. [Zygote germination, Mucorales.]

Brefeld, O. **1881.** Botanische Untersuchungen über Schimmelpilze. Leipzig. Heft 4. 191 pp. 10 pl.

Burgeff, H. **1915.** *Flora* **108:** 353–448. 13 figs. [Zygotes, Mucorales.]

Butler, E. J. **1907.** *Mem. Dept. Agr. India. Bot. Ser.* **1,** No. 5: 1–160. 10 pl. [*Pythium.*]

Callen, E. O. **1940.** *Ann. Bot.* N.S. **4:** 791–818. 40 figs. [*Rhizopus.*]

Claussen, P. **1908.** *Ber. Deutsch. Bot. Ges.* **26:** 144–161. 2 pl. [Gametogenesis, *Saprolegnia.*]

Coker, W. C. **1927.** *Jour. Elisha Mitchell Sci. Soc.* **42:** 207–226. 10 pl. [Saprolegniales.]

Coker, W. C., and J. Leitner. **1938.** *Ibid.* **54:** 311–318. 2 pl. [Saprolegniales.]

Cook, W. R. I. **1935.** *Arch. Protistenk.* **86:** 58–89. 4 pl. [*Lagenidium.*]

Couch, J. N. **1926.** *Ann. Bot.* **40:** 849–881. 4 pl. 3 figs. [Saprolegniales.]

1932. *Jour. Elisha Mitchell Sci. Soc.* **47:** 245–260. 4 pl. [*Rhizophydium.*]

1935. *Mycologia* **27:** 160–175. 64 figs. [*Rhizophydium.*]

1941. *Amer. Jour. Bot.* **28:** 704–713. 58 figs. [Flagella.]

1945. *Mycologia* **37:** 163–193. 78 figs. [Monoblepharidales.]

Couch, J. N., and Alma J. Whiffen. **1942.** *Amer. Jour. Bot.* **29:** 582–591. 66 figs. [Blastocladiales.]

Curtis, K. M. **1921.** *Phil. Trans. Roy. Soc. London* B. **210:** 409–478. 5 pl. [*Synchytrium.*]

Cutter, V. M. **1942.** *Bull. Torrey Bot. Club* **69:** 480–508, 592–616. 87 figs. [Meiosis, Mucorales.]

Davis, B. M. **1900.** *Bot. Gaz.* **29:** 297–311. 1 pl. [*Albugo.*]

1903. *Ibid.* **35:** 233–249, 320–349. 2 pl. [Gametogenesis, *Saprolegnia.*]

DeBary, A. **1863.** *Ann. Sci. Nat. Bot.* 4 ser. **20:** 5–148. 13 pl. [*Albugo.*]

Drechsler, C. **1939.** *Phytopathology* **29:** 391–422. 14 figs. [*Pythium.*]

1940. *Ibid.* **30:** 189–213. 8 figs. [*Pythium.*]

1941. *Ibid.* **31:** 478–507. 13 figs. [*Pythium.*]

1946. *Ibid.* **36:** 781–864. 29 figs. [*Pythium.*]
Edson, H. A. **1915.** *Jour. Agr. Res.* **4:** 279–291. 5 pl. [*Pythium.*]
Emerson, R. **1941.** *Lloydia* **4:** 77–144. 16 figs. [*Allomyces.*]
1950. *Ann. Rev. Microbiology* **4:** 169–200. [Aquatic phycomycetes.]
Emerson, R., and C. W. Wilson. **1949.** *Science* **110:** 86–88. 2 figs. [Meiosis, *Allomyces.*]
Foster, J. W. **1949.** Chemical activities of fungi. New York. 648 pp.
Frey, R. **1950.** *Ber. Schweiz. Bot. Ges.* **60:** 199–230. [Cell wall.]
Goldstein, Bessie. **1923.** *Bull. Torrey Bot. Club* **50:** 317–328. 1 pl. [*Empusa.*]
1927. *Mycologia* **19:** 97–109. 3 pl. [*Empusa.*]
Gregory, C. T. **1912.** *Phytopathology* **2:** 235–249. 7 figs. [*Plasmopara.*]
Güssow, H. T. **1917.** *Ann. Appl. Biol.* **3:** 150–158. 1 pl. [*Empusa.*]
Hanson, Anne M. **1945.** *Amer. Jour. Bot.* **32:** 479–487. 61 figs. [*Rhizophydium.*]
Harper, R. A. **1899.** *Ann. Bot.* **13:** 467–525. 3 pl. [*Synchytrium, Rhizopus.*]
Hatch, W. R. **1933.** *Jour. Elisha Mitchell Sci. Soc.* **49:** 163–170. 1 pl. [*Allomyces.*]
1935. *Ann. Bot.* **49:** 623–649. 33 figs. [*Allomyces.*]
Hatch, W. R., and R. C. Jones. **1944.** *Mycologia* **36:** 369–381. [*Allomyces.*]
Höhnk, W. **1932.** *Ibid.* **24:** 489–507. 1 pl. 9 figs. [*Pythium.*]
Kanouse, Bessie B. **1927.** *Amer. Jour. Bot.* **14:** 287–306, 335–357. 7 pl. [Leptomitales.]
Karling, J. S. **1931.** *Amer. Jour. Bot.* **18:** 526–557. 3 pl. [*Cladochytrium.*]
1935. *Ibid.* **22:** 439–452. 29 figs. [*Cladochytrium.*]
1937. *Mem. Torrey Bot. Club* **19:** 1–92. 6 pl. 2 figs. [*Cladochytrium.*]
1939. *Bull. Torrey Bot. Club* **66:** 281–286. 1 pl. [*Rhizophydium.*]
1939A. *Amer. Jour. Bot.* **26:** 512–519. 18 figs. [Anisochytridiales.]
1943. *Ibid.* **30:** 637–648. 21 figs. [*Anisolpidium.*]
Kevorkian, A. G. **1935.** *Mycologia* **27:** 274–285. 2 pl. [Leptomitales.]
Klebs, G. **1899.** *Jahrb. Wiss. Bot.* **33:** 513–593. 2 figs. [*Saprolegnia.*]
Kniep, H. **1929.** *Ber. Deutsch. Bot. Ges.* **47:** 199–212. 7 figs. [*Allomyces.*]
1930. *Zeitschr. Bot.* **22:** 433–441. 2 figs. [*Allomyces.*]
Köhler, E. **1931.** *Phytopath. Zeitschr.* **4:** 43–55. 17 figs. [*Synchytrium.*]
Krafczyk, H. **1935.** *Beitr. Biol. Pflanzen* **23:** 349–396. 31 figs. [Zygotes, Mucorales.]
Kusano, S. **1912.** *Jour. Coll. Agr. Imp. Univ. Tokyo* **4:** 141–199. 3 pl. [*Olpidium.*]
1930. *Japanese Jour. Bot.* **5:** 35–132. 19 figs. [*Synchytrium.*]
Laibach, F. **1927.** *Jahrb. Wiss. Bot.* **66:** 596–630. 2 pl. 12 figs. [*Monoblepharis.*]
Lendner, A. **1908.** *Matér. pour la Flore Crypt. Suisse* **3**[1]**:** 1–180. 3 pl. 59 figs. [Mucorales.]
Lugg, J. **1929.** *Trans. Wis. Acad.* **24:** 343–355. 1 pl. [*Allomyces.*]
McCranie, J. **1942.** *Mycologia* **34:** 209–213. 1 fig. [*Allomyces.*]
McLarty, D. A. **1941.** *Bull. Torrey Bot. Club* **68:** 75–99. 81 figs. [*Olpidiopsis.*]
Mäckel, H. G. **1928.** *Jahrb. Wiss. Bot.* **69:** 517–548. 26 figs. [*Saprolegnia.*]
Manton, I., B. Clark, and A. D. Greenwood. **1951.** *Jour. Exper. Bot.* **2:** 321–331. 8 pl. [Flagella.]
Martin, G. W. **1950.** Outline of the fungi. Dubuque, Iowa. 82 pp. 116 figs.
Melhus, I. E. **1911.** *Univ. Wis. Agr. Exper. Sta. Res. Bull.* **15:** 25–91. 10 figs. [*Albugo.*]
Miyake, K. **1901.** *Ann. Bot.* **15:** 653–667. 1 pl. [*Pythium.*]
Nabel, K. **1939.** *Arch. Mikrobiol.* **10:** 515–541. 7 figs. [Cell wall.]
Nishimura, M. **1926.** *Jour. Coll. Agr. Hokkaido Imp. Univ.* **17:** 1–61. 5 pl. [*Plasmopara.*]
Olive, E. W. **1906.** *Bot. Gaz.* **41:** 192–208. 2 pl. [*Empusa.*]
Palm, B. T. **1932.** *Ann. Mycol.* **30:** 421–426. 3 figs. [*Albugo.*]
Raper, J. R. **1936.** *Jour. Elisha Mitchell Sci. Soc.* **52:** 274–289. 3 pl. [Heterothallism.]
1939. *Amer. Jour. Bot.* **26:** 639–650. 27 figs. [Sexual hormones.]
1940. *Mycologia* **32:** 710–727. 4 figs. [Sexual hormones.]
1940A. *Amer. Jour. Bot.* **27:** 162–173. 14 figs. [Sexual hormones.]

1942. *Ibid.* **29**: 159–166. 6 figs. [Sexual hormones.]
1942A. *Proc. Nat. Acad. Sci. U.S.A.* **28**: 509–516. 2 figs. [Sexual hormones.]
1950. *Ibid.* **36**: 524–533. 5 figs. [Sexual hormones.]
Rees, Olive M. **1932.** *Amer. Jour. Bot.* **19**: 205–217. 3 pl. [*Empusa.*]
Riddle, L. W. **1906.** *Proc. Amer. Acad. Arts and Sci.* **42**: 177–197. 3 pl. [Entomophthorales.]
Rosenberg, O. **1903.** *Bih. Kgl. Svensk. Vetensk.-Ak. Handl.* **28,** Afd. 3, Nr. 10; 1–20. 2 pl. [*Plasmopara.*]
Ruhland, W. **1903.** *Jahrb. Wiss. Bot.* **39**: 135–166. 2 pl. [*Albugo, Plasmopara.*]
Salvin, S. B. **1940.** *Mycologia* **32**: 148–154. [Diplanetism.]
Sawyer, W. H. **1929.** *Amer. Jour. Bot.* **16**: 87–121. 4 pl. [*Empusa.*]
1931. *Mycologia* **23**: 411–432. 2 pl. 1 fig. [Entomophthorales.]
Scherffel, A. **1925.** *Arch. Protistenk.* **52**: 1–141. 5 pl. [Phylogeny.]
Shanor, L. **1939.** *Jour. Elisha Mitchell Sci. Soc.* **55**: 167–177. 1 pl. 1 fig. [*Olpidiopsis.*]
Sörgel, G. **1937.** *Zeitschr. Bot.* **31**: 401–446. [*Allomyces.*]
Sparrow, F. K. **1931.** *Amer. Jour. Bot.* **18**: 615–623. 1 pl. [*Cladochytrium.*]
1933. *Ann. Bot.* **47**: 517–542. 1 pl. 2 figs. [Monoblepharidales.]
1933A. *Mycologia* **25**: 513–535. 1 pl. 1 fig. [*Rhizophydium.*]
1936. *Jour. Linn. Soc. Bot. London* **50**: 417–478. 7 pl. 7 figs. [*Rhizophydium.*]
1939. *Papers Mich. Acad. Sci. Arts, Letters* **24**: part 1: 121–126. 2 pl. [*Rhizophydium.*]
1940. *Allan Hancock Pacific Expd.* **3**: 101–111. 2 pl. [Monoblepharidales.]
1942. *Mycologia* **34**: 113–116. [Classification.]
1943. Aquatic phycomycetes. Ann Arbor, Mich. 785 pp. 69 figs.
Speare, A. T. **1922.** *U.S. Dept. Agr. Bull.* **1117**: 1–18. 2 figs. [*Empusa.*]
Springer, Martha E. **1945.** *Amer. Jour. Bot.* **32**: 259–269. 46 figs. [Monoblepharidales.]
Stevens, F. L. **1899.** *Bot. Gaz.* **28**: 149–176, 225–245. 5 pl. [*Albugo.*]
1901. *Ibid.* **32**: 77–98, 157–169, 238–261. 4 pl. [*Albugo.*]
Stüben, H. **1939.** *Planta* **30**: 353–383. 17 figs. [Blastocladiales.]
Swingle, D. B. **1903.** *U.S. Dept. Agr. Bureau Plant Ind. Bull.* **37**: 1–40. 6 pl. [*Rhizopus.*]
Teter, H. E. **1944.** *Mycologia* **36**: 194–210. 3 figs. [*Allomyces.*]
Thaxter, R. **1888.** *Mem. Boston Soc. Nat. Hist.* **4**: 133–201. 8 pl. [Entomophthorales.]
1895. *Bot. Gaz.* **20**: 433–440. 1 pl. [*Monoblepharis.*]
1896. *Ibid.* **21**: 317–331. 3 pl. [*Sapromyces.*]
1897. *Ibid.* **24**: 1–15. 2 pl. [Mucorales.]
1914. *Ibid.* **58**: 353–366. 4 pl. [Mucorales.]
Thirumalachar, M. J., M. D. Whitehead, and J. S. Boyle. **1949.** *Ibid.* **111**: 487–519. 16 figs. [*Albugo.*]
Trow, A. H. **1895.** *Ann. Bot.* **9**: 609–652. 2 pl. [*Saprolegnia.*]
1901. *Ibid.* **15**: 269–312. 2 pl. [*Pythium.*]
Vanterpool, T. C. **1939.** *Mycologia* **31**: 124–127. [*Pythium.*]
Vlk, W. **1939.** *Arch. Protistenk.* **92**: 157–160. 1 fig. [Flagella.]
Wager, H. **1896.** *Ann. Bot.* **10**: 295–342. 2 pl. [*Albugo.*]
Wettstein, F. von. **1921.** *Sitzungsber. Akad. Wiss. Wien.* (Math.-Nat. Kl.) **130**^{1}: 3–20. [Cell wall.]
Whiffen, Alma J. **1944.** *Farlowia* **4**: 583–597. [Classification, Chytridiales.]
Wilson, C. M. **1952.** *Bull. Torrey Bot. Club* **79**: 139–160. 23 figs. [Meiosis, *Allomyces.*]
Wisselingh, C. van. **1898.** *Jahrb. Wiss. Bot.* **31**: 619–685. 2 pl. [Cell wall.]
Wolf, F. T. **1941.** *Mycologia* **33**: 158–173. 2 figs. [*Allomyces.*]
Ziegler, A. W. **1948.** *Jour. Elisha Mitchell Sci. Soc.* **64**: 13–40. 6 pl. [Zygotes, Saprolegniales.]
1953. *Amer. Jour. Bot.* **40**: 60–66. 52 figs. [Meiosis, Saprolegniales.]

CHAPTER 12

ASCOMYCETAE

All Ascomycetae produce a distinctive type of sporangium, the **ascus,** containing a definite number of **ascospores** that are formed immediately after meiosis and by a unique method of endoplasmic cytokinesis (**free cell formation**). The typical number of ascospores in an ascus is a multiple of four. Most species have eight ascospores within an ascus; but there are species with a smaller number of spores, or where the number is larger and is 16, 32, 64, 128, 512, or 1,024. In addition to ascospores, many species produce one or more other types of spore that reduplicate the mycelium.

According to a recent estimate[1] there are about 1,650 genera and 12,000 species.

Occurrence. Ascomycetes may be parasitic or saprophytic throughout their entire life cycle; or they may begin development as parasites and continue growth as saprophytes after death of infected portions of the host. Mycelia of most parasitic species grow within tissues of the host, but certain ascomycetes, as the powdery mildews (Erysiphales), grow superficially upon the host. Most parasitic species are restricted to a single host species or a group of closely related species. Many of the diseases of cultivated plants are caused by ascomycetes. In crop plants these include the leaf spot of alfalfa, the ear rot of corn, and the foot rot of various grains. Ascomycete diseases of fruit trees include the brown rot of stone fruits, apple scab, and peach leaf curl. Methods for controlling these diseases and thus reducing the loss to the grower include sprays toxic to the fungus, dusts toxic to the fungus, and the breeding of races resistant to the fungus. In some cases plant pathologists have been unsuccessful in developing methods of control. The most spectacular example of this is the chestnut blight caused by *Endothia parasitica* (Murr.) And. and And. This disease was first noted on the American chestnut [*Castanea dentata* (Marsh.) Borkh.] on trees in New York City. Shortly after it was first discovered in 1904 it spread rapidly throughout the chestnut forests of New York and neighboring states, and within a few

[1] Ainsworth and Bisby, 1950.

years practically all American chestnut trees in the United States were killed.

Saprophytic ascomycetes are found in a wide variety of habitats, many of them growing on rotting logs, on leaf mold, or in soil rich in humus, produce fruiting bodies (**ascocarps**) of macroscopic size and definite shape. These fungi, as in cup fungi and morels, may produce their ascocarps above ground or, as in truffles, may form subterranean ascocarps. Other saprophytic ascomycetes grow on the surface of decaying fruits, vegetables, or meat, as well as on damp leather and a great variety of plant and animal substances. Among these fungi are the yeasts and the blue and the green molds. Many saprophytic ascomycetes, especially *Penicillium* and the yeasts, are of industrial importance. *Penicillium* has become well known to the layman because it is the source from which the antibiotic penicillin is obtained. This fungus is also the one imparting the characteristic flavor and color to Roquefort cheese. Blue and green molds are used in various commercial processes. Some are able to change starch to sugar and serve as "starters" in alcoholic fermentation. Others are used in the production of oxalic, citric, and gluconic acids; and in the production of various vitamins.

Vegetative Structure. Except for yeasts and a few other forms, the thallus of an ascomycete is of a mycelial type. The hyphae appear to be multicellular and with transverse walls. Actually, a so-called transverse wall is an incomplete septum with a central perforation that is frequently large enough to permit a streaming of cytoplasm and nuclei from cell to cell. The portion of the protoplast between two successive septa generally contains a single nucleus; but, as in *Pyronema* (page 458), it may be multinucleate.

The vegetative portion of thalli of many mycelial ascomycetes is a loosely interwoven amorphous mass of hyphae similar to that found in a majority of phycomycetes. At times the major portion of the mycelium has the hyphae densely interwoven into a pseudoparenchymatous mass (**sclerotium**).

Asexual Reproduction. A production of ascospores is contingent upon sexual reproduction, or at least upon the formation of sex organs. Spores other than ascospores are asexual reproductive bodies. Except for the numerous genera found in lichens, a large majority of ascomycetes regularly produce one or more types of nonflagellated spore. Many ascomycetes, as the powdery mildews, produce asexual spores throughout their growing season and form ascospores only at the end of the season. In some ascomycetes, as in many blue and green molds, reproduction by means of asexual spores may continue indefinitely.

The most frequently encountered type of spore is the **conidium,** a spore that is borne at the free end of a special hypha (**conidiophore**).

Conidia are cut off in acropetalous succession by a conidiophore and usually in such rapid succession that there is a chain of conidia. Some genera have conidiophores that stand free from one another, and are either unbranched (Fig. 254, page 445) or branched (Fig. 252, page 442). Other genera have the conidiophores laterally abutting one another in a continuous spore-forming layer. The most frequently encountered of these conidia-producing areas are the **acervulus** and the **pycnidium.** An acervulus is a flattened fertile layer that is generally formed subepidermally. A pycnidium is a cup- or flask-shaped cavity that is open from the beginning and is lined with spores. Spores within a pycnidium are generally called **pycnospores** instead of conidia.

Instead of forming spores in succession at the end of a conidiophore, there may be a simultaneous formation of them throughout the length of a hypha. Spores formed in this manner are often called **oïdia.** In addition to forming conidia, pycnospores, or oïdia, a mycelium may also form large thick-walled spores. These **chlamydospores** are produced singly or in short catenate series.

Sexual Reproduction. Sex organs of ascomycetes are developed at the apices of hyphae and generally on short lateral branches. Such Hemiascomycetae as produce morphologically recognizable sex organs have those of opposite sex similar in shape and usually have the two equal in size. These may be uninucleate as in *Eremascus* (Fig. 246, page 434), or multinucleate as in *Dipodascus* (Fig. 248, page 435). Sex organs of Hemiascomycetae lie adjacent to each other and fusion of their protoplasts is immediately followed by a fusion of nuclei.

Male and female sex organs of Euascomycetae differ morphologically. The female sex organ (**ascogonium**) is cylindrical to globose and either unicellular or multicellular. The apex of an ascogonium is usually prolonged into a **trichogyne** and genera with multicellular ascogonia may also have intercalary cells producing trichogynes. Most genera have unbranched trichogynes but certain genera, as *Neurospora* (Fig. 257, page 449), have branched ones. The male sex organ (**antheridium**) is smaller than an ascogonium and is usually more or less cylindrical. Antheridia and ascogonia are produced in pairs adjacent to each other. When mature, the protoplast of an antheridium migrates into the ascogonium, either through a lateral pore or though the trichogyne. In Euascomycetae fusion of protoplasts (plasmogamy) is not immediately followed by fusion of nuclei (karyogamy) (see page 427).

There are also many Euascomycetae that produce ascogonia but do not produce antheridia. In them, sexual reproduction is effected by a process known as **spermatization.** Species that do not form antheridia frequently form conidium-like unicellular bodies that are called **spermatia.** Spermatia are borne more or less remote from the ascogonia. Some species produce spermatia in flasked-shaped cavities (**spermogonia**) that look very much like pycnida. Other species produce their spermatia (sometimes called **microconidia**) singly or in clusters on special hyphae (**spermatiophores**). Spermatia borne within spermogonia may be transported to trichogynes or to the vicinity of ascogonia. The same holds for spermatia borne on spermatiophores. When spermatia lodge in the vicinity of an ascogonium there is a growth of trichogynes to the spermatia. Spermatization may also be effected by means of either conidia or ascospores. For heterothallic species of *Neurospora* there has been a repeated demonstration that contact between a trichogyne and a spermatium or a conidium is necessary for the ultimate development of ascospores. It is also definitely established[1] for this genus that at the time of spermatization the protoplast of a spermatizing conidium migrates into the trichogyne.

Two vegetative mycelia may come in contact, anastamose, and have a migration of nuclei from one mycelium to the other. If the nuclei of the two mycelia differ genetically, the mycelium into which a nucleus or nuclei has migrated is **heterokaryotic.** Once heterokaryosis is established, nuclei derived from one mycelium may travel a distance of several millimeters through the other mycelium, the migration from cell to cell being through the perforations in the transverse septa. Heterokaryosis between two mycelia of opposite sex may be followed by a nuclei from one mycelium migrating into ascogonia borne by the mycelium of opposite sex. This has been shown to occur in *Neurospora.*[2] The ultimate result of this bringing together of sexually unlike nuclei by vegetative means (**somatogamy**) is similar to that due to a union of gametes.

Sexuality of Mycelia. Mycelia of ascomycetes derived from single ascospores or conidia are of various types with respect to their sexuality. The manner in which the terms homothallic and heterothallic should be applied to these various types is a matter of dispute.[3] As originally proposed[4] in connection with a study of sexuality in Mucorales, heterothallism was defined as the condition where "two complementary individuals . . . are needed for sexual reproduction"; and homothallism was defined as the condition where "the zygospores thus originate from a single mycelium." As a corollary it was held[5] that "the mycelium of a homothallic species is bisexual; while the mycelium of a heterothallic species is unisexual."

On the basis of the original definition, those ascomycetes in which two mycelia are essential for gametic union and the production of asco-

[1] Backus, 1939. [2] Dodge, 1936.

[3] Compare Buller, 1941; Dodge, 1936, 1945; Drayton and Groves, 1952; Hansen and Snyder, 1943; Whitehouse, 1949.

[4] Blakeslee, 1904, p. 208. [5] Blakeslee, 1904, p. 314.

spores may be considered heterothallic, and those in which a single mycelium can accomplish this may be considered homothallic.

Relatively few ascomycetes are morphologically heterothallic, with male mycelia producing only spermatia or antheridia, and the female mycelia producing only ascogonia. Most of them belong to the Laboulbeniales, but this has also been found[1] among a few members of other orders.

Heterothallism may also be of the type sometimes called **physiological heterothallism.** This was first discovered[2] in *Pleurage anserina* (Ces.) Kuntze but has since been found[3] to occur in a considerable number of other ascomycetes. A physiologically heterothallic mycelium produces both kinds of sexual elements but is self-sterile. However, it is interfertile with certain other mycelia of the same species. In an ascus of these morphologically homothallic but physiologically heterothallic species half the ascospores develop into self-sterile mycelia of one "mating type" and the other half develop into self-sterile mycelia of the opposite "mating type."

Homothallic species in which male and female elements of a single mycelium can initiate the development of ascospores are not all alike with respect to sexual genes of their nuclei. Most homothallic species have all nuclei of an ascus genetically alike (homokaryotic) with respect to genes for sex. Homothallism of the type in which all nuclei within an ascus are homokaryotic has been called[3] **primary homothallism.**

There are a few homothallic ascomycetes with binucleate spores in which the two nuclei are genetically unlike with respect to sex. In these species, as was first shown[4] for *Neurospora tetrasperma* Shear and Dodge, half of the nuclei in a developing ascus are genetically of one mating type and the other half are of the complementary type. When binucleate ascospores are delimited after the completion of nuclear division (Fig. 258, page 450) in a developing ascus the two kinds of nuclei are so oriented with respect to one another that each binucleate ascospore contains both kinds of nuclei. Homothallic mycelia developed from such ascospores are heterokaryotic with respect to genes for sex, and homothallism due to the heterokaryotic nature of the mycelium has been called[3] **secondary homothallism.** In addition to being produced by heterokaryotic binucleate ascospores, a secondarily homothallic heterokaryotic mycelium may be formed by somatogamy between two sexually compatible heterothallic mycelia.

Formation of Asci. The Hemiascomycetae producing evident gametangia have a direct development of the zygote into a single ascus or have a parthenogenetic development of a gametangium into an ascus. In the species with uninucleate gametangia[5] there is a fusion of the two nuclei

[1] Drayton and Groves, 1952; Hirsch, 1949. [2] Ames, 1934.
[3] Whitehouse, 1949. [4] Dodge, 1936. [5] Stoppel, 1907; Guillermond, 1909.

in the young zygote, now the ascus. This ascus enlarges to several times its original size and after the fusion nucleus has divided to form either four or eight daughter nuclei there is a formation of four or eight uninucleate ascospores (Fig. 246, page 434). In one hemiascomycete with multinucleate gametangia (*Dipodascus*[1]), only one nucleus from each gametangium functions as a gamete nucleus and the single fusion nucleus divides to form many daughter nuclei. The solitary asci of hemiascomycetes are always without an enveloping sheath of sterile hyphae.

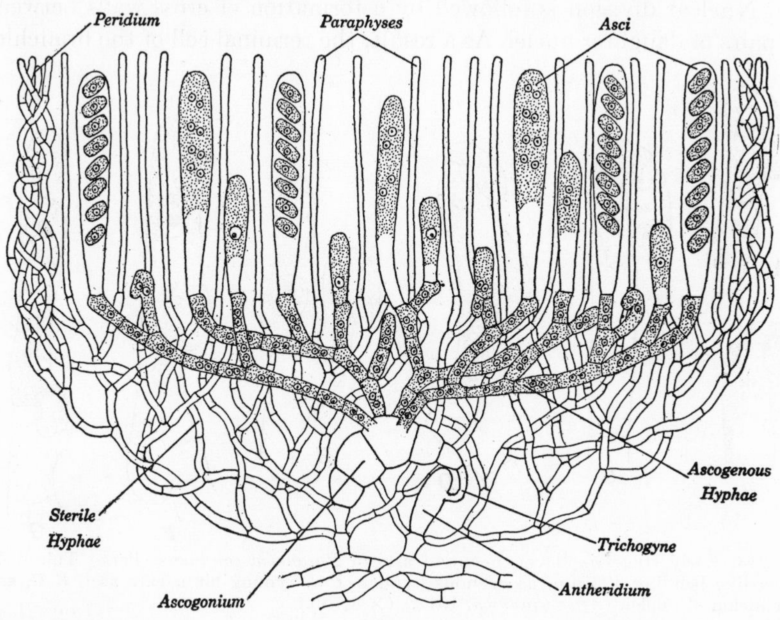

FIG. 242. Vertical section of a hypothetical ascocarp showing relationship of sex organs, ascogenous hyphae, and sterile hyphae.

At one time it was thought that a fusion of gamete nuclei took place within ascogonia of many Euascomycetae but more careful cytological study and the evidence from genetics show that this is not the case (see page 431). Instead of developing directly into an ascus, the ascogonium of euascomycetes gives rise to one or more **ascogenous hyphae** (Fig. 242). In some cases the ascogenous hyphae are unbranched; more often they are profusely branched and intertwined with one another. A relatively small number of species have ascogenous hyphae that do not form cross walls until late in their development; but most species have ascogenous hyphae with cross walls throughout all stages of development. All cells of an ascogenous hypha, or only the cells in the upper portion, are binucleate. In these binucleate cells one of the nuclei is a descendant of a

[1] Dangeard, 1907; Juel, 1902.

male nucleus entering the ascogonium, and the other is a descendant of a female nucleus in the ascogonium.

Many species have each ultimate branchlet of the ascogenous hyphae terminating in a recurved binucleate cell (Fig. 243*A*), These cells, often called **croziers,** have the two nuclei dividing simultaneously (Fig. 243*B*) and in such a manner that one pair of the resultant daughter nuclei lies in the arch of the crozier. One nucleus of the sister pair is at the extreme tip of the crozier; the other lies in the upper region of the uncurved portion. Nuclear division is followed by a formation of cross walls between the pairs of daughter nuclei. As a result, the terminal cell of the branchlet

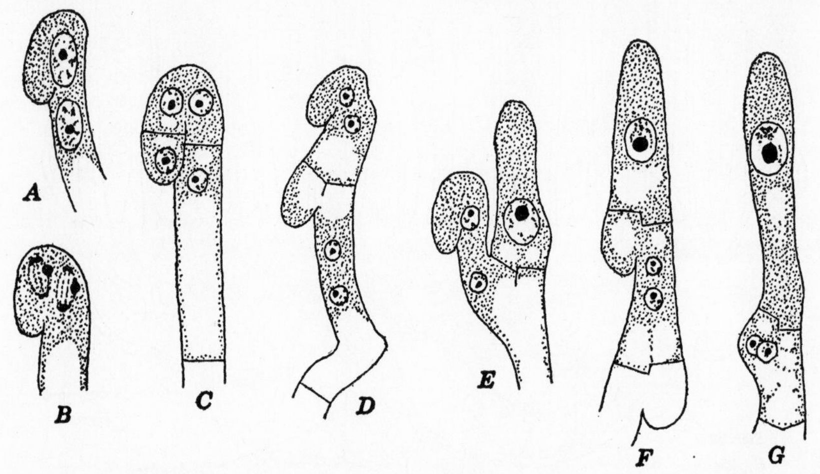

Fig. 243. Early stages in development of asci of *Pyronema confluens* (Pers.) Tul. *A–B*, crozier-like bending of tip of ascogenous hyphae. *C–D*, young binucleate asci. *E–G*, asci after fusion of nuclei. (*After Claussen*, 1912.) (× 1,750.)

is uninucleate, the penultimate cell is binucleate, and the antepenultimate cell is uninucleate (Fig. 243*C*). The binucleate penultimate cell is the one that develops into an ascus. The uninucleate terminal and antepenultimate cells usually unite with each other to form a binucleate cell subtending the young ascus (Fig. 243*D*, *F–G*).

The binucleate cell developing into an ascus enlarges to many times its original size and becomes more or less club-shaped. During enlargement there is a fusion of the two nuclei; and this is followed by a meiotic division of the fusion nucleus and a mitotic division of the four nuclei resulting from meiosis (Fig. 244*A–F*). Nuclear division generally stops at the octonucleate stage, but species are known in which it continues until there are 32,[1] 128,[2] 512,[3] or even 1,024[4] nuclei. The ascospores are formed after completion of the last series of nuclear divisions. At this

[1] Overton, 1906. [2] Sax, 1918. [3] Bessey, 1935. [4] Dodge, 1928.

time the nuclei are more or less pyriform and with a centrosome-like body at the pointed pole. Soon each nucleus develops an umbrella-shaped set of radiating fibers that extend outward from the centrosome into the cytoplasm.[1] Each curving set of rays grows downward until it is some distance beyond the rounded posterior pole of the nucleus; then it recurves to delimit a broad ellipsoidal mass of cytoplasm around the nucleus (Fig. 244*G–H*). The uninucleate protoplasts thus encircled by astral rays are the young ascospores. The portion of the cytoplasm not included

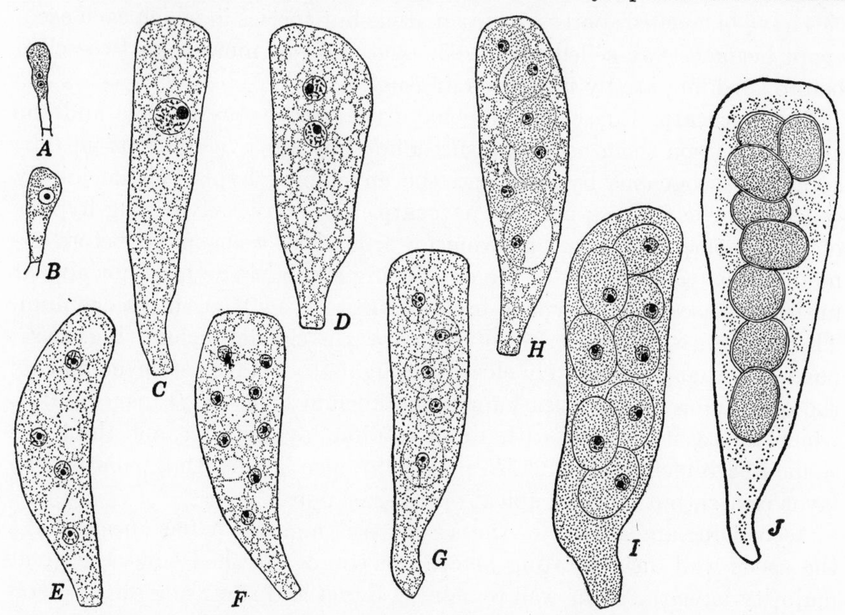

FIG. 244. Stages in development of asci of *Erysiphe aggregata* (Pk.) Farlow. *A*, ascus before fusion of nuclei. *B–C*, early and late uninucleate stages. *D–F*, stages in development to octonucleate stage. *G–H*, formation of ascospores. *I–J*, formation of ascospore walls. (× 650.)

within the ascospores is the **epiplasm.** The number of ascospores delimited within an ascus is not always the same as the number of nuclei at the time of ascospore formation. An octonucleate ascus may delimit ascospores around only two[2] or only four[3] of the nuclei and have the remaining six or four nuclei disintegrating. There are also cases[4] where two nuclei lie within a common set of astral rays delimiting an ascospore and where there is regularly a formation of four binucleate spores (Fig. 258, page 450). Conversely, an ascus that is octonucleate at the time of ascospore formation may contain more than eight ascospores because each of the eight ascospores divides into two daughter spores.[5]

[1] Harper, 1897, 1905. [2] Harper, 1905. [3] Faull, 1912. [4] Dodge, 1927.
[5] Lewis, 1911.

When an ascospore is first delimited, its plasma membrane lies immediately next to an inner limiting membrane of the epiplasm (Fig. 244*I*). Later on, there is a secretion of a spore wall around each ascospore and a gradual disappearance of the epiplasm as the spore walls develop (Fig. 244*J*). The wall of a mature ascospore may be smooth or may have a characteristic ornamentation of spines or ridges. Many species have the ascospores lying in a single linear series, but other species have them in a double series or parallel to one another in a fasciculate cluster. Most species have one-celled spores within an ascus but species in which each ascospore becomes two-celled (Fig. 263, page 457) or more than two-celled before shedding are by no means unusual.

The Ascocarp. Euascomycetae have the ascogenous hyphae and the asci borne upon them becoming surrounded by an enveloping tissue. The asci, the ascogenous hyphae, and the enveloping hyphal tissue jointly constitute the fruiting body or **ascocarp.** The sterile enveloping hyphae of an ascocarp may begin growing up around an ascogonium before gametic union takes place, or the enveloping sterile tissue may not appear until after ascogenous hyphae have begun to grow from an ascogonium. There are three general types of ascocarp: the **cleistothecium** (Fig. 255*G*, page 446) that is completely closed throughout all stages of development; the open, more or less cup-shaped, **apothecium** (Fig. 264*D*, page 459) in which the cavity is lined with a palisade-like layer of asci; and the flask-shaped **perithecium** (Fig. 257*B*, page 449), also lined with a palisade-like layer of asci, but with an apical opening or pore.

Ascospores are shed after the ascocarp is mature. A few species have the ascus wall disintegrating before ascospores are shed;[1] but the great majority have the ascus wall remaining intact and rupturing at the distal end. The ruptured end may split irregularly, it may split into two parts, or there may be a lid-like opening of the ascus apex. Many species have an explosive discharge of ascospores that hurls them several centimeters from the ascocarp. The discharge of ascospores from an apothecium may be in such profusion that an evident cloud of spores is formed.

Nuclear Cycle of the Ascomycetae. Hemiascomycetae with mycelia bearing gametangia have a union of gamete nuclei in the zygote and a division of the zygote nucleus into four, eight, or more daughter nuclei. Division of the zygote nucleus has been shown[2] to be meiotic in one of them and the same is probably true for the others. In these fungi all nuclei in the mycelia are haploid and the zygote nucleus is the only diploid nucleus in the life cycle. Among yeasts, the nuclei of vegetative cells may be haploid or diploid (see page 439).

Mycelia derived from ascospores of Euascomycetae contain haploid nuclei. At one time certain euascomycetes were thought to have a fusion

[1] Young, 1931. [2] DeLamater, 1952.

of gamete nuclei in the ascogonium, diploid nuclei in binucleate cells of ascogenous hyphae, and a fusion of diploid nuclei in the ascus. For certain of them, the fusion nucleus of an ascus was described as undergoing a double reduction in number of chromosomes (**brachymeiosis**). Cytological reinvestigation of many of these ascomycetes shows that there is no karyogamy in the ascogonium, and chromosome counts[1] show that division of the fusion nucleus in an ascus is not brachymeiotic.

Numerous genetic studies based on serial dissection of the linearly arranged ascospores from asci of *Neurospora* and other genera show that ascospores with contrasting pairs of characters (alleles) are arranged two by two in an ascus (Fig. 245). This shows that segregation of characters

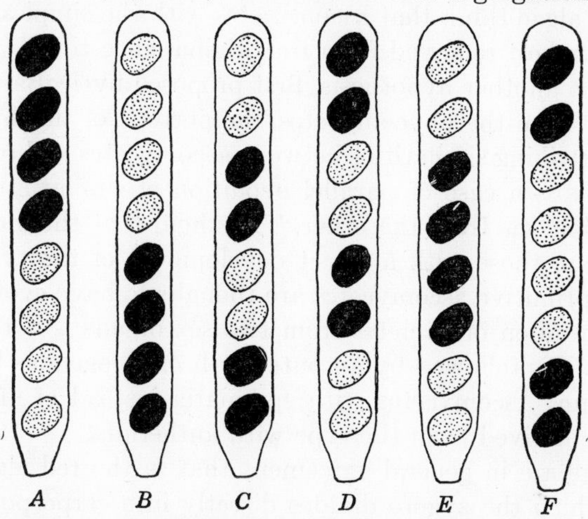

FIG. 245. Diagram showing the observed distribution of a pair of characters (alleles) to ascospores of an ascus. *A–B*, when segregated in the first meiotic division. *C–F*, when segregated in the second meiotic division.

occurs in the first and second divisions, but not in the third. If division in an ascus were brachymeiotic a segregation of characters would also at times take place in the third division and so result in an alternate arrangement of ascospores with contrasting characters. These cytological and genetic studies show that the fusion nucleus in the ascus of Euascomycetae is the only diploid nucleus in the life cycle and that all other nuclei are haploid.

Origin and Evolution of the Ascomycetae. Two widely divergent hypotheses have been proposed to account for the origin of the Ascomycetes. According to one hypothesis, first proposed by Sachs,[2] they have arisen from the Rhodophyta and presumably from the Florideae. Advocates[3] of this hypothesis point to the striking reproductive features com-

[1] Hirsch, 1950; Olive, 1950. [2] Sachs, 1875.

[3] Bessey, 1914, 1925, 1942, 1950; Dodge, 1914; Harper, 1900; Jackson, 1944; Thaxter, 1896.

mon to certain red algae and certain ascomycetes. These include the presence of a trichogyne on the female sex organ, gametic union by means of nonmotile spermatia, and analogies between ascogenous hyphae and gonimoblast filaments. According to such an origin the first ascomycetes to be evolved were those with spermatia and they probably evolved from Florideae with gonimoblast filaments growing directly from the carpogonium. These ascomycetes are thought to have given rise to those with an antheridium adjoining an ascogonium. The first of the ascomycetes with antheridia had ascogenous hyphae growing from the ascogonium. This type eventually evolved into one lacking ascogenous hyphae and where the zygote functions directly as the ascus. Those believing in a derivation from red algae think that ascomycetes with the simplest sexual system are the farthest removed from the original ancestors.

According to another hypothesis, first proposed by DeBary,[1] the ascomycetes arose from the phycomycetes. Supporters[2] of this hypothesis do not deny the striking similarities between ascomycetes and red algae, but think that this is a case of parallel evolution of similar structures and not a derivation one from the other. They hold that the most primitive ascomycetes are those with a direct development of the zygote into an ascus. These primitive ascomycetes are thought to have evolved into the type in which union of gametes from two sex organs is not followed by karyogamy and is followed by an outgrowth of ascogenous hyphae from the ascogonium. Ascomycetes with spermatia instead of antheridia are thought to be derived from the type with antheridia.

Phycologists are in general agreement that in the red algae the Bangioideae in which the zygote divides directly into carpospores are more primitive than Florideae in which the carpogonium gives rise to gonimoblast filaments bearing sporangia containing carpospores (see page 305). This gives support to the view that ascomycetes with a formation of ascospores in the zygote are more primitive than those in which the ascogonium gives rise to ascogenous hyphae bearing asci. Evolution to a condition where there are gonimoblast filaments or ascogenous hyphae may be looked upon as a device which permits the production of an unlimited number of spores as a result of a single gametic union. When considered as not being derived from those of red algae, the spermatia may be looked upon as minute detachable antheridia borne remote from instead of adjacent to an ascogonium.

Classification. On the basis of the presence or absence of ascogenous hyphae and ascocarps the ascomycetes fall into two major groups. Many mycologists consider this difference of sufficient magnitude to segregate

[1] DeBary, 1887.

[2] Atkinson, 1915; Claussen, 1912; Dangeard, 1907; Fitzpatrick, 1930; Gäumann, 1952; Guilliermond, 1928.

the Ascomycetae into two subclasses, the Hemiascomycetae and the Euascomycetae.

SUBCLASS 1. HEMIASCOMYCETAE

The Hemiascomycetae include those ascomycetes in which there is no formation of either ascogenous hyphae or ascocarps. The subclass includes about 50 genera and 250 species. These are placed in two orders, the Endomycetales and the Taphrinales.

ORDER 1. ENDOMYCETALES

The Endomycetales are hemiascomycetes in which plasmogamy is immediately followed by karyogamy. Plasmogamy may take place between the protoplasts of two gametangia, between two ascospores, or between two vegetative cells.

There are about 45 genera and 140 species. Some of the Endomycetales are saprophytic; others are parasitic. A few of the saprophytic genera have a true mycelium; but the great majority of them, including the yeasts, have a greatly reduced plant body. The systematic position of certain genera referred to the order is open to question because they have not been found producing asci.

Eremascus is one of the genera with a typical mycelium. One of the species (*E. fertilis* Stoppel) was first discovered as a mold on glasses of apple jelly.[1] This species has a branched mycelium with cross walls. Cells in the older part of a mycelium are usually uninucleate; those toward tips of hyphae contain 2 to 15 nuclei. *E. fertilis* does not produce asexual spores.

Sexual reproduction may begin within five days after a mycelium has begun to develop from an ascospore. Reproduction begins with an outgrowth of small vertical protuberances. These are developed in pairs, one on each of two adjoining cells and near the transverse wall separating the two (Fig. 246*A–C*). The tips of a pair of protuberances soon become apposed to each other, and the walls disappear in the region of mutual contact. Shortly afterward a nucleus migrates from each of the two cells into the fused protuberances, and the two nuclei soon unite with each other. Sooner or later there is the formation of a transverse wall (Fig. 246*E, G*) that cuts off the enlarging zygote, now the ascus, from the parent cells.[2] The zygote nucleus gives rise to eight daughter nuclei (Fig. 246*H*), and its division is meiotic.[3] The last step in ascus development is a free cell formation that divides the protoplast into eight uninucleate ascospores and a certain amount of epiplasm (Fig. 246*I–J*). The ascospores are liberated by a disintegration of the ascus wall.

[1] Stoppel, 1907. [2] Guilliermond, 1909; Harrold, 1950; Stoppel, 1907.
[3] DeLamater *et al.*, 1953.

Instead of fusing with each other, both of an apposed pair of protuberances may develop into an ascus. This is obviously due to parthenogenesis (Fig. 247). So, also, is the development of an ascus from a solitary

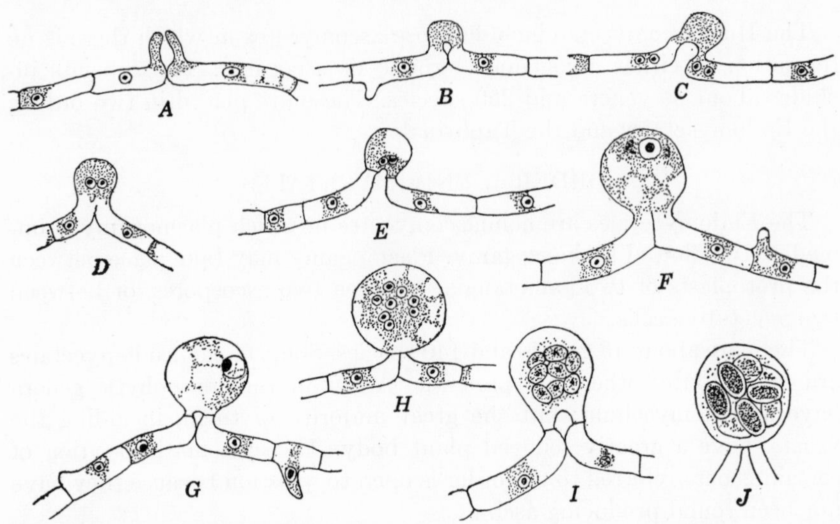

FIG. 246. *Eremascus fertilis* Stoppel. *A–D*, stages in conjugation. *E*, young binucleate zygote. *F–G*, zygote after nuclear fusion. *H*, octonucleate zygote. *I–J*, formation of ascospores. (*After Guilliermond*, 1909.)

protuberance on a mycelium. The same is also the case where a cell becomes greatly swollen, and its protoplast forms ascospores without sending out any protuberance.

Dipodascus is another of the Hemiascomycetae with a typical myce-

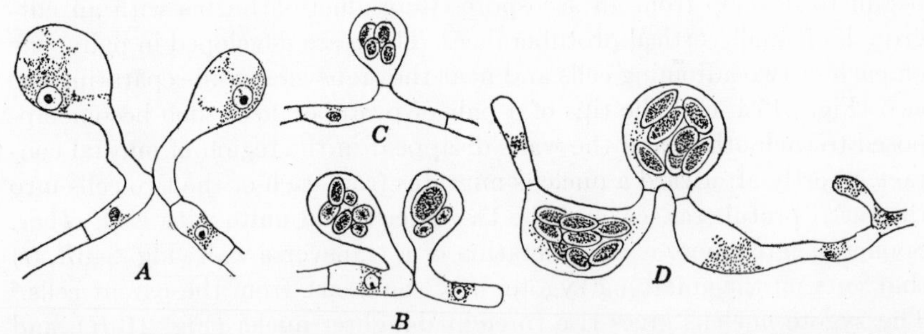

FIG. 247. Parthenogenetic formation of ascospores of *Eremascus fertilis* Stoppel. (*After Guilliermond*, 1909.)

lium. There are two species. The type species, *D. albidus* Lag., was first found growing saprophytically in slime fluxes exuding from trees. Its mycelium is sparingly branched and transversely septated into multinucleate cells of varying length (Fig. 248*A*). The other species has uninucleate cells.[1] There is no regular formation of asexual spores, but under certain conditions a hypha may break up into a chain of oïdia.[2]

Sexual reproduction of *D. albidus* begins in much the same manner as in *Eremascus* and with a formation of two lateral protuberances adjacent to a transverse septum. Each of the two protuberances contains several nuclei.[3] There is soon a terminal fusion of the two protuberances (Fig. 248*B*). Following this, each protuberance forms a transverse basal cross wall which blocks off its protoplast from that of the parent cell. One gametangium (the male) of the fused pair develops no further, and most

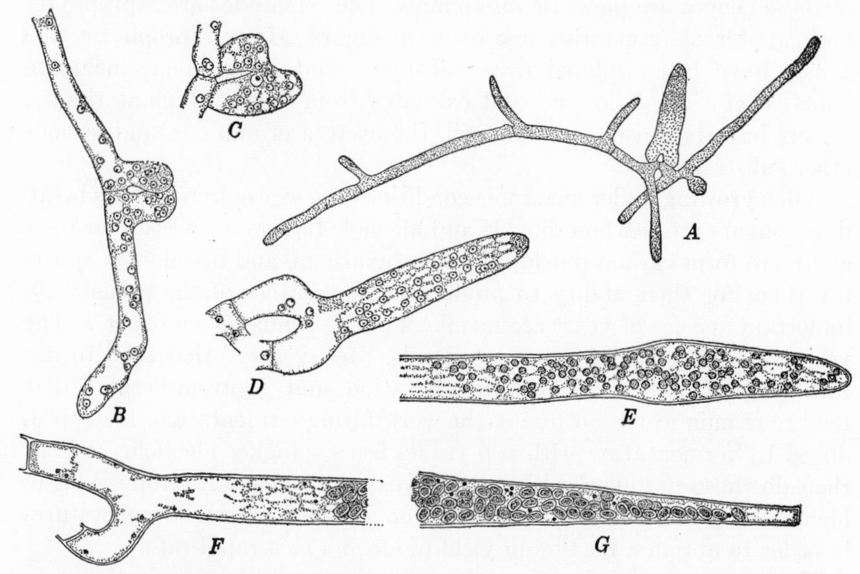

FIG. 248. *Dipodascus albidus* Lag. *A*, thallus with a young ascus. *B–C*, early stages in conjugation. *D–E*, early and later stages in development of zygote. *F–G*, basal and upper portion of ascus after the formation of ascospores. (*A*, *after Lagerheim*, 1892; *B–G*, *after Juel*, 1902.) (*B–G*, × 675.)

of its nuclei migrate into the other (female) gametangium. The female gametangium continues growth until its height is twelve or more times that at the time of gametangial fusion. Shortly after the male nuclei migrate into the female gametangium, one of them fuses with a female nucleus. The fusion nucleus is somewhat larger than other nuclei in the young zygote (Fig. 248*C–D*). It divides and redivides to form 100 or more daughter nuclei, each of which becomes the nucleus of a young ascospore. The nonfusing gamete nuclei remain undivided[4] and persist until ascospore formation, when they lie in the epiplasm delimited about the ascospores (Fig. 248*F–G*). The apex of an ascus ruptures or gelatinizes

[1] Biggs, 1937. [2] Lagerheim, 1892. [3] Dangeard, 1907; Juel, 1902.
[4] Juel, 1902, 1921.

at maturity, and the spores are extruded in a sticky matrix derived from the epiplasm. The extruded mass of spores often forms a sticky ball that remains attached to the ascus apex.[1]

Most yeasts are unicellular, nonmycelial, and with the ability to ferment certain sugars. Some[2] place all yeasts in a single family, the Saccharomycetaceae, and place this family in the Endomycetales. Others[3] exclude from the Endomycetales those yeasts which do not form ascospores.

When restricted to the ascosporic yeasts, sometimes called the "true yeasts," the Saccharomycetaceae include 14 genera and 68 species.[3] Three of these genera are parasitic on animals. The remainder are saprophytes and capable of fermenting one or more sugars. Many saprophytic true yeasts have been isolated from substrata containing sugar, including fruits, nectaries of flowers, and exudates from wounded plant tissues. Others have been isolated from soil, the excreta of animals, and various other substrata.

When growing under anaerobic conditions the saprophytic yeasts break down sugars into carbon dioxide and alcohol. Bakers use yeasts for their ability to form carbon dioxide; brewers, vintners, and distillers of spirits use them for their ability to produce alcohol. Most of the industrially important species of yeast are members of the genus *Saccharomyces*. The yeasts used in brewing are of two kinds, "top yeasts" that tend to rise to the top of beer wort during fermentation, and "bottom yeasts" that tend to remain at the bottom of the wort during fermentation. Beers produced by fermentation with top yeasts have a higher alcoholic content than do those produced with bottom yeasts. Distillers use top yeasts of high activity and carry out fermentation at relatively high temperatures in order to obtain a maximum yield of alcohol at a rapid rate.

The yeasts which bring about fermentation of fruit juices in the making of wines and ciders are largely "wild yeasts." These yeasts live in or on the soil of vineyards and orchards and are carried with dust to the skins of the fruit. Yeasts used in the fermentation and baking industries are "cultivated yeasts." These are carefully selected strains of proved good qualities which are maintained in pure culture to prevent contamination with wild yeasts that might impart undesired qualities to the product. In culturing yeasts to make the compressed yeast sold to housewives, the aim is to obtain a maximum number of yeast cells with a minimum amount of fermentation. This is achieved by a vigorous aeration of the culture solution that reduces fermentation to a minimum.

From the vegetative standpoint, yeasts are of two general types, those in which a cell divides into two daughter cells of equal size (**fission yeasts**) and those in which a cell buds off a small daughter cell (**budding**

[1] Lagerheim, 1892. [2] Ainsworth and Bisby, 1950.
[3] Lodder and Kreger-Van Rij, 1952.

yeasts). There are also species in which cell division is intermediate between bipartition and budding.

Schizosaccharomyces, a genus with three species, is the best known of the fission yeasts. The cells are usually solitary and cylindrical to spherical, but in one species[1] there may be a development of a mycelium composed of uninucleate cells. Vegetative multiplication of *S. octosporus* Beijerinck, a unicellular species, is by cell division. The nucleus of a cell divides into two daughter cells and this is followed by a transverse cell division that forms two daughter cells of approximately equal size (Fig.

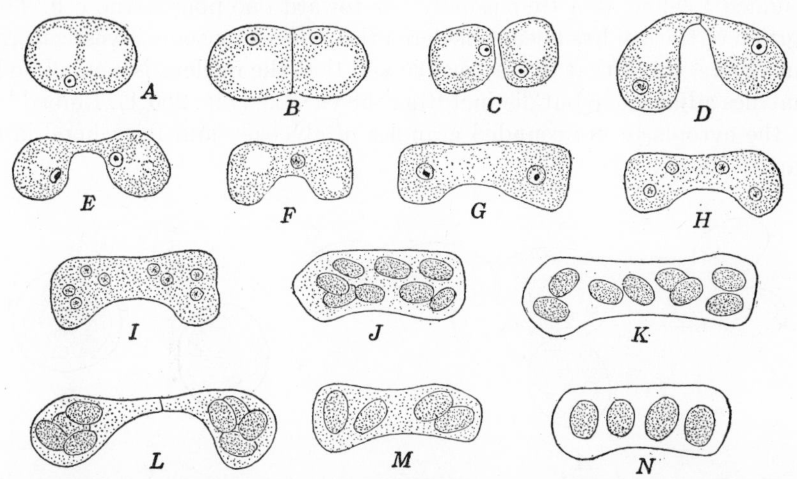

FIG. 249. *Schizosaccharomyces octosporus* Beijerinck. *A*, vegetative cell. *B*, cell division. *C–F*, stages in conjugation. *G–I*, stages showing increase in number of nuclei before ascospore formation. *J–K*, after formation of ascospores. *L–N*, parthenogenetic formation of ascospores. (× 1,950.)

249*A–B*). The two daughter cells remain attached to each other for a time, but they eventually reflex and separate from each other.[2]

S. octosporus is homothallic[3] and sexual reproduction occurs in abundance two or three days after a culture has been inoculated on a solid medium. It begins with an end to end apposition of two rounded cells. Sometimes the two are sister cells; sometimes they are not. In either case, each of the two cells sends out a short protuberance and the two protuberances unite with each other to form a conjugation tube.[4] The two nuclei migrate into the conjugation tube and there fuse with each other (Fig. 249*C–E*). The conjugation tube broadens after this, and according to the amount of broadening, the yoked cells develop into a dumbbell- or barrel-shaped zygote (ascus). The zygote nucleus divides to form eight daughter nuclei (Fig. 249*F–I*). An ascus wall remains in-

[1] Lodder and Kreger-Van Rij, 1952. [2] Coker and Wilson, 1911.
[3] Guilliermond, 1931. [4] Coker and Wilson, 1911; Guilliermond, 1903, 1905.

tact until germination of the ascospores within it. When an ascospore germinates, it enlarges somewhat and then divides transversely to form two daughter cells of equal size. Vegetative division may continue to form an indefinite number of cell generations. *S. octosporus* may also form ascospores without conjugation (Fig. 249*L–N*). These parthenogenetically developed asci usually contain four ascospores.

Saccharomyces, a genus with 30 species, is the most thoroughly investigated of the budding yeasts. It has more or less ovoid cells. The most conspicuous feature within a living cell of *S. cerevisiae* Hansen is a large rounded hyaline area that usually lies toward one pole of the cell. This portion of the cell has been considered the nucleus by some investigators,[1] but others[2] think that it is a vacuole and that the nucleus is a small body that lies adjacent to but distinct from the vacuole (Fig. 250*A*). Embedded in the cytoplasm are rounded granules of glycogen and mitochondria of various shapes.

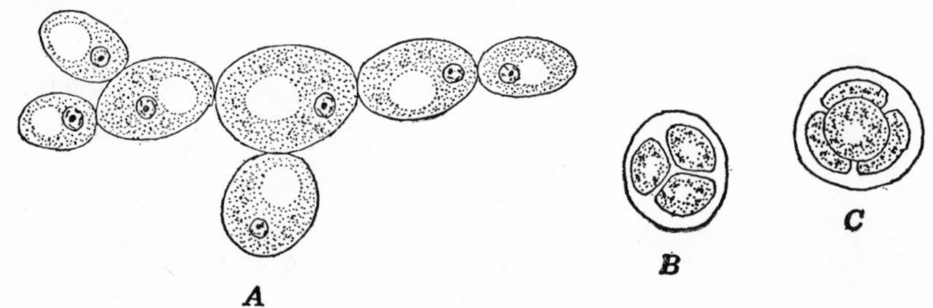

FIG. 250. *Saccharomyces cerevisiae* Hansen. *A*, budding of vegetative cells. *B–C*, ascospores. (× 2,600.)

Cell division of *S. cerevisiae* begins with a formation of a small outgrowth, the bud, at or near one pole of the cell. The nucleus divides as the bud is forming and one of the daughter nuclei migrates into the bud. A constriction in the plane of origin of the bud brings about a division into two daughter cells of very unequal size. The smaller of these, the former bud, enlarges rapidly. Usually the daughter cell formed by budding begins to form a bud before becoming separated from the parent cell. As a result, the cells of *Saccharomyces* tend to lie in short branched or unbranched chains (Fig. 250*A*).

According to their origin, vegetative cells of *S. cerevisiae* may be haploid or diploid. When cultured under appropriate conditions, the diploid cells develop directly into asci containing four ascospores (Fig. 250*B–C*). Genetic analyses of ascospores show that nuclear division in connection with the formation of ascospores is meiotic.[3] Usually the ascospores fuse in pairs to form vegetative cells before escaping from an ascus. The two

[1] Lindegren, 1949; Wager and Peniston, 1910.
[2] DeLamater, 1950; Guilliermond, 1905. [3] Winge, 1935.

ascospore nuclei unite in the vegetative cell thus formed, and after liberation from the ascus this diploid vegetative cell may multiply by budding for an indefinite number of cell generations.

Single ascospores dissected from asci before conjugation of ascospores takes place may develop into vegetative cells whose nuclei are haploid. These cells, which may be cultured for an indefinite number of cell generations, are distinguishable from diploid cells by means of their smaller size. Two haploid vegetative cells of opposite sex may fuse and their nuclei fuse to form a uninucleate vegetative cell with a diploid nucleus.

ORDER 2. TAPHRINALES

The Taphrinales have a mycelium producing asci that lie parallel to one another in a palisade-like layer that is without any enclosing peridium. There are about 6 genera and 125 species.

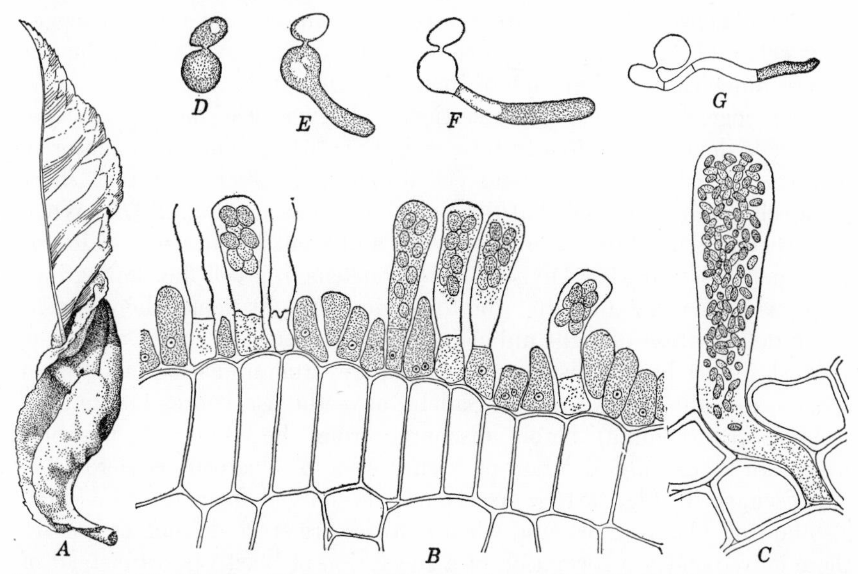

FIG. 251. *A–B*, *Taphrina deformans* (Fcl.) Tul. *A*, an infected peach leaf showing the characteristic malformation. *B*, asci at various stages of development. *C*, *T. johansonii* Sadeb.; ascus containing many blastospores. *D–G*, *T. epiphylla* Sadeb.; stages in the conjugation of blastospores and the formation of hyphae. (*D–G*, *after Wieben*, 1927.) (*A*, × ½; *B–C*, × 650.)

Taphrina, the type genus, has about 100 species. These are parasitic on ferns, Rosales, and Fagales. Two of the species, *T. deformans* (Fcl.) Tul. and *T. pruni* (Fcl.) Tul., cause serious diseases of orchard trees. The former produces a leaf curl of the peach (Fig. 251*A*); the latter causes a malformation of plum fruits.

Germinating spores of certain species give rise to a mycelium which at first has uninucleate cells and later has binucleate ones.[1] Other species

[1] Eftimu, 1927; R. E. Fitzpatrick, 1934; Wieben, 1927.

may have the spores giving rise to a mycelium that is binucleate from the beginning.[1] The binucleate condition may also arise through a conjugation of **blastospores** (conidia) or of ascospores (Fig. 251*D–G*). Two species in which conjugation of spores has been observed are heterothallic, four of the ascospores in an ascus being of one sex and four of the opposite sex.[2] Conjugation of ascospores may also take place in *T. deformans.*[3] However, the successful inoculation of the host by blastospores descended from a single ascospore shows that conjugation of spores is not essential for development of mycelia to a fertile condition in *T. deformans.*[4]

According to the species, the mycelium of *Taphrina* is intercellular, subcuticular, or grows within the walls of epidermal cells of the host.[5] Prior to ascus formation most species develop a compact mycelial layer, one cell in thickness, that lies between cuticle and epidermis of the host. Individual cells of this layer are more or less rounded and are the **ascogenous cells.** These are sometimes called chlamydospores. Each of them is at first binucleate, and in each of them there is a fusion of the two nuclei as the ascogenous cell elongates vertically. A few species have the ascogenous cells developing directly into asci (Fig. 251*C*). The great majority of species have each ascogenous cell dividing transversely into a short stalk cell and a sister cell that develops into an ascus (Fig. 251*B*). When an ascogenous cell divides into stalk cell and ascus the division of its fusion nucleus is mitotic.[6] Division of the nucleus in a cell developing into an ascus is meiotic[7] and after the formation of eight nuclei there is usually a delimitation of eight uninucleate ascospores.

Most species have a discharge of ascospores from an ascus; but certain species, including *T. johansonii* Sadeb., have the ascospores budding off blastospores (conidia) before discharge from the ascus. Blastospores within an ascus may also bud off a succession of blastospores before being discharged (Fig. 251*C*). Ascospores discharged from an ascus may also bud off blastospores, and when cultures are started from ascospores there is frequently a formation of a succession of blastospores instead of a development of mycelia. In some species, as in *T. epiphylla,* infection of the host occurs soon after discharge of ascospores; but in other species (presumably because only young and tender organs of the host can be infected) there is not an immediate infection of the host. It is thought[8] that production of successive generations of blastospores affords a means of survival during the prolonged period when the fungus is not growing within the host.

Many mycologists think that the Taphrinales are derived from the

[1] Ella M. Martin, 1924. [2] Wieben, 1927. [3] Mix, 1935.
[4] R. E. Fitzpatrick, 1934; Mix, 1935. [5] Mix, 1939. [6] Ella M. Martin, 1940.
[7] Eftimu, 1927; Juel, 1921; Ella M. Martin, 1940. [8] Mix, 1949.

Endomycetales. Some mycologists[1] disagree with this view and think that the Taphrinales are degenerate Euascomycetae in which there has been a disappearance of all portions of the thallus except the ascogenous hyphae.

SUBCLASS 2. EUASCOMYCETAE

The Euascomycetae include all the ascomycetes in which the asci are formed on ascogenous hyphae. These ascomycetes also produce ascocarps. According to one census[2] there are about 1,600 genera and 12,000 species.

Mycologists are in conflict concerning the number and composition of orders into which the Euascomycetae should be divided.[3] On the basis of the structure of the ascocarp the euascomycetes fall into the following three general types: the *Plectomycetes* in which the ascocarp is a cleistothecium; the *Pyrenomycetes* in which it is a perithecium; and the *Discomycetes* in which it is an apothecium. Instead of attempting to discuss all orders of the Euascomycetae, representative orders of Plectomycetes, Pyrenomycetes, and Discomycetes will be discussed on pages to follow.

PLECTOMYCETES

The Plectomycetes have ascocarps that are cleistothecia and in which exposure of asci and liberation of ascospores are effected by weathering of the wall (**peridium**) of the ascocarp. The cleistothecia contain more or less globose asci and these are irregularly arranged within the cleistothecium. Among the Plectomycetes, the Aspergillales have been selected to exemplify an order in which asci arise at various levels within the cleistothecium, and the Erysiphales as an order in which asci arise at a single level.

ASPERGILLALES (PLECTASCALES)

Cleistothecia of Aspergillales are borne within a loose mat of vegetative hyphae and in many cases the surface of the cleistothecium is not sharply delimited from the vegetative portion of the mycelium. The asci are formed at various levels within the cleistothecium and usually lie in a pulverent mass when mature. The two best-known genera, *Aspergillus* and *Penicillium*, are sometimes[4] included among the imperfect fungi because there are many species in which ascocarps are not known.

Penicillium is a saprophytic genus that grows on decaying vegetables, fruits, meats, and a great variety of moist plant and animal substances. The most recent monograph[5] of the genus recognizes 136 species. Most

[1] Bessey, 1950; Gwynne-Vaughan and Barnes, 1927.

[2] Ainsworth and Bisby, 1950.

[3] For some of the more modern systems compare Alexopolous, 1952; Bessey, 1950; Gäumann, 1949, 1952; G. W. Martin, 1950; Miller, 1949; Nannfeldt, 1932; and Wolf and Wolf, 1947.

[4] G. W. Martin. 1950. [5] Raper and Thom, 1949.

species cause economic loss; but a few of them, especially those involved in ripening of Camembert and Roquefort cheeses, are of economic benefit. There are also a few species pathogenic to man and animals. *Penicillium* is best known to the nonbotanist because it is the source from which the antibiotic penicillin is extracted. Penicillin was first discovered in *P. notatum* Westling and for a time this was the species from which penicillin was extracted. Later investigation has shown *P. chrysogenum* Thom to be better for this purpose, and irradiation of it with X rays and ultraviolet light has induced mutants with an even higher content of penicillin. Between June, 1943, and October, 1947, the discovery of better strains and greatly improved methods for culturing the fungus lowered the price of penicillin from $20 to 30 cents per 100,000 units.

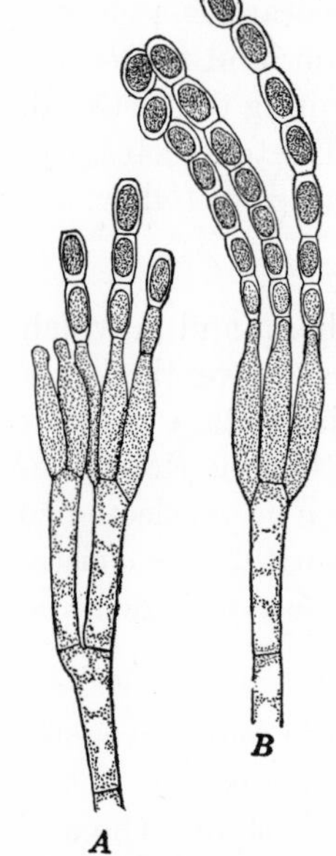

FIG. 252. Conidia of *Penicillium* spp. (× 975.)

The mycelium of *Penicillium* may grow superficially upon or penetrate deeply into the substratum. It is composed of freely branched hyphae whose cells are thin-walled and bi- to multinucleate. Anastamoses between hyphae of two mycelia may result in a heterokaryotic mycelium.[1] Some species may have the mycelium developing into a sclerotium.

Asexual reproduction is by the formation of brushlike tufts of conidia at the tips of multicellular conidiophores. A conidiophore grows vertically from a mycelium and to a more or less definite height. The conidiophore of some species is an unbranched axis terminating in a tuft of flask-shaped special cells (**phialides**), each of which forms conidia at its apex (Fig. 252*B*). Those of other species are branched at the upper end and with each branch terminating in a tuft of phialides (Fig. 252*A*). The upper cells of a conidiophore and the phialides are uninucleate.[1] Formation of conidia begins with a division of the nucleus of a phialide and a migration of one daughter nucleus into the narrow apex of the phialide. The terminal portion of the phialide is then cut off as a short cylindrical uninucleate cell that develops into a conidium. Additional cells are cut off in acropetalous succession at the phialide's apex and each of them develops into a conidium. The protoplast of a cell developing into a conidium secretes a spore wall distinct from the wall of the cell. According to whether the spore wall lies free from or is fused with the original wall of the cell, successively formed conidia lie a short distance from one another (Fig. 252) or abut on one another.[2]

[1] Baker, 1944. [2] Thom, 1914.

Somewhat more than 20 species are known to produce ascocarps. All critically studied species are homothallic and the heterothallism reported[1] for one species has not been confirmed in subsequent investigations. The structure of the sex organs and the manner in which ascogenous hyphae bear asci vary from species to species.[2] *P. vermiculatum* Dang. is one of the species with a simple type of ascogonium. It has a mycelium of uninucleate cells, and its ascogonia are developed from erect unicellular

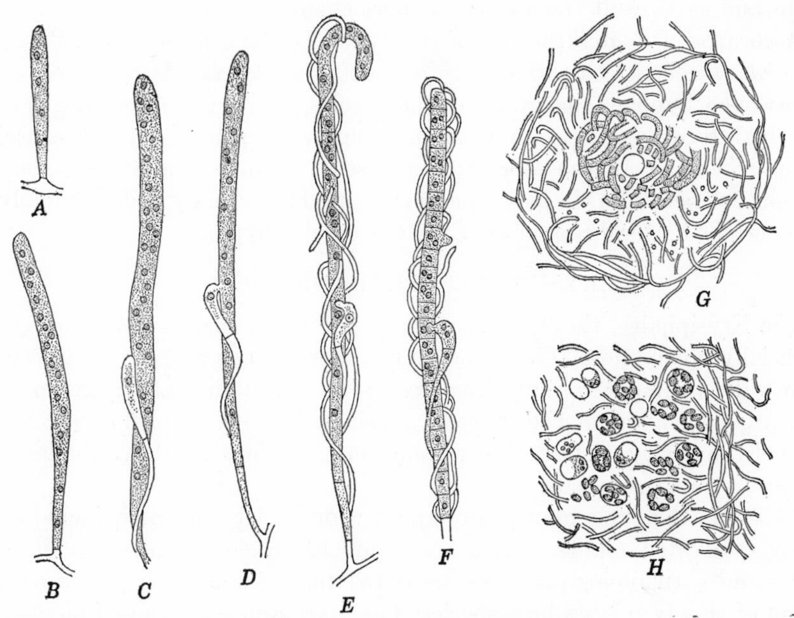

FIG. 253. *Penicillium vermiculatum* Dang. *A–B*, young ascogonia. *C–D*, ascogonia after development of the antheridium. *E*, ascogonium beginning to be surrounded by sterile hyphae. *F*, after formation of cross walls in ascogonium. *G*, transverse section of a young ascocarp showing the ascogonium surrounded by ascogenous hyphae (shaded). *H*, portion of a nearly mature ascocarp showing the asci intermingled with sterile hyphae. (*After Dangeard*, 1907.) (× 450.)

branches.[3] A young ascogonium is uninucleate, but, as it elongates, the nucleus divides and redivides to form 32 or 64 daughter nuclei (Fig. 253*A–B*). A slender uninucleate antheridial branch grows up in a lax spiral that makes several turns about the developing ascogonium. The antheridial branch eventually forms a short, somewhat inflated, uninucleate antheridium at its distal end. The tip of the antheridium is apposed to the ascogonium, and there is a dissolution of cell walls in the region of mutual contact (Fig. 253*C–D*). It has been held[4] that there is no gametic union after establishment of connection between antheridial

[1] Derx, 1925. [2] Dodge, 1933; Emmons, 1935.
[3] Dangeard, 1907; Emmons, 1935. [4] Dangeard, 1907.

and ascogonial protoplasts. Entangled sterile hyphae now grow up around the united antheridium and ascogonium (Fig. 253*E–F*) and ultimately develop into the sterile portion of the cleistothecium. Meanwhile, the ascogonium becomes transversely divided into a row of binucleate cells (Fig. 253*F*) and certain of these cells send out one or more branched ascogenous hyphae, also composed of binucleate cells. Each of the cells toward tips of branches of ascogenous hyphae develops into an eight-spored ascus and as a result the asci lie in short chains.[1]

Ascocarps of *Penicillium* are of two types. In the type to which *P. vermiculatum* belongs the wall (peridium) of the ascocarp is composed of interwoven hyphae. According to the species, the hyphae are loosely or closely interwoven. Species with this type of peridium have the asci borne in chains. In the other type of ascocarp there is a pseudoparenchymatous peridium. In this type the asci are borne singly and terminally on one-celled lateral branches of the ascogenous hyphae.

ERYSIPHALES (PERISPORIALES)

The Erysiphales, the "powdery mildews," are parasites that grow superficially on the host. The ascocarp is a more or less globose cleistothecium with a compact pseudoparenchymatous peridium that has no opening. Most members of the order havea single layer of parallel asci at the base of the cavity within the peridium, but a few of them have the layer reduced to a single ascus.

Erysiphe, the type genus, grows on a wide variety of hosts, including many cultivated plants. There are about 10 species, all cosmopolitan, and some with biological races restricted to a single host species or a group of closely related host species. The mycelium is composed of short uninucleate cells. It grows superficially on a host, upon either stem or leaf. Food is obtained by means of one-celled haustorial branches that pierce the walls of epidermal cells of the host. Haustorial branches of most species develop into globular or pyriform swellings after penetration into a host cell (Fig. 254*A*), but in one species[2] each haustorial branch has several parallel tubular processes.

Asexual reproduction begins shortly after a mycelium has become established upon a host and commences with an upgrowth of numerous short, erect, unicellular branches (conidiophores) from the mycelium. A unicellular conidiophore may cut off conidia in acropetalous succession from its distal end (Fig. 254*B–I*), or it may divide into a long stalk cell and a short terminal cell that successively cuts off conidia. Conidia are formed in profusion throughout most of the host's growing season. There is an immediate germination of conidia that have fallen upon a suitable host, and within a few days the new mycelium begins to form conidia.

[1] Emmons, 1935. [2] Smith, 1900.

Sexual reproduction of *Erysiphe* does not begin until the growing season of the host is drawing to a close. Most species seem to be homothallic, but one species has been shown[1] to be heterothallic. Sex organs are developed at the ends of pairs of hyphae lying parallel to and more or less twisted about each other. The terminal cell of one hypha becomes an ascogonium and that of the other hypha becomes an antheridium. The antheridial and ascogonial walls disappear in the region of mutual con-

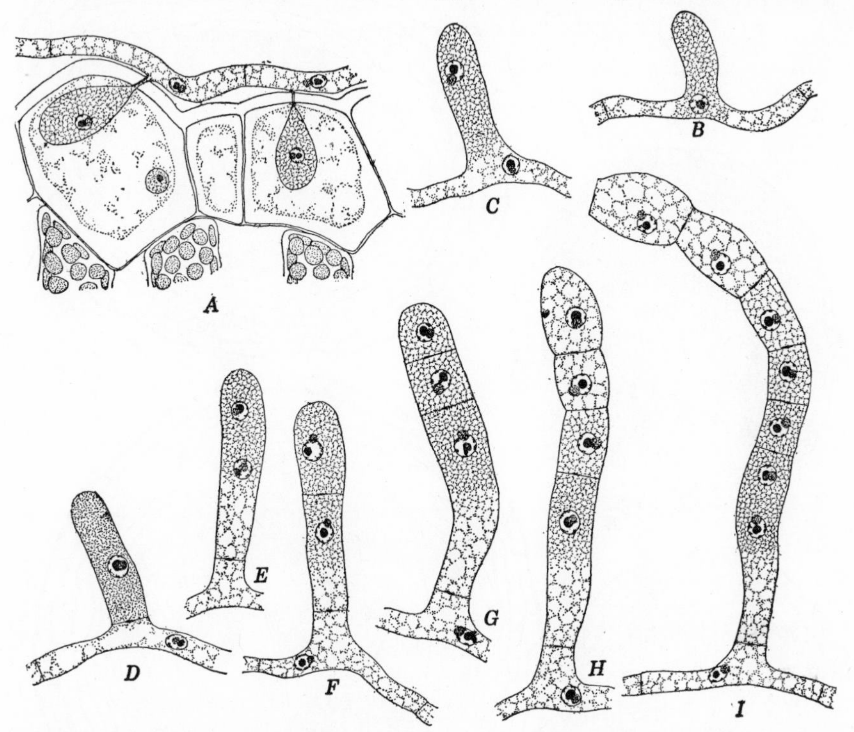

FIG. 254. *Erysiphe cichoraceum* DC. *A*, portion of a vegetative hypha with haustoria in epidermal cells of host. *B–I*, successive stages in development of conidia. (× 650.)

tact to form a pore through which the antheridial nucleus and sometimes the cytoplasm moves into the ascogonium. A fusion of the two nuclei now in the ascogonium has been recorded for *Erysiphe* and certain other Erysiphales by some investigators,[2] but this is denied by many others.[3] The number of nuclei within an ascogonium increases and then there is a formation of cross walls that divide it into a row of four to five cells (Fig. 255*A–C*). In this row the penultimate cell has two or more nuclei and ascogenous hyphae grow out from this cell.

[1] Yarwood, 1935. [2] Harper, 1896; Hein, 1927.

[3] Allen, 1936; Beatus, 1948, 1950; Bergman, 1941; Dangeard, 1907; Eftimu, 1929; Winge, 1911.

The ascogenous hyphae are so densely interwoven that their development cannot be followed in detail, but it has been shown[1] that those cells of it which develop into asci are binucleate and intercalary in position. Cells developing into asci increase greatly in size (Fig. 255*E–F*); the re-

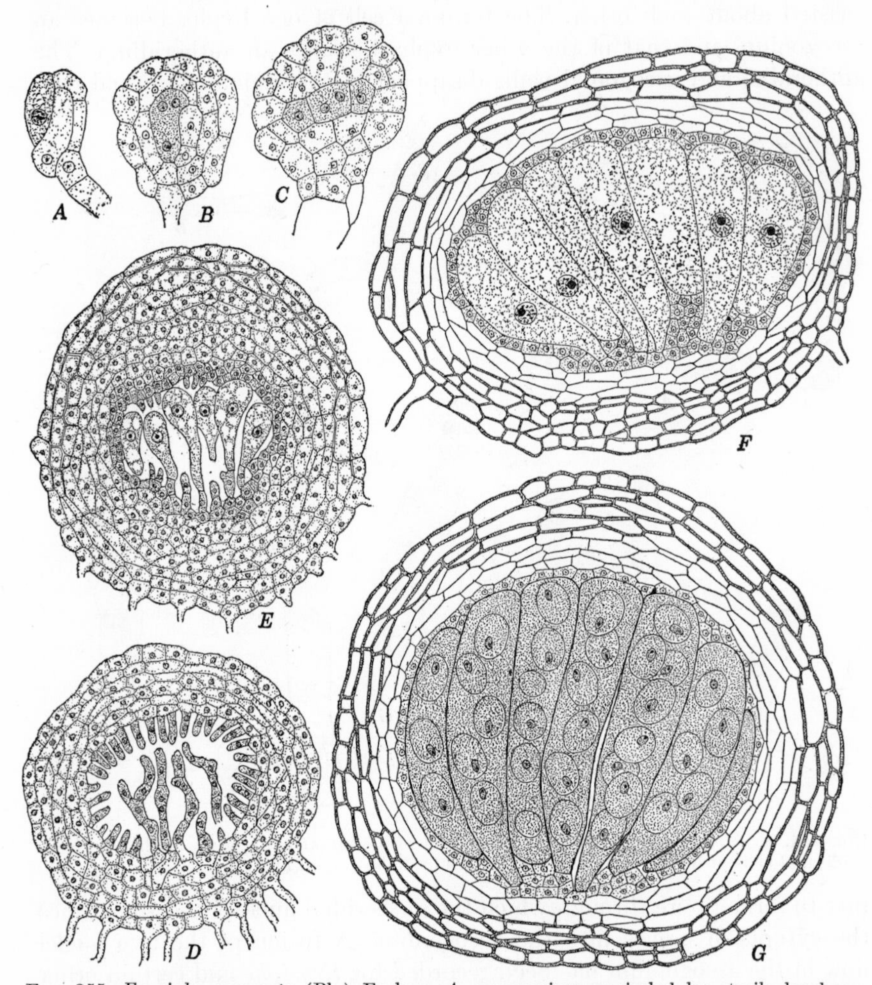

FIG. 255. *Erysiphe aggregata* (Pk.) Farlow. *A*, ascogonium encircled by sterile hyphae. *B*, multinucleate ascogonium. *C*, after formation of cross walls in ascogonium. *D*, young ascocarp after formation of ascogenous hyphae. *E–G*, successive stages in development of ascocarp and asci. (*A–C*, × 975; *D*, × 650; *E–G*, × 480.)

maining cells of the ascogenous hyphae lose their protoplasts and become compressed as the asci develop. There is a fusion of the two nuclei in a young ascus and as the ascus enlarges the fusion nucleus divides into eight daughter nuclei (Fig. 244, page 429). Division of the fusion nucleus

[1] Harper, 1896.

is meiotic. Asci of some species of *Erysiphe* form eight uninucleate ascospores after the octonucleate stage in development of an ascus (Fig. 255*G*). Asci of other species have a free cell formation of ascospores around only two of the eight nuclei in an octonucleate ascus, the remaining six nuclei lying in the epiplasm surrounding the two ascospores. Ascospores of some species of *Erysiphe* are not fully ripened and capable of germination until the following spring.

Immediately after gametic union the two sex organs become surrounded by a layer of densely compacted hyphae, most of which grow out from the cell subtending the ascogonium. At first this ensheathing layer (peridium) of a juvenile cleistothecium is one cell in thickness, but by the time the first ascogenous hyphae have appeared it has become three or more cells in thickness. Eventually the peridium becomes a layer 6 to 10 cells in thickness and one in which cells in the outer half are thick-walled and without protoplasts (Fig. 255*F–G*). Certain superficial cells of the peridium develop into elongate, hypha-like, unbranched appendages. A mature cleistothecium usually remains attached to the host, but it may become accidentally detached and blown about by the wind. The peridium usually remains intact over winter so that there is no exposure of asci and liberation of ascospores until the following spring. In most cases exposure of asci is due to an irregular cracking of the upper portion of the peridium; but in *E. graminis* DC. there is a transverse splitting in the equatorial plane[1] followed by a shedding of the upper half of the peridium. *E. graminis* has a forcible ejection of ascospores from the exposed asci and an ejection with sufficient force to hurl them more than 20 mm. Ascospores falling on a suitable host germinate immediately, and within a few days there is a production of conidia by the mycelium developing from an ascospore. The conidia, in turn, give rise to new mycelia producing conidia. When conditions are favorable this may result in a rapid spreading of the fungus to a large number of individuals of the host species.

PYRENOMYCETES

The Pyrenomycetes have an ascocarp in which escape of ascospores is through a circular pore or an elongated slit in the peridium. The asci are more or less cylindrical and are borne in a parallel series. In many pyrenomycetes the ascocarp is a perithecium with the upper end of the peridium prolonged into a neck terminating in a circular pore. Two of the orders described below have been selected as examples of those with perithecia, and two have been selected to exemplify those in which there is not a distinct perithecium.

[1] Salmon, 1903.

ORDER SPHAERIALES

The Sphaeriales have globose sessile perithecia standing free from the remainder of the mycelium. The peridium is usually dark in color and with the apex prolonged into a distinct neck terminating in a circular pore (**ostiole**). Perithecia of many species have sterile hairs (**paraphyses**) parallel to the asci, and have sterile hairs of another type (**periphyses**) just beneath the ostiole. According to the genus, development of asci is initiated by spermatization of a trichogyne or by lateral union of an antheridium and ascogonium. Some members of the order are saprophytes; others are parasitic on vascular plants.

One well-known genus of the order is *Neurospora*, the ascomycete most thoroughly studied by geneticists. This fungus is also of interest because of the elaborate trichogynes borne by the ascogonia. *Neurospora*, also

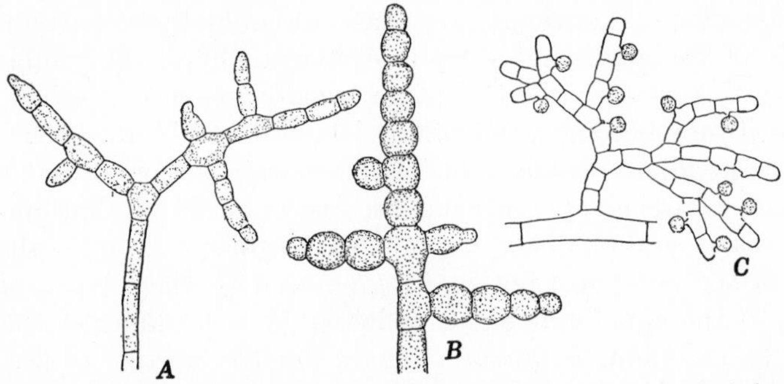

FIG. 256. *Neurospora sitophila* Shear and Dodge. *A–B*, conidia. *C*, spermatia (microconidia).

known as the red mold of bread, has long been known as a bakery pest causing considerable economic loss to bakers. At one time it was a difficult matter to eradicate the fungus once it had become established in a bakery. Today, its appearance in a bakery is no longer a problem because methods of controlling it have been devised.

For a long time this fungus was known only in the conidial stage and its species were placed among the imperfect fungi and in the genus *Monilia*. When the ascocarps were discovered[1] these species were removed from the Deuteromycetae and a new ascomycetous genus, *Neurospora*, was erected to receive them.

The mycelium of *Neurospora* grows superficially over the substratum; is freely branched; and has hyphae composed of cells, each with a dozen or more nuclei. Asexual reproduction is by means of conidia. These conidia, often called **macroconidia**, are borne in branched linear series at the end of a conidiophore growing erect from the mycelium (Fig. 256*A–B*). Most of these conidia contain several nuclei, but the terminal member of a file may be uninucleate.[2]

[1] Shear and Dodge, 1927. [2] Schönefeldt, 1935.

A mycelium may also produce an erect structure resembling a conidiophore but in which uninucleate spore-like bodies are budded off laterally from the cells.[1] These bodies are in reality spermatia, but they are often called **microconidia** because of their smaller size (Fig. 256*C*). Spermatia are capable of functioning as conidia and germinating to form mycelia.

Sexual reproduction of *Neurospora* is effected by spermatization, and with either spermatia or conidia. Typical strains of all species have each mycelium producing ascogonia, spermatia, and conidia; but not all species are alike with respect to their sexuality. *N. tetrasperma* Shear and

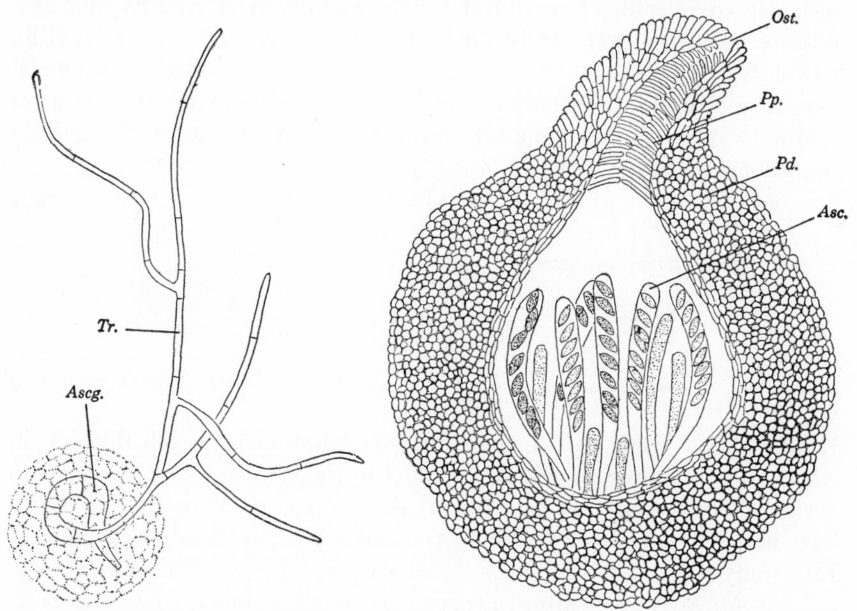

Fig. 257. *Neurospora sitophila* Shear and Dodge. *A*, diagram of a protoperithecium. *B*, vertical section of a nearly mature perithecium. (*Asc.*, asci; *Ascg.*, ascogonium; *Ost.*, ostiole; *Pd.*, peridium; *Pp.*, periphyses; *Tr.*, trichogyne.) (*A*, *based upon Backus*, 1939.) (*A*, × 210; *B*, × 150.)

Dodge is homothallic, but with a homothallism of the type called secondary homothallism (see page 426). *N. sitophila* Shear and Dodge and *N. crassa* Shear and Dodge are heterothallic, but with the type of heterothallism called physiological heterothallism (see page 426).

An ascogonium begins development as a coiled multinucleate lateral outgrowth from a hypha.[2] It soon becomes transversely divided into 5 to 10 multinucleate cells. Shortly after an ascogonium becomes multicellular sterile hyphae grow up from the lowermost of these cells and form a dense globose envelope surrounding the ascogonium. Next, several cells of the ascogonium usually send forth trichogynes, but in exceptional cases

[1] Dodge, 1932. [2] Backus, 1939; Dodge, 1935; Schönefeldt, 1935

only the terminal cell forms a trichogyne.[1] The trichogynes grow out through the envelope surrounding the ascogonium and they may become branched before or after emerging from the envelope. The structure thus developed has been called[2] a **protoperithecium** (Fig. 257*A*). If appropriate spermatia or conidia are not available for the trichogynes, there is no further development beyond the protoperithecial stage. When there are appropriate spermatia or conidia in the vicinity of a protoperithecium the trichogynes grow to and unite with them. It is thought[1] that growth of a trichogyne to a spermatium or a conidium is a chemotropic response to substances produced by the spermatia or conidia, but this has not been definitely established. However, it has been shown[1] that an establishment of a connection between the two is followed by a migration of spermatial or conidial nuclei into the trichogyne. Shortly after spermatization, the ascogonium produces a compact mass of irregularly shaped multinucleate cells. Certain cells at the surface of this mass of "ascogenous hyphae" are binucleate croziers. In them, a simultaneous

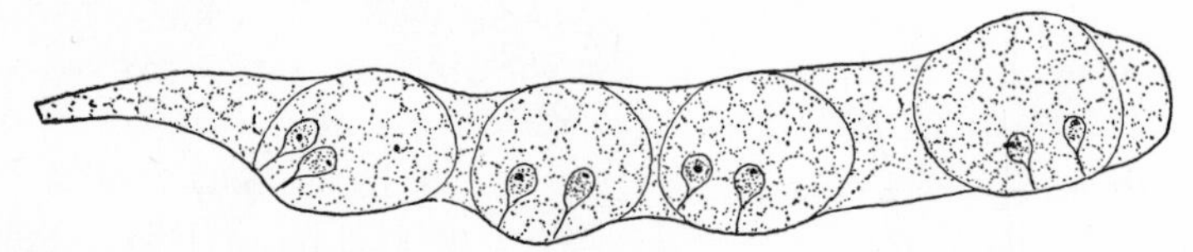

Fig. 258. *Neurospora tetrasperma* Shear and Dodge. Ascus just after delimitation of four heterokaryotic spores. (*After Dodge*, 1927.)

(conjugate) division of the two nuclei is followed by a cell division in which two daughter nuclei are included in the cell that develops into an ascus.[3] Genetic analysis has shown[4] that this binucleate cell is heterokaryotic. Further development of the ascus is in the manner typical for Euascomycetae (see page 428). Most species have a formation of eight uninucleate ascospores after the octonucleate stage, but in *N. tetrasperma*[5] the astral rays delimit four binucleate heterokaryotic ascospores (Fig. 258). Abnormal asci of this species may contain some ascospores that are either uninucleate or binucleate. In all species of *Neurospora* the number of nuclei in an ascospore increases prior to its discharge from an ascus.

After spermatization, portions of the protothecium other than the ascogonium develop into the sterile portion of a perithecium. A mature perithecium (Fig. 257*B*) has a pseudoparenchymatous peridium a dozen or more cells in thickness, and with the cells in the outer portion with dark-colored walls. The upper portion of the peridium is prolonged into an evident neck terminating in a circular pore (ostiole). As in many other Sphaeriales the canal of the neck is lined with periphyses, and there are paraphyses growing up between the asci. The periphyses are evident

[1] Backus, 1939. [2] Buller, 1941. [3] Colson, 1934; Singleton, 1953.
[4] Sansome, 1947. [5] Dodge, 1927.

in mature perithecia but the paraphyses are more or less evanescent structures.

ORDER LABOULBENIALES

The Laboulbeniales are minute ectoparasites in the cutinous integument of living insects. All genera have an ascogonium with a trichogyne and fertilization is effected by means of spermatia. The perithecium is borne on a stipe.

There are about 120 genera and 1,500 species. Many of the species are restricted to specific hosts and some hosts may harbor more than one species. For example, one of the beetles has been found[1] to be the host of six species of *Laboulbenia*, each occurring on specific portions of the host and certain of them found only on males or on females of the host.

Stigmatomyces baeri Peyritsch is relatively simple in structure as compared with many other Laboulbeniales. It grows upon the European housefly (*Musca domestica* L.). The fungus may be attached to any part of the fly, but more commonly it grows on the back of head and thorax or upon the anterior pair of legs.[2] Infection of the host is only by means of ascospores. An ascospore is broadly acicular, transversely divided into two cells, and with a gelatinous envelope that is characteristically thickened at one pole (Fig. 259*A*). The sticky envelope about a spore facilitates adherence when the basal end of it becomes attached to the host. Shortly after attachment to the host, the lower cell cuts off a short dark-colored foot cell (Fig. 259*B*). The uppermost cell of this three-celled stage eventually develops into the appendage bearing the antheridia and subtending parts; the median cell develops into the perithecium and subtending parts; the foot cell does not divide again and serves as an organ of attachment for the rest of the fungus.

Development of the antheridial portion begins with a succession of oblique divisions of the upper cell.[2] All daughter cells but the uppermost then divide in a plane perpendicular to the oblique wall (Fig. 259*C–F*). The upper daughter cell of each pair redivides transversely, and its superior daughter cell is metamorphosed into an antheridium (Fig. 259*H–I*). Each antheridium is flask-shaped, and, as it matures, there is a formation of an apical pore in the neck portion of the flask. The protoplast within an antheridium is uninucleate,[3] and it cuts off a minute uninucleate protoplast (the spermatium) that escapes through the pore in the antheridial wall. Escape of the spermatium is followed by a formation and a discharge of a second one. This may be repeated many times.

The median cell of the three-celled stage does not divide until the antheridia are well along in development.[2] It divides by a diagonally transverse wall into a small superior cell (that does not divide) and a

[1] Benjamin and Shanor, 1952. [2] Thaxter, 1896. [3] Faull, 1911.

large inferior cell (Fig. 259*F*). The inferior cell divides transversely (Fig. 259*G*) and its upper daughter cell divides transversely. The two lowermost of the three cells formed by division of the inferior cell do not divide further; the uppermost one is the perithecial initial from which the entire perithecium is developed (Fig. 259*H–I*). The perithecial initial elongates outward from other cells of the young thallus and then divides

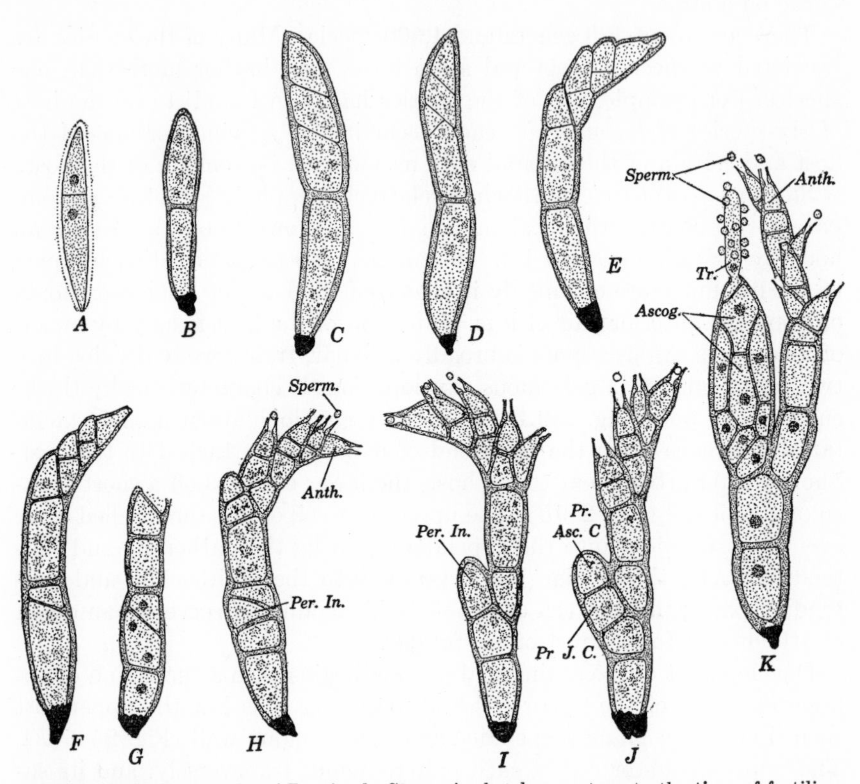

Fig. 259. *Stigmatomyces baeri* Peyritsch. Stages in development up to the time of fertilization. (*Anth.*, antheridium; *Ascog.*, ascogonium; *Per In.*, perithecial initial; *Pr. Asc. C.*, primary ascogonial cell; *Pr. J. C.*, primary jacket cell; *Sperm.*, spermatium; *Tr.*, trichogyne.) (*After Thaxter*, 1896.)

transversely (Fig. 259*J*). The upper daughter cell produced by this division is the **primary ascogonial cell**; the lower daughter cell is the **primary jacket cell** of the perithecial jacket (peridium). The primary ascogonial cell develops into an ascogonium that is four cells long and one in which the uppermost cell is a trichogyne. It is very probable that nuclear fusion takes place in the lowermost cell of the ascogonium after spermatia have lodged on the trichogyne. Meanwhile, the primary jacket cell has developed into a perithecial jacket (Fig. 259*K*). Eventually this becomes two cells in thickness and several cells in perimeter.[1] After fertilization, short stout ascogenic cells grow out from the base of the ascogonium, and each ascogenic cell gives rise to several asci. The ascogenic cells of Laboulbeniales are homologous with the ascogenous hyphae of other Euascomycetae. Nothing is known concerning the cytology of ascogenic cells in *S. baeri*, but it is known that they are binucleate in certain other Laboulbeniales.[2] In such Laboulbeniales the two nuclei divide conjugately, one pair of daughter nuclei migrating into an ascus budded off from the ascogenic cell, the other pair remaining in the ascogenic cell. This may be repeated several times. In the Laboulbeniales where ascus development has been studied,[2] the two nuclei in a young ascus unite with each other, and the fusion nucleus divides and redivides to form eight daughter nuclei. According to the genus, there is a formation of an ascospore about each nucleus or about four nuclei only. *S. baeri* is of the latter type.

ORDER CLAVICEPTALES

The Claviceptales include a number of genera whose mycelium forms a more or less pseudoparenchymatous cushion (stroma) of a soft texture, and one in which asci are formed within numerous perithecium-like cavities that are without a peridium but have an ostiole. These genera are usually placed in a single family, the Claviceptaceae, but opinion differs as to whether it should be placed in a separate order,[3] or referred to the Sphaeriales[4] or to the Hypocreales.[5]

The type genus, *Claviceps*, is parasitic on the ovaries of various Gramineae. During the course of development of the fungus, the ovary is replaced by a dark-colored compacted mass of fungus tissue, the **sclerotium** (Fig. 261*A*). The sclerotium of *Claviceps* is called **ergot.** There are a dozen or more species, the most important of which is *C. purpurea* (Fries) Tul., parasitic on rye and on several wild grasses. *C. purpurea* rarely causes an appreciable diminution in the yield of rye. On the other hand, a relative small percentage of ergot bodies in the harvested grain produces a serious physiological disease, known as **ergotism,** when the grain is used as food by man or domestic animals. Ergotism was fairly common among the people of Europe during the Middle Ages, but it has been greatly diminished in recent times on account of the introduction of modern methods of milling grain. Even today ergotism has not completely disappeared, and within the past quarter century there have been epidemics of ergotism in France and in Russia. Epidemics of ergotism among animals are chiefly in cattle grazing on grasslands badly infected with *Claviceps*. Ergot is an officially recognized drug that is used as an

[1] Thaxter, 1896. [2] Faull, 1911, 1912. [3] Gäumann, 1949, 1952.
[4] Miller, 1949. [5] G. W. Martin, 1950.

abortifacient and to control hemorrhage during childbirth. The active ingredients in ergot are alkaloids.

Infection of the host takes place only at the time of flowering and the region of infection seems to be restricted to the pistil. Hyphal branches developing from the spore soon invade and destroy the ovule, replacing it with a soft mycelial mass of much the same shape. The peripheral portion of the mycelial mass becomes greatly convoluted and there is a development of a palisade-like layer of short conidiophores over the entire surface.[1] Minute ovoid uninucleate conidia are cut off in acropetalous succession at the tip of each conidiophore (Fig. 260). These constitute the sphacelia stage in the life history, so-called because the conidia were once considered an imperfect fungus, *Sphacelia segetum* Lév. The conidia accumulate in a sweetish liquid exuding from the spikelet. This liquid, "honeydew," is eaten greedily by various insects, and there may be a certain amount of reinfection as an insect travels from flower to flower and plant to plant. The conidia remain viable during the winter[2] so that it is possible for them to infect flowers developed the next summer. Eventually the basal region of the hyphal mass ceases to produce conidia and develops into a densely compacted dark-colored tissue. This is followed by a progressively upward metamorphosis into compact tissue until the whole mycelium has been changed into a sclerotium that is capped with remnants of the sphacelial tissue. Mature sclerotia are considerably longer and broader than the normal grains in panicles of the Gramineae.

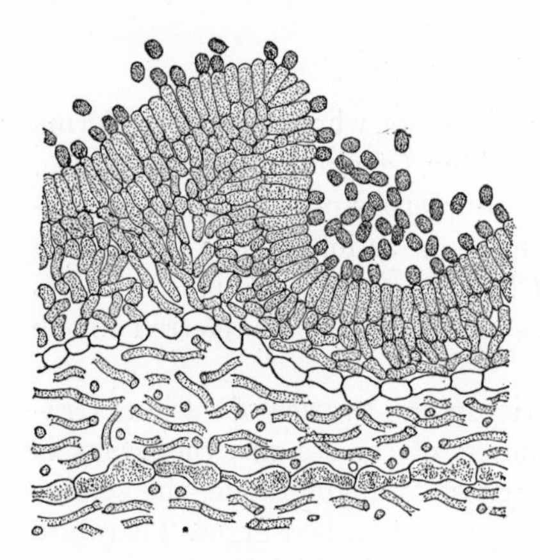

FIG. 260. Sphacelial stage of *Claviceps purpurea* (Fries) Tul. (× 650.)

Maturation of sclerotia coincides with ripening of the grains in a panicle. Some of the sclerotia on a panicle of rye fall to the ground; others become intermingled with the grain when rye is harvested and threshed. These may be returned to the same field or to other fields when a new crop of rye is sown. Sclerotia may also be dispersed by other agencies than man. In certain grasses the sterile portions of an infected flower mature into the barbed awns that effect a dispersal of normally developed grains of the species. Sclerotia of most grasses sink in water.[2] Those of grasses growing in marshes or along the banks of streams are often buoyant in water and thus may be transported some distance from the plant on which they developed.

[1] Tulasne, 1853. [2] Stäger, 1912.

Overwintering sclerotia that have not lost too much moisture produce perithecia the next spring. The relation between water content and viability becomes quite evident when sclerotia are brought into the laboratory. Sclerotia placed on moist sand soon after they are brought into the laboratory eventually germinate; those kept air-dry until spring and then placed on moist sand rarely germinate. A germinating sclerotium produces a half dozen or more small capitate outgrowths borne on stalks 10 to 20 mm. long (Fig. 261*B*). The capitate portion (stroma) of each out-

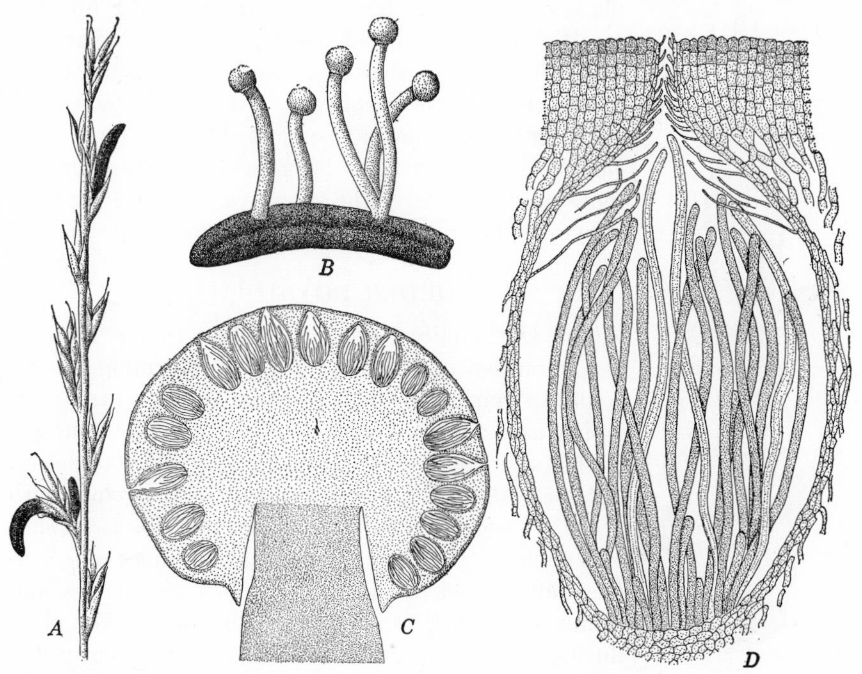

FIG. 261. *Claviceps purpurea* (Fries) Tul. *A*, panicle of *Agropyron repens* (L.) Beauv. with sclerotia of *Claviceps*. *B*, germinating sclerotium. *C*, vertical section of a fertile head. *D*, semidiagrammatic vertical section of a locule. (*A*, natural size; *B*, × 4; *C*, × 60; *D*, × 480.)

growth contains many perithecia (Fig. 261*C*). Certain branched hyphae somewhat below the surface of a stroma produce the sex organs. These hyphae may be distinguished from others on account of their richer protoplasmic content.[1] Antheridia and ascogonia are produced on the same hypha, each developing from the terminal cell of a lateral branch. Cells developing into sex organs soon become multinucleate, and those developing into ascogonia become broader than those developing into antheridia. An ascogonium develops a small lateral outgrowth that becomes applied to an antheridium. The cell walls dissolve in the region of mu-

[1] Killian, 1919.

tual contact, and the nuclei of the antheridium migrate into the ascogonium.[1] Ascogenous hyphae then grow from the ascogonium, and asci are formed at the tips of ascogenous hyphae bent into typical croziers.

The asci are produced in perithecia so deeply sunken in adjoining stromatic tissue that only the opening (the ostiole) protrudes. Each ascus contains eight elongate acicular ascospores that lie parallel to one another (Fig. 261*D*). The ascospores are forcibly discharged from an ascus, but this takes place only when a perithecium is vertically upright. At the time of spore discharge the stalk below the fertile head slowly twists and turns. As a result, every perithecium of the stroma is vertically upright for a short time.[2] Ascospores are ejected with a force sufficient to hurl them 20 to 80 mm.[3] Convection air currents may then carry the spores to the flowering head of rye, or the spores may be transported some distance by winds.

FIG. 262. A young branch of a cherry tree infected with *Plowrightia morbosa* (Schw.) Sacc. (× ¾.)

ORDER DOTHIDIALES

The Dothidiales have a mycelium that is more or less immersed in the substratum and forming a dark-colored stroma with one to many cavities (locules) in which asci are produced. According to one concept[4] of the order there are some 150 genera and 700 species.

Plowrightia (*Dibotryon*) is a parasitic genus with about 25 species. The best known of these is *P. morbosa* (Schw.) Sacc., the fungus that produces conspicuous galls (black knot) on branches of cherries and plums (Fig. 262). Infection of the host takes place during the spring and upon twigs of the current year's growth or upon those not over two or three years old. The mycelium does not produce spores until the following year. During the first year the cambial cells in an infected area of the host divide more rapidly than those in uninfected portions.[5] Only a relatively few of the cambial derivatives cut off toward the internal face of the cambium mature into wood. On the other hand, there is an increased production of parenchyma internal to the cambium and opposite wood rays more than one cell broad (multiseriate rays). The portion of each multiseriate ray formed after infection is very much broader and has the

[1] Killian, 1919. [2] Whetzel and Reddick, 1911. [3] Falck, 1910.
[4] G. W. Martin, 1950. [5] Stewart, 1914.

appearance of a compound ray. At the end of the first growing season the infected portion of a branch or twig is externally recognizable as a slight swelling.

When the host resumes growth the next spring, there is a very rapid swelling of the diseased area. The overlying bark soon ruptures and hyphae growing from the exposed cortex begin to develop into a dense pseudoparenchymatous tissue. The whole surface of this tissue becomes

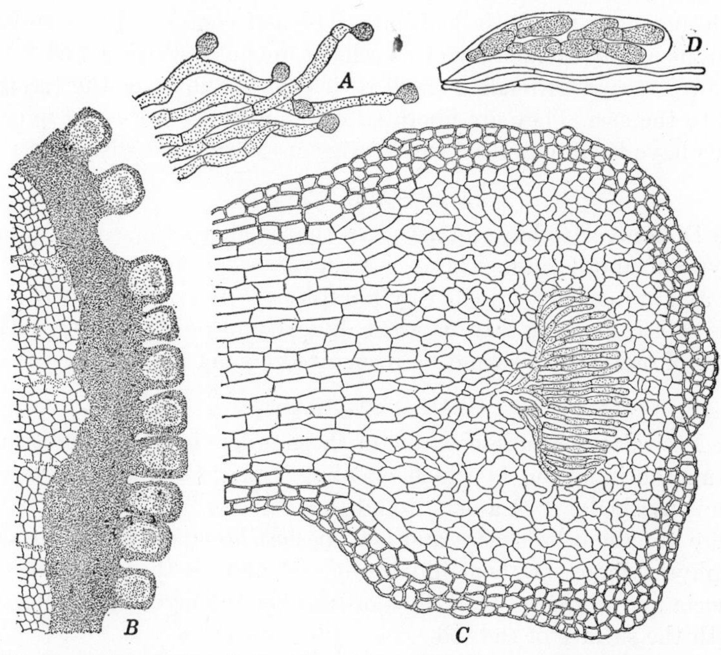

FIG. 263. *Plowrightia morbosa* (Schw.) Sacc. *A*, conidia. *B*, transverse section of a stroma bearing young locules. *C*, vertical section of a young locule in which there are sterile paraphyses in the region where asci will be formed. *D*, ascus. (*A*, *D*, × 650; *B*, × 30; *C*, × 325.)

covered with a velvety layer of simple or branched septate filaments. These are conidiophores, and at or near the tip of each of them there are one or more small ovoid conidia[1] (Fig. 263*A*). Conidia inoculated onto other individuals of the host produce typical infections.[2] The velvety layer of conidiophores disappears toward midsummer, and the underlying dense mycelial tissue becomes dead black and of a hard, brittle texture.

There is considerable uncertainty as to whether asexual reproduction by conidia is followed by a formation of pycnospores. Three types of pycnidia have been found[3] in the black stroma of *P. morbosa*, but at least one of these belongs to a saprophytic or parasitic fungus growing on the

[1] Farlow, 1876; Humphrey, 1891. [2] Gilbert, 1913. [3] Farlow, 1876.

stroma. On the other hand, there has been a production of pycnidia in cultures of a mycelium derived from the germination of an ascospore.[1]

After the disappearance of the conidiophores there is a formation of numerous rounded outgrowths on the surface of the stroma (Fig. 263*B–C*). The details of their development have not been followed, but it is known that they contain cavities in which asci are formed during the winter following their appearance. These outgrowths are sometimes called perithecia but their designation as such is open to question since they do not have a definite peridium. The asci contain eight ascospores, each transversely divided into two cells of unequal size (Fig. 263*D*). The ascospores escape through a small ostiole at the apex of the tissue external to the asci. They are liberated early in the spring and typical infections have been obtained[2] when twigs are inoculated with ascospores.

DISCOMYCETES

The Discomycetes have an ascocarp that is an apothecium or a modified type of apothecium. The asci are cylindrical, lie in a palisade-like layer, and are usually adjoined by paraphyses. As is the case with other groups of ascomycetes there is great diversity of opinion concerning the number of orders that should be recognized among the discomycetes.

ORDER PEZIZALES

The Pezizales are representative of those orders in which the ascocarp is an apothecium, and in which opening of asci for liberation of ascospores is by shedding of a definite lid (operculum).

There are about 60 genera and 500 species. Members of this order are saprophytic, many of them inhabiting soil and all these forming their apothecia above ground regardless of whether the mycelium grows at or beneath the surface of the soil.

Pyronema, with two or three species, is terrestrial and usually found on soil that has been burned over. Sometimes it is to be found in greenhouses or in seedbeds where the soil has been sterilized by steam.[3] The mycelium grows superficially on the soil and in the form of a white cottony layer. It is profusely branched and the hyphae are composed of relatively short cells, each with 6 to 12 nuclei.[4] There is no regular production of asexual spores, but certain erect hyphae of a mycelium may form chains of oïdia.[5]

The production of antheridia and ascogonia on a mycelium developed from a single ascospore shows that the mycelium is homothallic.[6] When cultured in the laboratory the two most important factors in inducing a formation of sex organs are light and a mechanical checking of increase

[1] Humphrey, 1891. [2] Gilbert, 1913. [3] Seaver, 1909.
[4] Claussen, 1912; Harper, 1900. [5] L. R. and C. Tulasne, 1865.
[6] Gwynne-Vaughan and Williamson, 1931; Robinson, 1926; Wilson, 1952.

in area of the mycelium.[1] At the time sex organs are formed a mycelium sends up short erect dichotomously branched hyphae two to four cells in height. The multinucleate terminal cell of one dichotomy develops into an antheridium and the multinucleate terminal cell of the other dichot-

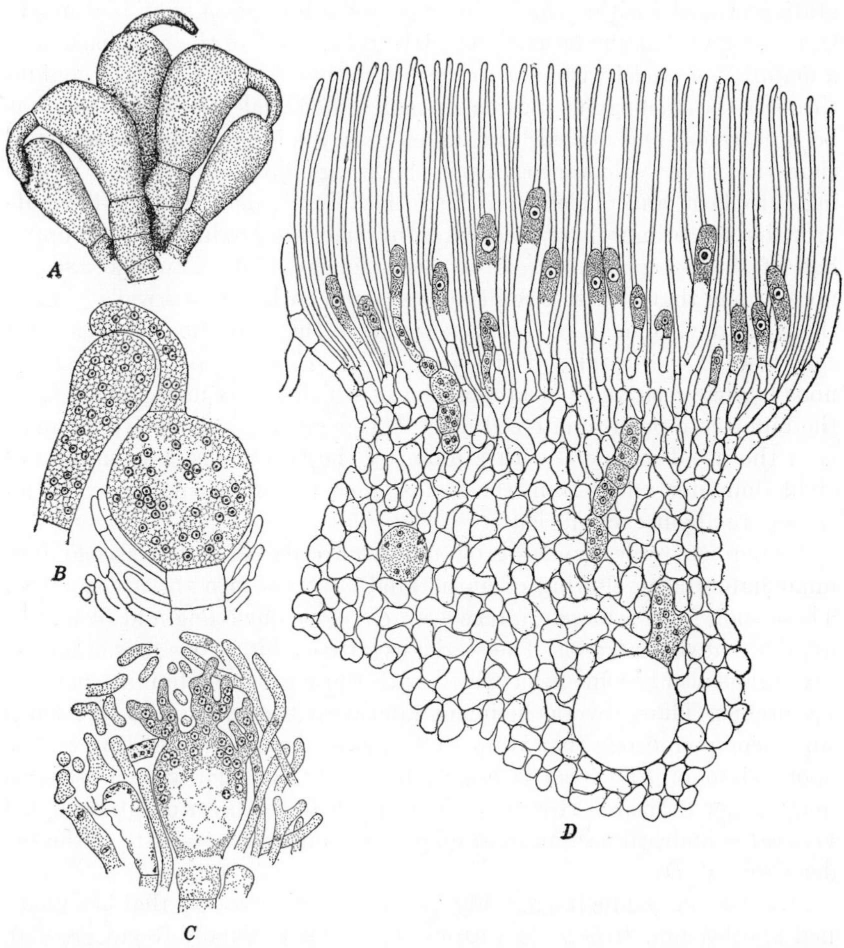

FIG. 264. *Pyronema confluens* (Pers.) Tul. *A*, surface view of a cluster of sex organs. *B*, vertical section of an apposed antheridium and ascogonium. *C*, vertical section of an ascogonium with young ascogenous hyphae. *D*, diagrammatic vertical section of a young ascocarp. (*C, after Gwynne-Vaughan and Williamson,* 1931.) (*A–B*, × 650; *C*, × 500; *D*, × 485.)

omy develops into an ascogonium (Fig. 264*A*). Cells developing into antheridia become club-shaped and their nuclei divide and redivide until there are a hundred or more. Those developing into ascogonia become subglobose and also come to contain a hundred or more nuclei. A devel-

[1] Kerl, 1937; Robinson, 1926; Wilson, 1952.

oping ascogonium produces a curved tubular apical outgrowth (trichogyne) whose tip grows toward and becomes applied to the upper end of an antheridium (Fig. 264*B*). This is followed by a dissolution of cell walls in the region of contact between trichogyne and antheridium, a disintegration of nuclei within the trichogyne, and a formation of an incomplete transverse wall at the base of the trichogyne. Most of the cytoplasm and a majority of nuclei within an antheridium then flow into the ascogonium through the trichogyne. Fusion of male and female nuclei in pairs has been affirmed[1] and denied,[2] but taken as a whole the evidence seems to show that there is no karyogamy in the ascogonium. Shortly after receiving cytoplasm and nuclei from the antheridium numerous knob-like outgrowths, the primordia of ascogenous hyphae, are produced on the upper half of the ascogonium. Each of them elongates into a tubular ascogenous hypha that at first is multinucleate and without cross walls.[3] Later, there is a development of transverse walls in the ascogenous hyphae, and cells toward the distal end of them are binucleate. Tips of the ascogenous hyphae recurve to form a crozier in which the ascus is formed from the binucleate penultimate cell (Fig. 243, page 428). Ascus development is in the usual manner—with a union of the two nuclei, a formation of eight daughter nuclei from the fusion nucleus, and a cutting out of an ascospore about each nucleus.

Numerous sterile hyphae grow out from cells below the ascogonium immediately after flowing of antheridial contents into the ascogonium. These soon form a loosely interwoven envelope encircling and overarching the united sex organs. The sterile hyphae enclosing one pair of united sex organs also become intertwined with those around adjoining pairs of sex organs. Thus, several incipient apothecia become united to form a single compound one that is up to 2 mm. in diameter at maturity. The apothecium of *Pyronema* is not so markedly cup-shaped as is that in many other Pezizales. However, the concave fertile layer of intermingled vertical cylindrical asci and paraphyses is quite characteristic of the order (Fig. 264*D*).

Helvella, the saddle fungus (Fig. 265*A*), has an ascocarp that is a modified apothecium. *Helvella* is a saprophyte that is usually found growing in soil, but it is sometimes found on decaying wood. The mycelium is subterranean and composed of many loosely interwoven multicellular hyphae in which each cell contains 2 to 16 nuclei.[4] The mycelium of *Helvella* has never been found producing asexual spores, but that of a closely related genus has been found bearing conidia.[5]

[1] Gwynne-Vaughan and Williamson, 1931; Harper, 1900; Tandy, 1927.
[2] Claussen, 1912; Dangeard, 1907; Hirsch, 1950; Moreau and Moreau, 1930.
[3] Claussen, 1912; Gwynne-Vaughan and Williamson, 1931; Wilson, 1952.
[4] McCubbin, 1910. [5] Molliard, 1904.

Ascocarps are formed in greatest abundance during the spring but there is also some fruiting of the fungus throughout the summer. Young ascocarps are subterranean, but, as they grow older, they push up through the soil and the above-ground portion eventually attains a height of 2 to 8 cm. The portion of the mycelium developing into an ascocarp is composed of hyphae that are shorter, thicker, and more profusely branched than other hyphae.[1] When an ascocarp is less than 1 mm. tall it consists of a stout stem terminating in a globose cap (Fig. 265*B–C*) and is without any internal differentiation of tissues. Soon there is a formation of a palisade-like layer of hyphae at the apex of the cap. Certain of the hyphae grow out beyond the palisade layer and become a thin overlying layer that disappears as the cap develops further. The palisade region of a cap grows more rapidly than does the region internal to it. As a result,

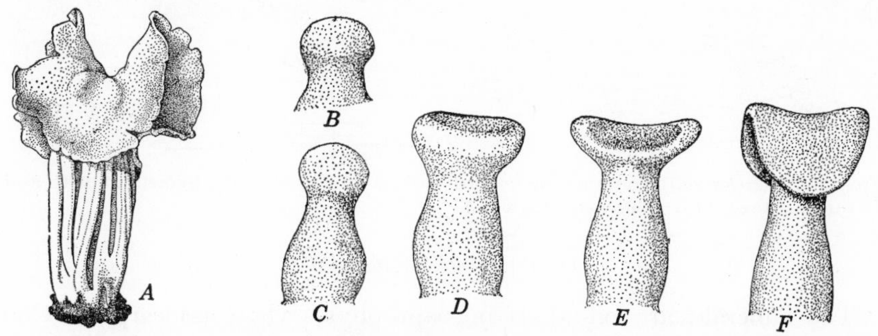

FIG. 265. *A*, mature ascocarp of *Helvella crispa* Fries. *B–F*, *H. elastica* Bull., early stages in development of an ascocarp. (*B–F*, *after McCubbin*, 1910.) (*A*, × ½; *B–E*, × 5½; *F*, × 3½.)

the cap soon assumes the saddle shape characteristic of the mature ascocarp (Fig. 265*D–F*).

Ascogonia have never been found in association with development of ascocarps of *Helvella*. Somatogamy (see page 425) has been recorded for *Helvella*[2] and for the closely related *Morchella*.[3] This occurs between cells of hyphae just below the palisade layer, and from these cells there is a development of hyphae in which the nuclei lie in pairs and divide conjugately. These hyphae lie in a matted web parallel to and a short distance below the palisade layer.[4] They have a breadth twice to three times that of other hyphae in the area. Erect branched hyphae (ascogenous hyphae) grow upward from them to the palisade layer, and the tips of the ascogenous hyphae become recurved to form croziers in which the penultimate binucleate cell develops into an ascus.[3] The two nuclei in a young ascus fuse and the fusion nucleus divides into eight daughter nuclei. An

[1] Molliard, 1904. [2] Carruthers, 1911; McCubbin, 1910. [3] Greis, 1940.
[4] McCubbin, 1910.

ascospore is delimited about each nucleus, and the eight ascospores thus formed lie in a linear series within an ascus (Fig. 266).

There is an explosive discharge of ascospores when they are liberated from an ascus and the period of spore discharge may last for several days because all asci do not mature at the same time. *Helvella* is one of the ascomycetes in which "puffing" of ascospores has been observed, and where discharge of ascospores is accompanied by a distinctly audible hissing sound.[1]

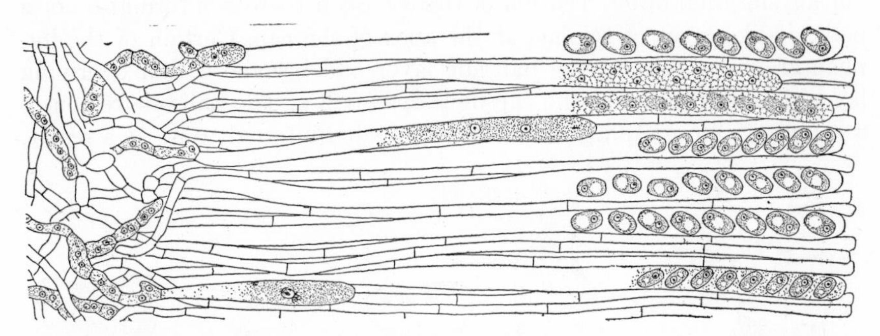

FIG. 266. *Helvella* sp. Diagrammatic vertical section of a portion of a hymenium with asci at various stages of development. (× 325.)

ORDER TUBERALES

The Tuberales are soil-inhabiting saprophytes whose ascocarps develop to maturity beneath the surface of the soil. Mature ascocarps do not have freely exposed asci but have them in a palisade-like layer (**hymenium**) that may surround a central cavity within an ascocarp, or may lie in irregular folds that completely fill the central cavity. The order contains some 30 genera and 140 species.

Several genera are of widespread distribution in the Mediterranean area of Europe. The Pacific Coast states are the region in this country where Tuberales have been found in greatest abundance. Truffles, the most highly esteemed of all edible fleshy fungi, include certain species of the genus *Tuber*, especially *T. melanosporum* Vittard. The gathering of truffles for the market is a regular industry in France and Italy, and in France the crop for the year 1949 was valued[2] at more than half a million dollars. Truffles are not evident to those searching for them because their ascocarps lie 10 to 30 cm. below the surface of the soil. Truffles have a very characteristic odor and the professional collector for the market trains pigs or dogs to scent out places where there are truffles growing in the soil. The collector digs up the truffles after the animal has found a place where they are growing. In this country truffles have not been

[1] DeBary, 1887. [2] France, Ministère de l'Agriculture, 1951.

found in sufficient abundance to make collecting of them commercially profitable.

The thallus of *Tuber* is a colorless subterranean mycelium composed of numerous branching hyphae consisting of very short uninucleate cells. The hyphae may run in all directions or may lie parallel to one another in thick strands (**rhizomorphs**). The mycelium of *T. melanosporum* seems to be a mycorhizal symbiont with roots of various trees; especially oaks

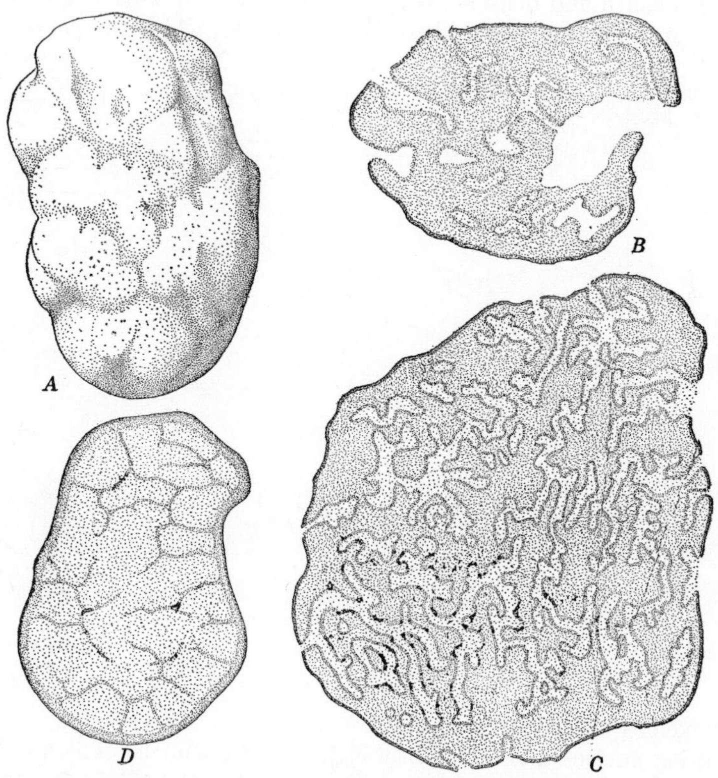

FIG. 267. *Tuber candidum* Harkn. *A*, surface view of a mature ascocarp. *B–C*, sections of young ascocarps. *D*, vertical section of a mature ascocarp. (*A*, × 2; *B–C*, × 9; *D*, × 3.)

and beeches.[1] Mycelia of certain other species, including *T. candidum* Harkn., are true saprophytes.

Young ascocarps have an early differentiation of the parallel multicellular paraphyses of the hymenial layer. This layer is irregularly folded and the folding becomes more pronounced as development continues (Fig. 267*B–D*). In *T. candidum* formation of the hymenium seems to be preceded by a localized pulling away from one another of hyphae within the ascocarp. Many hyphae then grow toward each cavity thus formed

[1] Dangeard, 1894.

and become arranged in a palisade-like layer encircling it. Ascogonia have not been found in developing ascocarps and sexual reproduction is by somatogamy (see page 425). The production of ascogenous hyphae is preceded by anastomoses between uninucleate intercalary cells of two hyphae. The nuclei in the binucleate cells thus formed divide conjugately and the cells give rise to ascogenous hyphae with binucleate cells.[1] Ascogenous hyphae below the hymenial layer may be recognized by their greater breadth and denser protoplasts (Fig. 268*A*). Tips of the ascogenous hyphae become recurved to form croziers in which the penultimate

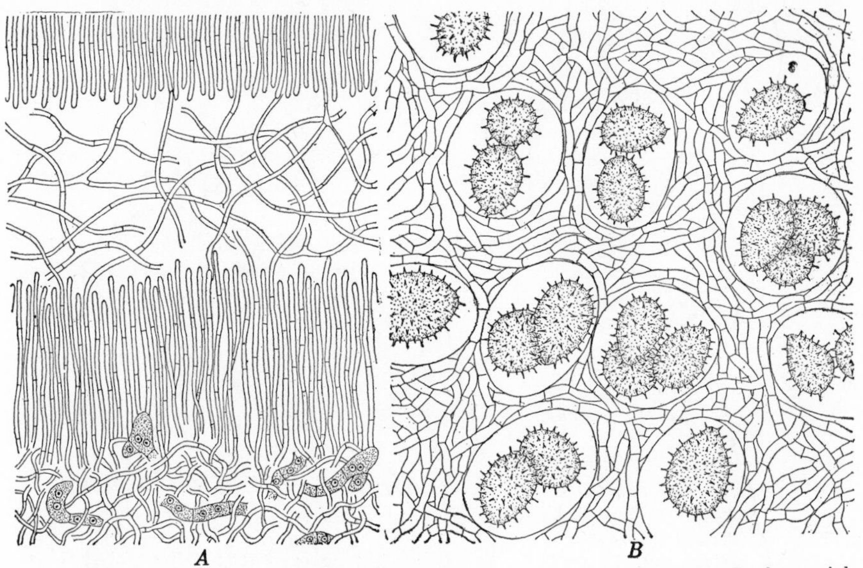

Fig. 268. *Tuber candidum* Harkn. *A*, young ascogenous hyphae beneath the hymenial layer. *B*, portion of the fertile region of a mature ascocarp. (*A*, × 650; *B*, × 430.)

cell develops into an ascus.[2] The two nuclei in a young ascus unite and the fusion nucleus divides to form eight daughter nuclei. The number of ascospores formed within an ascus is usually less than eight, because ascospores are cut out around only certain of the nuclei (Fig. 269). Mature ascospores of *Tuber* have the spore wall ornamented with spines or with reticulations (Fig. 268*B*).

A mature ascocarp (Fig. 267*A*) is more or less globose, has a smooth or warty surface, and is rarely more than 8 cm. in diameter. The outer portion of an ascocarp is composed of sterile thick-walled cells. This portion, the cortex, is derived in part from the outer region of a young ascocarp and in part from the ascogenous tissue. An ascocarp remains unopened after it is fully mature, and the ascospores are liberated only by a decay

[1] Greis, 1938, 1939. [2] Greis, 1938*A*, 1939; Schussnig, 1921.

of the cortex. Spore dispersal may be effected through the agency of animals, especially rodents. In California, certain of the Tuberales are a favorite food of wood rats[1] who detect them by means of their very characteristic odor. An ascocarp dug up by a rat may be eaten on the spot or may be carried to its burrow. In either case, crumbs falling on the ground may inoculate the soil. Spore dispersal may also be effected by undigested ascospores passing through the alimentary tract of an animal that has eaten an ascocarp.[2]

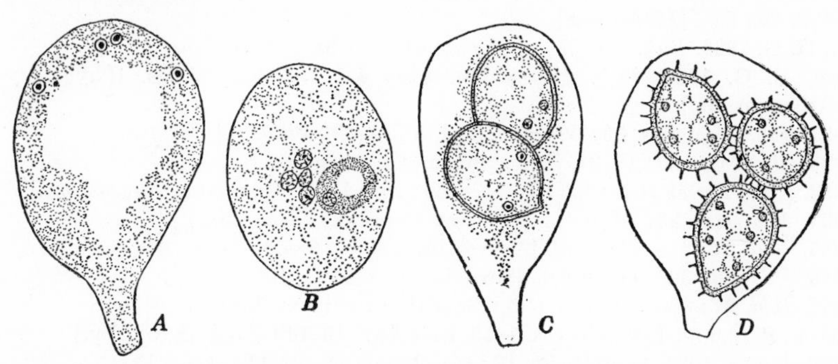

FIG. 269. *Tuber candidum* Harkn. *A*, young ascus. *B*, ascus just after delimitation of an ascospore. *C–D*, young and mature ascospores. (× 650.)

Bibliography

Ainsworth, G. C., and G. R. Bisby. **1950.** A dictionary of the fungi. Kew. 445 pp. 105 figs.

Alexopoulos, C. A. **1952.** Introductory mycology. New York. 482 pp. 187 figs.

Allen, Ruth F. **1936.** *Jour. Agr. Res.* **53:** 801–818. 7 pl. [*Erysiphe.*]

Ames, L. M. **1934.** *Mycologia* **26:** 392–414. 6 figs. [Physiological heterothallism.]

Atkinson, G. F. **1915.** *Ann. Missouri Bot. Gard.* **2:** 315–376. 10 figs. [Phylogeny of Ascomycetae.]

Backus, M. P. **1939.** *Bull. Torrey Bot. Club* **66:** 63–76. 4 pl. 1 fig. [*Neurospora.*]

Baker, Gladys E. **1944.** *Ibid.* **71:** 367–373. 10 figs. [*Penicillium.*]

Beatus, R. **1948.** *Zeitschr. Naturf.* **3B:** 42–51. 7 figs. [Erysiphales.]

1950. *Arch. Microbiol.* **15:** 253–269. [*Erysiphe.*]

Benjamin, R. K., and L. Shanor. **1952.** *Amer. Jour. Bot.* **39:** 125–131. 19 figs. [Laboulbeniales.]

Bergman, B. **1941.** *Svensk. Bot. Tidsskr.* **35:** 194–210. 3 figs. [Erysiphales.]

Bessey, E. A. **1914.** *Mycol. Centralbl.* **3:** 149–153. [Phylogeny of Ascomycetae.]

1925. *Papers Mich. Acad. Sci.* **4:** 67–80. 1 fig. [Phylogeny of Ascomycetae.]

1935. A text-book of mycology. Philadelphia. 495 pp. 139 figs.

1942. *Mycologia* **34:** 355–379. 5 figs. [Phylogeny of fungi.]

1950. Morphology and taxonomy of fungi. Philadelphia. 791 pp. 210 figs.

Biggs, Rosemary. **1937.** *Mycologia* **29:** 34–44. 50 figs. [*Dipodascus.*]

Blakeslee, A. F. **1904.** *Proc. Amer. Acad. Arts and Sci.* **40:** 205–319. 4 pl. [Sexuality.]

Buller, A. H. R. **1941.** *Bot. Rev.* **7:** 335–431. [Heterokaryosis.]

Carruthers, D. **1911.** *Ann. Bot.* **25:** 243–252. 2 pl. [*Helvella.*]

Claussen, P. **1912.** *Zeitschr. Bot.* **4:** 1–64. 6 pl. 13 figs. [*Pyronema.*]

[1] Parks, 1919. [2] Massee, 1909.

Coker, W. C., and Louise Wilson. **1911.** *Mycologia* **3:** 283–287. 1 pl. 2 figs. [*Schizosaccharomyces.*]
Colson, Barbara. **1934.** *Ann. Bot.* **48:** 211–224. 2 pl. 8 figs. [*Neurospora.*]
Dangeard, P. A. **1894.** *Le Botaniste* **4:** 61–87. 7 figs. [*Tuber.*]
1907. *Ibid.* **10:** 1–385. 91 pl. 10 figs. [*Dipodascus, Penicillium.*]
DeBary, A. **1887.** Comparative morphology and biology of the Fungi, Mycetozoa and Bacteria. Translated by H. E. F. Garnsey. Oxford. 525 pp. 198 figs.
DeLamater, E. D. **1950.** *Jour. Bact.* **60:** 321–332. 3 figs. [*Saccharomyces.*]
1952. *Science* **115:** 425. [*Eremascus.*]
DeLamater, E. D., S. Yaverbaum, and L. Schwartz. **1953.** *Amer. Jour. Bot.* **40:** 475–492. 209 figs. [*Eremascus.*]
Derx, H. G. **1925.** *Bull. Soc. Mycol. France* **41:** 373–381. [*Penicillium.*]
Dodge, B. O. **1914.** *Bull. Torrey Bot. Club* **41:** 157–202. 13 figs. [Phylogeny of Ascomycetae.]
1927. *Jour. Agr. Res.* **35:** 289–305. 3 pl. 5 figs. [*Neurospora.*]
1928. *Mycologia* **20:** 18–21. [Development of ascospores.]
1932. *Bull. Torrey Bot. Club* **59:** 347–359. 2 pl. 1 fig. [Spermatia, *Neurospora.*]
1933. *Mycologia* **25:** 90–104. 2 pl. 2 figs. [Ascocarp, *Penicillium.*]
1935. *Ibid.* **27:** 418–438. 4 pl. [*Neurospora.*]
1936. *Ibid.* **28:** 399–409. 2 figs. [Sexuality.]
1945. *Ibid.* **37:** 360–369, 629–635, 784–791. 1 fig. [Sexuality.]
Drayton, F. L., and J. W. Groves. **1952.** *Ibid.* **44:** 119–140. 8 figs. [Sexuality.]
Eftimu, Panca. **1927.** *Le Botaniste* **18:** 1–152. 3 pl. 38 figs. [*Taphrina.*]
1929. *Bull. Soc. Bot. France* **76:** 10–20. 2 pl. [*Erysiphe.*]
Emmons, C. W. **1935.** *Mycologia* **27:** 128–150. 16 figs. [Ascocarp, *Penicillium.*]
Falck, R. **1910.** *Zeitschr. Forst. u. Jagdw.* **43:** 202–227. [*Claviceps.*]
Farlow, W. G. **1876.** *Bull. Bussey Inst.* **1:** 440–454. 3 pl. [*Plowrightia.*]
Faull, J. H. **1911.** *Ann. Bot.* **25:** 649–654. [Laboulbeniales.]
1912. *Ibid.* **26:** 325–355. 4 pl. [Laboulbeniales.]
Fitzpatrick, H. M. **1930.** The lower fungi—Phycomycetes. New York. 331 pp. 112 figs.
Fitzpatrick, R. E. **1934.** *Scientific Agr.* **14:** 305–326. 10 figs. [*Taphrina.*]
France, Ministère de l'Agriculture. **1951.** Statistique agricole anuelle. 1949. Paris. 177 pp.
Gäumann, E. **1949.** Die Pilze. Basel. 382 pp. 440 figs.
1952. The Fungi. Translated by F. L. Wynd. New York. 420 pp. 440 figs.
Gäumann, E. A., and C. W. Dodge. **1928.** Comparative morphology of fungi. Translated and revised by C. W. Dodge. New York. 701 pp. 406 figs.
Gilbert, E. M. **1913.** *Phytopathology* **3:** 246–247. [*Plowrightia.*]
Greis, H. **1938.** *Biol. Zentralbl.* **58:** 617–632. 3 figs. [*Tuber.*]
1938A. *Jahrb. Wiss. Bot.* **86:** 81–106. 3 figs. [*Tuber.*]
1939. *Zeitschr. Bot.* **34:** 129–178. 3 pl. [*Tuber.*]
1940. *Jahrb. Wiss. Bot.* **89:** 244–253. 3 figs. [Helvellales.]
Guilliermond, A. **1903.** *Rev. Gén. Bot.* **15:** 49–66, 104–124, 166–185. 9 pl. 30 figs. [Saccharomycetaceae.]
1905. *Ibid.* **17:** 337–376. 4 pl. 11 figs. [Saccharomycetaceae.]
1909. *Ibid.* **21:** 353–391, 401–419. 8 pl. 33 figs. [*Eremascus.*]
1928. *Ibid.* **40:** 328–342, 397–414, 474–485, 555–574, 607–624, 690–704. 12 pl. 46 figs. [Phylogeny of Ascomycetae.]
1931. *Ibid.* **43:** 49–86. 6 pl. 10 figs. [Saccharomycetaceae.]
Gwynne-Vaughan, H. C. I., and B. Barnes. **1927.** The structure and development of the fungi. Cambridge. 384 pp. 285 figs.

Gwynne-Vaughan, H. C. I., and H. S. Williamson. **1930.** *Ann. Bot.* **44:** 127–145. 2 pl. 10 figs. [Pezizales.]
1931. *Ibid.* **45:** 355–371. 3 pl. 7 figs. [*Pyronema.*]
Hansen, H. N., and W. C. Snyder. **1943.** *Amer. Jour. Bot.* **30:** 419–422. 3 figs. [Sexuality.]
Harper, R. A. **1896.** *Jahrb. Wiss. Bot.* **29:** 655–685. 2 pl. [Development of asci.]
1897. *Ibid.* **30:** 249–284. 2 pl. [Development of asci.]
1900. *Ann. Bot.* **14:** 321–400. 3 pl. [*Pyronema.*]
1905. *Carnegie Inst. Wash. Publ.* **37:** 1–104. 7 pl. [Erysiphales.]
Harrold, C. E. **1950.** *Ann. Bot.* N. S. **14:** 127–148. 2 pl. 10 figs. [*Eremascus.*]
Hein, I. **1927.** *Bull. Torrey Bot. Club* **54:** 383–417. 2 pl. 5 figs. [Erysiphales.]
Hirsch, Hilde E. **1949.** *Amer. Jour. Bot.* **36:** 113–121. 11 figs. [Sexuality.]
1950. *Mycologia* **42:** 301–305. 6 figs. [*Pyronema.*]
Humphrey, J. E. **1891.** *Ann. Rept. Mass. Agr. Exper. Sta.* **8:** 200–210. 1 pl. [*Plowrightia.*]
Jackson, H. S. **1944.** *Trans. Roy. Soc. Canada* 3 ser. Sec. 5, **38:** 1–32. 5 figs. [Phylogeny of fungi.]
Juel, H. O. **1902.** *Flora* **91:** 47–55. 2 pl. [*Dipodascus.*]
1921. *Nova Acta Reg. Soc. Sci. Upsaliensis* 4 ser. **5,** No. 5: 1–43. 2 pl. 4 figs. [*Taphrina.*]
Kerl, Imgard. **1937.** *Zeitschr. Bot.* **31:** 129–174. 7 figs. [*Pyronema.*]
Killian, K. **1919.** *Bull. Soc. Mycol. France* **35:** 182–197. 8 pl. [*Claviceps.*]
Lagerheim, G. **1892.** *Jahrb. Wiss. Bot.* **24:** 549–565. 3 pl. [*Dipodascus.*]
Lewis, I. M. **1911.** *Bot. Gaz.* **51:** 369–373. 1 pl. [Many-spored asci.]
Lindegren, C. C. **1949.** The yeast cell, its genetics and cytology. St. Louis. 358 pp. 132 figs.
Lodder, J., and N. J. W. Kreger-Van Rij. **1952.** The yeasts. Amsterdam. 713 pp. 268 figs.
McCubbin, W. A. **1910.** *Bot. Gaz.* **49:** 195–206. 3 pl. 1 fig. [*Helvella.*]
Martin, Ella M. **1924.** *Trans. Wis. Acad.* **21:** 345–356. 2 pl. [*Taphrina.*]
1940. *Amer. Jour. Bot.* **27:** 743–751. 49 figs. [*Taphrina.*]
Martin, G. W. **1950.** Outline of the Fungi. Dubuque, Iowa. 82 pp. 116 figs.
Massee, G. **1909.** *Ann. Bot.* **23:** 243–263. 1 pl. [Tuberales.]
Miller, J. H. **1949.** *Mycologia* **41:** 99–127. 37 figs. [Classification.]
Mix, A. J. **1935.** *Phytopathology* **25:** 41–66. 6 figs. [*Taphrina.*]
1939. *Mycologia* **31:** 445–454. 2 figs. [*Taphrina.*]
1949. *Univ. Kansas Sci. Bull.* **33:** 3–167. 39 figs. [*Taphrina.*]
Molliard, M. **1904.** *Rev. Gén. Bot.* **16:** 209–218. 1 pl. [Helvellales.]
Moreau, F., and Mme. Moreau. **1930.** *Ibid.* **42:** 65–98. 7 pl. [Development of ascocarp.]
Nannfeldt, J. A. **1932.** *Nova Acta Reg. Soc. Sci. Upsaliensis.* 4 ser. **8:** 1–368. 19 pl. 47 figs. [Classification.]
Olive, L. S. **1950.** *Amer. Jour. Bot.* **37:** 757–763. 33 figs. [Brachymeiosis.]
Overton, J. B. **1906.** *Bot. Gaz.* **42:** 451–492. 2 pl. [Many-spored asci.]
Parks, H. E. **1919.** *Mycologia* **11:** 10–21. [*Tuber.*]
Raper, K. B., and C. Thom. **1949.** A manual of the Penicillia. Baltimore. 875 pp. 9 pl. 172 figs.
Robinson, W. **1926.** *Ann. Bot.* **40:** 243–272. 4 figs. [*Pyronema.*]
Sachs, J. **1875.** Text-book of botany. Translated and annotated by A. W. Bennett and W. T. Thiselton-Dyer. Oxford. 858 pp. 460 figs.
Salmon, E. S. **1903.** *Jour. Botany* **41:** 159–165, 204–212. [*Erysiphe.*]
Sansome, Eva R. **1947.** *Genetica* **24:** 59–64. [*Neurospora.*]

Sax, Hally J. **1917.** *Amer. Jour. Bot.* **5:** 61–78. 3 pl. [Many-spored asci.]
Schönefeldt, Maria. **1935.** *Zeitschr. Indukt. Abstamm. u. Vererb.* **69:** 193–209. 23 figs. [*Neurospora.*]
Schussnig, B. **1921.** *Sitzungsber. Akad. Wiss. Wien* (Math.-Nat. Kl.) **130**[1]**:** 127–146. 1 pl. 3 figs. [*Tuber.*]
Seaver, F. J. **1909.** *Mycologia* **1:** 131–139. 4 pl. [*Pyronema.*]
Shear, C. L., and B. O. Dodge. **1927.** *Jour. Agr. Res.* **34:** 1019–1042. 4 pl. [*Neurospora.*]
Singleton, J. R. **1953.** *Amer. Jour. Bot.* **40:** 124–144. 81 figs. [*Neurospora.*]
Smith, G. **1900.** *Bot. Gaz.* **29:** 153–184. 2 pl. [*Erysiphe.*]
Stäger, R. **1912.** *Mycol. Centralbl.* **1:** 198–201. [*Claviceps.*]
Stewart, A. **1914.** *Amer. Jour. Bot.* **1:** 112–126. 2 pl. [*Plowrightia.*]
Stoppel, Rose. **1907.** *Flora* **97:** 332–346. 2 pl. 6 figs. [*Eremascus.*]
Tandy, G. **1927.** *Ann. Bot.* **41:** 321–325. 1 pl. [*Pyronema.*]
Thaxter, R. **1896.** *Mem. Amer. Acad. Arts and Sci.* N.S. **12:** 197–429. 26 pl. [*Stigmatomyces.*]
Thom, C. **1914.** *Mycologia* **6:** 211–215. 1 fig. [*Penicillium.*]
Tulasne, L. R. **1853.** *Ann. Sci. Nat. Bot.* 3 ser. **20:** 5–56. 4 pl. [*Claviceps.*]
Tulasne, L. R., and C. Tulasne. **1865.** Selecta fungorum carpologia. Vol. 3. Paris. 221 pp. 22 pl.
Wager, H., and S. Peniston. **1910.** *Ann. Bot.* **24:** 45–83. 4 pl. 1 fig. [*Saccharomyces.*]
Whetzel, H. H., and D. Reddick. **1911.** *Phytopathology* **1:** 50–52. 1 pl. [*Claviceps.*]
Whitehouse, H. L. K. **1949.** *Biol. Rev.* **24:** 411–447. [Sexuality.]
Wieben, Magdalene. **1927.** *Forschungen auf d. Gebiet d. Pflanzenkrank.* **3:** 139–176. 32 figs. [*Taphrina.*]
Wilson, Irene M. **1952.** *Ann. Bot.* N.S. **16:** 321–339. 2 pl. 19 figs. [*Pyronema.*]
Winge, O. **1911.** *Bull. Soc. Mycol. France* **27:** 211–219. 2 pl. [Erysiphales.]
1935. *Compt. Rend. Trav. Lab. Carlsberg. Ser. Physiol.* **21:** 77–111. 3 pl. 16 figs. [*Saccharomyces.*]
Wolf, F. A., and F. T. Wolf. **1947.** The Fungi. Vol. 1. New York. 438 pp. 153 figs.
Yarwood, C. E. **1935.** *Science* **82:** 417–418. [*Erysiphe.*]
Young, Elaine. **1931.** *Amer. Jour. Bot.* **18:** 499–517. 3 pl. [Aspergillales.]

CHAPTER 13

BASIDIOMYCETAE

All Basidiomycetae produce a unique type of spore, the **basidiospore,** which is borne upon a unique type of sporangium, the **basidium.** The number of spores borne by a basidium is usually four, but it may be two or eight. Some basidiomycetes produce one or more other types of spore in addition to basidiospores. There are about 525 genera and 13,500 species. Fungi referred to the Basidiomycetae include the mushrooms and their allies, the puffballs and their allies, the jelly fungi, the smuts, and the rusts.

Primary Mycelia. Mycelia composed of uninucleate cells are **primary mycelia.** When a basidiospore germinates to form a primary mycelium

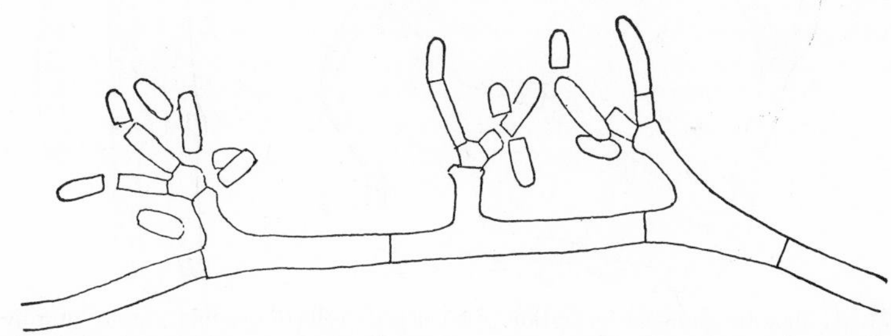

FIG. 270. *Coprinus fimentarius* L. Primary mycelium with oïdiophores and oïdia. (*After Bensaude*, 1918.)

the hyphae may be uninucleate from the beginning; or the first-formed hyphae may be multinucleate and then have a formation of transverse walls that divide them into uninucleate cells. A primary mycelium may grow to a limited or to an unlimited extent, but it never forms basidia and basidiospores. Multiplication of primary mycelia may be by means of conidia. It may also be by means of oïdia formed terminally on hyphae or formed on special outgrowths, **oïdiophores** (Fig. 270).

Secondary Mycelia. Mycelia composed of binucleate cells (**dikaryons**) in which the two nuclei divide simultaneously (conjugately) are **secondary mycelia.** These arise in various ways. Frequently they arise by somatogamy between two primary mycelia. In heterothallic species this takes place when two primary mycelia of opposite sex grow intermingled with each other (Fig. 271*A*). In homothallic species this may take place between two hyphae of a single primary mycelium. The dikaryotic cell formed by somatogamy may develop directly into a secondary (dikaryotic) hypha. Or, descendants of a nucleus entering a cell of a primary mycelium may migrate from cell to cell of this mycelium and so dikaryotize

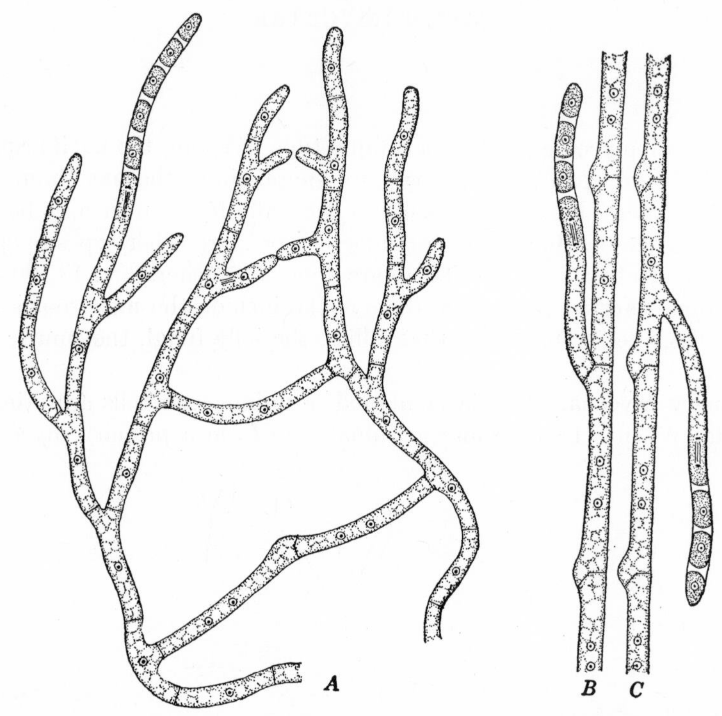

Fig. 271. *A*, diagram showing formation of binucleate cells of secondary mycelium by conjugation of uninucleate cells of primary mycelia. *B*, diagram showing the formation of uninucleate oïdia by binucleate cells of a secondary mycelium. (*Based upon Brodie*, 1936.)

the mycelium. Such a migration is possible because the transverse walls have a large perforation at the center. Dikaryotic secondary mycelia may also arise through a spermatization of a primary mycelium by oïdia or spermatia from another primary mycelium. Again, a dikaryotic mycelium may arise through conjugation between two basidiospores or conidia formed by them (Fig. 300*A–B*). In this case there is no formation of a primary mycelium prior to formation of the secondary mycelium.

One or more species of all orders except those to which rusts are referred have been found to form **clamp connections** during division of cells of the secondary mycelium. Here, cell division is usually restricted to terminal cells of the hyphae. In typical cases a cell about to divide sends forth a short, lateral, arcuate outgrowth that projects toward the base of the cell. One nucleus migrates into the outgrowth; the other remains within the cell.[1] There is next a simultaneous division of the two nuclei (Fig. 272*C*). Daughter nuclei of the nucleus in the cell come to lie some distance apart, one above and the other below the level of the outgrowth. One daughter nucleus of the nucleus within the outgrowth remains within the outgrowth; the other lies within the cell. Two transverse walls are now formed, one across the base of the outgrowth, the other across the cell and just below the level of the outgrowth (Fig. 272*D*). The outgrowth

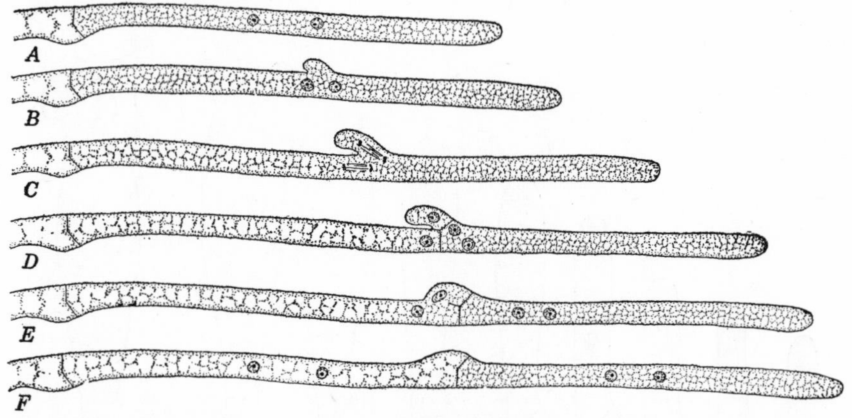

FIG. 272. Diagram showing the successive stages in formation of a clamp connection in a hypha of *Corticium varians* Kniep. (*Based upon Kniep*, 1915.)

is now a uninucleate **clamp cell.** The terminal daughter cell formed by transverse division of the original cell is binucleate; the subterminal daughter cell is uninucleate. Later on, the subterminal cell becomes binucleate by fusing with the clamp cell (Fig. 272*E–F*). The remains of the clamp cells are the clamp connections evident on the mycelium. In some cases clamp connections are evident on almost all cells of a secondary mycelium; in other cases only an occasional cell here and there along a hypha has a clamp connection.

Secondary mycelia may produce oïdia. The oïdia formed by them are usually dikaryotic and give rise to secondary mycelia when they germinate. However, cases are known where the oïdia are uninucleate (Fig. 271*B*) and where the oïdium forms a primary mycelium when it germinates.

Formation of Basidia. Basidia are formed from cells of a dikaryotic secondary mycelium. In many basidiomycetes, other than smuts and rusts, basidia are formed in a specialized portion of the mycelium or-

[1] Bensaude, 1918; Kniep, 1915, 1917.

ganized into a fruiting body (**basidiocarp**) of distinctive shape and usually of macroscopic size. The portion of the mycelium developing into a basidiocarp, sometimes called a **tertiary mycelium,** is dikaryotic. Basidia are of two general types, the **phragmobasidium** and the **holobasidium.** Phragmobasidia are vertically or transversely septate, or have a deeply incised apex. Holobasidia are more or less cylindrical, have a rounded apex, and are without septa. Almost all holobasidic species have the basidia borne in a palisade-like layer, the **hymenium.**

A young holobasidium is binucleate, and it may or may not have an evident clamp connection at its base (Fig. 273*A–D*). As it increases in

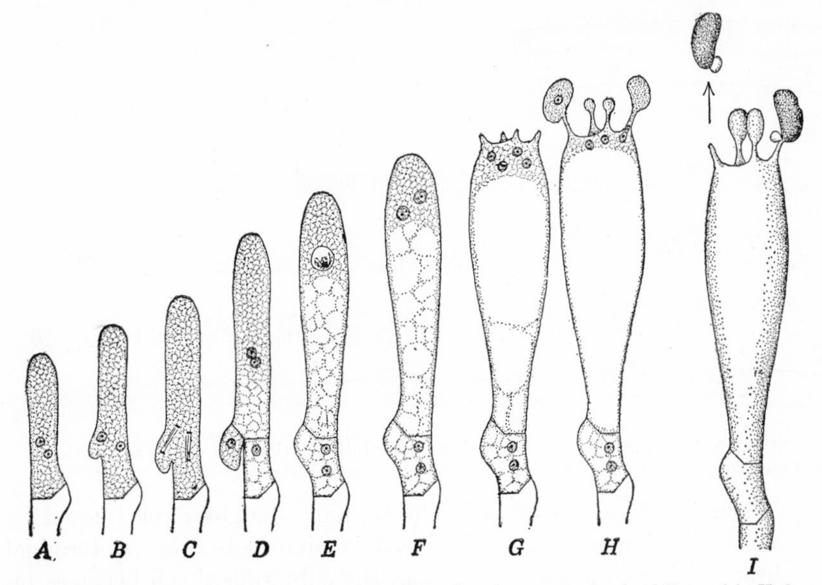

FIG. 273. Diagram showing successive stages in development of a basidium. (*A–H, based upon Kniep,* 1928; *I, based upon Buller,* 1922.)

size there is a fusion of the two nuclei and a migration of the fusion nucleus toward the apex of the basidium (Fig. 273*E*). The fusion nucleus soon divides meiotically into four daughter nuclei (Fig. 273*F–G*). In a few cases[1] each of the four nuclei undergoes one mitotic division to form eight nuclei within the basidium. After completion of the nuclear divisions there is a development of slender projections (**sterigmata**) at the distal end of the basidium. Four-nucleate holobasidia develop two or four sterigmata; eight-nucleate holobasidia may produce eight of them. Each sterigma swells at the upper end and a nucleus from the basidium migrates into the enlarging portion. A cross wall is eventually formed at the base of the enlargement, and the cell thus cut off is a basidiospore (Fig. 273*H–I*).

[1] Maire, 1902; Juel, 1916.

Phragmobasidia, similar to holobasidia, have a fusion of the two nuclei in the young basidium and a meiotic division of the fusion nucleus. Phragmobasidia are differentiated into a first-formed portion (the **hypobasidium**) and a later-formed portion (the **epibasidium**). Many genera with transversely septate phragmobasidia have the epibasidium borne apically on hypobasidium and have the transverse septa formed in the epibasidium. Such phragmobasidia have each of the four cells in the epibasidium producing a lateral sterigma (Fig. 293, page 497). Other transversely septate phragmobasidia have the septa formed in the hypobasidium and each of the cells thus formed producing a laterally borne epibasidium (Fig. 292, page 496). In some genera the phragmobasidium becomes vertically septate. Here, the septation is in the hypobasidium and with each of the cells into which it becomes divided producing an epibasidium at its apex (Fig. 290, page 494). There are also phragmobasidia where there is no septation and where epibasidia grow from the apex of the hypobasidium (Fig. 288, page 492).

The Basidiospore. Many basidiomycetes have an explosive abscission of basidiospores from a basidium,[1] and one that may hurl the spore 0.1 to 1.0 mm. Basidiospores that are explosively discharged have a small lateral outgrowth (the **hilum**) near the juncture with the sterigma. A minute or so before spore abscission, a small droplet of liquid appears upon the hilum. The droplet grows to about a fifth the size of the spore and then both droplet and basidiospore suddenly shoot off from the sterigma (Fig. 273*I*). The mechanism of this abrupt abscission is unknown. Basidiospores on a four-spored basidium are discharged in a regular sequence and not simultaneously. The time interval between discharge of the first and second spore may be a minute or more; that between discharge of the second and third, or third and fourth, may be somewhat longer.[2] There is also a successive ripening of basidia borne on a hymenium. Thus, the period of spore discharge from a basidiocarp continues for some time and, according to the species, may last for hours, days, or weeks. The number of basidiospores discharged from a basidiocarp is tremendous, and it has been estimated[3] that certain species shed basidiospores at the rate of a million a minute for 50 hours or more.

When conditions are favorable, basidiospores usually germinate to form a primary mycelium soon after discharge from a basidium. Instead of producing a primary mycelium a basidiospore may bud off one or a succession of conidia, each of which is capable of developing into a primary mycelium. This is of frequent occurrence in smuts, and here the conidia may be budded off before or after a basidiospore becomes detached from the basidium (Fig. 303, page 509).

[1] Buller, 1909, 1924. [2] Buller, 1924. [3] Buller, 1909.

Sexuality of Basidiomycetes. The sexual cycle of a basidiomycete includes an establishment of a dikaryotic phase by somatogamy or by spermatization of primary mycelia, karyogamy and meiosis in a basidium formed by the dikaryotic phase, and a return to the monokaryotic phase via the basidiospores. The sexuality of the primary mycelium produced from each of the four basidiospores borne on a basidium has been studied in numerous species. This has shown that primary mycelia of some species are homothallic and that those of other species are heterothallic. Heterothallic species are of two kinds. In **bipolar species** the four basidiospores of a basidium, and primary mycelia produced by these basidiospores, are of two mating types; whereas in **tetrapolar species** the four basidiospores on a single basidium produce primary mycelia of four mating types. Each of the four primary mycelia of a bipolar species is compatible with two of the other primary mycelia. On the other hand, each of the four primary mycelia of a tetrapolar mycelia may be compatible with but one of the other three primary mycelia. Exclusive of smuts and rusts, sexuality has been studied in 230 species of basidiomycetes.[1] Approximately 10 per cent of these are homothallic, 35 per cent are bipolar, and 55 per cent are tetrapolar.

Each nucleus in primary mycelia of bipolar heterothallic species bears a single factor for sex. In two compatible primary mycelia the sexual factor in nuclei of one mycelium is of opposite nature to that in nuclei of the other mycelium. These factors, sometimes designated as *A* and *B*, are borne on homologous chromosomes. Somatization or spermatization produces secondary mycelia composed of dikaryons in which one nucleus has the factor *A* and the other nucleus has the factor *B*. Karyogamy in the basidium results in a nucleus with the factor content *AB*. When four basidiospores are formed after meiotic division of a fusion nucleus with the factor content *AB*, two of them contain a nucleus with the factor *A*, and two with the factor *B*. In the four primary mycelia developing from these basidiospores a mycelium with the factor *A* is compatible with either of the two with the factor *B*, or vice versa.

Each nucleus in a primary mycelium of a tetrapolar heterothallic species contains two factors for sexuality; either A^1 or A^2 and either B^1 or B^2. The *A* and *B* factors in a nucleus of the primary mycelium are borne on separate chromosomes. The only primary mycelia that are compatible and capable of producing dikaryotic mycelia which form basidia are those in which neither the *A* nor the *B* factor in one mycelium is duplicated by either the *A* or the *B* factor of the other mycelium. Thus, when karyogamy occurs in a basidium, the content of sexual factors in the fusion nucleus is $A^1A^2B^1B^2$.

For tetrapolar species, the manner in which *A* and *B* factors are dis-

[1] Whitehouse, 1949*A*.

tributed to the four basidiospores of a basidium depends upon whether they become separated in the first or in the second meiotic division. If the factors become separated in the first meiotic division they may be distributed to the four basidiospores in either of the following two ways:

$$A^1B^1,\ A^1B^1,\ A^2B^2,\ A^2B^2$$
$$A^1B^2,\ A^1B^2,\ A^2B^1,\ A^2B^1$$

If they become separated in the second meiotic division the pairs of factors in the four basidiospores are distributed as follows:

$$A^1B^1,\ A^1B^2,\ A^2B^1,\ A^2B^2$$

The first two of the above three types behave in the same manner as a bipolar species, each of the four basidiospores producing primary mycelia that are compatible with two of the others. In the third of the above three types, each of the four is compatible with only one of the other three, and in the combination of either

$$A^1B^1 \times A^2B^2 \text{ or } A^1B^2 \times A^2B^1.$$

All individuals of heterothallic species have been found to be regularly bipolar or tetrapolar. On the other hand, a number of species have been found in which a basidiospore from one basidiocarp produces a primary mycelium that is interfertile (compatible) with all four primary mycelia from basidiospores borne on a basidium of another basidiocarp. This was first noted in basidiocarps from widely separated localities and so the basidiocarps were thought to belong to different **"geographical races."** It is now known that such races can occur close together in nature and even upon the same log or the same ball of horse dung.[1] The complete interfertility between the various stocks of a species is thought to be due to the fact that *A* and *B* factors in one race differ from the *A* and *B* factors in another race. The number of such multiple allelomorphs in a species is considerable, and it has been estimated[2] that the number may be a hundred or more.

Somatogamy to form a dikaryotic mycelium is usually between two primary (monokaryotic) mycelia, but there may be a dikaryotization of a monokaryotic mycelium by a dikaryotic mycelium. This is called the **Buller phenomenon** in honor of Buller,[3] who discovered it. In the Buller phenomenon there is somatogamy between a dikaryotic and a monokaryotic mycelium, and a dikaryotization of the monokaryotic mycelium by one of the two nuclei in a binucleate cell of the dikaryotic mycelium. Whether or not the dikaryotized monokaryotic mycelium will be one capable of producing basidia and basidiospores depends upon the nature of the dikaryotizing nucleus. Combinations in which the dikaryotizing nu-

[1] Raper, 1953. [2] Raper, 1953; Whitehouse, 1949, 1949*A*. [3] Buller, 1930.

cleus duplicates neither factor in the monokaryotic mycelium is called[1] a **legitimate combination** and results in a dikaryon which divides conjugately. An example of this would be a migration of a A^2B^2 nucleus from a dikaryotic $A^1B^1 + A^2B^2$ mycelium into a A^1B^1 mycelium. A combination in which either factor in the monokaryotic mycelium is duplicated by the entering nucleus is called an **illegitimate combination.** When this

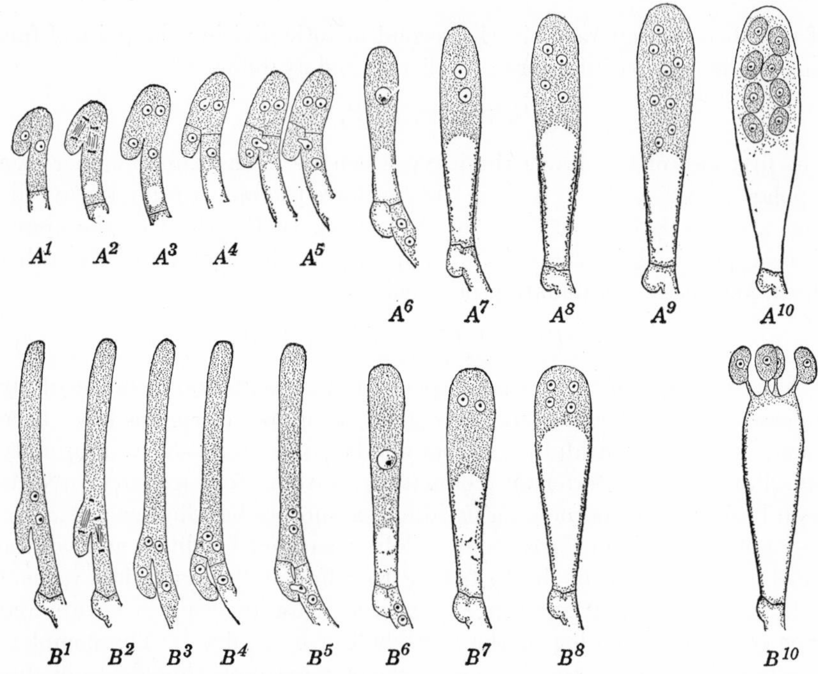

FIG. 274. Diagram showing similarities in development of an ascus (A^1–A^{10}) and a basidium (B^1–B^{10}). Homologous stages in the two lie vertical to each other. (*Modified from Gäumann and Dodge*, 1928.)

takes place there is not a development of a typical dikaryon because nuclei with either one or two factors in common do not attract each other and divide conjugately. An example of an illegitimate combination would be an entrance of a nucleus from an $A^1B^1 + A^2B^2$ dikaryotic mycelium into a monokaryotic mycelium each of whose nuclei have the factors A^1B^2.

Origin of the Basidiomycetae. At one time opinion was divided as to whether the Basidiomycetae arose from the Phycomycetae or the Ascomycetae. Practically every mycologist discussing the question during recent decades argues for a phylogenetic relationship between basidiomycetes and ascomycetes. The major factor inducing this swing to an

[1] Buller, 1941.

origin from ascomycetes was the suggestion[1] that basidiomycete hyphae with clamp connections are homologous with ascogenous hyphae and that there are homologies in early development of asci and basidia. According to this interpretation[1] the apparently terminal binucleate cell developing into a basidium is in reality a penultimate cell that lies posterior to a terminal uninucleate cell (Fig. 274). Thus, the only fundamental change in evolution of an ascus into a basidium would be a change from an endogenous to an exogenous method of spore formation.

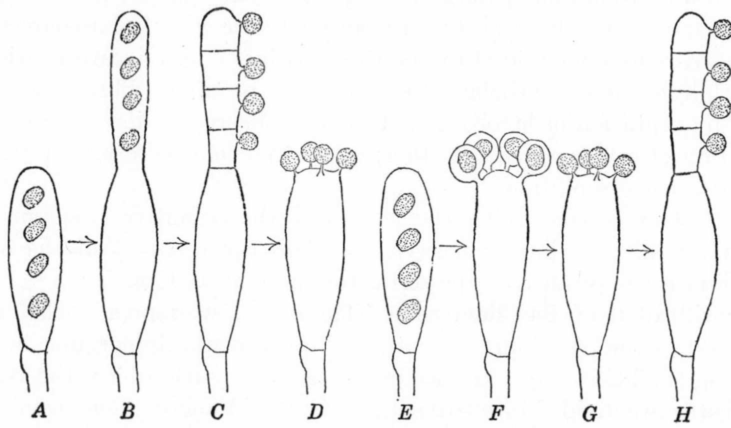

FIG. 275. Diagrams showing two theories on the evolution of an ascus into a basidium. For the sake of simplicity of diagram the basidium is derived from a four-spored ascus. *A–D*, according to the theory of Linder; *E–H*, according to the theory of Gäumann.

There are two theories concerning the manner in which this change took place. One theory[2] holds that an ascus evolved sporangiola (see page 410) at its apex and each of these sporangiola contained a single ascospore. From this was evolved a condition where the wall of the sporangiolum and that of the ascospore became firmly united with each other to become a basidiospore (Fig. 275*E–H*). The other theory[3] holds that ascomycetes giving rise to basidiomycetes were those in which the ascus wall has a thin elastic inner layer, and a rigid outer layer with a pore-like apex. After softening or rupture of the pore-like apex, the ascospores, still surrounded by the inner ascus wall layer, were protruded through the opening. This type gave rise to forms in which the protruded portion became tranversely septate and with each cell bearing an exogenously produced spore, the basidiospore (Fig. 275*A–D*).

Evolution within the Basidiomycetae. According to one interpretation, the basidiomycetes with phragmobasidia are the most closely related to the ancestral ascomycetes. Some[4] of those advocating this view think

[1] Kniep, 1915. [2] Gäumann, 1949, 1953. [3] Linder, 1940.
[4] Bessey, 1950; Dietel, 1928; Jackson, 1944; Linder, 1940.

that the rusts (Urediniales) were the first basidiomycetes to appear, but others[1] think that the jelly fungi (Auriculariales, etc.) are the most primitive of basidiomycetes with phragmobasidia. Evolutionary modification of the phragmobasidium is thought to have been along the line of simplification; and to have consisted of an obliteration of septation and an obliteration of differentiation into epi- and hypobasidium. The end result would be the holobasidium, a prominent feature of those basidiomycetes that many designate as the "higher basidiomycetes."

According to another interpretation,[2] basidiomycetes with holobasidia are the more primitive and the ones closest to the ancestral ascomycetes. Of the various holobasidial forms, those with the basidiocarp bearing a smooth hymenium are thought to be the most primitive. Phragmobasidia arose by septation of holobasidia. In one evolutionary line there was an evolution of a transverse septation; in another line there was an evolution of vertical septation.

Both theories concerning the nature of the primitive basidium are highly speculative, but as between the two the theory that the holobasidium is the primitive type seems the more attractive.

Classification of Basidiomycetae. There is a widespread belief that structure of the basidium is a feature of fundamental importance in segregating the basidiomycetes into major taxa. On such a basis the Basidiomycetae are divided into two subclasses, the Homobasidiomycetae and the Heterobasidiomycetae.

SUBCLASS 1. HOMOBASIDIOMYCETAE

The Homobasidiomycetae include the basidiomycetes with a holobasidium. There are about 300 genera and 7,500 species in this subclass.

Almost all members of the subclass produce basidiocarps. When segregated on the basis of structure of the basidiocarp the homobasidiomycetes fall into two groups, the Hymenomycetes and the Gastromycetes. The Hymenomycetes have the basidia borne in a basidium that is exposed from the beginning or becomes so before it is mature. The Gastromycetes have a basidiocarp in which the basidia do not become exposed before they are mature.

HYMENOMYCETES

The Hymenomycetes have a hymenium that is fully exposed before the basidiospores are mature and have a forcible ejection of basidiospores from the basidium.

There is great diversity of opinion concerning the content of orders referred to the Hymenomycetes. Some[3] place all Hymenomycetes in a single

[1] Alexopoulos, 1952; Martin, 1945.

[2] Gäumann, 1949, 1953; Gäumann and Dodge, 1928.

[3] Gäumann, 1949, 1953.

order, the Agaricales. Others[1] restrict the Agaricales to those Hymenomycetes in which the basidiocarp bears the basidia on gills, and place all others in another order, the Polyporales (Aphyllophorales). Still another treatment of the Hymenomycetes is to place[2] those without a basidiocarp in one order (Exobasidiales) and those with a basidiocarp in the Agaricales.

ORDER 1. EXOBASIDIALES

The Exobasidiales lack a basidiocarp and have a hymenium covering the infected portion of the host. There are three genera and about 15 species, all parasitic.

Exobasidium, the type genus, is parasitic on vascular plants and has about 10 species. One species causes a gall disease of cranberries and

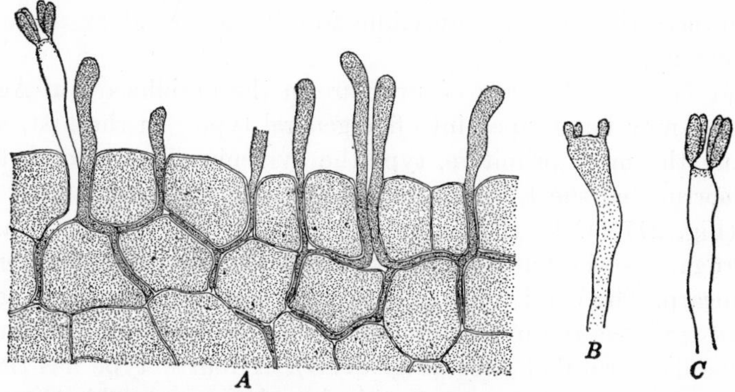

FIG. 276. *Exobasidium* sp. *A*, fruiting mycelium and host cells. *B–C*, stages in development of a basidium. (*A*, × 430; *B–C*, × 650.)

huckleberries; another causes a leaf blister of tea. *E. vaccinii* (Fckl.) Wor., the species parasitic on cranberries, infects both leaves and twigs of the host. Host cells in an infected area divide repeatedly and mature into a solid parenchymatous tissue of uniform texture.[3] An infected area is externally recognizable both on account of its gall-like appearance and on account of its red color. The mycelium of *E. vaccinii* is intercellular and composed of many very narrow hyphae. Most of them lie between subepidermal cells of the host, but some penetrate deeper. A mycelium may produce conidia. They may be borne on hyphae that project beyond the epidermis of the host or upon hyphae that lie intermingled with the basidia.[4]

Basidia develop terminally on erect unicellular hyphal branches growing up between and extending beyond epidermal cells of the host (Fig. 276). The basidia become club-shaped and several times broader than a hyphal branch. A young basidium is binucleate. During further develop-

[1] Bessey, 1950. [2] Martin, 1950.

[3] Pelluet, 1928; Eftimu and Kharbush, 1927. [4] Richards, 1896.

ment there is the usual fusion of the two nuclei and a subsequent division of the fusion nucleus.[1] The fact that a basidium may produce up to seven basidiospores shows that the fusion nucleus may form eight daughter nuclei. Basidiospores are developed on sterigmata borne terminally on the basidia.[2] Unlike most other homobasidiomycetes, the basidiospores are elongate and they may form one or two transverse septa before or after abscission. Germinating two- or three-celled basidiospores may bud off a conidium from each cell, and each conidium may bud off additional conidia in a yeast-like manner.

ORDER 2. AGARICALES

The Agaricales are all saprophytic and with a definite basidiocarp. Many members of this order have been shown to have clamp connections and to have the primary mycelium forming a secondary mycelium by somatogamy.

There is great diversity of structure in the basidiocarp of Agaricales but these may be grouped into five general types. In the first, and presumably the most primitive, type the hymenium is a smooth to somewhat corrugated sheet borne unilaterally on a crustose to erect basidiocarp (Fig. 277*A*). In the second type the hymenium is also a smooth to corrugated sheet, but completely encircles an erect, simple or branched, basidiocarp. The coral fungi (Clavariaceae) are of this type (Fig. 277*C*). A third type has the hymenium borne on downwardly projecting spines or spine-like protuberances (Fig. 277*D*). A fourth type has the hymenium lining small tubes or pores that face downward. This type includes the woody bracket fungi (Fig. 277*B*). It also includes the boletes which have a basidiocarp with the same differentiation into cap (pileus) and stem (stipe) as do the mushrooms. The fifth type has the hymenium borne on radially arranged gills (lamellae). Mushrooms are of this type (Fig. 280).

The mushrooms (Agaricaceae) may be selected as representative of the order. They are saprophytes but many of them are mycorhizal symbionts with forest trees. For this reason the mushroom floras of pine, oak-hickory, and beech-hemlock forests are quite different. The total number of species in the Agaricaceae is over 4,000, and these are segregated into about 90 genera.

Some agarics are highly esteemed as food, not so much for their nutritive value as for their flavor. Other agarics are not poisonous but have a disagreeable flavor. Still others are mildly to highly poisonous. Among the most poisonous of agarics are certain species of *Amanita* where there is enough of the poisonous substance (muscarine) in a single basidiocarp to kill a dozen or more people. There is a widespread belief that poisonous

[1] Eftimu and Kharbush, 1927; Maire, 1902. [2] Richards, 1896.

agarics may be recognized either by the color of their gills, or by the manner in which the "skin" peels off from the top of the cap, or by their ability to darken silver. All these tests for poisonous mushrooms are worthless. The only safe rule when proposing to eat mushrooms collected

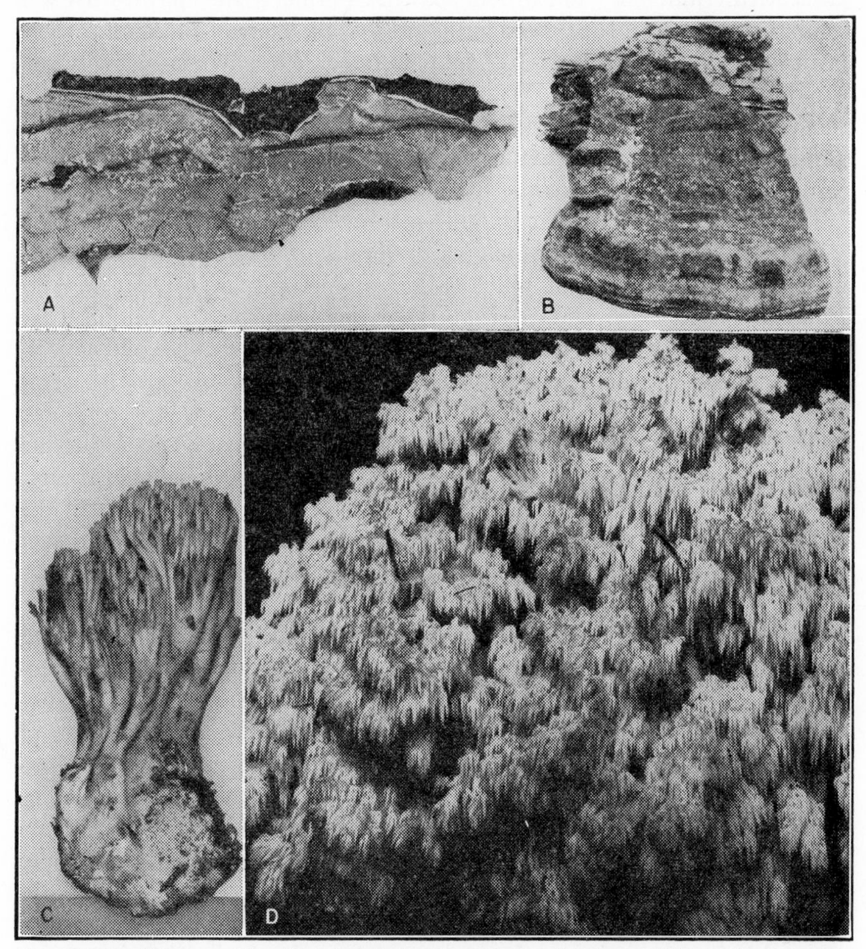

FIG. 277. Basidiocarps of various Agaricales. *A*, *Stereum cinerascens* Schw., with a smooth hymenium restricted to one face of the basidiocarp. *B*, *Fomes fomentarius* (Fr.) Kicx., with the hymenium lining small pores on the under side of the basidiocarp. *C*, *Clavaria fennica* Karst., with a smooth hymenium encircling all branches of the basidiocarp. *D*, *Hericeum coralloides* (Fr.) Gray, with the hymenium borne on small spine-like outgrowths. (*Photographs courtesy of Alexander H. Smith.*)

in the field is to identify them by means of the various handbooks describing mushrooms, and to eat only those species with such sharply defined characters that there can be no question about the identification.

The fresh and canned mushrooms sold in stores are almost always especially cultivated for the market. The mushroom usually grown for sale is one of the various strains of the field mushroom, *Psalliota campestris* (L.) Fries. It is grown in "mushroom cellars" and upon a substratum of well-rotted compost rich in nitrogenous compounds that has been inoculated with crumbs of "mushroom spawn." Formerly the spawn used was a mixture of substratum, mycelium, and basidiospores from a bed where mushrooms had been growing. Today, much of the spawn is specially cultured on various substrata. When the substratum used for growing mushrooms is inoculated under suitable conditions of temperature, moisture, and light there is soon an extensive development of a mycelium that continues to produce mushrooms (basidiocarps) for several months.

Hyphae of a mycelium may lie free from one another, or may lie adjoined in small rope-like strands (**rhizomorphs**). Certain of the hyphae in many rhizomorphs are of much larger diameter than others, and for *Psalliota* it has been shown[1] that the larger hyphae are produced by lateral fusion of smaller ones.

The sudden appearance of numerous basidiocarps above ground a few days after a heavy rain is well known to all. When a mycelium produces basidiocarps these develop to a certain size below ground and then do not increase greatly in size if the substratum becomes somewhat dry. The basidiocarps remain in this partially developed condition until the soil is thoroughly wetted by a rain. Then they enlarge rapidly, extend upward above the surface of the substratum, and mature within a few days.

Basidiocarps in which the hymenium is exposed from the beginning are **gymnocarpous.** Only a small percentage of the agarics are gymnocarpous. In the gymnocarpous *Omphalia* the primordium of a basidiocarp is cylindrical and tapering to a blunt apex.[2] The apical portion of the primordium develops into the pileus and the remainder develops into the stipe of the mature basidiocarp. The pileus is formed by a broadening and rounding up of the apex of the primordium (Fig. 278). The margins of the young pileus become downwardly curved and eventually there is a differentiation of gills on the lower side.

Basidiocarps in which the hymenium is at first enclosed but becomes exposed before maturity are **hemiangiocarpous.** In the hemiangiocarpous *Psalliota* the primordium of a basidiocarp is at first broadly ovoid (Fig. 279*A*–*B*). At the time it is about 1 mm. in height there is differentiation of a transverse internal ring of vertical hyphae. This is soon followed by a development of a transverse internal ring-shaped cavity, the **prelamellar chamber,**[3] between the vertical and the underlying hyphae (Fig. 279*C*). The portion of the primordium above the prelamellar cavity eventually develops into the pileus of the basidiocarp; that below it develops into

[1] Hein, 1930. [2] Blizzard, 1917. [3] Hein, 1930*A*.

the stipe. The tissue adjoining the upper side of the prelamellar cavity becomes concave and differentiated into alternate radial bands of slow- and fast-dividing cells. Each radial band of fast-dividing cells is the primordium of a lamella that soon projects downward into the prelamellar cavity (Fig. 279*D–G*). The diameter of a pileus increases greatly after the lamellae begin to develop. As a result, there is a constant broadening

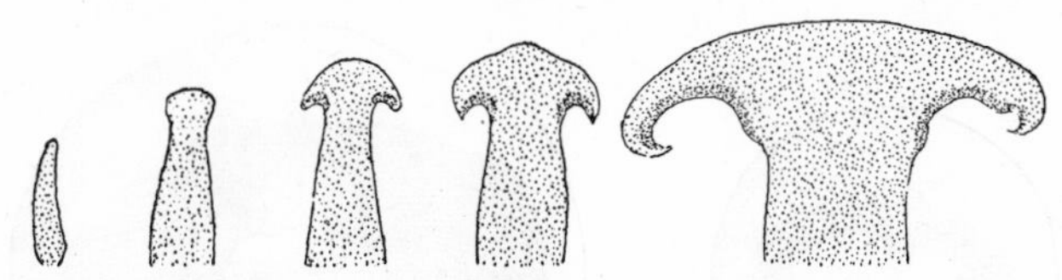

FIG. 278. *Omphalia chrysophylla* Fries. Diagrams of vertical sections of successive stages in development of the gymnocarpic basidiocarp. (*Based upon Blizzard,* 1917.) (× 12.)

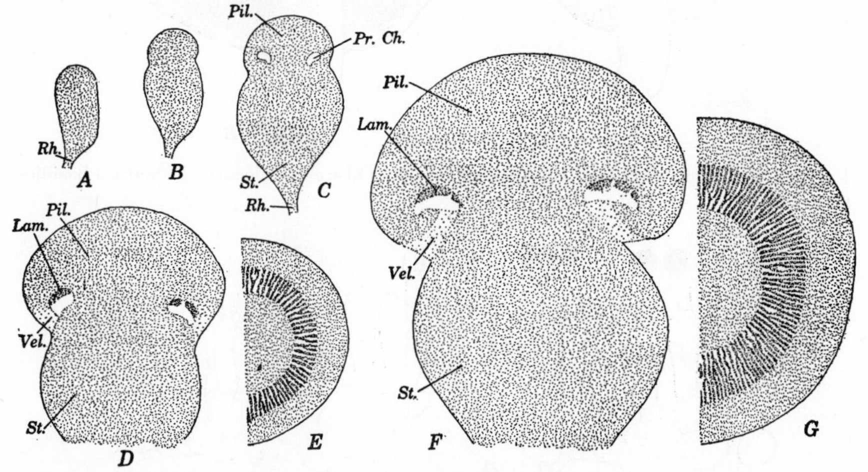

FIG. 279. *Psalliota campestris* (L.) Fries. Stages in development of the hemiangiocarpic basidiocarp. *A–B*, before formation of the prelamellar chamber. *C*, after formation of the prelamellar chamber and before formation of lamellae. *D–G*, vertical and transverse sections of basidiocarps with developing lamellae. (*Lam.*, lamellae; *Pil.*, pileus; *Pr. Ch.*, prelamellar chamber; *Rh.*, rhizomorph; *St.*, stipe; *Vel.*, velum.) (× 3.)

of the outer portion of the radial interspaces between the lamellae. Additional primordia of lamellae develop in the broadening interspace between two primary ones, but these secondary lamellae never have a radial length equal to that of primary ones. A young basidiocarp of *P. campestris* is about 1 cm. tall and with a breadth slightly less than the height at the time the secondary lamellae appear. Basidiocarps at this "button" stage of development have the edge of the pileus joined to the stipe by a thin sheet of tissue, the veil or **velum** (Fig. 279*D, F*). Enlargement of the pileus eventually ruptures the velum, but a ring-like remnant of it, the **annulus,** remains attached to the upper part of the stipe (Fig. 280).

As seen in cross section (Fig. 281) a lamella consists of three tissues. At the surface is the **hymenium**; beneath this is a **subhymenial tissue** of what seem to be isodiametric cells; and internal to this is a region of elongate cells, the **trama,** so oriented that their long axes lie parallel to the hymenium. The apparently parenchymatous subhymenial tissue is really composed of hyphae at right angles to those of the trama.

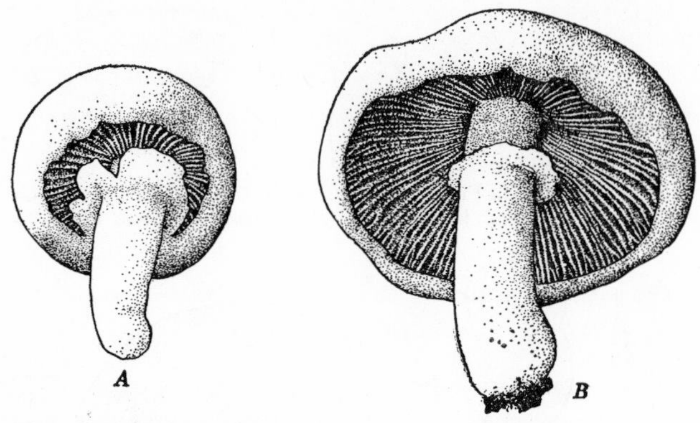

FIG. 280. *Psalliota campestris* (L.) Fries. *A*, nearly mature basidiocarp. *B*, mature basidiocarp. (× ⅔.)

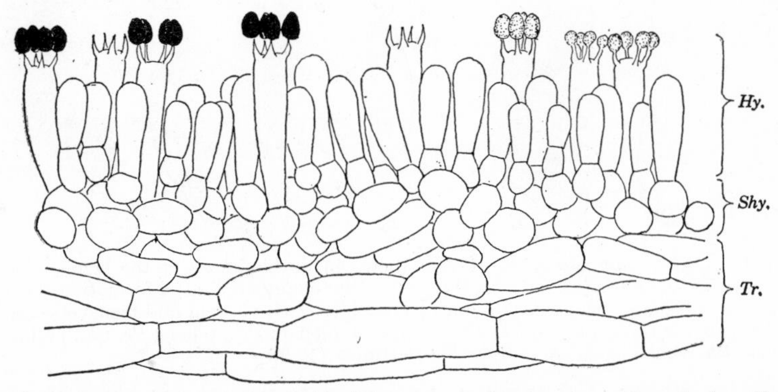

FIG. 281. *Psalliota campestris* (L.) Fries. Diagram of a transverse section of a lamella with basidia at various stages of development. (*Hy.*, hymenium; *Shy.*, subhymenium; *Tr.*, trama.) (*Based upon Buller*, 1922.) (× 500.)

All cells of the hymenium may develop into basidia, or some may develop into basidia and others develop into special sterile cells (**cystidia**) or into paraphyses. Basidial development is in the manner typical of homobasidiomycetes (see page 472) and, as already noted, there is not a simultaneous ripening of all basidia of a hymenium. A species usually has its basidia producing four basidiospores but there are species, as *P. campestris*, where some strains have four-spored basidia and others have two-spored ones.

Homobasidiomycetes have an explosive discharge of basidiospores immediately after they are mature. The forcible ejection of basidiospores (see page 473) is so nicely regulated that the spores are hurled beyond the hymenium, but not across the interlamellar space and against adjoining lamellae. After being shot horizontally into the interlamellar space, the spore falls vertically downward. The trajectory of basidiospores is unique among those of horizontally discharged projectiles. The trajectories of other projectiles are paraboloid curves; that of a basidiospore is a **sporobola**[1] and one that makes a right-angled downward turn.

GASTROMYCETES

The Gastromycetes are homobasidiomycetes in which the basidiocarp remains permanently closed or does not become open until after basidiospores have become detached from the basidia. Discharge of basidiospores from basidia is not explosive.

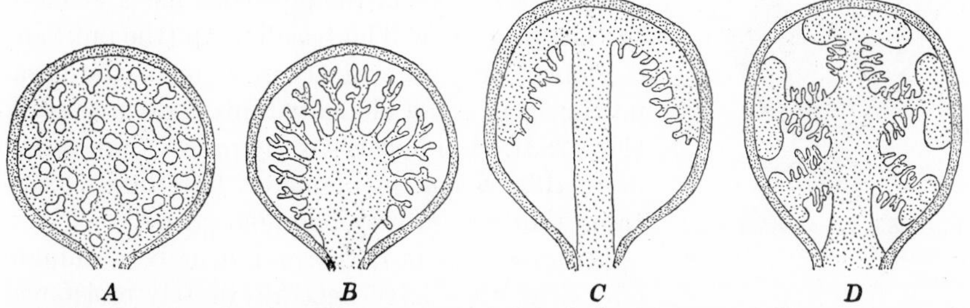

FIG. 282. Diagram showing different types of gleba in basidiocarps of Gastromycetes. *A*, lacunose type. *B*, coralloid type. *C*, unicapitate type. *D*, pluricapitate type. (*Modified from Fischer*, 1933.)

There are about 120 genera and 525 species, all saprophytic. Among them are the puffballs, the false truffles, the earth stars, the bird's-nest fungi, and the stinkhorns. At one time all Gastromycetes were usually grouped in a single order, the Lycoperdales, but the current practice is to group them in several orders. One such system[2] recognizes five orders and another[3] recognizes nine.

Mycelia of many species grow in the soil, but those of certain species grow in decaying wood. Terrestrial species may develop their basidiocarps above or below the surface of the soil. Basidiospores of some Gastromycetes with above-ground basidiocarps are dispersed by wind; those of other above-ground basidiocarps and of all subterranean basidiocarps are dispersed by animals feeding upon the basidiocarps. These animals include insects, slugs, and rodents. In many cases the subterranean basidiocarp emits a strong odor that attracts such animals as feed upon it.

Germinating basidiospores of several species are known to give rise to

[1] Buller, 1909. [2] Martin, 1950. [3] Zeller, 1949.

primary mycelia and the sexuality of four species is known[1] to be tetrapolar (see page 474). Clamp connections have been recorded for secondary mycelia of a number of species.

Basidiocarps developed on secondary mycelia consist of an outer sterile portion (**peridium**) and an inner fertile portion (**gleba**). There are four general types of gleba (Fig. 282). In the **lacunose type** numerous small cavities, each lined with a hymenium, develop within the gleba. In the **coralloid type** the gleba has numerous cylindrical to plate-like outgrowths from a central sterile region. The **unicapitate type** has the sterile portion of the gleba differentiated into an inverted cup-like apex with fertile projections from the interior of the cup. In the **pluricapitate type** the gleba has a branched sterile stipe with each branch terminating in a sterile cap. Sides of branches of the stipe bear numerous fertile outgrowths.

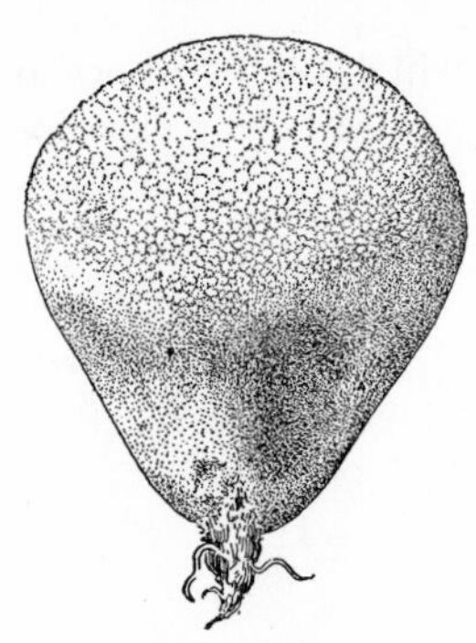

FIG. 283. *Lycoperdon pyriforme* Schaeffer. (Natural size.)

Lycoperdon, one of the puffballs, has a gleba of the lacunose type. The basidiocarp (the puffball) is globose to pyriform accordingly as the basal portion is or is not elongated into a definite stalk (Fig. 283). Basidiocarps of *Lycoperdon* are rarely more than 8 cm. in diameter, but those of certain other genera may be much larger.

Basidiospores of *Lycoperdon* usually germinate only after they have been alternately moistened and dried several times.[2] When a basidiospore germinates (Fig. 284*E*) it gives rise to a primary mycelium with short uninucleate cells. The dikaryotic secondary mycelium formed from primary mycelia frequently has its hyphae lying in a branching system of rhizomorphs. Rhizomorphs of *Lycoperdon*[3] may be more complex than those of *Psalliota* and composed of three concentric layers, an outer cortex of loose hyphae, a subcortical layer of compact hyphae, and a central core of parallel hyphae.

Primordia of basidiocarps usually arise terminally on a rhizomorph but they may arise laterally. They are formed by an outgrowth of hyphae from the central core.[3] Young primordia about 0.5 mm. in diameter are homogeneous in structure. Those slightly larger show a beginning of a differentiation into peridium and gleba. Differentiation of the peridium begins with an outgrowth of a compact palisade-like layer of hyphae over the entire surface of the primordium. The outer portion (**exoperidium**) of a young peridium becomes pseudoparenchymatous; the inner portion (**endoperidium**) remains palisade-like.[4] The exoperidium develops numerous cracks as a basidiocarp increases in size and eventually most of the

[1] Whitehouse, 1949*A*. [2] Swartz, 1929. [3] Lander, 1933; Swartz, 1933, 1936.
[4] Cunningham, 1926; Lander, 1933.

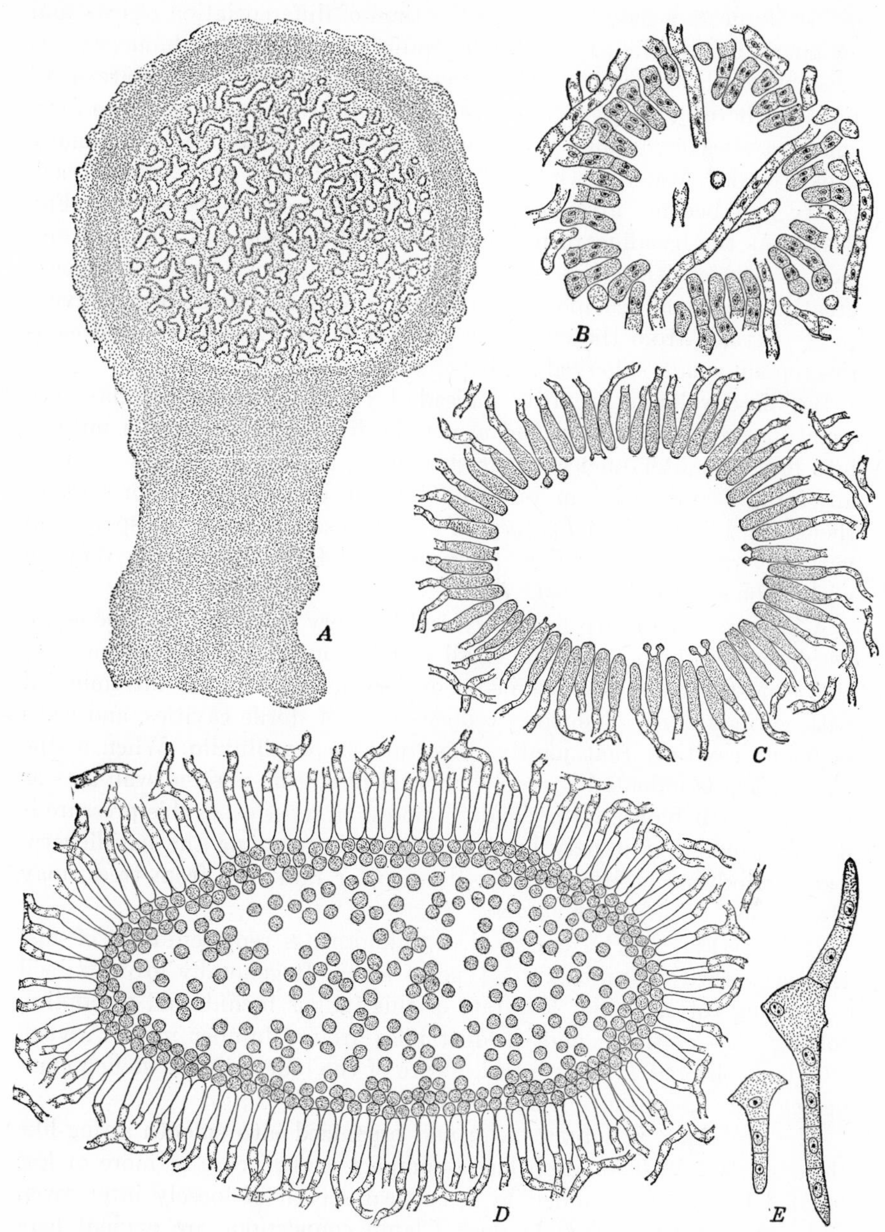

FIG. 284. *Lycoperdon gemmatum* Batsch. *A*, vertical section of a young basidiocarp. *B*, a very young glebal cavity before the formation of basidia. *C*, glebal cavity at the beginning of basidiospore formation. *D*, old glebal cavity. *E*, germination of basidiospores. (*E*, *after Swartz*, 1929.) (*A*, × 21; *B–D*, × 650; *E*, × 1,000.)

exoperidium may flake off. Up to the time of differentiation of exo- and endoperidium the inner region (the embryonic gleba) is a homogeneous mass of interlaced hyphae. Then, here and there in this tissue are small regions where the hyphae begin to pull away from one another to form small cavities containing very loosely interwoven hyphae with many broken ends.[1] Many newly formed hyphal branches grow toward each cavity and become arranged in an encircling palisade-like layer (Fig. 284*B*). As the basidiocarp increases in size there is a continuous formation of new cavities (Fig. 284*A*). The first-developed cavities increase greatly in size and become elongated and irregularly lobed. Basidia eventually develop from the encircling palisade layer. Later-developed cavities remain small, spherical in shape, and sterile.

Basidia developing from the palisade layer of fertile cavities have the usual fusion of two nuclei and a meiotic division of the fusion nucleus into four daughter nuclei.[2] Four sterigmata and basidiospores are usually formed on a basidium, but sometimes there are only two or three of them.[3] Basidiospores of *Lycoperdon* are globose and with the spore wall variously ornamented. When they are shed from the basidia they lie within the cavity (Fig. 284*C–D*).

A mature basidiocarp has a dry and leathery sterile jacket, the endoperidium, in which there is a small circular opening at the summit. At this time the gleba consists of a powdery mass of spores intermingled with various sterile elements (hyphae, walls of sterile cavities, and walls of fertile cavities) that jointly constitute the **capillitium.** When a ripe basidiocarp is indented by some external force, the peridial wall acts as a bellows that blows out a cloud of spores. In most cases this pressure is due to winds, but it may be due to animals touching the basidiocarp. Large raindrops falling on a basidiocarp, or rain drip from trees, may also cause a discharge of spores.[4]

Phallus (Fig. 285*A*), one of the stinkhorns, is representative of gastromycetes with a unicapitate type of gleba. It generally grows in soil containing rotten wood. Habitats of this fungus include old woodpiles, rotting piles of trash, and sawdust piles around lumber mills. Anyone who has collected *Phallus* is well aware of the indescribable stench emanating from the mature basidiocarps.

The mycelium is subterranean and organized into smooth string-like rhizomorphs. A rhizomorph has a compact central core of more or less parallel hyphae surrounded by a cortical sheath of loosely interwoven and irregularly branched hyphae. Clamp connections are evident here and there in the cortical sheath. Sometimes a rhizomorph develops into an irregularly shaped sclerotium.[5]

[1] Lander, 1933. [2] Ritchie, 1948. [3] Coker and Couch, 1928; Ritchie, 1948.
[4] Gregory, 1949. [5] Overholts, 1925.

Primordia of basidiocarps generally develop at the tips of rhizomorphs, and the diameter of a primordium soon increases to several times that of the rhizomorph. The only evident structure in a young primordium is a central dome-shaped region, the **columella.** The columella eventually develops into the gleba and the portion external to it develops into the peridium. The peridium soon becomes differentiated into a narrow, firm, exterior portion (the **outer volva**) and an interior gelatinous portion. The

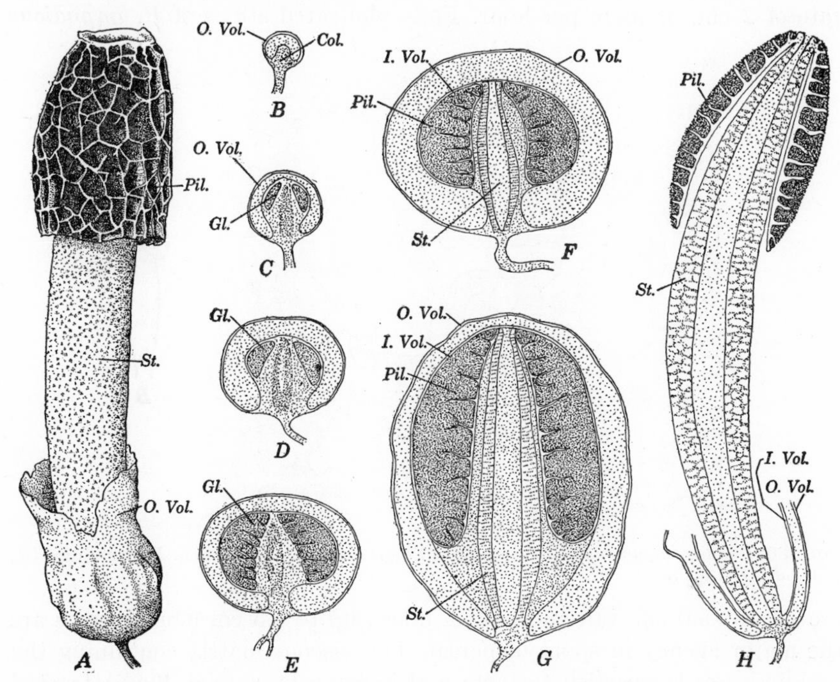

Fig. 285. *Phallus impudicus* L. *A*, surface view of a mature basidiocarp. *B–G*, vertical sections of "eggs" at successive stages of development. *H*, vertical section of a mature basidiocarp. (*Col.*, columella; *Gl.*, gleba; *I. Vol.*, inner volva; *O. Vol.*, outer volva; *Pil.*, pileus; *St.*, stipe.) (× ¾.)

columella becomes differentiated into a **stipe** terminating in an inverted cup-shaped fertile tissue, the **pileus,** which is overarched by a thin cap of sterile glebal tissue, the **inner volva** (Fig. 285*B–G*). The inner face of the cup-shaped pileus is much convoluted and with the surface covered with a hymenium (Fig. 286*A*). Mature basidia produced by the hymenium are club-shaped and with eight basidiospores at the distal end (Fig. 286*B*). Basidiospores of a nearly mature basidiocarp lie in a sticky viscous matrix resulting from disintegration of the basidia and sterile hyphae of the pileus.

Development of basidiocarps is subterranean until the basidiospores are mature and shed from the basidia. At this stage the basidiocarp is ovoid and that of *P. impudicus* L. may be up to 4.5 by 6 cm. Unopened subterranean basidiocarps are often called "eggs" and they may remain in the unopened egg stage for a considerable time (Fig. 285*G*). At any time when conditions are favorable, there is an elongation of the stipe that pushes the pileus through both the inner and outer volva (Fig. 285*A*, *H*). Eggs often open a few hours after they are removed from the ground, and the stipe pushing up through the volvae may elongate at a rate of 2 cm. or more per hour. Fully elongated stipes of *P. impudicus*

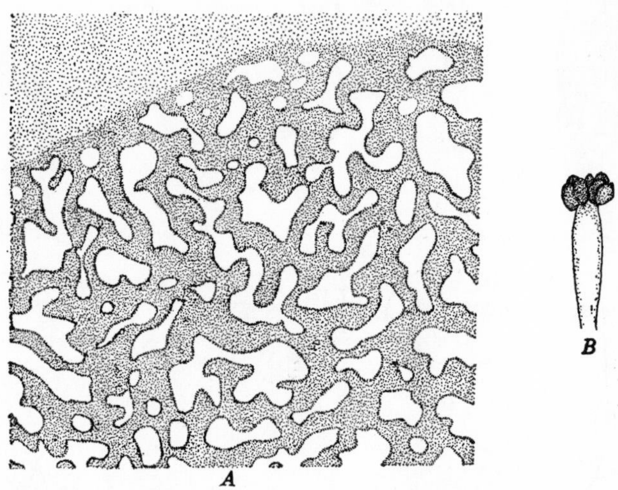

FIG. 286. *Phallus impudicus* L. *A*, section of a portion of a young gleba. *B*, basidium. (*A*, × 60; *B*, × 1,300.)

are 7.5 to 15.0 cm. tall and with a pileus up to 4.5 cm long. Insects are the major agency in spore dispersal. The viscous matrix containing the basidiospores is sweetish to taste and is eaten by carrion flies attracted by the strong putrescent stench of the mature basidiocarp. Spore dispersal may also be due to rains washing basidiospores from the pileus.

SUBCLASS 2. HETEROBASIDIOMYCETAE

The Heterobasidiomycetae have phragmobasidia that are usually differentiated into hypobasidium and epibasidium, and are almost always vertically or transversely septate. There are about 225 genera and 6,000 species. The jelly (tremelloid) fungi, the rusts, and the smuts are heterobasidiomycetes.

All rusts are placed in one order (Urediniales) and all smuts in another (Ustilaginales). All the remaining members are sometimes placed in a single order,[1] but the usual practice is to group them in three orders (Dacromycetales, Tremellales, Auriculariales). Those recognizing these

[1] Martin, 1945, 1950.

three orders usually place the Septobasidiaceae among the Auriculariales but there is considerable justification for the proposal[1] that they be placed in a separate order, the Septobasidiales.

ORDER 1. DACROMYCETALES

The Dacromycetales have basidia that are unseptate but in which the distal end of the hypobasidium bears two divergent epibasidia. These **Y**-shaped basidia are not overlain or intermingled with sterile hyphae at any stage of development. Basidiocarps are quite small, are gelatinous to waxy in texture, and have a definite or indefinite shape. There are about 7 genera and less than 100 species, all saprophytic on wood.

Dacromyces is a rather widely distributed genus, but its basidiocarps are apt to be overlooked because they are rarely more than 2 to 3 cm. in diameter. The basidiocarps (Fig. 287) are generally yellowish to a deep orange. In dry weather they are greatly shrunken and very difficult to find; after a rain they imbibe water and regain their former size and color.

FIG. 287. Basidiocarp of *Dacromyces aurantius* (Schw.) Farlow. (Natural size.)

A basidiospore is uninucleate and unicellular when discharged from a basidium,[2] but it soon becomes transversely divided into several uninucleate cells each of which may give rise to a primary mycelium (Fig. 288*C–E*). Sometimes each cell into which a basidiospore becomes divided buds off several conidia.[3] Primary mycelia are composed of relatively short uninucleate cells (Fig. 288*F*). Clamp connections have been found on secondary mycelia of several species.[4]

Growth of a basidiocarp of *D. deliquescens* (Bull.) Duby is at a relatively slow rate and basidia are not developed until the third year.[4] A developing basidiocarp of *Dacromyces* consists of a densely interwoven mass of branched dikaryotic secondary hyphae in which the hyphal interspaces are filled with a gelatinous substance. Hyphae at the surface of a developing basidiocarp lie in a palisade-like layer. During the second, and possibly the first, year there is a formation of oïdia at the surface of the basidiocarp. Hyphae producing oïdia are relatively stout (Fig. 288*A*) and each divides transversely into a number of binucleate oïdia.[5]

Basidia arise in a palisade-like tissue, often called the hymenium, at the surface of a basidiocarp. The hymenium is often described as consisting of fertile cells (basidia) and sterile ones (paraphyses), but there

[1] Couch, 1938. [2] Gilbert, 1911, 1921. [3] Brefeld, 1888. [4] Martin, 1942.
[5] Dangeard, 1895.

is good reason for believing that the so-called paraphyses are immature basidia. A young basidium is binucleate, and during its further development there is a union of the two nuclei and a meiotic division of the fusion nucleus into four daughter nuclei (Fig. 288*B*). During meiosis or shortly afterward, two widely divergent epibasidia grow out from the

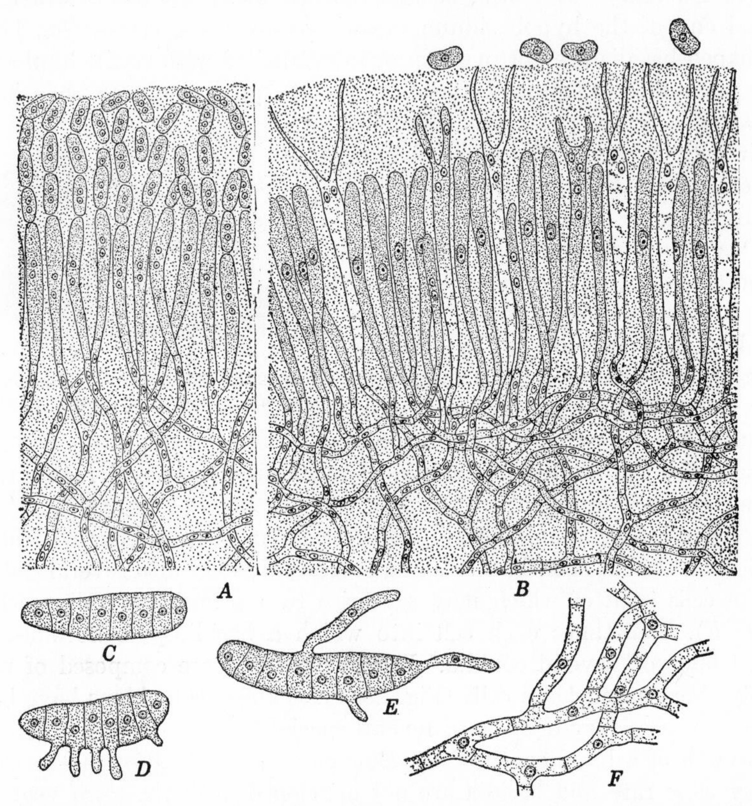

FIG. 288. *Dacromyces deliquescens* (Bull.) Duby. *A*, diagrammatic vertical section of a portion of a basidiocarp producing oïdia. *B*, diagrammatic vertical section of a portion of a basidiocarp with basidia at various stages of development. *C–E*, germination of spores. *F*, portion of a primary mycelium. (*A–B*, × 975; *C–F*, × 1,300.)

apex of the hypobasidium.[1] Each epibasidium develops a small apical sterigma after it has grown through the gelatinous matrix of the basidiocarp. A single nucleus migrates into the basidiospore developing on each sterigma. The other two nuclei remain in the hypobasidium[2] or in the epibasidia.[3] There is a forcible ejection of a basidiospore shortly after a droplet of liquid has accumulated on the hilum. Basidiospores of *D. deliquescens* are shot 0.5 to 0.65 mm. outward from the sterigmata.[4]

[1] Dangeard, 1895; Gilbert, 1921; Istvánffi, 1895; Juel, 1898.
[2] Gilbert, 1921. [3] Istvánffi, 1895; Juel, 1898. [4] Buller, 1922.

ORDER 2. TREMELLALES

The Tremellales have a basidium in which the hypobasidium becomes vertically divided into two, three, or four cells, each of which develops an epibasidium at the distal end. There is a basidiocarp of more or less indefinite shape and one which is usually gelatinous in texture. The order includes about 18 genera and over 100 species.

Tremella is a genus with about 40 species. One of them (*T. mycetophila* Peck) is parasitic on certain Agaricales; the others grow as saprophytes on decaying wood. The basidiocarp of *Tremella* is gelatinous in texture, is more or less rounded, and has a variously convoluted surface (Fig. 289).

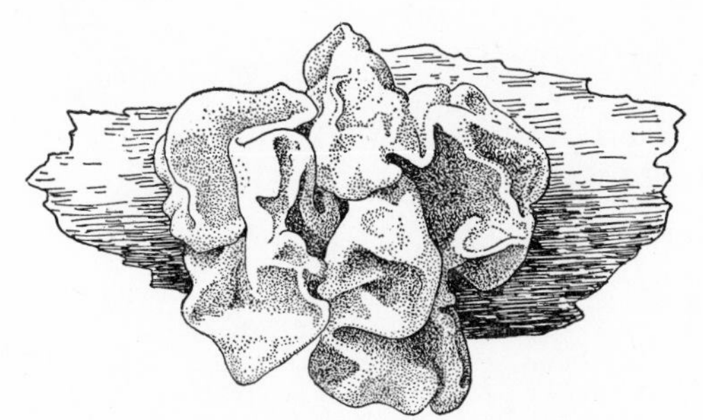

FIG. 289. Basidiocarp of *Tremella* sp. (Natural size.)

A germinating basidiospore gives rise to a primary mycelium which may form conidia after it has become a few cells in length.[1] A germinating basidiospore may also form a sterigma that produces a single secondary basidiospore at its apex[2] (Fig. 290*I*). The sexuality of primary mycelia of *Tremella* has not been investigated but that of certain other members of the order has been shown[3] to be bipolar. Secondary mycelia of several species are known[4] to have clamp connections.

The secondary mycelium ramifies through and absorbs food from the substratum. The basidiocarp is developed from hyphae projecting beyond the substratum. These hyphae are somewhat broader and more intertwined than those in the substratum, and all interspaces between them are filled with gelatinous material. A basidiocarp may form oïdia in catenate series from hyphal tips just within the periphery of the basidiocarp.[5] Unlike *Dacromyces*, oïdia are formed simultaneously with instead of prior to the formation of basidiospores.

Basidia are developed slightly below the entire surface of a basidiocarp. External to the basidia is a palisade-like layer of narrow, branched or unbranched, erect hyphal tips (paraphyses). Intermingled with the

[1] Brefeld, 1888. [2] Wheldon, 1934. [3] Barnett, 1937. [4] Martin, 1942.
[5] Dangeard, 1895; Wheldon, 1934.

paraphyses, and of approximately the same height, are much broader unicellular **cystidia** (Fig. 290*A*). The first indication of basidial development is a slight swelling of dikaryotic terminal cells of hyphae just below the paraphyses and cystidia. These cells, the hypobasidia, become globose, their two nuclei fuse with each other, and the fusion nucleus divides meiotically into four daughter nuclei[1] (Fig. 290*B–D*). Even before

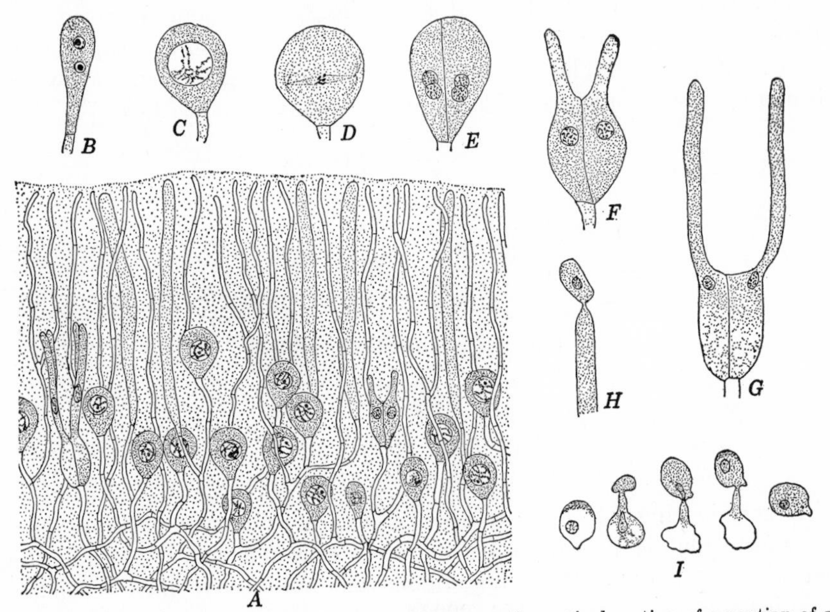

Fig. 290. *A–H*, *Tremella frondosa* Fries. *A*, diagrammatic vertical section of a portion of a hymenium with basidia at various stages of development. *B–G*, successive stages in development of a basidium. *H*, basidiospore on apex of epibasidium. *I*, formation of secondary basidiospores from basidiospore of *T. mesenterica* Retz. (*I*, *after Whelden*, 1934.) (*A*, × 650; *B–H*, × 1,300; *I*, × 575.)

the completion of meiosis a hypobasidium may begin to develop mamillate protuberances, the primordia of epibasidia, at the distal end.[2] However, in most cases the epibasidia do not begin to develop until the hypobasidia have divided vertically into four uninucleate cells (Fig. 290*E*). An epibasidium elongates until its apex projects beyond the gelatinous matrix of the basidiocarp. Then it develops a sterigma and a basidiospore at its distal end (Fig. 290*F–H*). A single nucleus moves into each elongating epibasidium and eventually into the basidiospore developing on the sterigma.[2] Discharge of basidiospores from the sterigmata is explosive.[3]

[1] Dangeard, 1895; Neuhoff, 1924; Wheldon, 1934.
[2] Wheldon, 1934. [3] Buller, 1922.

ORDER 3. AURICULARIALES

The Auriculariales have a basidium in which either the hypobasidium or the epibasidium becomes divided into four cells. If the hypobasidium becomes divided each cell forms a single epibasidium. The basidiocarps are of definite or indefinite shape. There are about 12 genera and 65 species, a few parasitic on mosses or on vascular plants, the great majority saprophytic.

Auricularia, with about 15 cosmopolitan species, is a saprophyte that grows on stumps or on dead trunks of various trees. Its basidiocarps (Fig. 291) are more or less saucer-shaped and so attached to the substratum that the concave side faces downward. A basidiocarp is gelatinous in texture when moist, but it gradually changes to a horny consistency as it dries out. During rainy weather a dried-out basidiocarp imbibes water, returns to a gelatinous condition, and resumes growth. Mature basidiocarps may be up to 10 cm. in diameter.

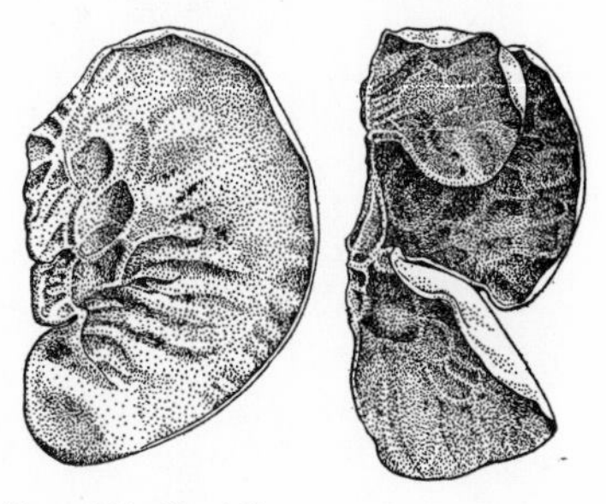

Fig. 291. Basidiocarp of *Auricularia auricula-judae* L. (× ½.)

A germinating basidiospore shed from a basidiocarp divides transversely into three or four cells, and then one or more of these cells sends out a primary mycelium.[1] The primary mycelia of certain species have been shown[2] to have a bipolar sexuality. Primary mycelia may form clusters of sickle-shaped conidia; and they may be produced shortly after a single primary hypha has grown from a cell of a basidiospore, or after the hypha has grown into an extensive primary mycelium.[1] A conidium may develop into a primary mycelium, or may bud off additional conidia in a yeast-like manner. Secondary mycelia formed from primary mycelia are dikaryotic and certain species are known[3] to have clamp connections.

The basidiocarp produced by a secondary mycelium is an intricately interwoven system of narrow hyphae with spaces between the hyphae filled with a gelatinous substance. The convex side of a basidiocarp bears a superficial layer of club-shaped sterile cells. Basidial development is restricted to the concave side. The basidia arise some distance in from the convex surface but they eventually extend to just beneath it. Developing hypobasidia are cylindrical, stand vertically, and lie intermingled with sterile hyphae (Fig. 292). The two nuclei in a young hypobasidium fuse and the fusion nuclei divide meiotically. A transverse wall is formed between the two nuclei resulting from the first meiotic division and between both pairs of nuclei formed by the second meiotic division[4] (Fig.

[1] Brefeld, 1888. [2] Barnett, 1937. [3] Martin, 1942. [4] Sappin-Trouffy, 1896.

292). The distal cell of the four-celled hypobasidium forms an epibasidium at its apex, and a single epibasidium is formed laterally on each of the other three cells. All epibasidia grow to the surface of the basidiocarp, and then each forms a sterigma and basidiospore at its apex. If a basidiocarp is so oriented that the basidia lie parallel to the ground, the basidiospores are hurled 0.4 to 0.5 mm. beyond their sterigmata.[1]

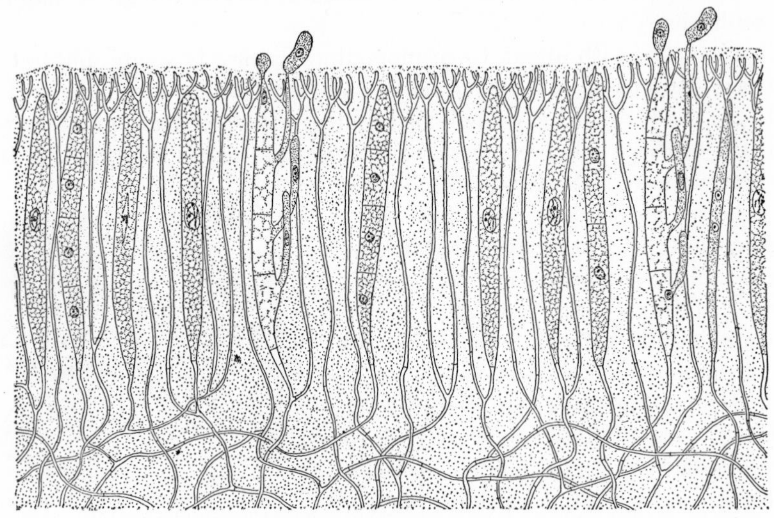

FIG. 292. *Auricularia auricula-judae* L. Diagrammatic vertical section of a portion of a hymenium with basidia at various stages of development. (× 650.)

ORDER 4. SEPTOBASIDIALES

The Septobasidiales have basidia in which development ceases for a time and is then resumed at a later stage. The hypobasidium is usually thick-walled. It may form a transversely septate epibasidium at its apex; or it may become transversely septate and with each cell producing an epibasidium. There are 2 genera and about 175 species.

The Septobasidiales are parasites of scale insects. The majority of species are found only in the tropics, but some 35 of them are known from the southern part of the United States.[2] The portion of the mycelium growing within a scale insect does not invade vital parts and thus kill the host. Hyphae also extend out from the host to form a felt-like layer covering portions of stems and branches of trees infested with scale insects. This felt affords shelter for other host individuals that are not infected with the fungus. Thus the relationship between fungus and scale insects is also symbiotic.

The mycelium of *Septobasidium* is perennial, with growth starting anew each spring and continuing until early in the autumn. Formation of hypo-

[1] Buller, 1922. [2] Couch, 1938.

basidia begins about the time that vegetative growth ceases and they are fully developed by early spring. Formation of epibasidia by the hypobasidia occurs during wet weather of spring and early summer.[1]

Hypobasidia of *Septobasidium* are developed at the tips of hyphae just beneath the upper surface of the felted portion of the mycelium external to the host. The commonest type is that in which the hypobasidium is thick-walled and one that forms a transversely septate epibasidium at its apex (Fig. 293*A–B*). The next commonest type is that in which the

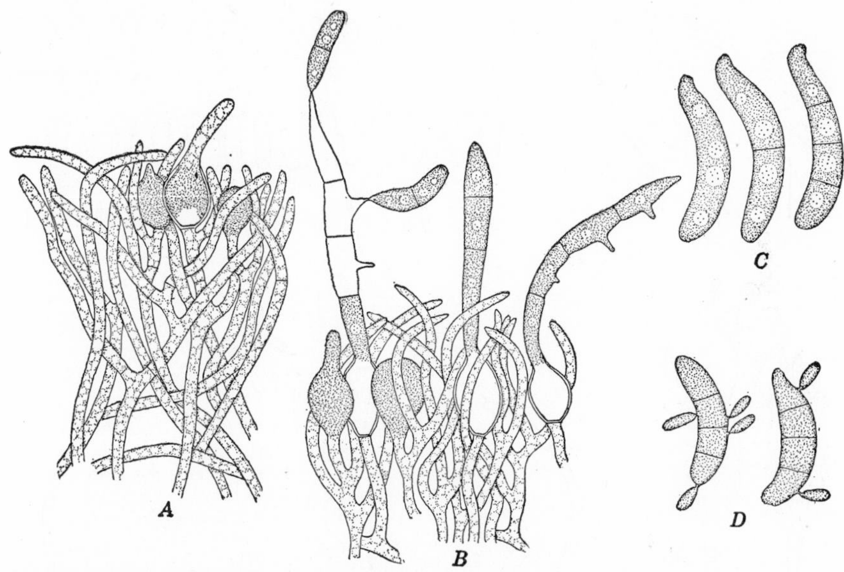

FIG. 293. *Septobasidium retiforme* (B. and C.) Pat. *A*, Vertical section of hymenial surface with young basidia. *B*, vertical section of hymenial surface with mature basidia. *C*, basidiospores. *D*, basidiospores forming conidia. (*After Coker*, 1920.) (*A–B*, × 540; *C–D*, × 1,080.)

hypobasidium is thin-walled, becomes transversely divided into three or four cells, and has each cell producing an epibasidium terminating in a sterigma and basidiospore. A few species have basidia of other types.[2] Many, but not all, species of *Septobasidium* have binucleate hypobasidia and a fusion of the two nuclei. Division of the fusion nucleus is meiotic and takes place at the time epibasidia begin to develop.[3] Basidiospores of most species are arcuate and become transversely divided into two or more cells before or after abscission from the sterigmata (Fig. 293*C*). One species is known[4] to have an explosive abscission of basidiospores similar to that in homobasidiomycetes. Basidiospores falling upon a suitable substratum, such a moist bark or a moist mycelium, may bud off

[1] Couch, 1935, 1938. [2] Couch, 1935, 1938; Olive, 1943. [3] Olive, 1943.
[4] Couch, 1935.

conidia (Fig. 293*D*) and the formation of conidia may continue for a long time.

ORDER 5. UREDINIALES

The Urediniales, the rusts, are obligate parasites of vascular plants. Dikaryotic mycelia of all Urediniales produce one- to several-celled **teleutospores** in which each cell is at first dikaryotic and then has a fusion

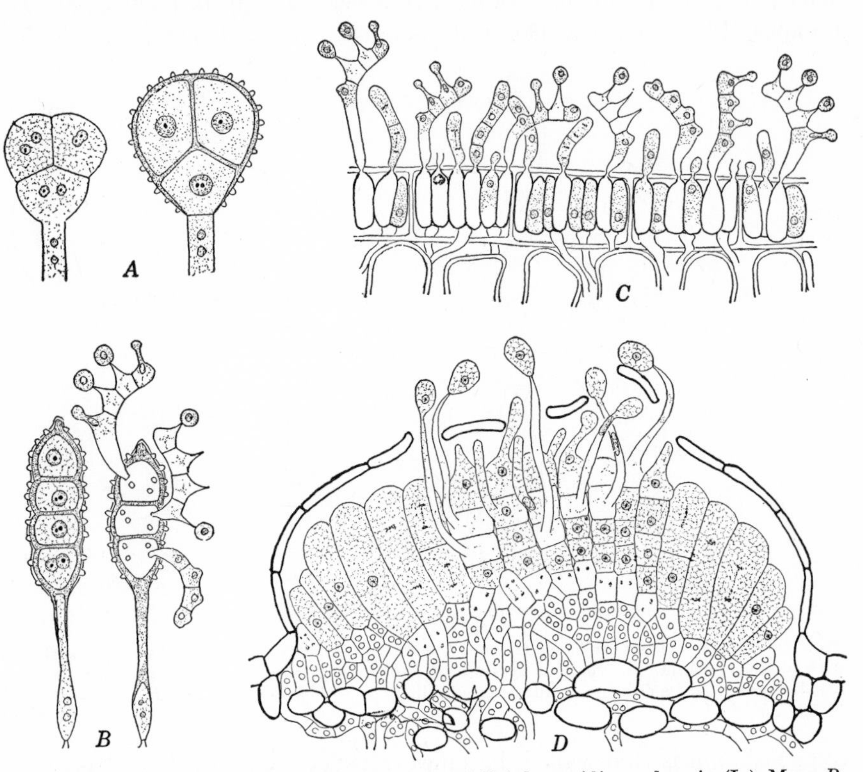

FIG. 294. *A*, young and mature teleutospores of *Triphragmidium ulmaria* (L.) Max. *B*, teleutospores of *Phragmidium rubi* (Pers.) Wint. before and after formation of epibasidia. *C*, teleutosorus of *Thekospora areolata* (Fr.) Mgn. *D*, teleutosorus of *Coelosporium sonchi* (Schum.) Lév. (*All after Sappin-Trouffy*, 1896.) (*A*, × 630; *B*, × 310; *C*, × 460; *D*, × 540.)

of the two nuclei. Many Urediniales also form either one or two kinds of dikaryotic spores in addition to teleutospores, but in these spores there is no fusion of the nuclei. There are about 125 genera and 6,000 species.

Teleutospores are borne in sori that are generally subepidermal and eventually become exposed by rupture of the overlying epidermis. Teleutospores may or may not be laterally adjoined in a crust-like layer, and they may be sessile or borne on stalks (Fig. 294). From the morphological standpoint each cell of a teleutospore is a dikaryotic hypobasidium and one in which there is a fusion of the two nuclei before the teleutospore is mature. Most genera have each hypobasidium of a teleutospore sending forth an epibasidium that becomes transversely divided into four cells, each of which forms a sterigma and basidiospore (Figs. 294*B–C*, 298*A*). Some genera have the hypobasidium becoming transversely divided into four cells and have each of the four cells forming an epibasidium terminating in a single sterigma and basidiospore (Fig. 294*D*).

A basidiospore falling upon a suitable host germinates to form a primary mycelium of uninucleate cells. Dikaryotization may be by somatogamy or it may be by spermatization. After dikaryotization there may be a formation of a dikaryotic mycelium that produces dikaryotic spores; or dikaryotization may be immediately followed by a formation of dikaryotic spores as is the case with aecidiospores (see page 504).

If no other dikaryotic spores other than teleutospores are produced during the complete life cycle, the rust is short-cycled or **microcyclic.**[1] If there is a production of one or additional types of dikaryotic spores, the rust is long-cycled or **macrocyclic.** Macrocyclic rusts may have the following three types of spore in addition to teleutospores and basidiospores: dikaryotic **aecidiospores** which always produce a dikaryotic mycelium when they germinate, dikaryotic **uredospores** which are always borne on a dikaryotic secondary mycelium and which always produce a dikaryotic secondary mycelium when they germinate, and uninucleate **spermatia** which are borne upon a primary mycelium with uninucleate cells. Microcyclic rusts may produce only teleutospores and basidiospores or they may also have the primary mycelium producing spermatia. Urediniales completing the entire life cycle on a single host are **autoecious,** and those with two hosts necessary for the complete cycle are **heteroecious.** Heteroecism is found only among macrocyclic rusts.

Puccinia graminis Pers., often called the wheat rust, is a macrocyclic rust in which the complete life cycle involves all possible types of spore. It is also heteroecious; with the primary mycelium parasitic on the barberry and the secondary mycelium parasitic on wheat, oats, rye, barley, and many grasses. Although there are no evident morphological differences between uredospores, or between teleutospores, from different host species there are many biological races within *P. graminis.* For example, uredospores from the wheat will not infect oats, rye, or barley. In addition, there are also biological races upon the same host species and numerous physiological races have been found in different agronomic varieties of wheat.

Infection of wheat with *P. graminis* is externally evident because of the vertically elongate, reddish-brown or blackish, granular pustules upon the stem and leaves. The first pustules (sori) appear late in the spring and are reddish brown. Since they contain uredospores only they are

[1] Arthur and Kern, 1936; Arthur *et al.*, 1929.

known as **uredosori.** Uredospores of a mature uredosorus are freely exposed, and they may become detached and carried to other plants by the wind. A uredospore is broadly ovoid, binucleate, and with four or five circular thin areas (**germ pores**) in the relatively thick wall. It germinates within a few hours after falling upon a suitable host plant and sends out a hypha (**germ tube**) through one or more of the germ pores (Fig. 295*A*). If it sends out two germ tubes, one grows more vigorously than the other. A germ tube grows over the surface of the epidermis of the host and, when it reaches a stoma, its tip develops into an elongate vesicle—the **appressorium.** The binucleate protoplast of the germ tube migrates into the

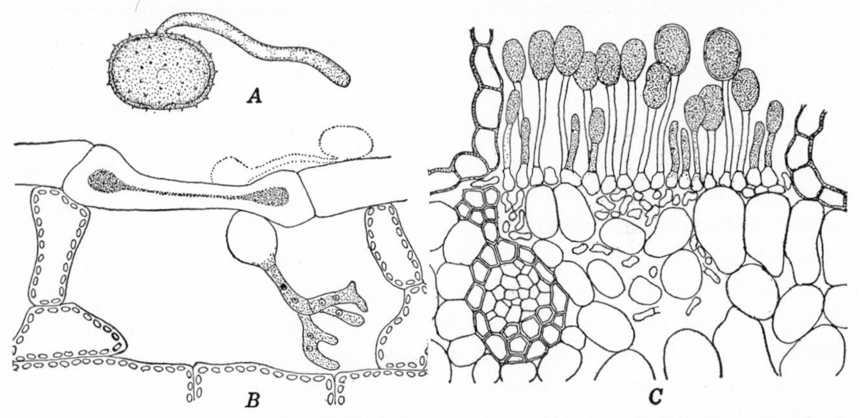

FIG. 295. *Puccinia graminis* Pers. *A*, germination of a uredospore. *B*, infection of a wheat plant by growth of a hypha through a stoma. *C*, uredosorus. (*A*, × 650; *B*, × 485; *C*, × 325.)

appressorium, and the empty germ tube becomes separated from the appressorium by a cross wall.[1] The appressorium then sends downward a wedge-like outgrowth whose distal end usually enlarges into a vesicle after it has grown through the stomatal slit. The contents of the appressorium migrate into the vesicle developed beneath the stoma, and a much-branched mycelium, composed of many short binucleate cells, then grows from the substomatal vesicle (Fig. 295*B*). Growth of the mycelium is intercellular and with a formation of many short haustorial branches that penetrate the host cells. A fully developed mycelium does not extend far from the point of entrance into the host. There is some killing of host cells in the infected area, but many of them appear to be normal. Hyphal branches of the mycelium are especially numerous just beneath the epidermis of the host, and within five or six days they begin to form uredospores. The first uredospores mature 10 to 12 days after infection. A very young uredosorus consists of a layer of binucleate **basal cells** that elongate vertically and divide transversely (Fig. 295*C*). The inferior

[1] Allen, 1923.

daughter cell, which does not divide, is the **foot cell.** The superior daughter cell divides transversely, the upper daughter cell maturing into a uredospore and the lower one into a **stalk cell.** Since there is a continual differentiation of new basal cells in a sorus, there may be a long-continued production of uredospores. Maturation of the first uredospores is followed by a rupturing of the overlying epidermis of the host and dispersal of the uredospores. The time interval between infection and development of the new mycelium to a fruiting condition is so short (10 to

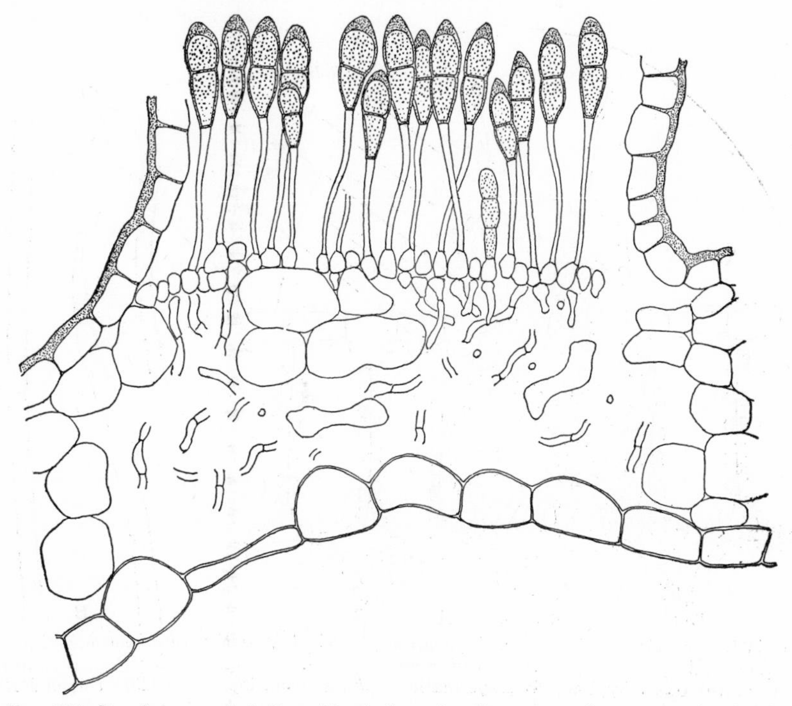

FIG. 296. *Puccinia graminis* Pers. Vertical section through a teleutosorus. (× 325.)

12 days) that several successive generations of uredospore-producing mycelia may be formed during the summer if conditions are favorable.

Toward the end of summer, the mycelium begins to produce teleutospores instead of uredospores. The first teleutospores are generally developed in a sorus containing uredospores; sori produced late in the development of the host contain only teleutospores. The change from uredo- to teleutospore production is dependent upon the photosynthetic activity of the host, and it has been shown[1] that under certain conditions there may even be a reversal from teleuto- to uredospore production. Teleutospore development is similar to uredospore development except that the

[1] Waters, 1928.

sister cell of the stalk cell divides into two binucleate cells which develop into a two-celled teleutospore (Fig. 296). Both cells of the teleutospore are hypobasidia and each secretes a thick wall with a single germ pore. The two nuclei in each hypobasidium fuse as the wall is maturing.[1]

Ordinarily the hypobasidia of a teleutospore do not "germinate" until the next spring. At this time teleutospores may be lying on the ground or may still be attached to dead host plants. One or both hypobasidia sends forth a tubular epibasidium. The fusion nucleus moves into the

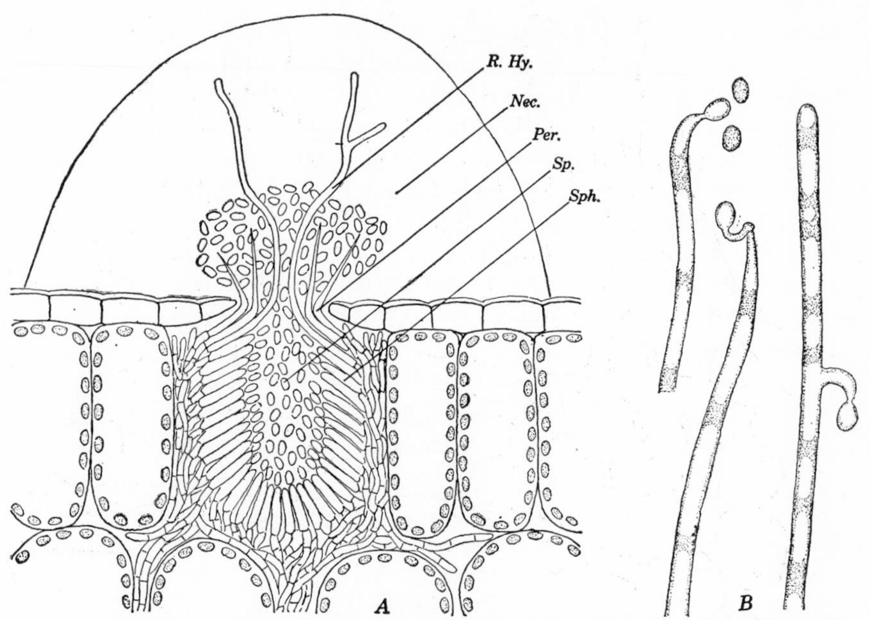

FIG. 297. *Puccinia graminis* Pers. *A*, diagram of a vertical section of a spermogonium. *B*, terminal and lateral spermatization of receptive hyphae. (*Nec.*, nectar; *Per.*, periphyses; *R. Hy.*, receptive hyphae; *Sp.*, spermatia; *Sph.*, spermatiophores.) (*Based upon Buller*, 1950.)

epibasidium and there divides meiotically into four daughter nuclei. Transverse walls are formed after both the first and the second meiotic divisions. Each of the four cells thus formed produces a lateral sterigma and basidiospore, but this generally takes place in the median cells before it does in the terminal ones (Fig. 298*A*). As in many of the homobasidiomycetes, abscission of basidiospores is explosive.[2]

Basidiospores are incapable of infecting wheat, and they can develop into a mycelium only if they fall upon a barberry. A basidiospore falling upon a leaf or a young twig of the barberry sends out a germ tube that grows directly through the outer wall of an epidermal cell and there forms

[1] Sappin-Trouffy, 1896. [2] Buller, 1924.

a hypha with four to six uninucleate cells.[1] This is the beginning of development of the primary mycelium, and the branches growing out from each cell of the hypha develop into a primary mycelium that grows between all cells between the upper and lower epidermis. About the fourth day after infection, dense mats of hyphae appear here and there between the upper epidermis and the palisade tissue of a leaf. These are the primordia of the **spermogonia (pycnia)**. A mature spermogonium (Fig. 297*A*) is oval to flask-shaped and with a pore-like opening, the **ostiole,** at its apex. Hyphae adjacent to the ostiole develop into straight pointed **periphyses** that project through and beyond the ostiole. The region adjacent to the ostiole also gives rise to **receptive hyphae** (**flexuous hyphae**) projecting farther beyond the ostiole than do the periphyses.[2] The cavity of the spermogonium is lined with a palisade-like layer of elongate uninucleate cells (**spermatiophores**) each of which cuts off a succession of **spermatia.** The spermatia are extruded through the ostiole and accumulate in a mass just external to it. As the spermatia are being extruded, the spermogonium secretes a droplet of a nectar-like liquid that covers the periphyses, the receptive hyphae, and the extruded spermatia (Fig. 297*A*).

Spermatia were generally thought to be functionless spore-like bodies until it was found[3] that they are an essential factor in inducing the formation of dikaryotic aecidiospores by the mycelium growing within the barberry. It was found that there was a production of aecidiospores only when there was a transfer of spermatia to the vicinity of an ostiole of another spermogonium. It was also found that a production of aecidiospores took place only when the spermatia from a mycelium of one sex were transferred to the vicinity of a spermogonium borne by a mycelium of opposite sex. The clue leading to this discovery was the chance observation[4] that a fly went from droplet to droplet of exuded nectar on a barberry leaf, and the realization that the resultant transfer of spermatia might be of significance. The manner in which a transfer of spermatia brings about diploidization was soon shown[5] to be by a spermatization of the receptive hyphae of a spermogonium (Fig. 297*B*). Under natural conditions, flies are not always essential for spermatization since this may also take place when two mycelia of opposite sex grow close together and there is a coalescence of droplets of nectar from their spermogonia.

A primary mycelium within a barberry leaf also produces a globose mass of hyphae just within the lower epidermis. This mass, the **protoaecidium,** has a more or less plate-like layer of **basal cells** on the side away from the lower epidermis, and a mass of **displacement cells** on the side facing the lower epidermis. If there is no spermatization there is no fur-

[1] Allen, 1930. [2] Buller, 1950. [3] Craigie, 1927, 1927*A*.
[4] Buller, 1950; Craigie, 1927, 1927*A*. [5] Craigie, 1933.

ther development of a protoaecidium. If there is spermatization, spermatial nuclei entering receptive hyphae migrate from cell to cell of the primary mycelium. Such a migration is possible because of the central pore in cross walls between the cells. The migrating nuclei eventually reach and dikaryotize the basal cells of a protoaecidium.[1] There is then

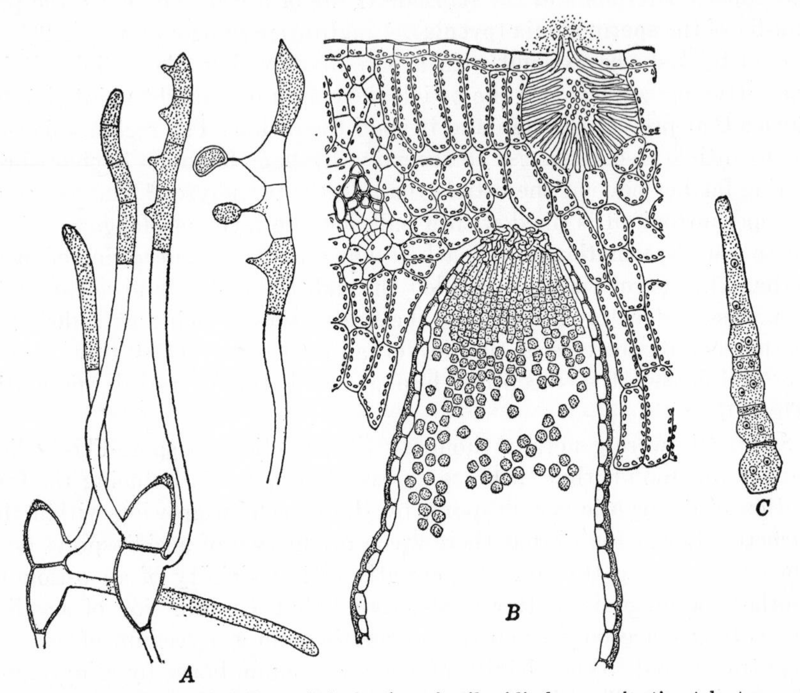

Fig. 298. *Puccinia graminis* Pers. *A*, formation of epibasidia by germinating teleutospores. *B*, vertical section of a barberry leaf showing a spermogonium and an aecidium. *C*, a chain of aecidiospores alternating with small sterile cells. (*A*, × 480; *B*, × 160; *C*, × 650.)

a development of the protoaecidium into an **aecidium.** Each of the dikaryotized basal cells cuts off a chain of dikaryotic cells on the side toward the lower epidermis of the host. The chains of dikaryotic cells grow into the cavity formed by gradual disintegration of the mass of displacement cells. Derivatives from basal cells at the periphery of the plate of basal cells do not redivide and they mature into the protective layer, **peridium,** of an aecidium. Derivatives cut off from all other basal cells immediately divide into a large and a small daughter cell. The large cell becomes an **aecidiospore**; the smaller one soon disintegrates (Fig. 298*C*). A developing aecidium elongates and pushes through the epidermis of the host. The apex of the peridium eventually ruptures, and the exposed aecidiospores are shed from the aecidium (Fig. 298*B*).

[1] Buller, 1950.

Aecidiospores are shed late in the spring. They cannot reinfect the barberry. An aecidiospore carried to and lodging upon a wheat plant may germinate and send forth a hypha that grows through a stoma. The mycelium developing within the wheat is dikaryotic, and within 10 to 12 days it begins to form uredospores.

In areas where the barberry is present, the first infection of wheat plants is by means of aecidiospores. In areas where there are no barberries within hundreds of miles there may also be an early appearance of *P. graminis* on wheat and other hosts. Here, infection may be due to uredospores surviving over winter if the climate is a mild one. This is not the case in regions with severe winters and where all uredospores are winter-killed. Infection of hosts in such regions is due to uredospores that have been carried by winds from regions where the mycelia in wheat plants have already begun the production of uredospores. The catching of uredospores in spore traps exposed in airplanes[1] flying hundreds of miles north of wheat-growing areas of North America shows that spores of *P. graminis* are carried long distances by winds.

The microcyclic rusts are generally interpreted as types that are derived from, instead of more primitive than, the macrocyclic rusts. Some microcyclic rusts produce spermatia; others do not. All species in which the sexuality has been studied are homothallic.[2]

Puccinia malvacearum Bert., the rust growing on leaves of the hollyhock, is representative of microcyclic rusts which form only teleutospores and basidiospores. Inoculation of the host with single basidiospores shows[3] that this rust is homothallic. The primary mycelium is intercellular and grows between all mesophyll cells of a leaf. The portion internal to the lower epidermis becomes dikaryotic,[4] presumably by somatogamy, and this portion gives rise to a teleutosorus that becomes exposed by rupture of the host's epidermis. Development of teleutospores[5] is similar to that in *P. graminis* and the nuclei in both hypobasidia fuse before the teleutospore is ripe (Fig. 299*A–B*). "Germination" of teleutospores may take place immediately after they are mature and without their becoming detached from the host. The fusion nucleus moves into the epibasidium growing out from each hypobasidium and there undergoes meiosis.[5] Transverse cross walls are formed between daughter nuclei of both the first (Fig. 299*E*) and the second meiotic divisions. Each of the four cells of an epibasidium sends out a sterigma that develops a basidiospore at its apex (Fig. 299*F–G*). Each basidiospore is uninucleate when first formed but it may become binucleate before germinating (Fig. 299*H*). A basidiospore infects the host immediately after it is shed and the mycelium developing from the spore soon produces teleutospores. Thus,

[1] Pady *et al.*, 1950. [2] Buller, 1950. [3] Ashworth, 1931; Brown, 1940.
[4] Ashworth, 1931; Allen, 1935. [5] Allen, 1933*A*.

there may be several successive generations of the fungus during a single growing season of the host.

Microcyclic rusts producing spermatia have not been critically investigated, but there is reason for assuming that similar to *P. graminis* the dikaryotic condition is initiated by spermatization.

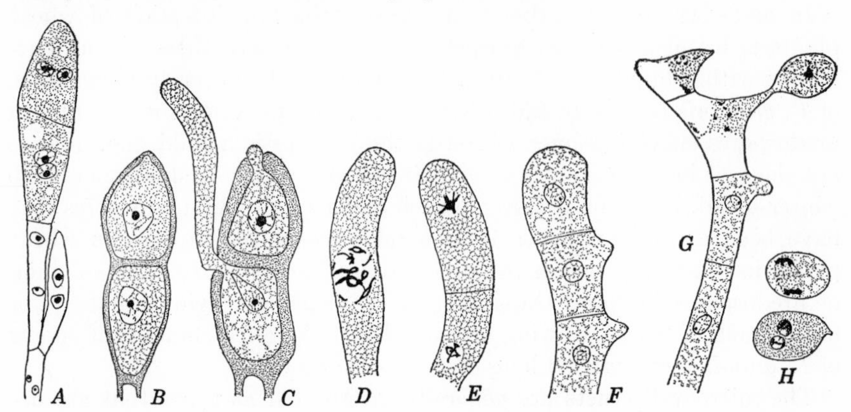

FIG. 299. *Puccinia malvacearum* Bert. *A*, young teleutospore. *B*, mature teleutospore. *C–G*, stages in development of epibasidia by germinating teleutospores. *H*, basidiospores. (*After Ruth F. Allen*, 1933*A*.) (*A–C*, × 700; *D–H*, × 1,125.)

ORDER 6. USTILAGINALES

The Ustilaginales, the smuts, are parasites in which the teleutospores (chlamydospores) are formed from intercalary cells of a dikaryotic mycelium. The teleutospores are one-celled hypobasidia which produce septate or unseptate epibasidia. There are about 40 genera and 700 species.

Ustilago is representative of genera with septate epibasidia. There are about 300 species and most of them are parasitic upon a single host species. Certain species are parasitic upon cereals. These are of considerable economic importance since they may reduce the yield of grain by 25 to 50 per cent.

Although parasitic, *Ustilago* may also be a facultative saprophyte and certain species have been grown from basidiospore to teleutospore on synthetic media.[1] Several species have been found to be heterothallic and with a typical infection dependent upon inoculation of the host with two basidiospores or two conidia of opposite sex. The sexuality of heterothallic species may be bipolar or tetrapolar. Establishment of the dikaryotic condition may take place at the earliest possible stage and by somatogamy between two cells of the four-celled epibasidium[2] (Fig. 300*C–D*). There may also be somatogamy between basidiospores or between conidia produced by them.[3] More frequently, somatogamy is between cells

[1] Sartoris, 1924. [2] Harper, 1899; Lutman, 1910; Rawitscher, 1912.
[3] Bowman, 1946; Harper, 1899; Lutman, 1910.

of primary mycelia resulting from germination of basidiospores or of conidia. In *U. maydis* (DC.) Cda. [*U. zea* (Beckm.) Ung.] a basidiospore or a conidium gives rise to a primary mycelium that immediately grows through the epidermis of the host and then grows horizontally beneath

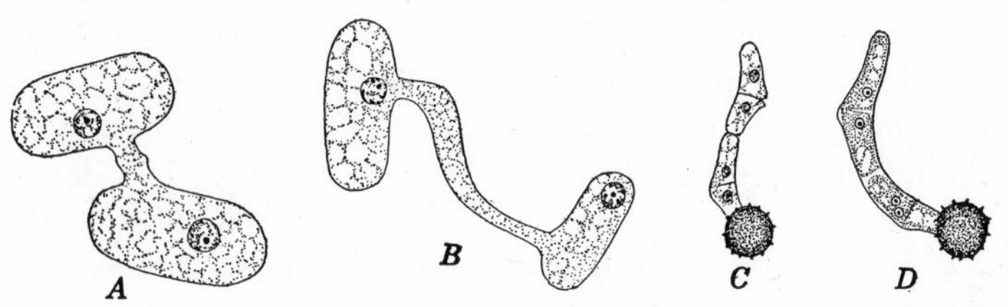

FIG. 300. *A–B*, conjugation of basidiospores of *Ustilago anthearum* Wint. *C–D*, conjugation between cells of epibasidium of *Ustilago carbo* Tul (*A–B*, *after Harper*, 1899; *C–D*, *after Rawitscher*, 1912.)

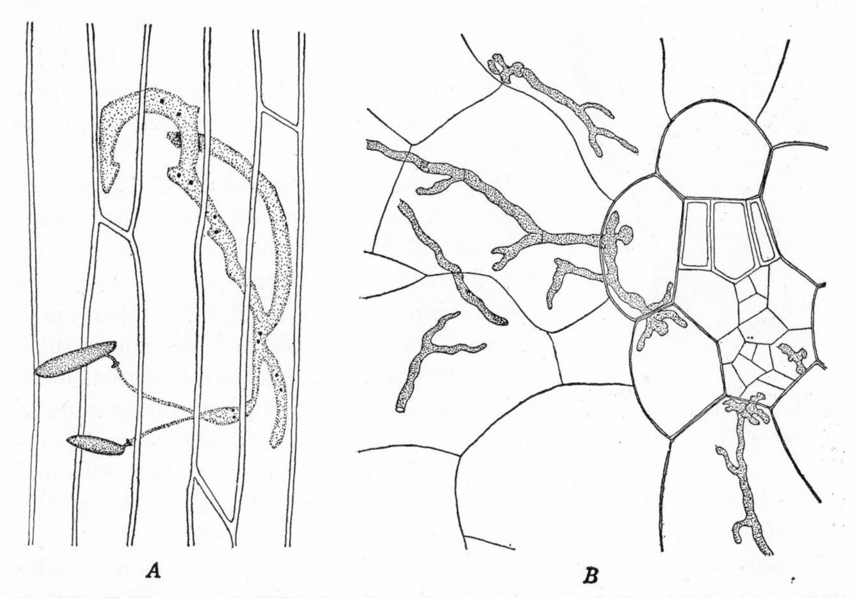

FIG. 301. *Ustilago maydis* (DC.) Cda. *A*, surface view of a corn leaf containing a secondary mycelium formed by conjugation of hyphae from two germinating conidia. *B*, vertical section of a corn leaf showing mycelium within hypertrophied host tissues. (*A*, *after Hanna*, 1929.) (*A*, × 540; *B*, × 650.)

it. Somatogamy with another primary mycelium may take place immediately after penetration into the host (Fig. 301*A*) or after there has been some growth of primary mycelia penetrating the host.[1] When corn plants are infected with a single spore of *U. maydis*, or with several spores of the same sex, there is a formation of a many-celled primary mycelium, but this never produces teleutospores or induces a formation of galls by the

[1] Hanna, 1929; Sleumer, 1931.

host.[1] When there is a formation of a dikaryotic secondary mycelium of *U. maydis* it grows to only a limited extent. This mycelium grows chiefly in intercellular spaces of the host tissue and sends short haustorial branches into the host cells (Fig. 301*B*). Evidence seems to be better favoring those who record clamp connections[1] than those[2] who deny that they are present. The production of a secondary mycelium induces an active division and redivision of host cells in the infected region, and many of them increase to an enormous size. This causes a gall-like swelling of the infected region (Fig. 302). Eventually there is a death of all host cells below the epidermis of the gall. Ordinarily the only spores formed in an infected area are teleutospores (chlamydospores), but under exceptional conditions certain hyphae may protrude through the epidermis of the host and form conidia. These conidia are always uninucleate and a single one is incapable of developing into a mycelium produces teleutospores when inoculated on the host.[2]

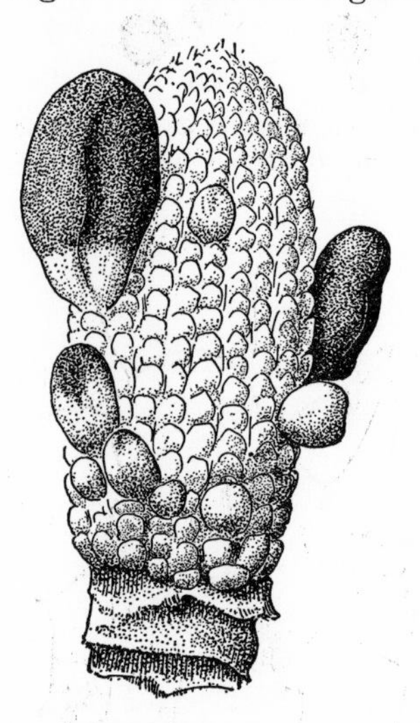

FIG. 302. An ear of corn with certain kernels infected with *Ustilago maydis* (DC.) Cda. (× ⅔.)

When growth of the dikaryotic secondary mycelium ceases, most of the cells become globose and develop into thick-walled unicellular hypobasidia (teleutospores). A young hypobasidium is dikaryotic but there is a fusion of the two nuclei as it develops a thick wall. The gall of *U. maydis* now consists of an epidermal layer overlying a powdery mass of innumerable hypobasidia (teleutospores) intermingled with dried remains of host cells and sterile hyphae. The epidermis of a gall may dry out and rupture at any time after the hypobasidia are mature.

Hypobasidia of *U. maydis* may "germinate" and produce epibasidia immediately after they are shed from a gall, but it is very probable that the great majority of them do not do so until the following spring. At the time of "germination" the wall cracks open and a tubular outgrowth, the epibasidium, begins to extend out through the opening (Fig. 303*A*). In *U. maydis* the fusion nucleus divides into two daughter nuclei, one of which migrates into the epibasidium. Both nuclei divide again, and one or both daughter nuclei of the nucleus remaining within the hypobasidium migrate into the epibasidium.[1] The three- or four-nucleate epibasidium then becomes divided into four cells. The nucleus within each

[1] Hanna, 1929. [2] Sleumer, 1931.

epibasal cell divides into two daughter nuclei. One of them migrates into a basidiospore budding off from the cell; the other remains within the cell. Ordinarily the nucleus remaining within the cell divides again and there is a budding off of a second basidiospore. Numerous genetic studies have shown that division of the fusion nucleus is meiotic, and that two cells of the epibasidium produce basidiospores of one sex and the other two cells produce basidiospores of the opposite sex. The chances for an infection of the host are greatly increased because of the budding off of conidia from the basidiospores. This may take place before (Fig. 303*E*) or after detachment of a basidiospore from the basidium.

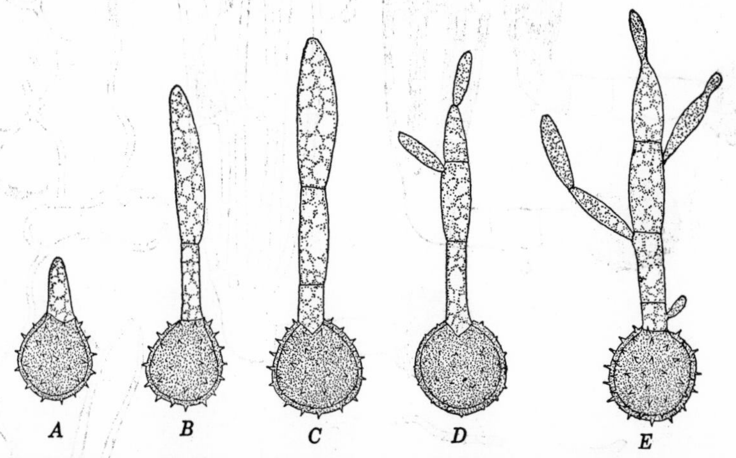

FIG. 303. *Ustilago maydis* (DC.) Cda. Stages in the formation of epibasidia by germinating hypobasidia and the production of conidia by the budding of basidiospores. (× 1,300.)

Tilletia is representative of the genera with epibasidia that do not become transversely divided into uninucleate cells. There are about 40 species. Two of these [*T. tritici* (Bjerk.) Wint. and *T. foetans* (B. and C.) Trel.] are parasitic on wheat. Collectively these two species cause the disease known as bunt or stinking smut. This is not a serious disease in this country, except in the Pacific Northwest. Heads of wheat infected with *Tilletia* have an odor resembling that of decaying fish.

Infection of wheat plants normally takes place only during the seedling stage. If teleutospores are used as the inoculum, there is considerable infection for the first six days after seeds are planted and none after the tenth day.[1] If conidia are used as the inoculum there is considerable infection for the first eight days and none after the twelfth. Development of the mycelium within a seedling keeps pace with that of host tissues. The presence of the fungus within the host is not externally evident, and it is impossible to distinguish between infected and uninfected individuals

[1] Sartoris, 1924.

until the time of flowering. At this time, flowers of infected plants have ovaries about twice the normal size and have abortive stamens of small size. There is a rapid increase in the amount of dikaryotic mycelium

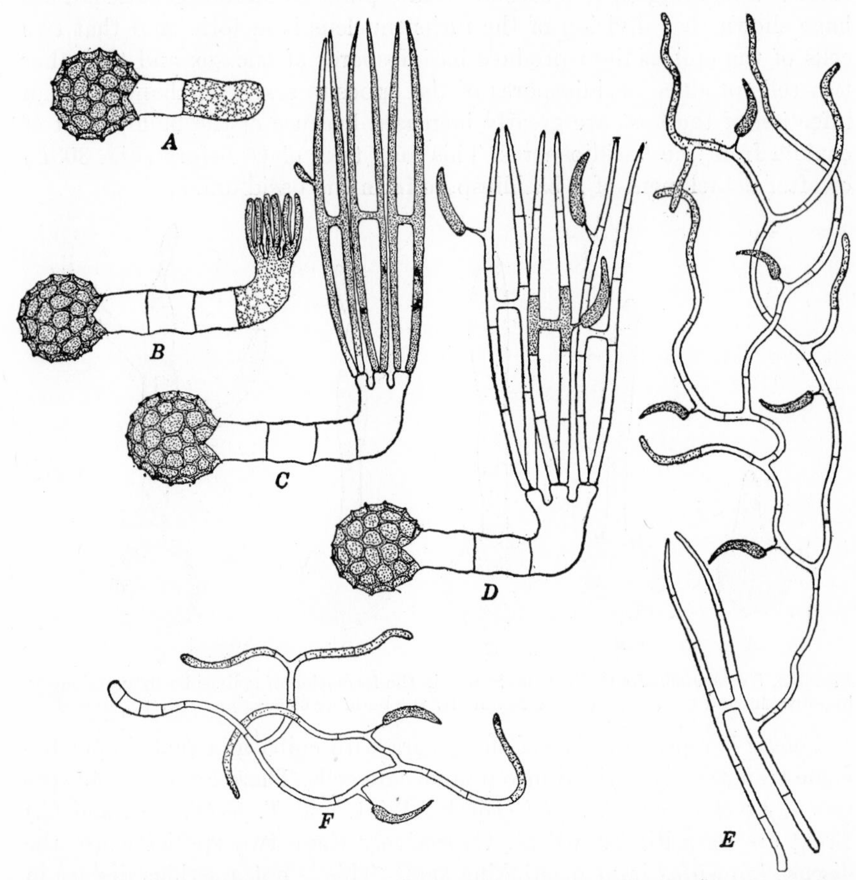

Fig. 304. *Tilletia tritici* (Bjerk.) Wint. *A–B*, diagrams showing the formation of epibasidia by germinating hypobasidia and the beginning of formation of basidiospores *C–D*, diagrams showing the conjugation of basidiospores and the formation of conidia. *E*, diagram showing the development of a mycelium and conidia from a conjugated pair of basidiospores. *F*, diagram of the production of secondary conidia by a mycelium formed from a primary conidium. (*Diagrams based upon Buller*, 1933.) (× 300.)

within the developing ovaries, and this is followed by most of the dikaryotic cells developing into unicellular globose hypobasidia (teleutospores). These changes result in a wheat kernel with a normal seed coat but one in which the interior of the kernel is filled with hypobasidia. Such kernels are called **smut balls.** Under normal conditions the smut balls do not break open and liberate the contained hypobasidia until the following spring. When wheat is threshed there is a breaking of a certain percentage of the smut balls as the wheat passes through the threshing machine. Many of the hypobasidia from these broken smut balls lodge upon normal kernels passing through the machine and are accidentally sown with the kernels when the next crop of wheat is planted.

The two nuclei in a young hypobasidium (teleutospore) fuse as it is maturing, and when the hypobasidium "germinates" to form an epibasidium the fusion nucleus moves into the epibasidium and there divides meiotically to form 8, 16, or more daughter nuclei. An elongating epibasidium may have its protoplasm restricted to the distal portion and form a succession of transverse septa as the basal portion is evacuated[1] (Fig. 304*A–B*). Frequently there is no formation of transverse septa.[2] Eight to 24 elongate, acicular, arcuate, uninucleate basidiospores are formed at the distal end of the epibasidium. Genetic analysis[3] of these basidiospores has shown that *Tilletia* is heterothallic and in some cases tetrapolar. Basidiospores frequently conjugate in pairs before becoming separated from the epibasidium (Fig. 304*C*). The protoplast of one basidiospore then migrates to and fuses with the protoplast of the other basidiospore. The basidiospore containing the united protoplasts may give rise to a single dikaryotic conidium or it may send forth a single branching hypha that bears several conidia (Fig. 304*D–E*). In turn, conidia produced by basidiospores, or by hyphae growing from them, may give rise to hyphae bearing conidia (Fig. 304*F*). Abscission of conidia is by a forcible discharge similar to that of basidiospores of many homobasidiomycetes.[4] Conidia infecting the host are dikaryotic and give rise to a dikaryotic mycelium. When infection takes place a hypha grows between the host's epidermal cells and develops into a mycelium that lies within the tissues of the host.[5]

Bibliography

Alexopoulos, C. J. **1952.** Introductory mycology. New York. 482 pp. 187 figs.

Allen, Ruth F. **1923.** *Jour. Agr. Res.* **23:** 131–151. 6 pl. [*Puccinia graminis.*]

1930. *Ibid.* **40:** 585–614. 17 pl. [*Puccinia graminis.*]

1933. *Ibid.* **47:** 1–16. 6 pl. [*Puccinia graminis.*]

1933A. *Phytopathology* **23:** 574–586. 4 figs. [*Puccinia malvacearum.*]

1935. *Jour. Agr. Res.* **51:** 801–818. 9 pl. [*Puccinia malvacearum.*]

Arthur, J. C., and F. D. Kern. **1926.** *Mycologia* **18:** 90–93. [*Urediniales.*]

Arthur, J. C., in collaboration with F. D. Kern, C. R. Orton *et al.* **1929.** The plant rusts (Urediniales). Philadelphia. 446 pp. 186 figs.

Ashworth, Dorothy. **1931.** *Trans. Brit. Mycol. Soc.* **16:** 177–202. 2 pl. 7 figs. [*Puccinia malvacearum.*]

Barnett, H. L. **1937.** *Mycologia* **29:** 626–649. 3 figs. [Sexuality.]

Barrus, M. F. **1916.** *Phytopathology* **6:** 21–28. 3 figs. [*Tilletia.*]

[1] Brefeld, 1883; Buller, 1933. [2] Dastur, 1921; Rawitscher, 1914; Yen, 1936.
[3] Becker, 1936; Flor, 1932; Hanna, 1934.
[4] Buller and Vanterpool, 1925; Buller, 1933. [5] Sartoris, 1924.

Becker, T. **1936.** *Phytopath. Zeitschr.* **9:** 187–228. [*Tilletia.*]
Bensaude, Mathilde. **1918.** Recherches sur le cycle évolutif et la sexualité chez les Basidiomycètes. Nemours. 156 pp. 13 pl. 30 figs.
Bessey, E. A. **1950.** Morphology and taxonomy of fungi. Philadelphia. 791 pp. 210 figs.
Blizzard, A. W. **1917.** *Amer. Jour. Bot.* **4:** 221–240. 6 pl. [Gymnocarpic basidiocarps.]
Bowman, D. H. **1946.** *Jour. Agr. Res.* **72:** 233–243. 2 figs. [*Ustilago maydis.*]
Brefeld, O. **1883.** Untersuchungen aus dem Gesammtgebiete der Mykologie. Heft 3. Leipzig. 220 pp. 13 pl.
1888. *Ibid.* Heft 7. 178 pp. 11 pl.
Brodie, H. J. **1936.** *Amer. Jour. Bot.* **23:** 309–327. 41 figs. [Oidia.]
Brown, A. M. **1940.** *Canad. Jour. Res.* **18,** Sect. *C*: 18–25. 3 pl. [*Puccinia malvacearum.*]
Buller, A. H. R. **1909.** Researches on fungi. Vol. 1. London. 287 pp. 5 pl. 83 figs.
1922. *Ibid.* Vol. 2. London. 492 pp. 157 figs.
1924. *Ibid.* Vol. 3. London. 611 pp. 227 figs.
1930. *Nature* **126:** 686–689. [Sexuality.]
1933. Researches on fungi. Vol. 5. London. 416 pp. 174 figs.
1941. *Bot. Rev.* **7:** 335–431. [Diploidization.]
1950. Researches on fungi. Vol. 7. Toronto. 458 pp. 124 figs.
Buller, A. H. R., and T. C. Vanterpool. **1925.** *Nature* **116:** 934–935. 1 fig. [*Tilletia.*]
Coker, W. C. **1920.** *Jour. Elisha Mitchell Sci. Soc.* **35:** 113–182. 39 pl. [*Tremella, Septobasidium.*]
Coker, W. C., and J. N. Couch. **1928.** The Gasteromycetes of the eastern United States and Canada. Chapel Hill, N.C. 201 pp. 123 pl.
Colson, Barbara. **1935.** *Ann. Bot.* **49:** 1–18. 49 figs. [*Psalliota.*]
Couch, J. N. **1935.** *Jour. Elisha Mitchell Sci. Soc.* **51:** 1–77. 44 pl. [*Septobasidium.*]
1938. The genus Septobasidium. Chapel Hill, N.C. 480 pp. 114 pl. 60 figs.
Craigie, J. H. **1927.** *Nature* **120:** 116–117. 1 fig. [*Puccinia graminis.*]
1927A. *Ibid.* **120:** 765–767. 2 figs. [*Puccinia graminis.*]
1928. *Phytopathology* **18:** 1005–1015. 3 figs. [*Puccinia graminis.*]
1931. *Ibid.* **21:** 1001–1040. 14 figs. [*Puccinia graminis.*]
1933. *Nature* **131:** 25. [*Puccinia.*]
Cunningham, G. H. **1926.** *New Zealand Jour. Sci. and Technol.* **8:** 228–232. 7 figs. [*Lycoperdon.*]
Dangeard, P. A. **1895.** *Le Botaniste* **4:** 119–181. 24 figs. [*Tremella, Dacromyces.*]
Dastur, J. F. **1921.** *Ann. Bot.* **35:** 399–407. 1 pl. 9 figs. [*Tilletia.*]
Dietel, P. **1928.** Hemibasidii. In A. Engler and K. Prantl, Die natürlichen Pflanzenfamilien. 2d ed. Bd. 6. pp. 1–98. 80 figs.
Eftimu, Panca, and S. Kharbush. **1927.** *Rev. Path. Vég. et Ent. Agr.* **14:** 62–88. 1 pl. 9 figs. [*Exobasidium.*]
Flor, H. H. **1932.** *Jour. Agr. Res.* **44:** 49–58. [*Tilletia.*]
Gäumann, E. **1949.** Die Pilze. Basel. 382 pp. 440 figs.
1953. The fungi. Translated by F. L. Wynd. New York. 420 pp. 440 figs.
Gäumann, E. A., and C. W. Dodge. **1928.** Comparative morphology of the fungi. Translated and revised by C. W. Dodge. New York. 701 pp. 406 figs.
Gilbert. E. M. **1911.** *Science* N.S. **33:** 264. [*Dacromyces.*]
1921. *Trans. Wis. Acad.* **20:** 387–397. 1 pl. 1 fig. [*Dacromyces.*]
Gregory, P. H. **1949.** *Trans. Brit. Mycol. Soc.* **32:** 11–15. 1 pl. 1 fig. [*Lycoperdon.*]
Hanna, W. F. **1929.** *Phytopathology* **19:** 415–442. 1 pl. 3 figs. [*Ustilago maydis.*]
1934. *Proc. Fifth Pacific Sci. Congr.* 3195–3201. [*Tilletia.*]
Harper, R. A. **1899.** *Trans. Wis. Acad.* **12:** 475–498. 2 pl. [Ustilaginales.]
Hein, Illo. **1930.** *Amer. Jour. Bot.* **17:** 197–211. 2 pl. [*Psalliota.*]
1930A. *Ibid.* **17:** 882–915. 4 pl. [*Psalliota.*]

Hennings, P. **1897.** Hymenomycetineae. In A. Engler and K. Prantl, Die natürlichen Pflanzenfamilien. Bd. 1. Abt. 1. 105–276. 59 figs.

Hills, Patricia L. **1942.** *Amer. Midland Nat.* **28:** 756–760. 5 figs. [Clamp connections.]

Istvánffi, G. von. **1895.** *Ber. Deutsch. Bot. Ges.* **13:** 452–467. 3 pl. [*Dacromyces, Tremella.*]

Jackson, H. S. **1944.** *Trans. Roy. Soc. Canada* 3d ser. **38,** Sect. 5: 1–32. 5 figs. [Phylogeny.]

Juel, H. O. **1898.** *Jahrb. Wiss. Bot.* **32:** 361–388. 1 pl. [*Dacromyces.*]

1916. *Nova Acta Reg. Soc. Sci. Upsaliensis* 4 ser. **5,** Nr. 5: 1–43. 2 pl. [Development of basidia.]

Kniep, H. **1915.** *Zeitschr. Bot.* **7:** 369–398. 1 pl. 20 figs. [Phylogeny of basidia.]

1916. *Ibid.* **8:** 353–359. 1 pl. [Development of basidia.]

1917. *Ibid.* **9:** 81–118. 3 pl. 14 figs. [Formation of clamp connections.]

Lander, Caroline A. **1933.** *Amer. Jour. Bot.* **20:** 204–215. 3 pl. [*Lycoperdon.*]

Linder, D. H. **1940.** *Mycologia* **32:** 419–447. 6 figs. [Evolution of basidium.]

Lutman, B. F. **1910.** *Trans. Wis. Acad.* **16:** 1191–1244. 7 pl. [*Ustilago.*]

Maire, R. **1902.** Recherches cytologiques et taxonomiques sur les Basidiomycètes. Paris. 209 pp. 8 pl.

Martin, G. W. **1942.** *Mycologia* **34:** 132–138. [Clamp connections.]

1945. *Ibid.* **37:** 527–542. 1 fig. [Classification, Tremellales.]

1950. Outline of the fungi. Dubuque, Iowa. 82 pp. 116 figs.

Neuhoff, W. **1924.** *Bot. Arch.* **8:** 250–297. 4 pl. 7 figs. [*Auricularia, Tremella.*]

Olive, L. S. **1943.** *Mycologia* **35:** 557–572. 3 figs. [*Septobasidium.*]

Overholts, L. O. **1925.** *Ibid.* **17:** 108–112. 2 pl. [*Phallus.*]

Pady, S. M., B. Peterson, and G. J. Greene. **1950.** *Phytopathology* **40:** 632–641. 1 fig. [Spores in the air.]

Pelluet, D. **1928.** *Ann. Bot.* **42:** 637–664. 2 pl. 5 figs. [*Exobasidium.*]

Raper, J. R. **1953.** *Quart. Rev. Biol.* **28:** 233–259. [Tetrapolar sexuality.]

Rawitscher, F. **1912.** *Zeitschr. Bot.* **4:** 673–706. 1 pl. 20 figs. [Ustilaginales.]

1914. *Ber. Deutsch. Bot. Ges.* **32:** 310–314. 4 figs. [*Tilletia.*]

Richards, H. M. **1896.** *Bot. Gaz.* **21:** 101–108. 1 pl. [*Exobasidium.*]

Ritchie, D. **1948.** *Amer. Jour. Bot.* **35:** 215–219. 35 figs. [*Lycoperdon.*]

Sappin-Trouffy, P. **1896.** *Le Botaniste* **5:** 59–244. 69 figs. [Urediniales.]

Sartoris, G. B. **1924.** *Amer. Jour. Bot.* **11:** 616–647. 2 pl. [*Ustilago, Tilletia.*]

Sleumer, H. O. **1931.** *Zeitschr. Bot.* **25:** 209–263. 1 pl. 33 figs. [*Ustilago.*]

Swartz, D. **1929.** *Papers Mich. Acad. Sci.* **9:** 299–304. 1 pl. [*Lycoperdon.*]

1933. *Amer. Jour. Bot.* **20:** 440–465. 2 pl. [*Lycoperdon.*]

1936. *Ibid.* **23:** 4–7. 11 figs. [*Lycoperdon.*]

Waters, C. W. **1928.** *Phytopathology* **18:** 157–213. 3 figs. [*Puccinia graminis.*]

Wheldon, R. M. **1934.** *Mycologia* **26:** 415–425. 3 pl. 11 figs. [*Tremella.*]

Whitehouse, H. L. K. **1949.** *Biol. Rev.* **24:** 411–447. [Heterothallism.]

1949A. *New Phytol.* **48:** 212–244. [Heterothallism.]

Yen, W. Y. **1936.** *Compt. Rend. Soc. Biol.* **121:** 1304–1306. 14 figs. [*Tilletia.*]

Zeller, S. M. **1949.** *Mycologia* **41:** 36–58. [Classification, gastromycetes.]

CHAPTER 14

DEUTEROMYCETAE

The Deuteromycetae (the imperfect fungi) include those fungi in which there is no formation of zygotes, or ascospores, or basidiospores at any known stage in development of the fungus. They are the fungi in which the "perfect stage" (that is, zygote, ascus, or basidium) has not been discovered or is lacking. The class is wholly artificial and is erected for the temporary reception of species pending discovery of structures showing that they belong to either the Phycomycetae, Ascomycetae, or Basidiomycetae. The Deuteromycetae also include certain fungi that never form spores at any known stage of their development. These *Mycelia sterila* are recognizable only when they are of a distinctive type, as sclerotia; or grow in distinctive habitats, as is the case of certain mycorhizal fungi.

According to the strictest interpretation, the Deuteromycetae should include phycomycetes known only in the sporangial stage; rusts in which only aecidiospores or uredospores are known; and certain species of ascomycetous genera, as *Penicillium*, which are known only in the conidial stage. However, such species known only in the "imperfect" stage have such characteristic fructifications that there is little doubt concerning their proper systematic position.

Removal of species from the Deuteromycetae has been going on for more than a century. Examples of this are seen in the demonstration that *Sphacelia segetum* Lev. is the conidial stage of *Claviceps purpurea* (Fries) Tul. (page 454); and that certain species of *Monilia* belong in *Neurospora* (page 449). On the other hand, the list of imperfect fungi is continually expanding because new species are being added more rapidly than old ones are being removed. At present about 1,300 genera and 11,000 species are referred to the Deuteromycetae.

It is very probable that almost all the fungi assigned to the deuteromycetes are ascomycetes. The evidence for this includes the similarity between their conidial stages and those of ascomycetes, the lack of unseptate mycelia characteristic of phycomycetes, and the lack of clamp connections found in basidiomycetes. Sooner or later there will be a dis-

covery of the "perfect stage" of certain species now referred to the Deuteromycetae. On the other hand, one cannot assume that there will be an eventual transfer of all species from the class because it is very probable that many species have lost the ability to form the perfect stage.

The imperfect fungi include many species that cause serious diseases among plants and animals. Examples of the former are the anthracnose of beans, the leaf spot of beets, and the early blight of potatoes. The much-publicized "athlete's foot" is an example of a disease of man caused by an imperfect fungus.

Attempts have been made to arrange the Deuteromycetae according to a natural system, but these have been founded upon such inadequate bases that there is no assurance that they show the real phyletic relationships. For this reason it is better to follow the widely used and purely artificial system that divides the Deuteromycetae into orders differing from one another in the manner in which the spores are borne. These are:

Moniliales in which the conidia are borne directly upon an undifferentiated mycelium or upon specialized conidiophores. The conidiophores may be simple or compound and solitary or adjacent to one another. If the conidiophores are adjacent, they never lie in an acervulus or in a pycnidium. There are about 660 genera and 4,100 species.

Melanconiales in which the fungi are parasitic and with the conidiophores in a subepidermal or subcortical acervulus. The order includes some 90 genera and 1,000 species.

Sphaerosidales in which the conidia are borne in a pycnidium or in a modified type of pycnidium. There are about 500 genera and 5,200 species.

Mycelia sterila in which there is no formation of spores, and in which the mycelium has a characteristic structure or mode of growth. About 20 genera and 200 species are placed in this order.

CHAPTER 15

LICHENES (LICHENS)

A lichen consists of two separate plants, a fungus and an alga, so associated with each other that they appear to be a single plant. The fungus almost always envelops the algal component of the association and the combined growth of the two results in a structure of such constant definite form and internal structure that lichens may be segregated into genera and species. There are some 400 genera and 15,000 species.[1]

The proper assignment of lichens to one of the divisions of the plant kingdom presents a problem. Lichenologists universally consider them a class (Lichenes) distinct from classes in either the algae or the fungi. In this they are in accord with the International Code of Botanical Nomenclature in which (Article 23-*d* of the Code as revised in 1950) they are recognized as a distinct group. According to another interpretation both the algal and the fungal component of a lichen should be given a binomial name. Many mycologists take this view[2] and hold that the binomial given to a lichen should apply only to the fungus portion of it, and that the fungus should be referred to one of the classes of the Eumycophyta. Phycologists have seldom objected to this because one is rarely able to carry identification of the algal component beyond the genus. On the other hand, relatively few mycologists or phycologists have been interested in the lichens and the major contributions to their taxonomy have been by botanists specializing in lichens. Thus there is justification for treating lichens by themselves instead of in connection with fungi or with algae.

In four genera the fungal component is a basidiomycete; in all others it is an ascomycete. The algal component may belong to the Cyanophyta or to the Chlorophyta, and may be filamentous or nonfilamentous. Lichens have also been described[3] in which fungi are associated with autotrophic bacteria (purple bacteria) but it has also been held[4] that these bacteria are not an essential component of these lichens.

The relationship between alga and fungus in a lichen is a matter of

[1] Zahlbruckner, 1922–1932.
[2] For example, Alexopoulos, 1952; Bessey, 1950; Martin, 1950.
[3] Uphof, 1925, 1926. [4] Suessenguth, 1926.

controversy. Some agree with the statement that "a lichen is a fungus which lives during all or a part of its life in parasitic relation with the algal host and also sustains a relation with an organic or an inorganic substratum."[1] The strongest argument that the relationship between fungus and alga is one of parasitism is the demonstration[2] that haustorial branches or appresoria penetrate the algal cells of many lichens. Others think that the lichen is a partnership (**consortium**) of a symbiotic nature. The fungus absorbs and retains moisture necessary for the consortium; the alga synthesizes the carbohydrates necessary for the two members of the consortium. If the relationship is symbiotic it is of the type known as **helotism** because the partnership is decidedly at the expense of the alga.

Lichens grow on a wide variety of substrata including the leaves and bark of trees, soil, and rocks. In most cases a given species is restricted to a particular substratum and in the case of those growing on rocks there are marked differences in the composition of the lichen flora on igneous and limestone rocks. Many lichens thrive and multiply in habitats where other vegetation is practically nonexistent. Such habitats include bare rocks and extremely cold regions. The best example of the latter is the arctic tundra where large areas are covered with "reindeer moss" (*Cladonia rangifera* Web.) that grows in clumps 15 to 30 cm. in height. Other lichens, especially those growing on leaves and on the bark of trees, thrive best when there is an abundance of moisture. This is well exemplified by the luxuriant development of lichens in tropical rain forests and in the restriction of the "Californian Spanish moss" (*Ramalina reticulata* Kremp.) to trees growing in the more humid canyons of the Coast Range.

Lichens are of considerable ecological importance as pioneers in colonization of rocky habitats by plants. Growth of a lichen upon a cliff or boulder is accompanied by a disintegration of the portion of the rock immediately beneath it. If the rock is a limestone there is more or less dissolving of the stone. Several lichens growing on limestone are endolithic and with all vegetative cells embedded in the rock.[3] Disintegration of rocks other than limestone is almost wholly mechanical. This has been ascribed[4] to varying stresses and strains induced by expansion and contraction of the gelatinous body of the lichen. When a lichen dies, its decaying remains, together with rock particles, form a soil in which other plants may grow. The first successors are generally mosses, but sooner or later vascular plants begin to grow in the soil.

When recognized as a class, the Lichenes are divided into two subclasses, the Ascolichenes and the Basidiolichenes.

[1] Fink, 1913. [2] Bornet, 1873; Fry, 1928; Geitler, 1937. [3] Fry, 1922.
[4] Fry, 1924, 1927.

SUBCLASS 1. ASCOLICHENES

The Ascolichenes include all lichens in which the fungal component is an ascomycete. All but four of the genera of Lichenes belong to this subclass.

A few Ascolichenes have a gelatinous thallus with alga and fungus uniformly distributed through a gelatinous matrix (Fig. 309*B*). The great majority of them are more or less leathery in texture, internally differentiated, and with the algal component restricted to a definite portion of the thallus (Fig. 306*A*). Some of these lichens are **crustose** and with a

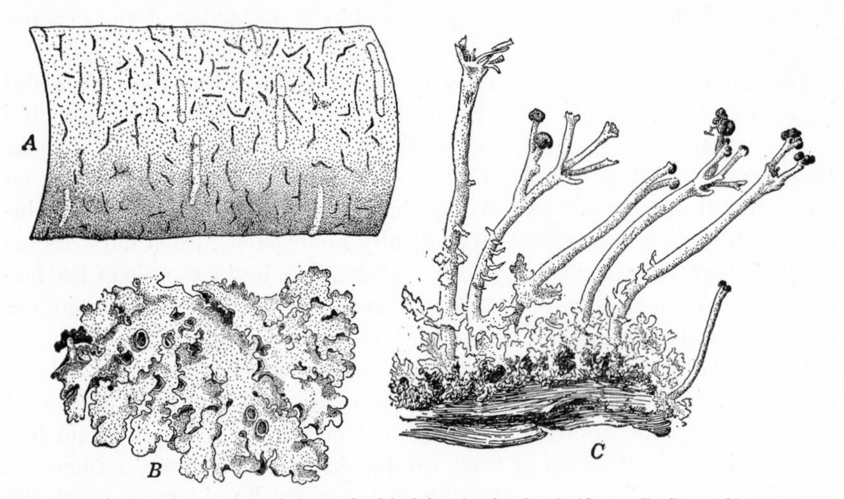

FIG. 305. *A*, *Graphis scripta* Ach. embedded in the bark of *Alnus*. *B*, *Parmelia flavicans* Tuck. *C*, *Cladonia flabelliformis* (Fkl.) Wainio. (*A*, × 1½; *B–C*, × ½.)

flattened thallus closely adherent to the substratum. In some crustose lichens the only evident portions of them are the ascocarps of the fungus (Fig. 305*A*). Other lichens are **foliose** (Fig. 305*B*) and with a leaf-like, lobed to deeply incised, thallus that is attached to the substratum by outgrowths (**rhizines**) from the lower surface. A rhizine may consist of a single branched or unbranched hypha, or of a number of parallel hyphae that lie closely applied to one another. A foliose lichen may be attached to the substratum by a single rhizine growing from the center of the lower face or it may be attached by several rhizines. Still other lichens are **fruticose** and have a much-branched cylindrical to ribbon-like thallus that may be erect or pendant (Fig. 305*C*). Fruticose lichens are attached to the substratum in the basal portion only. The foregoing distinctions between the various types of thallus in ascolichens are not absolute. There are intergrading forms all the way from the simplest of crustose lichens to the most highly differentiated of the fruticose ones.

Structure. Thalli of most foliose lichens are internally differentiated into four tissues (Fig. 306*A*). The uppermost region consists of more or less vertical hyphae that are without interspaces or with the interspaces filled with gelatinous material. This **upper cortex** may or may not be externally limited by an epidermis-like layer of hyphae. Beneath the upper cortex is the **algal layer.** It consists of rather loosely interwoven hyphae intermingled with algae. At one time the algae were thought to be the reproductive cells of a lichen and were called **gonidia.** This misnomer is

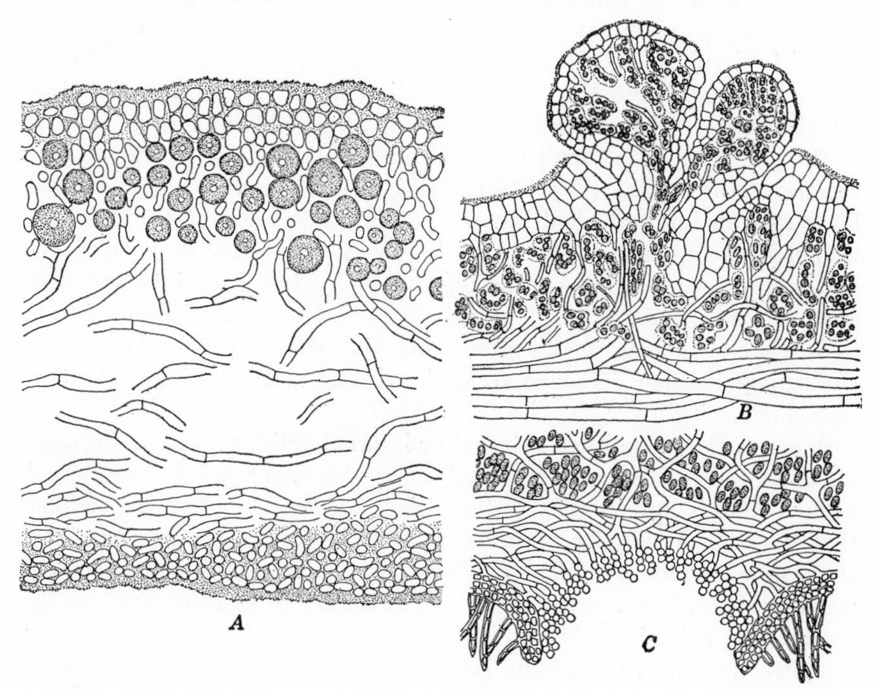

FIG. 306. *A*, vertical section of a portion of thallus of a species of *Physcia*. *B*, isidia of *Peltigera praetexta* (Fkl.) Zopf. *C*, cyphella of a species of *Sticta*. (*B*, *after Darbishire*, 1926; *C*, *after Schneider*, 1897.) (*A*, × 480; *B*, × 150.)

still in common use and the algal layer is often called the **gonidial layer.** Beneath the algal layer is a **medulla** composed of very loosely interwoven hyphae. Below this is the **lower cortex,** which consists of compacted hyphae. In some genera the hyphae are more or less perpendicular to the lower face of the thallus; in others they lie parallel to it. The rhizines grow out from the underside of the lower cortex.

Thalli of fruticose lichens generally have a cortical layer at the outside, an algal layer beneath this, and a central axis of medullary tissue.

In addition to the tissues just enumerated, a thallus may have other vegetative structures. Some foliose and fruticose lichens have a localized differentiation of the cortex into **breathing pores** that facilitate gaseous exchange between interior and exterior of the thallus. Breathing pores of foliose lichens are always developed in the upper cortex. A breathing pore is an area in the cortex where the hyphae are loosely interwoven, and the tissue beneath it is more or less medullary in nature. A breathing pore may be flush with the surface of the thallus, or it may be a cone-like elevation. The concave circular depressions (**cyphellae**) developed in the lower cortex of a few foliose lichens are also aerating organs (Fig. 306*C*). They are circular breaks in the lower cortex that have been replaced by hyphae which have grown out from the medulla.[1] Cyphellae bear a superficial resemblance to pycnidia because empty, rounded, terminal cells of the hyphae are abstricted in a spore-like manner.

Many lichens have small coralloid outgrowths (**isidia**) from the free surface of the thallus (Fig. 306*B*). Isidia consist of an external cortical layer and an internal algal layer. The alga is the same as that in the thallus. Development of an isidium is generally preceded by a rupturing of the upper cortex, after which medullary hyphae grow into and protrude beyond the wound.[2] The primary function of an isidium seems to be that of increasing the photosynthetic surface of a thallus. Sometimes they become detached from the thallus and serve as vegetative reproductive bodies.

A lichen may also have external or internal gall-like growths (**cephalodia**) in which there are both algal cells and fungal hyphae. An external cephalodium is immediately distinguishable from an isidium by the fact that the cephalodial alga is different from that in the algal layer of the thallus. Cephalodia formed on different individuals of the same species generally contain the same alga.[3] Furthermore, these algae are usually species that enter into the composition of other lichens. In some species the development of cephalodia is due to propagative bodies (**soredia**) of other lichens falling upon young portions of the thallus. Thus, a cephalodium may be looked upon as a small sterile thallus of another lichen and as having no organic connection with the thallus bearing it. Internal cephalodia also contain algae different from those in the algal layer.

Vegetative Multiplication. Continued marginal growth of a lichen may be accompanied by death and decay of the older portions. In these lichens, as in many liverworts, progressive growth and death increase the number of plants. Accidentally several portions of a thallus may develop into a new plant provided they contain both symbionts. This is of frequent occurrence in the "Californian Spanish moss" (*Ramalina reticulata* Kremp.) where detached portions of the pendant thallus are carried to other trees by winds and there develop into new plants. Reproduction

[1] Schneider, 1897. [2] Darbishire, 1926. [3] Smith, 1921.

may also be due to a breaking off of outgrowths, especially isidia, from the thallus.

The commonest method of vegetative propagation is by the development of minute bud-like outgrowths (**soredia**) on the upper surface of a thallus. A soredium consists of one or more algal cells enclosed by a few hyphae (Fig. 307*C–D*). They may develop over the entire surface of a thallus or in localized pustule-like areas (**soralia**). Soredia arise in the algal layer in places where there are breaks in the overlying upper cortex. A hypha from the algal layer produces branches that enfold one, two, or more algal cells, and the soredium thus formed is pushed outward by an

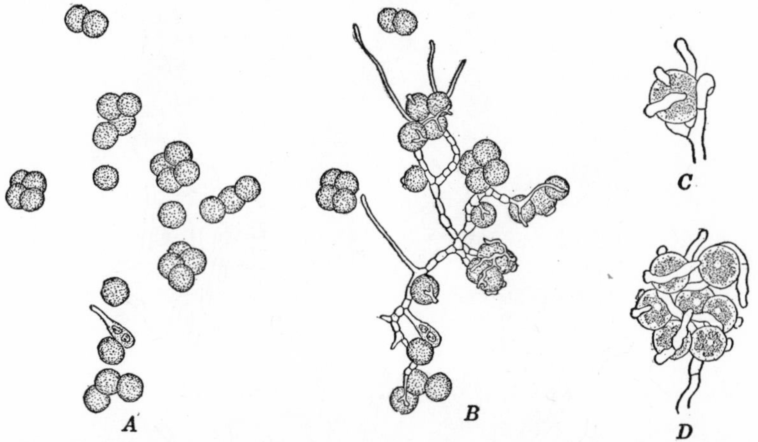

FIG. 307. *A–B*, early stages in synthesis of a lichen thallus. *A*, a culture of "*Protococcus*" (*Trebouxia?*) containing a germinating ascospore from *Physcia parietina* DeNot. *B*, the same culture five days later. *C–D*, soredia of a species of *Parmelia*. (*A–B*, *after Bonnier*, 1889.) (*A–B*, × 250; *C–D*, × 650.)

elongation of the underlying portion of the hypha. The attachment of soredia to the thallus is easily broken, and they are carried in all directions by the wind. If a soredium falls upon a suitable substratum and conditions for growth are favorable, it will immediately develop into a thallus. If conditions are unfavorable for thallus development but not sufficiently unfavorable to check all growth, it will develop other soredia. Sometimes this "soredial dust" forms an extensive coating on trees.

Spore Formation. The fungus of an ascolichen regularly forms spores. When the spore germinates, it sends out hyphal branches that grow in all directions. If one of them comes in contact with a suitable alga (Fig. 307*A–B*), it forms additional branches that enfold the alga.[1] Combined growth of the alga and fungus eventually results in a lichen. If none of the hyphal branches comes in contact with appropriate algae, the hypha dies. However, hyphae of germinating spores may grow indefinitely in

[1] Bonnier, 1889.

artificial cultures when supplied with the proper foods. Under such conditions the mycelium may grow for months and have an external form and internal differentiation of tissues somewhat comparable to that when it grows in association with algae.[1]

Ascolichens may form asexual spores in addition to ascospores. One lichen has been described[2] as producing conidia, but this has been questioned.[3] There are also a few well-established cases where the hyphae break up into oïdia that may germinate into hyphae.[3] Many lichens produce large numbers of small spore-like bodies within flask-shaped cavities

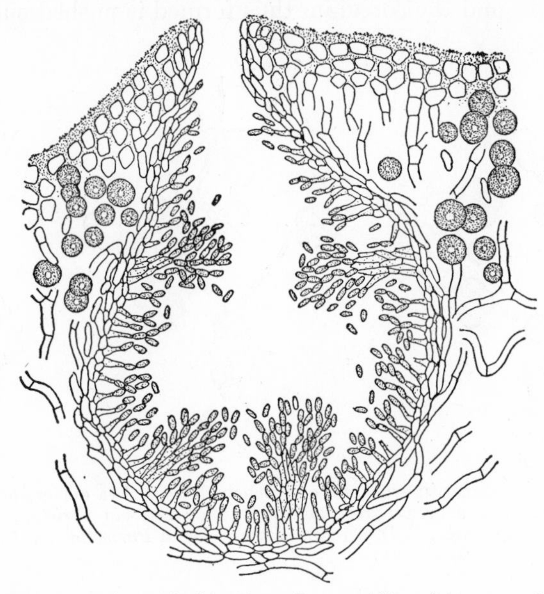

Fig. 308. Semidiagrammatic vertical section of a pycnidium (spermogonium?) of a species of *Physcia*. (× 430.)

immersed in the thallus (Fig. 308). In certain species the spores are capable of germination, and the hyphae developing from them produce a lichen if they come in contact with appropriate algae.[4] This shows that the flask-shaped cavities of these species are **pycnidia** and that the spore-like bodies within them are **pycnospores.** In the case of certain other species the cavities seem to be **spermogonia** that contain spermatia.

Asci produced by the fungus may be borne in apothecia or perithecia. These may be embedded in the thallus, stand somewhat above it, or be subtended by long stalks. Ascocarp development begins with the differentiation of an ascogonium from hyphae deep in the algal layer. The ascogonia are many-celled and usually have several coils in the lower por-

[1] Tobler, 1909; Werner, 1926; Killian and Werner, 1924. [2] Bonnier, 1889.
[3] Smith, 1921. [4] Hedlund, 1895.

tion. Ascogonia of most lichens are composed of uninucleate cells, but in certain species the cells are multinucleate.[1] In a large number of species[2] the upper end of an ascogonium is differentiated into a tricogyne whose tip projects beyond the surface of the thallus (Fig. 309*A*). Fertilization in lichens with protruding trichogynes has been described as being by means of spermatia.[3] The spermatia are produced in flask-shaped spermogonia that lie near the ascogonia. The evidence that the spermatia function as male gametes includes the discovery of spermatia lodged

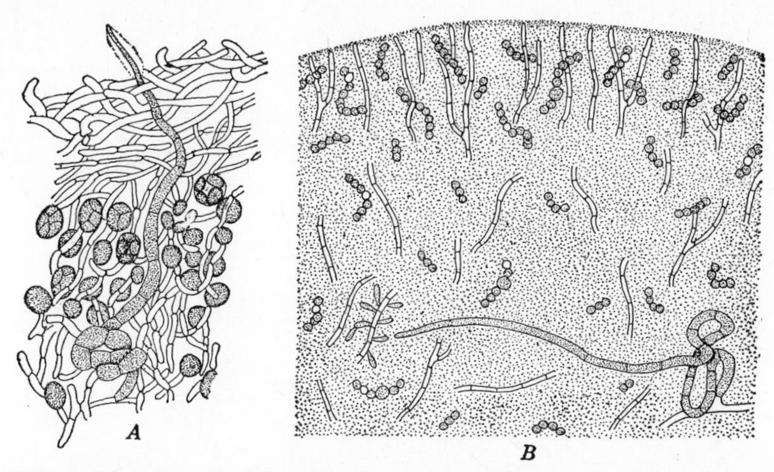

FIG. 309. *A*, *Anaptychia ciliaris* (L.) Kbr. Ascogonium with an externally protruding trichogyne. *B*, *Collemodes bachmannianum* Fink. Diagram showing an ascogonium with a trichogyne that remains within the thallus. (*A*, *after Bauer*, 1901; *B*, *based upon Bachmann*, 1913.)

against the sticky protruding tips of trichogynes[3] and the fact that thalli with numerous ascogonia but lacking spermatia rarely produce ascocarps.[4] This is not accepted by all who have studied development of the ascogonia, and it has been held[1] that there is never a fertilization of protruding trichogynes by spermatia. There is at least one species (*Collemodes bachmannianum* Fink) where the trichogynes never project beyond the thallus (Fig. 309*B*). Instead, a trichogyne grows more or less horizontally through the thallus until it comes in contact with a cluster of spermatia borne laterally on an internal hypha.[5] The discovery of empty spermatia in contact with such a trichogyne seems to indicate that their protoplasts have migrated into the trichogyne,[6] but an actual migration of male nuclei down the trichogyne has not been seen.

[1] Moreau and Moreau, 1928.

[2] Stahl, 1877; Bauer, 1898, 1901, 1904; Darbishire, 1900.

[3] Stahl, 1877; Bauer, 1898, 1901, 1904.

[4] Bauer, 1898.

[5] Bachmann, 1912, 1913; Fink, 1918.

[6] Bachmann, 1913.

Fertilization is followed by a development of ascogenous hyphae from the basal portion of the ascogonium. In some cases[1] there is a parthenogenetic development of ascogenous hyphae without any preceding formation of ascogonia. The ascogenous hyphae are freely branched and with cells containing one, two, or several nuclei each. Asci are produced at the ends of the ascogenous hyphae. Sometimes[2] the ends are bent in typical croziers, and the binucleate penultimate cell develops into the ascus;

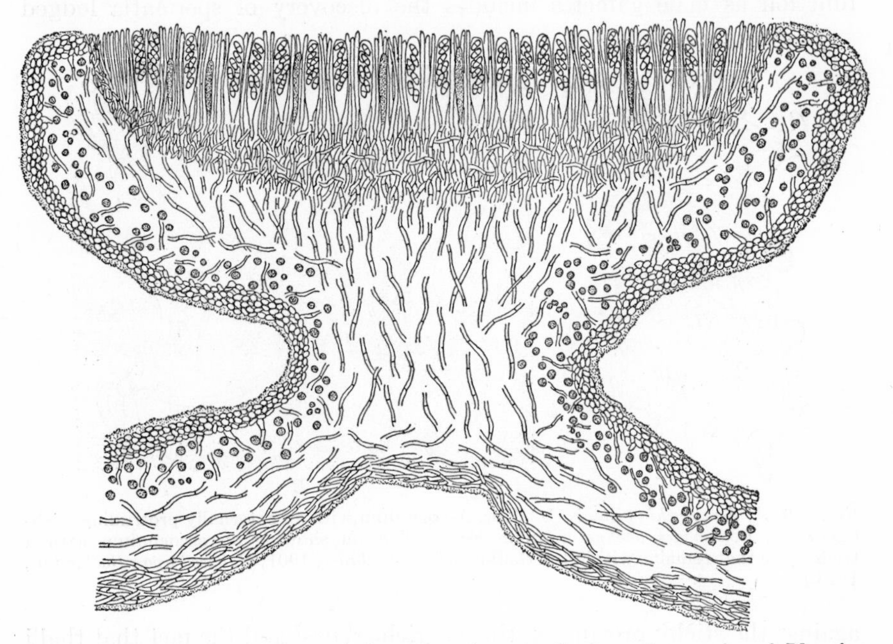

FIG. 310. Semidiagrammatic vertical section of an apothecium of a species of *Physcia*. (× 160.)

sometimes there is a direct development of an ascus from the terminal cell. Ascus development is in the usual manner. When there are two nuclei in a young ascus, the two unite with each other,[3] and the fusion nucleus divides and redivides to form eight daughter nuclei. Eight ascospores are formed by free cell formation, and in most genera each ascospore characteristically divides into two or more cells before liberation.

The ascocarp, whether apothecium or perithecium, is lined with a palisade-like layer of paraphyses (Fig. 310). The asci grow vertically upward between the paraphyses but never project beyond them. Ascus development is never simultaneous and in certain lichens an apothecium may continue the production of asci for several years.[4] Discharge of asco-

[1] Darbishire, 1914. [2] Bauer, 1904; Moreau and Moreau, 1928.
[3] Bachmann, 1913; Moreau and Moreau, 1932. [4] Smith, 1921.

spores from perennial apothecia is discontinuous and takes place only during wet weather.[1]

The Ascolichenes are divided into two series: the *Pyrenocarpeae* in which the ascogonium is a perithecium and the *Gymnocarpeae* in which it is an apothecium. The external morphology of the thallus, its internal structure, the nature of the algal symbiont, and the structure of the ascocarp are characters used in redividing each series into families. Sixteen families are recognized among the Pyrenocarpeae[2] and 35 among the Gymnocarpeae.

SUBCLASS 2. BASIDIOLICHENES

There are four genera of lichens in which the fungal component is a basidiomycete. In all of these the fungus is thought to be related to the Thelophoraceae, one of the simpler families of the Agaricales. The algal component is always a member of the Myxophyceae and either nonfilamentous (*Chroococcus*) or filamentous (*Scytonema*). All four genera of Basidiolichenes are tropical in distribution and found growing upon bare soil, rocks, or trees.

FIG. 311. *Cora pavonia* Weber and Mohr, a basidiolichen. (*After Johow*, 1884.)

The best-known member of the subclass is *Cora pavonia* Weber and Mohr, a species that is widely distributed in Central and South America on bare soil and on trees. The much-lobed thallus bears a superficial resemblance to a bracket fungus (Fig. 311). When it grows on trees, *C. pavonia* is laterally attached to the substratum by rhizines. As seen in vertical section, the thallus is differentiated into three layers.[3] The uppermost portion (the **superior layer**) is a loose felt of more or less perpendicular hyphae; beneath this is the **algal layer** in which hyphae run in all directions. The algal component is a species of *Chroococcus*. The **inferior layer** lies below the algal layer and is a rather dense felt of hyphae that run in all directions.

The lower surface of the thallus bears concentrically arranged arcuate outgrowths of more or less perpendicular hyphae. Each outgrowth (**subhymenium**) is radially divided into a number of segments. The lowermost face of each subhymenium bears a palisade-like layer of basidia. Sometimes this is described as consisting of intermingled basidia and unicellular paraphyses, but it is very probable that the so-called paraphyses

[1] Hilitzer, 1926. [2] Zahlbruckner, 1926. [3] Mattirolo, 1881; Johow, 1884.

are immature basidia. Each basidium bears four terminal sterigmata and basidiospores.[1]

Bibliography

Alexopoulos, C. J. **1952.** Introductory mycology. New York. 482 pp. 187 figs.
Bachmann, Freda M. **1912.** *Ann. Bot.* **26:** 747–760. 1 pl. [Internal spermatia.]
1913. *Arch. Zellf.* **10:** 369–430. 7 pl. [Internal spermatia.]
Bauer, E. **1898.** *Ber. Deutsch. Bot. Ges.* **16:** 363–367. 1 pl. [Development of ascocarp.]
1901. *Flora* **88:** 319–332. 2 pl. [Development of ascocarp.]
1904. *Bot. Zeitg.* **62:** 21–44. 2 pl. 1 fig. [Development of ascocarp.]
Bessey, E. A. **1950.** Morphology and taxonomy of fungi. Philadelphia. 791 pp. 210 figs.
Bonnier, G. **1889.** *Ann. Sci. Nat. Bot.* 7 ser. **9:** 1–34. 5 pl. 6 figs. [Synthesis of lichens.]
Bornet, E. **1873.** *Ibid.* 5 ser **17:** 45–110. 11 pl. [Nature of lichens.]
Darbishire, O. V. **1900.** *Jahrb. Wiss. Bot.* **34:** 329–345. 1 pl. [Development of ascocarp.]
1914. *British Assoc. Adv. Sci. Rept.* 83rd meeting, Birmingham. **1913:** 713–714. [Development of ascocarp.]
1926. *Ann. Bot.* **40:** 727–758. 4 pl. [Development of ididia.]
Fink, B. **1913.** *Mycologia* **5:** 97–166. [Nature of lichens.]
1918. *Ibid.* **10:** 235–238. 1 pl. [Development of ascocarp.]
Fry, E. Jennie. **1922.** *Ann. Bot.* **36:** 541–562. 1 pl. 9 figs. [Endolithic lichens.]
1924. *Ibid.* **38:** 175–196. 10 figs. [Disintegration of rocks.]
1927. *Ibid.* **41:** 437–460. 2 pl. 22 figs. [Disintegration of rocks.]
1928. *Ibid.* **42:** 141–148. 6 figs. [Nature of lichens.]
Geitler, L. **1937.** *Arch. Protistenk.* **88:** 161–179. 7 figs. [Algal-fungal relationship.]
Hedlund, T. **1895.** *Bot. Centralbl.* **63:** 9–16. [Germination of pycnospores.]
Hilitzer, A. **1926.** *Acta Bot. Bohemica* **4:** 52–58. 3 figs. (Ref. *Biol. Abstrs.* **3,** No. 2935: 1929.) [Spore discharge.]
Johow, F. **1884.** *Jahrb. Wiss. Bot.* **15:** 361–409. 5 pl. [*Cora.*]
Killian, C., and R. G. Werner. **1924.** *Compt. Rend. Acad. Sci. Paris* **179:** 1339–1342. 10 figs. [Cultivation of fungus.]
Martin, G. W. **1950.** Outline of the fungi. Dubuque, Iowa. 82 pp. 116 figs.
Mattirolo, O. **1881.** *Nuovo Gior. Bot. Ital.* **13:** 245–267. 2 pl. [*Cora.*]
Moreau, F., and Mme. Moreau. **1928.** *Le Botaniste* **20:** 1–67. 35 figs. [Development of ascocarp.]
1932. *Rev. Gén. Bot.* **44:** 305–315. 4 pl. [Development of ascocarp.]
Schneider, A. **1897.** A text-book of lichenology. Binghamton, N.Y. 230 pp. 76 pl.
Smith, Annie L. **1921.** Lichens. Cambridge. 464 pp. 135 figs.
Stahl, E. **1877.** Beiträge zur Entwicklungsgeschichte der Flechten. Leipzig. Heft **1,** 55 pp.; Heft 2, 32 pp. 4 pl.
Suessenguth, K. **1926.** *Ber. Deutsch. Bot. Ges.* **44:** 573–578. [Bacteria of lichens.]
Tobler, F. **1909.** *Ibid.* **27:** 421–427. 1 fig. [Cultivation of fungus.]
Uphof, J. C. T. **1925.** *Amer. Jour. Bot.* **12:** 97–103. 6 figs. [Bacteria of lichens.]
1926. *Biol. Zentralbl.* **46:** 492–503. 5 figs. [Bacteria of lichens.]
Werner, R. G. **1926.** *Bull. Soc. Mycol. France* **41:** 385–387. 1 fig. [Cultivation of fungus.]
Zahlbruckner, A. **1922–1932.** Catalogus lichenum universalis. Vol. 1, 696 pp.; Vol. 2, 815 pp.; Vol. 3, 899 pp.; Vol. 4, 754 pp.; Vol. 5, 814 pp.; Vol. 6, 618 pp.; Vol. 7, 784 pp.; Vol. 8, 612 pp.
1926. Lichenes. In A. Engler and K. Prantl, Die natürlichen Pflanzenfamilien. **2d ed.** Bd. 8. pp. 61–270. 96 figs.

[1] Johow, 1884.

INDEX

Numbers in **boldface** type refer to pages on which the subject is illustrated or especially described.

A

Acervulus, 424, 515
  nature of, 424
Acetabularia, **119–121**
  crenulata, **120**
  mediterranea, **121**
  wettsteinii, 121
Achlya, 390, 396
  bisexualis, **397**, 398
Acotyledones, 1
Acrasieae, 10, 347, **358–362**
  nature of, 358
Acrasin, 360
Acrochaetium, **302**
Actinoptychus undulatus, **197**
Aecidiospores, 499, **504**
  formation of, 504
  germination of, 505
  nature of, 499
Aecidium, **504**
Aethalium, **350**
  nature of, 349
Aflagellatae, 376, **407–417**
  nature of, 409
Agar, **293–294**
Agardhiella, **331–333**
  coulteri, **331, 333**
Agaricaceae, **480–485**
Agaricales, 479, **480–485**
Aglaozonia, 239
Akinete, **22**, 48, 66, **73**, 115, **116**, 174, 181, **278, 280**, 284, **285**, 298
  germination of, 48, **180**, 285, **287**
  nature of, 21
Alaria, 218
Albugo, **401–404**
  candida, 401, **402, 403**
Algae, ancestral to fungi, **366–367**
  annual, 240, 258, 313
  blue-green (*see* Cyanophyta)
  brown (*see* Phaeophyta)
  classes of, 5, **9–10**
  classification of, **3–6**
  divisions of, 5, **9–10**
  economic uses, **195–196, 218–219, 293–294**
Algae, fossil, **119**, 122, **194–196**, 227
  golden-brown (*see* Chrysophyceae)
  interrelationships among, **7–9**
  longevity of, 221
  organisms belonging to, **2–3**
  perennial, 240, 258, 303
  pigments of, **4**
  red (*see* Rhodophyta)
  as subdivision, **2**
  thermal, 275
  vertical zonation of, **292**
  yellow-green (*see* Xanthophyceae)
Algin, **218–219**, 220
  chemical composition, 218
  uses of, **218–219**
Allomyces, 366, **383–387**
  anomalus, 387
  arbuscula, **384**
  cystogenes, 386
  moniliformis, 386
Alternation of generations, 111
  heteromorphic, 45, **52**, 226, 228, 245, 246, 249, 253, **255**, 257, 262, **386**
    nature of, 25
  isomorphic, 45, 61, 62, 67, 68, 118, 226, 228, **231**, 234, 236, 237, 240, **385**
    nature of, 25
Amanita, 480
Amitosis, 16, 120
Amoeba proteus, 159
Amoeboid cells, 146, 159, **160, 171**, 172, 187, 189
  (*See also* Myxamoebae; Plasmodium; Rhizopodial stage)
Amoeboid movement, 181, 186, 188, 348
Amylum star, 125
Anabaena, 280, 282
  circinalis, **278–280**
  oscillarioides, **287**
  sphaerica, **287**
Anadyomene, 118
Anaptychia ciliaris, **523**
Androsporangium, 75, **76**
  nature of, 75
Androspore, nature of, 75
Angiospermae, relationships of, **9**

Anisochytridiales, 376, **418–419**
Anisogamy, 32, 33, **36**, **37**, 59, **62**, 91, 94, 102, **106**, 108, **109**, 114, **170**, **179**, 224, 234, **238**, 255, 365, 373, **384**
  nature of, 22
Anisolpidium, 418–419
  ectocarpi, 418
Antapical plates, **156**
Antheridial filament, **126**, 127
Antheridial initial, 238
Antheridial mother cell, 74
Antheridium, 23, **54**, 55, **58**, **74**, **76**, **116**, 225, **236**, **243**, **252**, 253, **263**, 365, **388**, 393, **395**, **400**, **408**, 424, **427**, **443**, 451, **452**, 455, **459**
  development of, 182, **183**, 243, 264, 267, **268**, **395**, 396, 400, **403**
  nature of, 23
Antherozoid, **41**, **49**, 50, **58**, 59, **74**, **75**, 116, **126**, 127, **129**, **210**, 224, **236**, **269**, **270**, 365, 375, **388**
  liberation of, **74**, 268, 269
  nature of, 22
Anthocerotae, 10
Aphyllophorales, 479
Apical cap, **69**, **71**
Apical cell, **123**, **233**, 241, **242**, 256, **266**, **302**, **303**, 319, **320**, **334**, 337, **338**
  differentiation of, 271
  division of, **242**, 266
  growth and, 123, 221, 242
Apical plates, 156, **157**
Aplanatae, 376, 409
Aplanogamete, **80**, **81**, 365, 373, 391, **413**, **418**
  nature of, 23
Aplanogamy, 81, 154, **206**, **207**, 391, 393, **395**, **403**, 406, 407, **413**, **418**
  nature of, 23
Aplanospore, 47, **48**, 52, 66, 87, **91**, **95**, 98, **99**, **110**, 153, 163, 168, **175**, 177, **178**, 181
  germination of, 48, **95**, **178**
  nature of, 21
Apothecium, 430, **459**, 522, **524**
  development of, 460
  nature of, 430
Appresoria, **500**
Arthrodesmus incus, **87**
Ascocarp, **427**, 444, **446**, **461**, **463**
  development of, **461**, **463–464**
  nature of, 423
  relation to sex organs, **427**
  types of, **430**
  (*See also* Apothecium; Cleistothecium; Perithecium)
Ascogenous cells, **439**, 440
Ascogenous hyphae, **427**, **428**, **443**, **446**, **459**, 461, **462**
  croziers of, **428**
  nature of, 427
Ascogonial cell, **452**
Ascogonium, **427**, **443**, 445, **446**, **452**, 455, **459**, **523**
  development of, **443–444**, **459**
  multicellular, **449**
  nature of, 366, 424
Ascolichenes, 517, **518–525**
  classification of, **525**
  crustose, **518**
  foliose, **518**
  fruticose, **518**, 519
  nature of, 518
  spore formation by, **521–525**
  structure of, **519–529**
  synthesis of, **521**
  vegetative multiplication, **520–521**
Ascomycetae, 6, 10, 365, 369, **442–468**, **518–525**
  ascocarps of, **430**
  ascus formation by, **426–430**
  asexual reproduction, **423–424**
  classification of, **432–433**
  Deuteromycetae and, 514
  nature of, 422
  nuclear cycle in, **430–431**
  occurrence of, **442–443**
  origin of, 267, **431–432**
  sexual reproduction of, **424–425**
  vegetative structure of, **423**
Ascospore, **434**, **435**, **438**, 442, **443**, **446**, **449**, **462**, **464**, **465**, **521**
  discharge of, 440, 447, 456, 462, 524
  dispersal of, 465
  formation of, **437**
  heterokaryotic, 426, **450**
  two-celled, **457**
Ascus, 369, **438**, 442, **443**, **446**, **449**, **450**, **455**, 456, **457**, **462**, **464**, **465**, **524**
  ascogenous hyphae and, **427**
  development of, **426–430**, 440, 461, **462**
  formation from zygote, 427, **434**, **435**
  nature of, 366
  number of spores, 422, 429, 464, 465
Asparagopsis armata, 307
Aspergillales, **441–444**
Aspergillus, 441
Astasia, **142**
Asterocytis, **297–298**
  ramosa, **298**
  smaragdina, **298**
Auricularia, **495–496**
  auricula-judae, **495**, **496**
Auriculariales, 478, 490, **495–496**

Autocolony, **98, 100**
formation of, 98, 101
nature of, 21
Autogamy, 144, 209, **211**
nature of, 144
Autospore, 89, **99,** 100, **153, 169**
liberation of, **169**
nature of, 21
Auxiliary cell, **318,** 319, **324, 325, 327, 330, 331,** 332, **333, 335, 339**
nature of, 306
Auxiliary cell filament, **324, 325, 335,** 336
Auxospore, 204, **205**
of Centrales, **209–211**
formation of, **210, 211**
nature of, 193, 205
of Pennales, **205–209**
formation of, **206–208**
Axial field, 199
Axial filament, **320, 323, 341**
Axoneme, **16,** 143
nature of, 16
Azygote, 80

B

Bacillariophyceae, 5, 9, **193–212**
auxospores of, **205–211**
cell division in, **203–205**
cell wall of, **196–199**
classification of, **211–212**
fossil, **194–196**
locomotion of, **201–203**
nature of, 193
occurrence of, **194**
pigments of, **4**
relationships of, 165
statospores of, **211**
structure of protoplast, **199–201**
Badhamia foliicola, 349
Bangiales, **297–301**
Bangioideae, **297–301**
ascomycetes and, **432**
Barberry, *Puccinia graminis* and, **502–504**
Basal cell, 267
Basidiocarp, 480, **481, 485, 486, 491, 493, 495**
development of, **487, 489, 491–492**
gymnocarpous, **483**
nature of, 482
hemiangiocarpous, **483, 484**
nature of, 482
nature of, 472
Basidiolichenes, 517, **525–526**
Basidiomycetae, 6, 366, 369, **469–513, 525–526**
basidiospores of, **473**
Basidiomycetae, classification of, **478**
Deuteromycetae and, 514
evolution within, **477–478**
formation of basidia, **471–474**
nature of, 469
origin of, **476–477**
primary mycelium of, **469, 470,** 480, 491, **492,** 493, 495, 499, 503
dikaryotization of, 504, **505**
nature of, 469
primitive, **477–478**
secondary mycelium, **469–471,** 480, 486, 491, **492,** 493, 495, **507,** 508, 510
formation of, **470**
nature of, 469
tertiary mycelium, 472
Basidiospore, **472, 479, 484, 496–498, 506, 509**
conidium formation by, 473, 480, **497,** 506, **509, 510**
discharge of, **473,** 485, 488, 492, 494, 497
dispersal of, 490
germination of, 486, **487, 492**
infection by, 502
secondary, 493, **494**
somatogamy between, 506, **507, 510**
Basidium, 369, **479, 484, 487, 490**
development of, **471–474, 479, 496**
homologies with ascus, **476**
nature of, 366
origin of, **477**
(*See also* Epibasidium; Hypobasidium)
Batrachospermum, 301
Biddulphia mobiliensis, **209**
smithii, **197**
Biflagellatae, 376, **389–409**
nature of, 389
Bisporangium, 308
nature of, 307
Bispore, 328
diploid, 329
haploid, 329
nature of, 307
Black knot, 456
Blade, **260**
structure of, **261**
Blakeslea trispora, **410**
Blastocladiales, 376, **383–387**
cell wall of, 372
Blastodiniaceae, 162
Blastospore, **438,** 439, 440
budding of, 430
conjugation of, 430, **438**
Blepharoplast, 17, 53, 72, **141,** 143
Bonnemaisonia, 307
Botrydiopsis, **176–177**
arhiza, **177**

Botrydium, 94, 166, **168, 177–179**
granulatum, **170, 178**
wallrothii, **178**
Brachyallomyces, 387
Brachymeiosis, **431**
Breathing pores, 520
Bryophyta, 2, 8, **10**
classes of, **10**
relationships of, 8, 9, **27**
Bryopsidaceae, **101–104**
Bryopsis, **102–104**
corticulans, 102, **103**
plumosa, 102
Buller phenomenon, **475–476**
Bunt, 509

C

Calamophyta, 7, 8, 10
relationships of, **9**
Callose, 13, 105
Capillitium, **350**, 488
formation of, **251**
nature of, 351
Capitulum, 127
primary, **126**
secondary, **126**
Carotenes, **4**, 12, 281
alpha-carotene, **4**
beta-carotene, **4**, 14, 57, 139, 148, 166, 166, 184, 193
eta-carotene, **4**
Carpogonial filament, **310, 314**, 323, **324, 325, 327, 331**, 334, **335**, 336, **339**
nature of, 304
Carpogonium, 291, 296, **298**, 304, **308, 310, 314, 321, 324, 325, 327, 330, 331, 335, 339**
formation of, 300
nature of, 304
Carpomitra, **248–250**
cabrerea, **249, 250**
Carposporangium, **314, 321, 327, 333, 340**
nature of, 306
Carpospore, 291, 295, **299**, 305, **309**, 321, **327**, 334
amoeboid, **299**
development of, **305–307**
discharge of, **299**, 301
germination of, **307**
Carposporophyte, 311, **321, 330**, 332, **333, 340**
development of, 315
diploid, **309**, 321, **324**
haploid, **309, 314, 318**
nature of, 307
Carpotetrasporangia, **310**
Carpotetrasporangia, nature of, 307
Carpotetraspore, nature of, 307
Carpotetrasporophyte, **310**
nature of, 307
Carrageenin, 294
Caulerpa, **104–106**
crassifolia, 105
cupressoides, **105**
prolifera, **105, 106**
Caulerpaceae, **104–106**
Cell division, **70**, 79, 83, **86, 143**, 152, **158**
by budding, **438**
segregative, 116, **117**
Cellulose, 13, 56, 67, 69, 82–84, 149, 151, 220, 277, 294, 361, 389
Central body, division of, **279**
Central cell, **128**
Centrales, 212
Centrosome, 220, 520
Ceramiales, 313, **337–342**
Ceratiomyxa, **353–356**
Ceratium, 154, 157
hirundinella, **158**
Chaetomorpha, 67
Chaetophoraceae, 25, **50–52**
Chamaesiphon incrustans, **287**
Chamaesiphonales, 288
Chantransia, 301
Chara, 16, **123**, 124, 126, **128, 129**
crinata, **130**
foetida, **126, 129, 130**
intermedia, **125**
Characeae, **122–130**
Characiaceae, **93–94**
Characium, 16, **93–94**
sieboldii, **93**
Charales, **122–130**
Charophyceae, 5, **121–130**
asexual reproduction of, **125**
cell structure in, **124–125**
classification of, **122**
nature of, 121
occurrence of, **122**
sexual reproduction of, **125–128**
vegetative structure, **122–124**
zygote germination in, **128–130**
Chitin, 13, 68, 69
fungus, 372
Chlamydomonadaceae, **30–34**
Chlamydomonas, 3, 14, **17**, 19, 22, 24, 30, **31–34**
braunii, 33
coccifera, 33
dorsoventralis, **16**
eugametos, 32, 34
intermedia, 34
nasuta, 16

Chlamydomonas, oögamum, 33
reinhardi, 34
snowiae, **31, 33**
Chlamydospore, 388, 412, 417, 424, 508
nature of, 424
Chlorarachnion, **173,** 347
reptans, 172, **173**
Chlorochytrium, 25, **92–93**
inclusum, **92**
lemnae, 92
Chlorococcales, 29, **88–101**
relationships of, **27**
Chlorococcum, **89–90**
humicola, **90**
Chlorogibba trochisciaeformis, **169**
Chlorogonium, 22
Chloromeson, **171**
agile, **170, 171**
Chloromonadales, 10
Chlorophyceae, 3, 5, 9, **28–121**
classification of, **28–30**
interrelationships among, **27**
nature of, 28
pigments of, **4**
(*See also* Chlorophyta)
Chlorophylls, **4**
chlorophyll *a*, **4,** 12, 148, 166, 193, 275, 281
chlorophyll *b*, **4,** 12
chlorophyll *c*, **4,** 148, 193
chlorophyll *d*, **4**
chlorophyll *e*, **4,** 166
Chlorophyta, 5, 9, **12–138,** 294
asexual reproduction of, **20–22**
cell division in, **18–19**
cell structure in, **13–18**
cell wall of, **13**
chloroplasts of, **13–15**
classes of, **28**
evolution among, **26–28**
life cycles of, **24–26**
nature of, 12
occurrence of, **12**
relationships of, **9**
sexual reproduction of, **22–23**
vegetative multiplication of, **19–20**
zygotes of, **23–24**
Chloroplast, **13–15, 46, 48, 51,** 61, **64, 66,** 68, **69,** 79, **83,** 86, **91, 95, 103,** 115, **118, 141,** 145
division of, 19
loss of pigments, 141
shape of, 14
of zygote, 81
Chondrus, 294
Chondrus, crispus, 294
Chordariales, **245–248**
relationships of, **227**
Chromatophore, 150, **156,** 168, 173, **175,** 177, 178, 187, **188, 189,** 191, **200,** 220, 294, **298, 299**
(*See also* Chloroplast)
Chromoplasm, 279
structure of, 280
Chromulina, **187**
dubia, 187
freiburgensis, **186**
globosa, **187**
Chroococcales, 277, 282, 283, **288**
Chroococcus, 283, 525
turgidus, **277, 279**
Chrysamoeba, **189**
radians, **189**
Chrysocapsales, **189–191**
Chrysomonadales, **187–188**
Chrysophaerales, **192–193**
Chrysophyceae, 5, 9, **184–193,** 347
asexual reproduction of, **185–186**
cell structure in, **184–185**
classification of, **186–187**
nature of, 184
occurrence of, **184**
pigments of, **4**
relationships of, 165
Chrysophyta, 5, 9, **165–216**
nature of, 165
relationships of, **9**
Chrysotrichales, **191–192**
Chylocladia ovalis, 333
Chytridiales, 372, **376–383**
Chytrids, 369, **376–383, 390–392, 418–419**
Cilium (*see* Flagellum; Mastigoneme)
Cladochytrium, **382–383**
replicatum, **383**
Cladonia flabelliformis, **518**
rangifera, 517
Cladophora, 13, 16, 21, 26, **67–69**
glomerata, **67,** 68
kuetzingianum, **67**
trichotoma, 68
Cladophoraceae, 25, **67–69**
Cladophorales, **29, 66–69**
relationships of, **27**
Clamp cell, **471**
Clamp connection, 470, **472,** 480, 488, 491, 493, 495
formation of, **471**
Classification, **1–11**
artificial systems, **1**
basis of, 2
natural systems, 1
of spore-producing plants, **1–10**
Clavaria fennica, **481**
Claviceps, **453–456**
purpurea, 453, **455, 456,** 514

Claviceptales, **453–456**
Cleft, funnel, 201, **202**
polar, 201, **202**
Cleistothecium, 340, **443, 446**
development of, **446–447**
nature of, 430
Closterium calosporum, **87**
moniliforme, **85**
Clubroot, 356
Cocconeis pediculus, **198,** 206
placentula, **206, 208**
Codiaceae, **111–115**
Codium, **112–115**
fragile, **112,** 113, **114**
Coelosphaerium, 280, 283
naegelianum, **277**
Coelosporium sonchi, **498**
Coenobium, **36, 37, 39, 97, 98, 100**
formation of, 35
nature of, 34
Coenocyst, 96
Coenocyte, 26, 57, 58, 89, 90, **93,** 102, 105, **107, 110,** 115, 178, 179, 324, **379**
nature of, 16, 364
Colaciales, **145–146**
Colacium calvum, **145**
Coleochaetaceae, **53–55**
Coleochaete, 24, 25, 45, **53–55**
nitellarum, 55
pulvinata, **54,** 55
scutata, **54,** 55
Collemodes bachmannianum, **523**
Colony, **36, 37, 43, 188**
formation of, **40**
reproduction of, 188
Columella, **411, 489**
formation of, **412**
Companion cell, **391**
Conceptacle, **264**
cystocarpic, 326, **327**
development of, **266,** 267
oögonial, **268**
spermatangial, 326, **327**
tetrasporic, **328**
Conchocelis rosea, 301
Conidiophore, 423
Conidiosporangium, 404, **405,** 406, **416**
development of, **402, 416**
discharge of, **416**
germination of, **402,** 404, **405**
nature of, 373
Conidium, 373, 423, 440, **442,** 444, **445,** 447, **448, 454, 457,** 462, 491
dikaryotic, 511
formation of, **442**
germination of, **507**
somatogamy between, 506
Conjugales, 78
Conjugation, 83, 87, **206, 207**
lateral, 81
scalariform, **80,** 81, **82**
(*See also* Anisogamy; Isogamy)
Conjugation tube, 23, **80,** 81
Connecting band, 196
Connecting filaments, 259, **261**
Consortium, 517
Coprinus fimentarius, **469**
Cora pavonia, **525**
Coral reefs, 326
Corallinaceae, **326–329**
Corona, **128, 129**
inferior, **120**
superior, **120**
Corticating filaments, **123**
initials of, 124
Cortication, 229, **252,** 253
Cortex, 260, **266**
development of, **261**
lower, **519**
upper, **519**
Cosmarium, **88**
reniforme, **85**
Cover cell, **341**
Crozier, **428,** 456, 460, 461
development of, **428**
nature of, 428
Cryptogamia, 1
Cryptogamic plants, **1–10**
classes of, **9–10**
divisions of, **9–10**
nature of, 1
Cryptonemiales, 313, **322–326**
Cryptophyceae, 6, 10, 148
relationships of, 148
Cumagloia, 313
andersonii, **303**
Cutleria, **237–240**
adspersa, **237, 240**
multifida, **237, 238, 240**
Cutleriales, 220, 224, **237–240**
relationships of, 227
Cyanophyceae, 3, 275
(*See also* Cyanophyta)
Cyanophycin granules, 280
Cyanophyta, 5, 10, **275–290**
chromatic adaptation in, **281–282**
classification of, **288**
filamentous, **278**
fixation of nitrogen by, **282**
movements of, **282–283**
nature of, 275
nonfilamentous, **277**
occurrence of, **275–276**
organization of thallus, **276–277**
relationships of, **9**
spore formation by, **284–286**

Cyanophyta, structure of protoplast, **279–284**
vegetative reproduction, **283–284**
Cyclosporeae, 228, **264–271**
nature of, 264
origin of, **227–228**
Cyclotella, 210
meneghiniana, **211**
Cylindrocapsa, **49–50**
geminella, **49**
involuta, **49**
Cylindrocapsaceae, **49–50**
Cylindrospermum, 287
muscicola, **285**
Cymatopleura solea, **200**
Cymbella lanceolata, **198, 207**
Cyphella, **519**
nature of, 520
Cyst, **120**, 153, **154**, 156, **160**, 352
germination of, **121**, 160
(*See also* Statospore)
Cystidium, 484, **494**
Cystocarp, nature of, 307
(*See also* Carposporophyte)
Cystogenes, 386
Cystopus, 401
Cytokinesis (*see* Free cell formation; Progressive cleavage)
Cytopharynx, **141**
Cytoplasmic streaming, 125, 201
locomotion and, **203**
Cytostome, 141

D

Dacromyces, **491–492**, 493
aurantius, **491**
deliquescens, 491, **492**
Dacromycetales, 490, **491–492**
Dasycladaceae, **119–121**
Dasycladales, 29, **119–121**
relationships of, **27**
Derbesia, 27, **109–111**
marina, 109, **110**
Dermocarpa pacifica, **287**
Desmarestia, 218, 221–223, **250–253**
aculeata, **252**
herbacea, **251, 252**
latissima, 250
Desmarestiales, 224, **250–253**
relationships of, **227**
Desmidiaceae, 78, **84–88**
Desmidium aptogonum, **85**
Desmids, placoderm, 84
saccoderm, 82
(*See also* Desmidiaceae; Mesotaeniaceae)
Desmokontae, 148, 149
Desmophyceae, 9, **149–150**
nature of, 129
Deuteromycetae, 6, 10, 369, **514–515**
Diatomaceous earth, **194–195**
Diatoms, centric, **197**, 198
pennate, **198**
(*See also* Bacillariophyceae)
Diatoxanthin, **4**
Dibotryon, 456
Dichotomosiphon, **115–116**
pusillus, 115
tuberosus, 115, **116**
Dichotomosiphonaceae, **115–116**
Dicotyledones, 1
Dictyosiphon, **256–257**
foeniculaceus, **256**
Dictyosiphonaceae, **255–257**
Dictyosiphonales, 224, 254, **255–257**
relationships of, 227
Dictyostelium, **359–362**
discoideum, **360, 361**
Dictyota, 221, **241–244**
dichotoma, **242, 243**
Dictyotales, 220, 224, 226, **240–244**
relationships of, 227
Dictyuchus, 396
Didymium, **348**
Dikaryons, 470, 476, **492**, 498
formation of, **470**
nature of, 469
sexuality of, **474–476**
Dikaryotization, 475, 499, 505
Dinamoebidium, **159–160**
varians, 159, **160**
Dinastridium sexangulare, **153**
Dinocapsales, **160–161**
Dinoclonium conradi, **161**
Dinococcales, **162–163**
Dinoflagellates (*see* Dinophyceae)
Dinophyceae, 5, 9, 148, **150–164**
asexual reproduction of, **152–154**
cell walls of, **151**
classification of, **155**
nature of, 150
occurrence of, **150–151**
pigments of, **4**
sexual reproduction of, **154–155**
structure of protoplast, **151–152**
Dinophysidales, **158–159**
Dinophysis acuta, **159**
Dinothrix paradoxa, **161**
Dinotrichales, **161–162**
Dinoxanthin, **4**
Dioecism, 22, 113, 266
(*See also* Heterothallism)
Diplanetism, **389–390**, 391, 393
nature of, 389

Dipodascus, 424, 427, **434–435**
albidus, 434, **435**
Discomycetes, **458–462**
nature of, 458
Displacement cells, 503
Distigma, **142**
Dothidiales, **456–458**
Draparnaldia, 20
Dudresnaya, **322–326**
coccinea, 324
crassa, **323, 324**
verticillata, **323**

E

Ectocarpales, 224, **228–232**
relationships of, **227**
Ectocarpus, 221, **229–232**, 234, 246
acutus, **230**
cylindricus, **230**
life cycle of, **231**
Egg, **41, 49**, 50, 55, **58**, 59, **75**, 127, **210**, 224, **252**, 253, 263, **268, 270**, 365, 374, **388, 395, 400**, 406
liberation of, **269**
nature of, 22
Embryo, development of, **270**
polarity of, **270**
Empusa, **415–418**
muscae, 415, **416**
Endochite, 267, 268, **269**
Endomycetales, **433–439**
Endoperidium, nature of, 486
Endosome, **143, 152**
Endosphaeraceae, **91–93**
Endospore, 285, **287**
formation of, 286
Endosporeae, **347–357**
germination of spores, **351–353**
nature of, 347
plasmodium of, **348–349**
sporangia of, **349–351**
Endothia parasitica, 442
Enteromorpha, 26, 61
Entomophthorales, 373, **415–418**
cell walls of, 372
Entosiphon sulcatum, **140**
Epibasidium, **492, 496–498**, 502, **506, 509, 510**
nature of, 473
Epichrysis, **192–193**
paludosa, **193**
Epilithon, **326–329**
mediocris, **327**, 328
membranaceum, **326**
Epiplasm, **429, 446, 467**
nature of, 429
Epitheca, of diatom, 196, **203**
Epitheca, of diatom, formation of, **204**
of dinoflagellate, 156, **157, 159**
Equisetinae, 10
Eremascus, **431–432**
fertilis, 433, **434, 435**
Ergot, 453
Ergotism, 453
Erysiphales, **444–447**
Erysiphe, **444–447**
aggregata, **429**
cichoraceum, **445**
graminis, 447
Euallomyces, 385, 386
Euascomycetae, 433, **441–465**
nature of, 441
Euastrum affine, **85**
Eucapsis alpina, **277**
Eudorina, 35, **36–38**
unicocca, **37**
Euglena, 141, **142**
intermedia, **140, 141**
Euglenales, **139–145**
asexual reproduction of, **144**
cell shape, **140–141**
cell structure, **141–144**
classification of, **145**
sexual reproduction of, **144–145**
Euglenarhodone, 14, 141
Euglenocapsales, 145
Euglenophyceae, 5, 9, **139–147**
pigments of, **4**
Euglenophyta, 6, 9, **139–147**
nature of, 139
relationships of, **9**
Eumycophyta, 6, 10, **364–513**
classification of, **369**
evolution among, **368–369**
nature of, 364
origin of, **266–268**
relationships of, **9**
sexual reproduction of, **365–366**
spores of, **364–365**
Eunotia diodon, **200**
Exit tube, 376, **383, 391, 392**
Exobasidiales, **479–480**
Exobasidium, **479–480**
vaccinii, 479
Exochite, 267
Exoperidium, 488
nature of, 486
Exospore, 286
Exosporeae, 347, **353–356**
nature of, 353
Extrusion papilla, **106**
Exuviaella, **149–150**
marina, **149**
Eyespot, **17**, 39, **141, 187**
division of, 143

Eyespot, lens of, **17**
  photosensitive substance of, **17**
  pigment cup of, **17**
  structure of, **17**, 143

F

False branching, 277, **278**
Fats, 200
  (*See also* Oils)
Fertile disk, **120, 121**
Fertile sheet, 267
Fertilization, **41**, 55, 77, 128, 253, **270**, 315, **330**
  (*See also* Oögamy)
Fertilization tube, 393, **395**, 396
Filament, of Cyanophyta, **278**
  nature of, 276
Fissure, inner, 201, **202**
  outer, 201, **202**
Flagellatae as ancestors of fungi, **368**
Flagellum, **31, 141**, 187, **352, 355, 381, 388, 392, 407**
  dimorphic, **149**, 152
  formation of, 72, 144
  tinsel type, 3, 179, 185, 188, 222, 372, **373**, 389, 391, 394, 418
    structure of, **142**
  trailing, 168
  whiplash type, 3, **16**, 152, 168, 179, 185, 188, 222, 356, 372, **373**, 389, 391, 394
    structure of, **16**
Flavicin, **4**
Flavoxanthin, **4**
Flexuous hyphae, 503
Florideae, 297, **301–342**
  alternation of generations in, **309–311**
  ascomycetes and, **432**
  carpospore development in, **305–307**
  classification of, **312–313**
  diphasic, **309**, 311, 315, 319
  evolution among, **311–312**
  fertilization in, **305**
  gametophyte of, **304–307**
  monoaxial, **302, 320**, 323
  multiaxial, 215, 302, **303**, 316, 329, **334**
  nature of, 301
  spermatia of, **305**
  tetrasporophyte, **307–309**
  triphasic, 310, 311, 319, 322, 329, 337
  vegetative structure, **301–304**
Fomes fomentarius, **481**
Foot cell, **500**, 501
Free cell formation, **429**, 442, 447
Fruiting body, 349, **350**
Frustule, 196
Fucaceae, 217
Fucales, 220, **264–271**
  relationships of, 227
Fucosan granules, nature of, 220
Fucoxanthin, **4**
Fucus, 244, **265–271**
  furcatus, **269**
  serratus, **266**, 267
  vesiculosus, 265, **266**, 267, **268**
Fungi, 2, **346–513**
  classes of, 6, **10**
  classification of, **6**
  as division, **6**
  divisions of, **10**
  eucarpic, 371–373, **377–379**
    nature of, 371
  evolution of, **8**
  holocarpic, 373, **379–380, 390–393**, 418
    nature of, 371
  imperfect (Deuteromycetae), 6, 10, 369, **514–515**
  polycentric, 379
  as subdivision, **2**
Fungus chitin, nature of, 372
Fuscorhodin, 279

G

Gaidukov phenomenon, 281, 282
Gametangial ray, **120**
Gametangium, **56**, 57, **112**, 234, **247, 255, 357**, 373, **434, 435**
  development of, 108, **109**, 113, **413**
  female, **103**, 108, **114**, 224, **238, 384**, 391, **435**
  male, 108, **114**, 224, **238, 384**, 391, **435**
  nature of, 23
  (*See also* Antheridium; Oögonium)
Gametophyte, 45, 63, **231, 235, 237, 246, 247, 249, 255**, 257, 262, **263, 304–307, 309, 314, 317, 327–328, 330–332, 334–336, 338–341**, 385
  female, 244, **252**, 253, **263**
  male, 243, **252**, 253, 263
Gastroclonium, **333–337**
  coulteri, 333, **334, 336**
  ovale, **335**
Gastromycetes, 478, **485–490**
  nature of, 485
Gelidiales, 313, **319–322**
Gelidium, 293, **319–322**
  capillaceum, **320**
  cartilagineum, 319, **320, 321**
Gemma, 394
Germ pore, **500**
Germ tube, 396, 406, **408, 413, 500**
Gigartina, **329–331**
  corymbifera, 292
  cristata, 292

Gigartina, leptorhynchos, **329**
papillata, 292, **329**
Gigartinales, 313, **329–333**
Girdle, 150
Girdle view, 196, **197, 198**
Gleba, 486, **487, 489, 490**
nature of, 486
types of, **485**, 486
Glenodinium, 157
lubiniensiforme, **154**
uliginosum, **154**
Globule, **128**
development of, **126–127**
nature of, 125
Gloeocapsin, 279
Gloeochloris, **173–174**
smithiana, **174**
Gloeocystis, 13
Gloeodinium, **160–161**
montanum, 160, **161**
Gloeothece, 283
Gonidial layer, **519**
Gonidium, of algae, **39**
division of, **40**
nature of, 35
of lichens, 519
nature of, 519
Gonimoblast filament, **310**, 314, 315, **318, 321, 324, 325, 327, 330, 333, 335, 340**, 341
initial of, **340**
nature of, 301, 305
Gracilaria, 294
Graphis scripta, **518**
Grinnellia, **302**
Gymnocarpeae, **525**
Gymnodiniales, **155–156**
Gymnodinium neglectum, **156**
Gymnogongrus griffithsiae, 311
Gymnospermae, relationships of, **9**

H

H-piece, 47, 48, **167**, 174
Haematococcus, 14, 17
Halicystidaceae, **106–111**
Halicystis, **107–111**
ovalis, **107**, 108, **109**
Halosaccion glandiforme, 292
Haplospora, **235–236**
globosa, **235, 236**
Haplosporangium bisporalis, **410**
Haplostichineae, **245–253**
nature of, 245
Haptera, 79, **258, 260**
Haustorial filament, **330, 333**
Haustorium, 404, **445**
nature of, 401
Helminthocladia, 309, 312
hudsonii, **310**
Helotism, 517
Helvella, **460–462**
crispa, 461, **462**
elastica, 461
Hematochrome, 34, 36, 41, 57
chemical composition of, **14**
Hemiascomycetae, 426, **433–441**
nature of, 433
Hemicellulose, 70
Hemidinium nasutum, **154**
Hepaticae, 10
Hericeum coralloides, **481**
Heterobasidiomycetae, 478, **490–511**
classification of, **490–491**
nature of, 490
Heterocapsales, **173–174**
Heterochloridales, **171**
Heterococcales, **176–177**
Heterocyst, **278**, 284, **285–287**
development of, **286**
function of, **287**
nature of, **286–287**
Heterogeneratae, 10, **245–264**
nature of, 245
Heterokaryosis, 425, 442
nature of, 414
Heterokontae, 3, 166
(*See also* Xanthophyceae)
Heterosiphonales, **177–184**
Heterospory, 223, 225
Heterothallism, 32, 36, 38, 40, 44, 50, 54, 63, 68, 96, 118, 154, 179, 181, 224, 232, 238, 253, 300, 317, 326, 330, 331, 334, 413, 414, 425, 506, 509, 511
bipolar, **474–476**
gynandromictic, **397**, 401
nature of, 22, 373
original definition of, 425
physiological, 449
tetrapolar, **474–476**
Heterotrichales, **174–175**
Heterotrichy, nature of, 45
Hilum, 473
Holdfast, 64, 72, **73**
(*See also* Haptera)
Holobasidium, **472**, 478
nature of, 472
Homobasidiomycetae, **478–490**
nature of, 478
Homokaryosis, nature of, 414
Homothallism, 32, 40, 50, 55, 96, 116, 121, 179, 181, 300, 314, 317, 385, 394, 413, 414, 458, 474
nature of, 22, 373

Homothallism, original definition of, 425
physiological, **426**
primary, **426**
secondary, **426**
Hormogonales, **288**
Hormogonium, 283, **284**
nature of, 283
Hormospore, **284**
Hydrodictyaceae, 89, **96–99**
Hydrodictyon, 14, **15**, 16, 18
Hydrurus, **190–191**
foetidus, **190**
Hymenial layer, **464**
Hymenium, **484**, 491, **492**, **494**
nature of, 472
Hymenomycetes, **478–485**
nature of, 478
Hypha, of fungi, **364**
of Phaeophyta, 259, **261**
trumpet, 259, **261**
Hyphal body, 415, **416**, 417
Hypnospore, 44, 98, 177–179, 181
nature of, 21
Hypobasidium, **492**, **494**, **496–498**, 499, 502, **504**, **506**, **509**, **510**
nature of, 473
Hypochytriales, 375, 418
Hypocreales, 453
Hypothallus, **350**
Hypotheca, of diatom, 196, **203**
formation of, 204
of dinoflagellate, 156, **157**, **159**

I

Intercalary plates, 156
anterior, 156, **157**
posterior, **157**
Internode, initial of, **123**
Involucre, **243**
Iridophycus, 294
flaccidum, 292
splendens, 292
Isidium, **519**, 520
function of, 520
structure of, **520**
Isogamy, 32, **33**, 44, **46**, 52, 68, **80**, 90, 91, 94, **95**, 118, **154**, 170, 175, 179, **206**, **207**, 224, **230**, 234, 245, **352**, **355**, **357**, 365, 373, **378**, **379**, 380, 381, **382**, **413**, **418**, **434**, **435**
nature of, 22
Isogeneratae, 10, **228–244**
nature of, 228
Isthmia enervis, **197**
Isthmus, 84, **85**, **86**
nature of, 84

K

Karyogamy, 82, 366, 373, 424, **428**, **472**, 474, 498
nature of, 365
Kelps, 217
(*See also* Laminariales)
Kombu, 219

L

Laboulbenia, 451
Laboulbeniales, **451–453**
Labyrinthulae, 347
Lagenidiales, **390–393**
cell wall of, 372
Lagenidium, 390, **392–393**
rabenhorstii, **392**
Lamella, **483**
structure of, **484**
Laminaria, 218, 225, **258–264**
andersonii, **260**, **261**
digitata, **261**
ephemera, 258
farlowii, **260**
flexicaulis, **263**
Laminariales, 217, 220, 224, 253, 254, **257–264**
relationships of, **227**
Laminarin, chemical composition of, **220**
Leaf, of Charales, **123**
fertile, **125**
Leathesia, 218, 221–223, **246–248**
amplissima, **248**
difformis, **247**
Lepidophyta, 7, 8, 10
relationships of, **9**
Leptomitaceae, **399–401**
Leptomitales, **399–401**
cell walls of, 372
Leucoplast, 15, 115
Leucosin, 166, 168, 177, 188, 191, 192, 200
Liagora, 312
Lichenes, **516–526**
algae of, **516**
classification of, **517**
ecological importance of, **517**
fungi of, **516**
nature of, 516
occurrence of, **517**
Lithophyllum, 107
Lithothamnion, 107
Lomentaria ovalis, 333
Lorica, **140**, 141, 184
Lutein, **4**
Lychnothamnus, 126
Lycoperdon, **486–488**
gemmatum, **487**

Lycoperdon, pyriforme, **486**
Lycopodinae, 10
Lycopsida, as division, **7**
  nature of, 6
  as subdivision, 7
Lyngbya birgei, **284**

M

Macdonald-Pfitzer law, **204–205**
Macroconidia, 448
Macrocystis, 218, **219**, 260
  pyrifera, 257, **258**
Macrosporangium, 225
Macrospore, 225
Mannitol, 220
Manubrium, **126**
Mastigoneme, **142, 168,** 185, 222
  nature of, 142
Medulla, 259, **266, 519**
Meiosis, 24, 34, 41, 47, 52, 55, 64, 68, 77, 84, 88, 92, 96, 103, 113, 118, 129, 145, 179, 206, 207, 210, 211, 223, 225, 231, 244, 253, 262, 264, 267, 301, 305, 308, 319, 328, 366, 386, 403, 406, 428, 430, 433, 474, 488, 505, 509
  distribution of characters and, 431
Meiosporangium, 384
Melanconiales, **515**
Melosira islandica, **205**
  varians, **210**
Merismopedia elegans, **277**
Meristem, growth and, 259
Mesochite, 267, **269**
Mesotaeniaceae, **82–84**
Mesotaenium, 16
  greyii, **83**
Micrasterias apiculatum, **85**
Microaplanospore, 181
Microcladia borealis, 292
Microcoleus vaginatus, **278**
Microconidia, **448**
  nature of, 425, 449
Microdictyon, 118
Microspora, 18, 21, **47–49**
  willeanum, **48**
Microsporaceae, **47–40**
Microsporangium, 225
Microspore, of diatom, 209, 210
    nature of, 209
  of Phaeophyta, 225
Microzoospore, 51
Mildew, downy, 404
  powdery, 444
Mitosis, **143, 152**
Mold, black, 409
  fish, 393
  red, 448
Monilia, 448, 514
Moniliales, **515**
Monoblepharidales, 376, **387–389**
Monoblepharis, **387–389**
  polymorpha, **388**
Monocotyledones, 1
Monoecism, 22, 113, 266
  (*See also* Homothallism)
Monosporangium, 297, 304, **317**
Monospore, 295, 297, 301, 304, 317
  nature of, 297
Morchella, 461
Mucilage duct, 261
Mucorales, 373, **409–415**
  cell wall of, 372
Muscarine, 480
Musci, 10
Mushrooms, **480–485**
  edible, **480–481**
    cultivation of, **481**
  poisonous, **480**
Mycelia sterila, 514, **515**
Mycelium, nature of, 364
Mycetozoa, 6
Myrionema, **245–246**
  strangulans, 217, 245, **246**
Myxamoebae, **352, 357,** 359, **360**
  aggregation of, **361**
  nature of, 346
Myxomycetae, 6, 10, **347–356**
  nature of, 347
Myxomycophyta, 6, 10, **346–363**
  classification of, 346–347
  nature of, 349
  relationships of, **9**
Myxophyceae, 3, 5, 10, **275–290**, 525
  pigments of, **4**
  (*See also* Cyanophyta)
Myxoxanthin, **4**
Myxoxanthophyll, **4**

N

Nannandrium, nature of, **76**
Nannocyte, 286
Navicula oblonga, **203**
  radiosa, **200**
  rhyncocephala, **198**
Nectar, 502
Nemalion, **313–316**
  multifidum, **314**
Nemalionales, **313–316**
Nemathecia, 326
Neodinoxanthin, **4**
Neofucoxanthin A, **4**
Neofucoxanthin B, **4**
Neoxanthin, **4**

Nereocystis, 221, 260, 298
luetkeana, **258**
Netrium digitus, **83, 84**
Neuromotor apparatus, **16, 17, 142,** 152
Neurospora, 424, 425, 431, **448–451,** 514
sitophila, **448, 449**
tetrasperma, 426, 449, **450**
Nitella, 123, 124, 126, 128
gracilis, **125**
Nitrogen fixation by algae, **282**
Node, initial of, **123**
Nodularia spumigena, **285**
Nodule, central, 199, 201
polar, 199, 201
Nostoc muscorum, **287**
Nostocaceae, 282
Nostochopsis lobatus, **278**
Nowakowskiella elegans, **373**
Nucule, **128, 129**
development of, **127–128**
nature of, 125
Nurse cell, **324, 325**
nature of, 306
Nurse tissue, **330,** 332, **333**
nature of, 306

O

Ochromonas crenata, **186**
Odonthalia, 254
Oedogoniaceae, **69–78**
Oedogoniales, 18, 29, **69–78**
macrandrous, **74–75**
nature of, 74
nannandrous, 74, **75–77**
evolution of, **77**
nature of, 74
relationships of, **27**
Oedogonium, 13, 15, 16, 24, 25, 50, **69–78**
concatenatum, **76**
crassum, **69, 70, 74, 75**
Oidia, 424, **469, 470,** 471
nature of, 424
Oidiophore, **469**
Oils, 16, 151, 168, 176
Olpidiopsis, **390–392**
achlyae, **391**
Olpidium, **377–379**
viciae, **377, 378**
Omphalia, 482
chrysophylla, **483**
Oöblast, **324, 325,** 332
function of, **332**
Oöcystaceae, **99–100**
Oöcystis, **99–100**
borgei, **99**
eremosphaeria, **99**
lacustris, **99**
parva, **99**
Oögamy, 22, 23, 32, 33, 40, **41,** 50, 54, **58,** 59, 73, 116, 170, **210,** 224, **236,** 244, 263, **270,** 365, 374, **388,** 389, 391, 393, **395, 403,** 406, 407
nature of, 22
Oögonial mother cell, 74, **76,** 127, **128**
Oögonium, **49,** 50, **54,** 55, **58, 75, 76, 116,** 127, **128,** 225, **243, 252,** 253, **263, 269, 388,** 393, **395, 400, 403,** 405, **408**
development of, 182, **183,** 244, **268, 394–395,** 400, 402, **403**
nature of, 23
types in Fucales, **265**
Oömycetae, 367, 375
Oöspore, 365
Ophiocytium, 167
Oscillatoria, 282
formosa, **278**
limosa, **278**
princeps, **279**
Oscillatoriaceae, 282
Oscillatoriales, **278**
Ostiole, 267, **268,** 448, **449,** 503
Oxyrrhis marina, **152**

P

Palaeodasycladus mediterraneus, **119**
Palmella stage, **31,** 32, 51, 90, 146, **161,** 187, **190, 192**
nature of, 31
Pandorina, **35–36**
morum, **36**
Paradesmose, 17
Paramylum, 139, 141
Paraphysis, 254, **255, 260,** 267, **268, 427,** 448, **459, 524**
antheridial, **269**
fertile, **249**
Paraspore, 295, 308
nature of, 308
Parmelia, **521**
flavicans, **518**
Parthenogenesis, 57, 63, 68, **95, 208,** 224–226, 231, 257, 380, 386, 403, 408, **434, 437**
nature of, 23
Parthenospore, 77, 80, 87, 396, 408, 417
nature of, 77
Pectic compounds, 13, 57, 67, 69, 79, 82–84, 105, 196, 277, 294
Pediastrum, 21, **96–99**
boryanum, **97–99**
Pedicel, **126, 128**
Peltigera praetexta, **519**
Penicillin, 423, 442
Penicillium, 423, **441–444**
chrysogenum, 442

Penicillium, notatum, 442
vermiculatum, **443**
Pennales, **212**
Pericarp, 316, **318, 339, 340**
Pericentral cell, **320**, 337, **338**
fertile, **339**
Peridiniales, **156–158**
Peridinin, **4**
Peridinium wisconsinensis, **157**
Peridium, 347, **351, 427, 444, 446, 449, 504**
nature of, 486
Periphysis, 267, **268**, 448, 450, **502**
nature of, 267
Periplasm, **400, 403**
nature of, 400
Periplast, 140
Perisporiales, 444
Perithecial initial, **452**
Perithecium, 430, **449, 455**, 522
nature of, 430
Peronosporales, 390, **401–409**
cell wall of, 372
Pezizales, **458–462**
Phacus, 144
Phaeophyceae, 3, 5
pigments of, **4**
(*See also* Phaeophyta)
Phaeophyta, 5, 10, **217–274**
alternation of generations in, **225–226**
asexual reproduction of, **222–223**
cell structure, **219–220**
classification of, **228**
distribution of, **217–218**
economic uses, **218–219**
evolution among, **226–228**
interrelationships among, **227**
nature of, 217
relationships of, **9**
reserve foods of, **220–221**
sexual reproduction of, **223–225**
vegetative structure, **221–225**
Phaeothamnion, **191–192**
confervicola, **191**
Phallus, **488–490**
impudicus, **489, 490**
Pharyngeal rod, **142**
Phialide, **442**
Phialopore, 35, **40**
Phormidium foevalarum, 282
Phragmidium rubi, **498**
Phragmobasidium, 473, 478, **492, 494, 496–498, 504, 506, 509, 510**
nature of, 472
Phycobilins, **4**, 5
Phycocyanins, **4**
c-phycocyanin, **4**, 275
r-phycocyanin, **4**, 295
Phycoerythrins, **4**
c-phycoerythrin, **4**, 275, 281
r-phycoerythrin, **4**, 295
photosynthesis and, 295
Phycomyces, 414
Phycomycetae, 6, 10, 347, 365, 369, **371–421**
asexual reproduction of, **372–373**
classification of, **375–376**
Deuteromycetae and, 514
evolution among, **375**
life cycles of, **374–375**
Brachyallomyces type, **386**
Cystogenes type, **386**
Euallomyces type, **386**
nature of, 371
occurrence of, **371**
origin of, **366–367**
sexual reproduction of, **373–374**
vegetative structure, **371–372**
Phyllophora, 311
brodiae, 311
Physarum alpinum, **350**
polycephalum, 348, 349, **352**
Physcia, **519, 522**
parietina, **521**
Phytodinads, 151
Phytodiniaceae, **162–163**
Pileus, **483, 484, 489**
Pilobolus, 414
Pinnularia, **202, 203**
Pinnule, 102, **103**
Pithophora oedogonia, **22**
Placental cell, **314, 327**, 328, **340**, 341
formation of, 315
Plakea, 35, 39, **40**
nature of, 35
Plasmodiocarp, **350**
nature of, 349
Plasmodiophora, **356–358**
brassica, 356, **357, 358**
Plasmodiophoraceae, **356–358**
Plasmodiophorales, 346, 352, **356–358**
Plasmodiophoreae, **356–358**
nature of, 356
Plasmodium, **348–349, 357, 358**
nature of, 346
net, **172**, 347
Plasmogamy, 365, 373, 433
nature of, 365
Plasmopara, **404–406**
viticola, 404, **405**, 406
Plectascales, 441
Plethysmothallus, **226**, 247
nature of, 226
Pleurococcus, 52
Plowrightia, **456–458**
morbosa, **456, 457**

Plumaria elegans, 308
Pocockiella, 241
Polarity, 269, 270
Polycystis, 280
  aeruginosa, **277**
Polyeder, 98, **99**
  germination of, **99**
Polyporales, 479
Polysiphonia, **337–342**
  flexicaulis, **338–340**
  nigrescens, 338, 341
  pacifica, **340**
Polysiphony, **233**, 235, **338**
Polysporangium, 308, **336**
  nature of, 307
Polyspore, 295, **336**
  nature of, 307
Polystichineae, 245, **254–264**
  nature of, 254
Polytoma, 14, 22, 30
Pore plate, **159**
Porphyra, 293, 296, **298–301**
  naiadum, 298
  nereocystis, 298
  perforata, 292, **299**
  tenera, 299
  umbilicalis, 301
Porphyrosiphon notarisii, **278**
Postcingular plates, 156, **157**
Postelsia palmaeformis, 258, **259**
Prasiola, **65–67**, 296
  meridionalis, **66**
  mexicana, **66**
Prasiolaceae, 65
Prasiolales, 65
Precingular plates, 156, **157**
Prelamellar chamber, 482, **483**
Procarp, **330, 339, 340**
  nature of, 306
Progametangium, **413**
Progressive cleavage, 68, 90, **93**, 94, **97**, 111, 350, **351, 354**, 380, 385, 390, **412**
  nature of, 20
Propagulum, 222, **233**, 234
  development of, **233**, 234
Protoaecidium, 503
Protococcaceae, **52–53**
Protococcus, 18, 44, **52–53**
  viridis, **52**
Protoflorideae, 297
Protonema, 130
  primary, **130**
  secondary, **130**
Protonematal initial, 129, **130**
Protoperithecium, **449**, 450
  nature of, 450
Protosiphon, 26, **94–96**
  botyroides, 94, **95**, 96
Protosiphonaceae, **94–96**
Protozoa, ancestral to fungi, 368
Psalliota, 482, 486
  campestris, 482, **483, 484**
Pseudobryopsis, 102
Pseudocilia, **43**
Pseudoplasmodium, 360, 358, **361**
  migrating, 360, **361**
  nature of, 346
Pseudopleurococcus stage, 53
Pseudopodium, 157, **189**
Pseudoraphe, 199
Pseudovacuole, **280–281**
Psilophyta, 10
  relationships of, **9**
Psilophytinae, 10
Psilopsida as subdivision, **7**
Pteridophyta, 2
  validity of, **6–7**
Pteridophytes, 10
  classes of, **10**
  divisions of, **10**
  primitive, 8
Pterophyta, 7, **10**
Pteropsida, 6, 7
  as division, 7
  nature of, 6
  as subdivision, **7**
Pterygophora, 221
Puccinia, **499–506**
  graminis, **499–505**
  malvacearum, **505–506**
Puffballs, 486
Pulsules, 152
Punctariales, 220, 224, **254–255**
  relationships of, 227
Pycnia, 503
Pycnidium, 424, **522**
  nature of, 424
Pycnospores, 424, **522**
  nature of, 424
Pyrenocarpeae, **525**
Pyrenoid, of Chlorophyta, **14–15**, 61, 69
    division of, 25
    formation of, **15**, 87
  naked, 168, 173, 184, 200, 294, **299**
Pyrenomycetes, **447–458**
  nature of, 447
Pyronema, 423, **458–460**
  confluens, **428, 459**
Pyrrophyta, 6, 9, **148–164**
  nature of, 148
  relationships of, **9**
Pythium, **406–409**
  aphanidermatium, 408
  helicoides, **407**
  intermedium, **408**
  paroecandrium, **407**

Pythium, periilum, **407**
salpingophorum, **408**

R

Ramalina reticulata, 517, 520
Raphe, 199
structure of, **201–202**
Receptacle, 250, **251**, 264, 267
Receptive hyphae, **502,** 503
function of, **503**
Reproduction, fortnightly, 63, 68, 108, 242
monthly, 243
seasonal, 82, 102, 105, 262, 266
Reservoir, **141**
Rhabdomonas incurvum, **143**
Rhizine, nature of, 518
Rhizochloridales, **172–173**
Rhizochrysidales, **188–189**
Rhizodiniales, **159–160**
Rhizoid, **62, 117, 178, 240, 243, 270, 411**
primary, **130**
secondary, **130**
Rhizoidal initial, 129, **130**
Rhizome, **107**
Rhizomorph, 463, 482, **483**, 488
nature of, 463
Rhizomycelium, 376, 380
nature of, 376
Rhizophydium, 373, **380–381**
ovatum, 380, **381, 382**
Rhizoplast, 17, 143
Rhizopodial stage, 169, 187
Rhizopus, **411–414**
nigricans, **411, 412, 413**
sexualis, 413
Rhodomela, 254
larix, 292
Rhodophyceae, 3, 5, 10, **291–346**
pigments of, **4**
(*See also* Rhodophyta)
Rhodophyta, 5, 10, **291–345**
ascomycetes and, **432**
cell structure in, **294–295**
classification of, **297**
distribution of, **291–293**
economic uses, **293–294**
nature of, 291
pigments of, 295
relationships of, **9**
reproduction of, **295–297**
(*See also* Bangioideae; Florideae)
Rhodymeniales, 313, **333–337**
Rhoicosphenia curvata, **200**
Rivularia dura, **278**
Rockweeds, 217
(*See also* Fucales)
Rod organs, 142
Rusts, 490
hollyhock, 505
wheat, 499
white, 401
(*See also* Urediniales)

S

Saccharomyces, **438–439**
cervisiae, **438**
Saccharomycetaceae, **436–439**
Saprolegnia, **393–396**
ferax, **373, 394,** 395
Saprolegniales, 390, **393–399**
cell wall of, 372
Sapromyces, **399–401**
androgynus, **400**
reinschii, **400**
Sargassum natans, 222
Scaphospora speciosa, 236
Scenedesmaceae, **100–101**
Scenedesmus, 14, **100–101**
quadricauda, **100**
Schizochlamys, 16
Schizogoniaceae, **65–67**
Schizogoniales, 29, **65–67**
relationships of, **27**
Schizomeridaceae, **64–65**
Schizomeris, **64–65**
leibleinii, **64**
Schizosaccharomyces, **437–438**
octosporus, **437**
Schizymenia epiphytica, 311
Scinaia, **316–319**
furcellata, **316–318**
Sclerotium, 349, 423, **453, 455**
germination of, **455**
maturation of, 454
overwintering of, 455
Scytonema, 525
Semicell, 84, **85**
formation of, **86**
nature of, 84
Separation disk, 283, **284**
Septobasidiaceae, 491, **496–498**
Septobasidiales, 491, **496–498**
Septobasidium, **496–498**
retiforme, **497**
Seta, 53
Sex determination, genotypic, 63, 78, 244, 262
Sexual reproduction (*see* Anisogamy; Isogamy; Oögamy)
Sexuality, **397–398, 414–415, 425–426, 431, 474–476**
bipolar, **474–476,** 493, 495, 506
hormones and, **397–398**

Sexuality, tetrapolar, **474–476,** 486, 506, 511
"geographical races" and, 475
Sheath initial, **128**
Shield cell, **126**
Sieve plate, 260
Sieve tube, 260
Silica, 166
Siliceous plates, 188
Silicification, 176, 193
nature of, 197
Silicon, diatoms and, 197
Simultaneous cleavage, 20
Sinus, 84, **85**
Siphonae verticillatae, **119**
Siphonales, 13, **29, 101–116**
relationships of, **27**
Siphonocladales, **29, 116–118**
relationships of, **27**
Slime molds (*see* Myxomycophyta)
Smut, 490
stinking, 509
(*See also* Ustilaginales)
Smut balls, 510
Somatogamy, 461, **470,** 474, 475, 499, 506, **507**
nature of, 425
Soralia, 521
Soranthera, **254–255**
ulvoidea, 254, **255**
Soredia, nature of, **521**
Soredial dust, 521
Sorocarp, **353, 359,** 360, **361**
nature of, 352
Sorogen, 360
Sorophore, **359,** 360, 361
nature of, 360
Sorophore sheath, **361**
Sorus, **238, 240, 243, 260, 359,** 360
Spermatangial filament, 326, **327**
Spermatangial mother cell, 304
Spermatangium, 296, 304, **314, 317, 320, 323, 338**
development of, 305
nature of, 296
Spermatiophore, 425, **502,** 503
Spermatium, of fungi, 366, 424, **448, 452, 502, 523**
of Rhodophyta, 291, 295, **299,** 338
formation of, 300
liberation of, **299**
Spermatization, 424, 450, 474, 499, **502,** 503
nature of, 424
Spermocarp, **54,** 55
germination of, **54**
nature of, 55
Spermogonium, **502,** 523
nature of, 424
Spermothamnion turneri, 308
Sphacelaria, 218, 222, **232–234**
bipinnata, **234**
californica, **233**
radicans, **233**
Sphacelariales, 220, 224, **232–234**
relationships of, **227**
Sphacelia segetum, 454, 514
Sphacelial stage, **454**
Sphaeriales, **448–451,** 453
Sphaeroplea, 18, 27, **58–60**
annulina, **58, 60**
cambrica, **58,** 59, **60**
Sphaeropleaceae, **57–60**
Sphaeropleineae, 45, **57–60**
Sphaeropsidales, **515**
Sphaerozosma aubertianum, **86**
Sphenopsida, as division, 7
as subdivision, 7
Spirogyra, 13, 15, 16, 18, 19, 23, 25, 79, 81
Spirotaenia condensata, **83**
Spongomorpha, 67
Sporangiolum, **410**
nature of, 373, 410
Sporangiophore, 372, **405, 411, 416**
development of, 411, **412, 416**
nature of, 401
Sporangium, 57, **110, 350, 351,** 383, **391, 400, 407, 410, 411,** 419
development of, 57, **349–351,** 382, 387, **388, 393–394,** 399, 406
germ tube, 396, **405,** 406, **408, 413**
intercalary, **407**
nature of, 20
neutral, 223, **230, 235,** 236, 246, **247**
plurilocular, 222, 223
nature of, 223
resistant, **384,** 385
development of, 385
resting, 381
"summer," **377,** 380
unilocular, 222, **230,** 235, **240, 246, 249,** 252–254, **255, 256, 260**
development of, 222, 229, 262
nature of, 222
"winter," **378,** 379, 380
Spore, 355, **358, 360**
formation of, 351
germination of, **351–353,** 355, **357**
neutral, of Phaeophyta, 223
of Rhodophyta, 295, 297, **298**
formation of, 300
resting, 381
"summer," **377, 379**
viability of, 352

Spore, "winter," **378,** 380
(*See also* Aecidiospore; Aplanospore; Ascospore; Basidiospore; Bispore; Blastospore; Conidium; Monospore; Oidium; Paraspore; Polyspore; Teleutospore; Tetraspore; Uredospore; Zoospore)
Sporobola, 485
Sporochnales, **248–250**
relationships of, **227**
Sporochnus, 248
Sporophore, **342,** 353
Sporophyll, 257
Sporophyte, 64, 68, **231, 235,** 239, **240, 246, 247, 249, 251, 252,** 253, **255, 256, 260, 384**
Stalk cell, 127, **128,** 267, **341,** 500, 501
primary, 238
Starch, **14–15,** 148, 151, 157, 160
cyanophycin, 280
floridean, 295
pyrenoids and, 14, **15**
stroma, 70
Statolith, 86
Statospore, 165, **170,** 171, **185,** 187–189, **190,** 192, 211, **212**
formation of, 169, **170, 185–186**
germination of, **186**
Staurastrum curvatum, **85**
fucigerum, **87**
splendens, **350**
Stereum einerascens, **481**
Sterigma, **405, 472,** 488, **494, 496, 498**
Stichococcus, 19
Sticta, **519**
Stigeoclonium, 20, **50–52**
lubricum, **51**
Stigma, 17
Stigmatomyces baeri, **451–453**
Stigonema, 297
Stinkhorn, 488
Stipe, **260, 483, 484, 489**
Stolon, **411**
Stoneworts, 121
Stylodinium globosum, **162**
Suffultory cell, 74, **76**
nature of, 74
Sulcus, 155, **156, 159**
nature of, 155
Supporting cell, **330,** 334, **335, 339, 340**
nature of, 304
Surirella saxonica, **205,** 206
Suspensor, 409, **413**
Suture, 158
Syncephalis pycnospora, **410**
Synchytrium, **379–380**
endobioticum, **379**
Syngamy, nature of, 24
Synura, **188**
adamsii, **188**
uvella, **188**

T

Tabellaria fenestrata. **198**
Taphrina, **439–441**
deformans, **439,** 440
epiphylla, 440
johansonii, **439,** 440
pruni, 439
Taphrinales, **439–441**
relationships of, 441
Teleutosorus, **498, 501**
Teleutospore, **498, 506,** 508, **510**
formation of, **501–502**
germination of, **498,** 502, **504–506,** 508, **509,** 511
nature of, 498
Tetraspora, **42–44**
cylindrica, **43**
gelatinosa, **43**
Tetrasporales, 28, **42–44**
relationships of, **27,** 42
Tetrasporangium, of Phaeophyta, **243**
development of, 244
of Rhodophyta, 308, 322
cruciate, **320,** 322, **329**
nature of, 308
pyramidate, 336, **341**
nature of, 308
zonate, **323, 328, 333**
nature of, 308
Tetraspore, of Phaeophyta, 241, **243**
of Rhodophyta, 295, 328, **329, 333, 336, 341**
nature of, 307
Tetrasporophyte, **309,** 312, 321, **331–333,** 336, **341–342**
nature of, 307
sporangia of, **307–309**
Thallophyta, nature of, 2
validity of, **2**
Thecospora areolata, **498**
Tidal levels, vertical zonation and, **292**
Tides, gamete liberation and, 63, 68, 108
periodic reproduction and, 63, 68, 242–243
zoospore liberation and, 63, 68
Tilletia, **509–511**
foetans, 509
tritici, 509, **510**
Tilopteridales, **234–236**
relationships of, **227**
Tolypella, 126
prolifica, **125**
Tolypothrix tenuis, 278

Tongue cell, 267
Trabecula, 105, **106**
Trachelomonas volvocina, **140**
Tracheophyta, 7
Trama, **484**
Trebouxia, **90–91**
  cladoniae, 90, **91**
Tremella, **493–494**
  frondosa, **494**
  mesenterica, **494**
Tremellales, 490, **493–494**
Trentepohlia, 14, 18, **56–57**
  aurea, **56**
Trentepohliaceae, **55–57**
Tribonema, 166, **168, 174–175**
  bombycinum, **167, 175**
Trichoblast, 337, **338**
  initial of, 337
  nature of, 337
  spermatangial, **338**
Trichogyne, **54**, 55, 296, 304, **314, 318, 321, 324, 327, 330, 331, 335, 339**, 424, **427, 449, 452, 459, 523**
  nature of, 296
Trichome, **278**, 283
  nature of, 276
Trichothallic growth, **237**, 239, **246, 247, 250, 252**
  nature of, 221
Triphragmidium ulmaria, **498**
Truffles, 462
Tube cells, **128**
  decay of, 129
Tuber, **462–465**
  candidum, **463–465**
  melanosporum, 462
Tuberales, **462–465**
Turbinate organ, 382

U

Ulothrix, 19, 21, 23, 24, **45–47**, 54
  zonata, 45, **46**, 47
Ulotrichaceae, **45–47**
Ulotrichales, 29, **44–60**
  relationships of, **27**
Ulotrichineae, **45–57**
Ulva, 23, 26, **61–64**, 68, 245
  lactuca, 23
  lobata, 23, **62**, 63
  stenophylla, **62**
Ulvaceae, 25, **61–64**
Ulvales, 29, **60–65**
  relationships of, **27**
Uniflagellatae, **376–389**
  nature of, 376
Urceolus cyclostomus, **140**
Urediniales, 478, 490, **498–506**
  autoecious, 499, **505–506**
    nature of, 499
  heteroecious, **499–505**
    nature of, 498
  macrocyclic, **499–505**
    nature of, 499
  microcyclic, 499, **505–506**
    nature of, 499
Uredosorus, **500**
Uredospore, 499
  formation of, **500**
  germination of, **500**
  infection by, 501
  nature of, 499
Urococcus insignis, 160
Urospora, 67
Ustilaginales, 490, **506–511**
Ustilago, **506–509**
  anthearum, **507**
  carbo, **507**
  maydis, **507, 508**
  zea, 507
Utricle, **112, 114**

V

Vacuole, central, **18**
  contractile, **17–18**, 141, 188, 190
  noncontractile, 150
  pulsating, 17
Valonia, **117–118**
  aegagropila, **117**
  macrophysa, **117**
  utricularis, **117**, 118
  ventricosa, 118
Valve, 196
Valve view, 196, **197, 198**
Vaucheria, 115, 177, **179–184**, 367
  sessilis, 182, **183**
Vaucheriaceae, 115, **179–184**
Velum, **483**
Ventral plate, **157**
Violaxanthin, **4**
Volva, inner, **489**
  outer, **489**
Volvocaceae, **34–42**
Volvocales, 28, **30–40**
  relationships of, **27**
Volvox, 3, **17**, 34, 35, **38–42**
  aureus, **39**
  rouseletii, 39

W

Water blooms, 275
Westiella lanosa, **284**
Wheat, *Puccinia graminis* and, **499–502**

X

Xanthidium antilopaeum, **35**
Xanthophyceae, 3, 5, 9, **166**–184, 347
asexual reproduction of, **168–169**
cell structure in, **166–168**
classification of, **170–171**
nature of, 166
occurrence of, **166**
pigments of, **4**
relationships of, **165**
sexual reproduction of, **169–170**
Xanthophylls, **4**, 12, 148, 151, 184, 193, 217, 275, 281

Y

Yeasts, **426–439**
bottom, 436
budding, **438–439**
cultivated, 436
diploid, 438
fission, **437–438**
haploid, 438
top, 436
true, 436
wild, 436

Z

Zanardinia, 237
Zeaxanthin, **4**
Zonaria, 241
Zoogamete, **43, 46, 51, 56, 67**, 68, 90, 91, 93, **95**, 98, 118, **154**, 175, **230**, 234, 257, **352, 355, 357**, 365, 373, **378, 379**, 380, 381, **382**
female, **36, 37, 62, 103, 109, 114, 170, 238**, 255, 382, **384**
liberation of, **114**
formation of, **62**, 68, 179
liberation of, **67**, 104, **106, 107**
male, **36, 37, 62, 103, 106, 109, 114, 170, 238**, 255, **382, 384**
liberation of, **114**
nature of, **22**
Zoosporangium, **384**
development of, 385
Zoospore, 24, 38, 42, 44, **46**, 50, 55, 65, 68, **73, 90, 99, 110**, 118, 153, 154, **160, 161**, 163, **168**, 173, 174, **175, 177**, 185, **186, 190**, 191, 193, 229, **240**, 248, 372, **373, 381**, 383, 387, **388, 391, 392**, 399, **402, 403, 405, 407, 409, 418**
diploid, 375
formation of, **20–21**, 46, 51, 53, **72**, 91, 111, **162**, 176, 181, 387, **392, 407**
gametic union of, 223, 232
germination of, **180**, 191, 262, **383**
haploid, 375
liberation of, **21, 48**, 68, **73, 93, 98, 161**, 162, 229, **381, 383, 391, 407, 418, 419**
factors inducing, **20**
time of, 97
multiflagellate, **180**
nature of, 20
neutral, **230**
Zygnema, 13, 23, 24, **79–82**
Zygnemataceae, 13, **79–82**
Zygnematales, **78–88**
relationships of, **27**
Zygomycetae, 367, 375, 409
Zygospore, 78, 365
Zygote, **33, 36**, 38, **41, 43, 46**, 50, 52, **60, 75**, 77, **80**, 83, **87, 95, 99, 106, 116, 154**, 170, **210**, 257, 300, 353, **357**, 365, **378, 382, 384, 388, 391, 395**, 400, **403, 408, 413, 418**, 434
chloroplasts of, 24
formation of, **82, 84, 88**
(*See also* Anisogamy; Isogamy; Oögamy)
germination of, **24, 33, 34**, 36, 38, 42, 44, 47, 52, 60, 63, 69, **77–78, 82, 84, 88**, 96, **99**, 104, **106, 114**, 115, **130, 154**, 155, 184, 250, **379, 384, 388**, 389, **391**, 392, 393, 396, **403**, 404, **405**, 406, **408**, 409, **413**, 414
meiosis and, **24**
twin, 87